Yuqing Weng

Ultra-Fine Grained Steels

Yuqing Weng

Ultra-Fine Grained Steels

With 482 figures

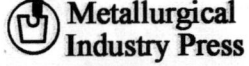 Metallurgical Industry Press

 Springer

EDITOR:

Yuqing Weng

China Iron & Steel Research Institute Group, 100081 Beijing

China

E-mail:weng@csm.org.cn

Based on an original Chinese edition:

《超细晶钢——钢的组织细化理论与控制技术》(Chaoxijing Gang——Gang de Zuzhi Xihua Lilun yu Kongzhi Jishu), Metallurgical Industry Press, 2003.

ISBN 978-7-5024-4415-0	Metallurgical Industry Press, Beijing
ISBN 978-3-540-77229-3	Springer Berlin Heidelberg New York
e ISBN 978-3-540-77230-9	Springer Berlin Heidelberg New York

Preface

This book is composed of ten chapters. Based on systematic description of research achievements of the project of ultra-fine grain steels and their engineering applications, new theories of microstructural refinement and the newly developed technologies in production of high strength and high toughness steels are introduced. The book features the integration of materials science with engineering technology. In the scope of theories of the strengthening and toughening of ultra-fine grain steels, the theory of deformation induced ferrite transformation (DIFT) for ferrite-pearlite steels has been put forward. The phenomenon of ultra-fine grain refinement effect by the existing precipitates of nanometer size in the steel produced by using thin slab casting and rolling (TSCR) has been discovered and analyzed. The theory of deformation induced precipitation and medium temperature phase transformation control for bainitic steels has been proposed. The theory of resistance against delayed fracturing of high strength and high toughness alloy structural steels has been established.

In the aspect of production technologies, some production technologies for obtaining ultra-fine grains and high strength high toughness of steels are introduced. The chemical metallurgy, solidification technique, and welding technique etc. for ultra-fine grain steels are introduced. In the aspect of engineering applications of ultra-fine grain high strength and high toughness steels, all the trial applications and commercial applications in the areas of civil constructions, automobile manufacturing and engineering machinery etc. are described.

The book provides theoretical concepts and engineering application technologies for the research, production, and application of ultra-fine grain steels. It is a good reference for researchers, scientists, engineers, university teachers, students and postgraduates in the fields of steel structural materials research, metal materials and metallurgical engineering research, university & school teaching, and production & application engineering.

Acknowledgements

This book is a systematic report on theoretical achievements, research on new technology, and applications developed under the Important Fundamental Research Program of New Generation Steel Materials—one of National Important Basic Research Programs in the past ten years in China.

The Program has been financially supported by the Ministry of Science and Technology of China. The main steel corporations in China provided great help including laboratory test apparatus and expertise, and in production trials. It has been technically supported by the famous academies and universities in China undertaking technically research and development of steel structural materials, including China Iron and Steel Research Institute Group, Institute of Metal Research of Chinese Academy of Sciences, University of Science and Technology Beijing, Northeastern University and Tsinghua University.

I would like to acknowledge the renowned scholars of steel materials of China, namely, professor Changxu Shi, professor Jun Ke, professor Hengde Li as well as the renowned scholars of metallurgy in China, namely, professor Ruiyu Yin, professor Tieyong Zuo and so on, who have paid their attention to and directed this work. In addition, this work was given sufficient attention to and supported by many individuals of Chinese Academy of Engineering and Ministry of Science and Technology of China, etc. I would like to express my gratitude to them.

Some 400 researchers from more than 20 companies have contributed to the contents of this book with their ideas and conceptions for the past ten years. Without the work that they had done, this book would not have been accomplished.

Ultra fine grain steel is a topic with both traditional and modern significance. We hope some work we have done is useful for the future work of colleagues in materials field. Finally, we wish further success in R&D of ultra-fine grained steels in the future!

Yuqing Weng

2008-5

List of contributors

Chapter 1
Yuqing Weng
Dr. and Professor
46 Dongsixi Dajie Beijing, 100711 China
E-mail: weng@csm.org.cn

Chapter 2
Zhongmin Yang
Dr. and Professor
Central Iron & Steel Research Institute
E-mail: yangzhongmin@nercast.com

Chapter 3
Han Dong
Dr. and Professor
Central Iron & Steel Research Institute
E-mail: donghan@public.net.cn
Xinjun Sun
Dr.and Profossor
E-mail: sunxinjun@nercast.com

Chapter 4
Yonglin Kang
Dr. and Professor
School of Material Science and Engineering
University of Science and Technology Beijing
E-mail: kangylin@mater.ustb.edu.cn
Delu Liu
Dr. and Professor
Central Iron & Steel Research Institute
E-mail: deluliu@sina.com

Chapter 5
Xinlai He
Professor
School of Material Science and Engineering
University of Science and Technology Beijing
E-mail:hexl@mater.ustb.edu.cn
Chengjia Shang
E-mail: cjshang@mater. ustb. edu.cn

Chapter 6
Weijun Hui
Dr. and Professor
Central Iron & Steel Research Institute
E-mail: Wjhui@sina.com

Chapter 7
Bingzhe Bai
Dr. and Professor
Department of Material Science and Engineering
Tsinghua University
E-mail: bzbai@mail.tsinghua.edu.cn

Chapter 8
Xinhua Wang
Dr. and Professor
Metallurgical Engineering School
University of Science and Technology Beijing
E-mail: wangxinhua@metall.ustb.edu.cn

Chapter 9
Pei Zhao
Dr. and Professor
Central Iron & Steel Research Institute
E-mail: zhaopei@atmcn.com

Chapter 10
Zhiling Tian
Dr. and Professor
Central Iron & Steel Research Institute
E-mail: tianzhl@cisri.com.cn
Yun Peng
Dr. and Professor
Central Iron & Steel Research Institute
E-mail: pengyun@nercast.com

Contents

1
Overview

Steel are the basic materials in human civilization. Sufficient quantity of high quality steel materials is necessary for realization of industrialization of countries in the world and for providing conditions for the modern life of mankind.

In the history of materials, twentieth century could be considered as the century of steel. The world output of crude steel in the year of 1900 was 31.04 million tons and that in the year of 2000 reached 846 million tons. In the early years of twenty first century, due to the rapid economic development in China and other new rising countries, the world steel output reached 1220 million tons in the year of 2006, which was more than 40 times than that of 1900.

Steel materials structural materials occupies more than 90% of the total amount of steel materials consumption. Table 1.1 lists the changes of shares of iron and steel structural materials and iron and steel functional materials in China in recent years.

Table 1.1 Percentages of the outputs of two kinds of steel materials in China in recent years

Year	Steel materials structural materials	Steel materials functional materials
2003	95.94%	4.06%
2004	96.13%	3.87%
2005	96.78%	3.22%
2006	96.10%	3.90%

Nowadays, production processes of iron and steel are highly automatic and realized in large-scale production mills. A hot strip rolling line can produce up to 5 million ton steel products annually. A hot bar rolling line can produce up to 1 million ton steel products annually. In accordance with the demand of sustainable development from society and with the self-development rules of steel materials, the properties of steel materials and their production technology should meet the following five basic requirements.

1. Under conditions of sufficient toughness and application performances, further strengthening is required while service safety is ensured.
2. To further increase service life of steel materials structures and of machinery constructions made of steels.
3. To develop new production technology in order to save energy and natural resources.
4. To reduce the burden on the environment and to reduce the emission of CO_2 and other gases, liquids,(water) and solid stuffs (slag) in accordance with the demand of cycle economy and to strengthen the recycling of wastes.
5. To reduce the production and management costs in order to increase the property to price ratio.

1.1   The Technology of Controlled Rolling and Controlled Cooling (Thermo-mechanical Controlled Processing, TMCP)

The technology of controlled rolling and controlled cooling (Thermo-mechanical controlled processing, TMCP) contributes to the development of fine grained steels. It is one of the main production methods of high strength and high toughness structural steel materials.

The demand for strengthening of engineering structures induces the invention and production of high strength low alloy steels. In 1870, in the city of Saint Louis, USA a riveted arciform bridge crossing the Mississippi river was constructed by using steel containing 1.5%~2.0% Cr. Later on, welding technology was applied to manufacturing of steel structures. It is then required that carbon content and carbon equivalent (C_{eq}) in the steel should be lowered. In order to maintain strength level while carbon content is lowered, European countries starting with UK applied rolling technology based on low temperature rolling in the second decade of 20th century. The essential of this practice was the microstructural refinement of austenite leading to grain refinement strengthening contributing to strength increment in addition of solid strengthening by alloy elements and precipitation strengthening. During world war II, multi-times of fracturing accidents of fully welded steel ship structures sent out warnings that low temperature toughness property should be guaranteed for these steel structures. In 1950s, in former Soviet Union, controlled rolling technique was developed from the low temperature rolling and applied for production of pipeline steels used for arctic area and fine grained steels suitable to low temperature service were produced. Meanwhile in the years of 1951~1958, Hall and Petch did separate research on the effect of grain size of low carbon steels and proposed the Hall-Petch formula depicting the relationship of yield strength and grain size that is shown as follows:

$$R_p = R_0 + kd^{1/2}$$

where R_p is yield strength; R_0 is lattice friction force of ferrite; k is a constant; d is grain size.

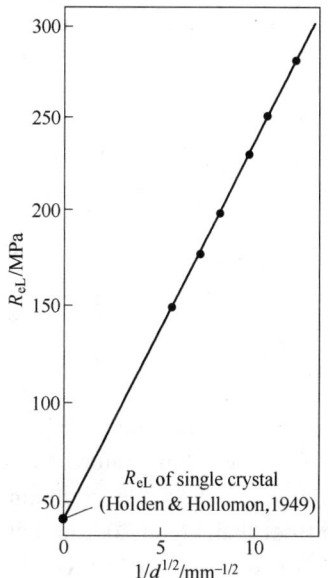

Figure 1.1 Relationship of strength and grain size(Hall)

Typical experimental results are shown in Figure 1.1 (Dong T, 1999).

Later, Petch did further research and found that the fracturing stress has similar relation with grain size. The established formula expressing the relationship of impact toughness transition temperature T_c and grain size d is as follows:

$$T_c = a - bd^{-1/2}$$

where a, b are constants.

The two formulae, as mentioned above, illustrate that yield strength R_p increases and toughness-brittleness transition temperature T_c decreases as grain size are refined.

In the meantime, together with the development of fine grained steels, there is equally important development of clean steel technology. In 1940s, production of aluminum killed steel started leading to the important improvement of steel quality. Later on, the effect of second phase particles was studied. In 1948, Orowan mechanism of dislocation by-passing particles was put forward (this will be discussed in the later part on steel microalloying.) laying the theory basis of precipitation strengthening by particles of nanometer scale. The formation, classification, and function of oxide inclusions and sulphide inclusions and especially measures ensuring plasticity level lead to the progress of steel-making technology. Ladle metallurgy technology was industrialized by the end of 1950s and at the beginning of 1960s. Ladle furnace (LF) was started in the years of 1952~1953. Vacuum degassing unit (VD) was started in 1955. Only in 1959, 100 ton RH unit was formally equipped (Hiroyuki Kajioka, 1997). Afterwards, steel cleanness had been drastically increased. Figure 1.2 shows the development of steel cleanness of deep drawing steel grades (Weng Y Q, 2006). It proved that the development of fine grained steels and that of steel-making technology of clean steels laid the bases for the production of modern high strength high toughness steels.

Controlled rolling technology was later developed in two directions. One direction was to study the behavior of deformed austenite. In 1960s, in USA kinetics

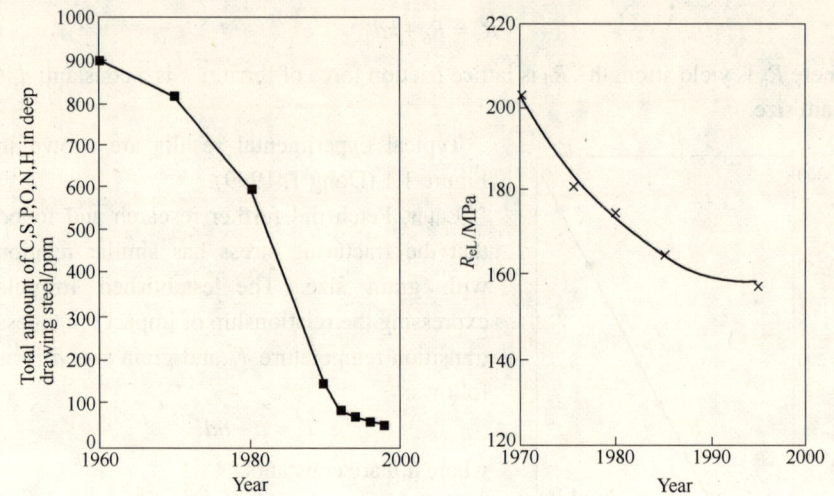

Figure 1.2 Cleanness improvement of deep drawing steel grade

of austenite recrystallization was interpreted qualitatively. In the early 1980s, "recrystallization controlled rolling", i.e. rolling in higher temperature zone to obtain grain refinement. By using this technology, it is possible to obtain refined austenite grain size to about 40 μm much finer than about 200μm that was common in the 1920s and 1930s. The other direction was the emerge of microalloyed steel that is one of the most important progresses and can be considered as the most vigorous category of steels. In 1960s, the effects of micro-amount additions of Nb, V, and Ti on the microstructures and properties of steels were studied in many countries in the world. In 1968, Gray and Yeo observed second phase particles of niobium carbonitrides in magnitude of nanometer (Gray J M, 1968). Precipitation strengthening due to precipitated particles of nanometer magnitude can be explained by using Orowan mechanism. Typical calculation and experimental results are shown in Figure 1.3 (Dong T, 1999). The second effect of addition of microalloying elements is the pinning of grain boundaries preventing from their movement, thus retarding grain growth resulting grain refinement strengthening. The third effect is to increase the recrystallization stop temperature. During hot rolling precipitated carbonitrides of microalloy elements exert grain boundary pinning force that is larger than recrystallization driving force resulting in increase of recrystallization stop temperature (T_{nr}). An example is shown in Figure 1.4. Ever since, non-recrystallization controlled rolling started to work. Finish rolling is realized in the temperature zone below recrystallization stop temperature. In consequence, nucleation rate during the $\gamma \rightarrow \alpha$ transformation is increased and the formed ferrite grains are therefore much refined.

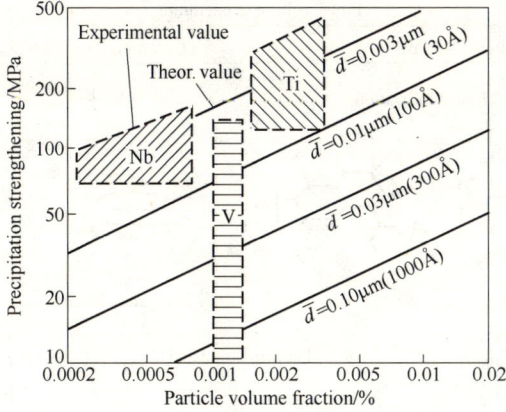

Figure 1.3 Relations of precipitation strengthening with precipitated particle size ($\bar{d}$) and volume fraction (f) and experimental data ranges

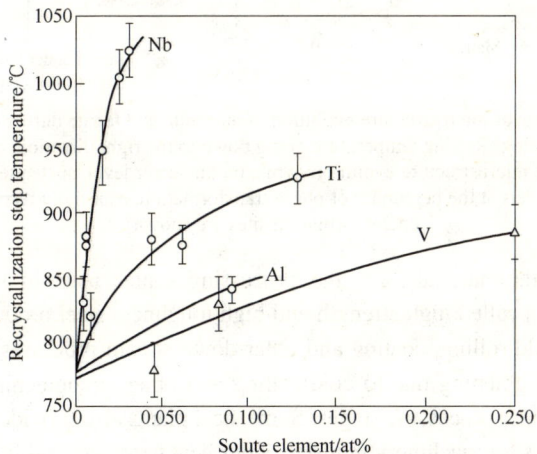

Figure 1.4 Relations of recrystallization stop temperature and solid solute content of microalloying elements in steel of 0.07C-0.225Si-1.40Mn

In 1980s, during the development of shipbuilding plate steels, one type of the plate steel products, microalloying principles of non-recrystallization controlled rolling and after rolling phase transformation leading to grain refinement had been applied. Moreover, technology of after rolling controlled cooling, especially, on-line accelerated cooling of thick plates was developed. Combination of controlled rolling and controlled cooling lead to the formation of complete TMCP (Thermo-mechanical controlled processing) technology. Figure 1.5 shows schematically the microstructure evolution during TMCP.

Application of TMCP technology for grain refinement and clean steel-making technology, together with the application of physico-metallurgical principles of solid solution strengthening, precipitation strengthening, and grain refinement strengthening lead to the formation of main stream of strengthening and toughening

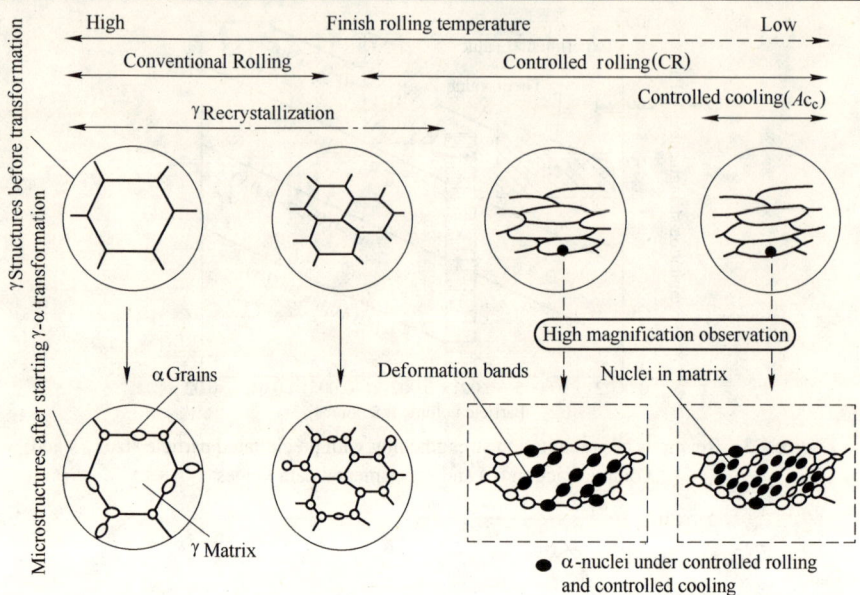

Figure 1.5   Models of microstructure evolution of austenite and ferrite during controlled rolling and controlled cooling (Rolling temperature going down to the right direction, on the upper level there is austenite microstructure evolution; while on the lower level, austenite microstructure models at the beginning of phase transformation, especially ferrite nuclei formation sites are shown)

of steel structural materials, i.e. the processing routes used in steel plants for production of hot rolled high strength and high toughness steel products. Of course, there still are cold rolling, coating and other down-stream processes in steel plants. Dislocation strengthening due to cold rolling and other strengthening mechanisms are involved in later processing stages. Some steel plants also provide semi-parts and semi-components for machinery industry. After heat treatment and finish machining, these parts and components will have their final properties guaranteed. Nevertheless, fine grained high strength high toughness steels produced by using TMCP has been recognized as one of the greatest progresses in the second half of 20th century. Table 1.2 shows the finest grain sizes of the TMCP processed low carbon steels. Here, the theoretically calculated values are obtained under conditions that nucleation of ferrite is taking place along grain boundaries during $\gamma \rightarrow \alpha$ transformation after hot rolling and grain growth under the best controlled cooling.

Table 1.2   The finest grain sizes of TMCP processed low carbon steels at present time

Grain size	γ Grain size /μm	α Grain size /μm	The finest α grain size /μm
γ Recrystallization rolling	40	15~20	
TMCP carbon steel		15~20	
TMCP microalloyed steel		10(industrial)	5(calculated)

1.2 R & D Program of "Super Steels" and "New Generation Steel Materials"

When entering the 1990s, increasingly serious competition was waged among various structural materials. Engineering plastic materials were increasingly applied for longitudinal structures subject to not very high loading. Audi car made of whole aluminum structure did appear in Europe posing threat to cars made of steel structure due to its self-weight reduction, reducing oil-consumption, and alleviation of gas emission. IISI (International Iron & Steel Institute) organized 35 steel companies from North America and Europe to jointly start a project on the development of "Ultra Light Steel Auto Body". In the project, it is required that strength level of auto body structure should be increased by 80%, the weight of auto body be reduced by 25%, Oil consumption of family car be reduced to 3L/100 km, and the amount of CO_2 emission reduced by 2%~3%. The development of high strength automotive sheet steels and longitudinal beam steels and the development of high strength and high toughness sheet steels will increase the competitiveness of steel materials against other engineering materials. The project certainly is an important project contributing to continuous optimization of air environment.

Japanese iron and steel industry made great contributions in R & D of high strength steels. From 1995 to 1997 in Japan, an investigation work was done for two years. Their reached conclusion was that postwar high speed industrialization in Japan has already come to the maturity period and great change period will come in the 21st century (Akira Sato Tekkon Kai, 1997). Maintenance costs of major basic structures built in postwar high speed development period are increasing as they are entering the revamping period. The revamping expenses occupied more than 50% of the country's total investment for capital construction. Due to very large consumption of steel after world war II, large amount of steel scrapes are being brought about. Re-melting of steel scrapes makes many alloy elements contained useless. Therefore, newly developed steel materials are not relying on alloying to ensure properties and natural resources must be saved. From the viewpoint of social development, Japan has entered into an aged society. One of every four people in Japan is above 65 years old. Social burden and environment protection put forward the task requiring more efficient industrial activities. Based on the above-mentioned concepts, "Creation of Ultra-Steels for the 21 Century" and "Ultra-Steel" were proposed in Japan. This concept in Japan is to develop new steel grades possessing double strength level and double service lifetime. Aiming at double strength level and double service life, under the sponsorship of Japanese Science Bureau, a 10 years long national research project named as STX-21 had been initiated in April, 1997. What's STX-21? STX-21 stands for structural materials for the 21st century. ST means science and technology and the letter X symbolizes a number of creative outputs expected. From FY1997(financial year of 1997) to FY2001, the Basic Mining Bureau of the Ministry of International Trade and Industry provided financial assistance to the program of "Super Metal Technology" which was conducted by NEDO (New Energy and Industrial Technology Development Organization). Within the program, there was one of four projects concerning iron and steel structural materials. This project required the development of technology controlling low carbon sheet steel with homogeneous multi-phase microstructure of ferrite and pearlite and with grain size reaching 1μm. The project was called "Technology for Creating Mesoscopic Structure Steel".

Under the promotion of Japanese program of "Ultra Steel", Republic of Korea started program of "High Performance Structural Steel for the 21 Century— HIPERS-21" which is a ten years national research program (1998~2008). The Korean program is similar to the Japanese program of "Double Strength Level and Double Service Lifetime". However, their managements are different. In Japan, NIMS (National Institute for Material Science) is the main organizer while in ROK, POSCO (Pohan Steel Corporation) is the main organizer.

In China, preparation work was done in 1996 and the new national program of "Basic Research of New Generation Microalloyed High Strength and High Toughness Steels" was formally started in 1997. In October, 1998, when China initiated national plan on important basic research programs, " Important Basic Research of New Generation Steel Materials" (from October, 1998 to October, 2003) was included among 10 programs being started as the first series of important research programs. This program was a program aiming at strength increase to double strength level for 3 kinds of structural materials. A program of "Metallurgy Basic Research on Iron and Steel Quality Improvement and Service Lifetime Increase" (October, 2004~October, 2009) was started in October 2004. It is a program to double the service lifetime of materials.

After initiation of similar programs in China, in Japan, and in Korea, EU (European Union) started a program of "Ultra Fine Grained Steels" in July, 2001. Corresponding research institutes in Italy, GB, Germany, and Belgium are taking part in the program work. At the same time, some European steel corresponsive companies (Corus, VAI) provide promotion from the industry.

In January of 2001, when the first phase work was completed, a new project "The Basic Technological Research on Environment Friendly Ultra Fine Grained Steels" was arranged. At the same time, a new concept on "New structural steels and new designs of engineering structures" was put forward. All these indicated that application of ultra steels to the basic constructions was emphasized.

Under the joint initiation and promotion of China, Japan, and Korea, ICASS (International Conference on Advanced Structural Steels) was held consecutively in Tsukuba, Japan in 2002 and in Shanghai, China in 2004, and in Gyeongju, Korea in 2006. Every time, the conference was attened by about 300 people from about 20 countries contributing to the new development of steel materials.

Here-in-after, it is necessary to briefly introduce the procedure of definition of "New generation steels" (NG Steels for short) in China.

The author of this paper, as the Chief Scientist of three consecutive national programs in China, started preparation work in 1995. Since 1996, I have been engaged in research of new generation structural materials for 12 years. Personally, in my opinion, advanced materials do not only include new biological materials, nanometer materials, and functional materials, but also include thousand years traditional materials optimally developed with low cost and high properties. When we look at the steel materials that are of more than 3000 years history, their actual strength potential has only been exploited one sevenths in nowadays industrial application of ultra high strength steels. Up till present time, steel materials are the most important man-made structural materials. Moreover, they are the most applied functional materials. Figure 1.6 demonstrates the change of world steel output during the modern metallurgy period beginning from the invention of LD convertor steelmaking, i.e. more than 50 years period. From the figure, we do not see any shadow of maturity, attenuation, and setting sun at all. On the contrary, it indicates that its vitality is still strong.

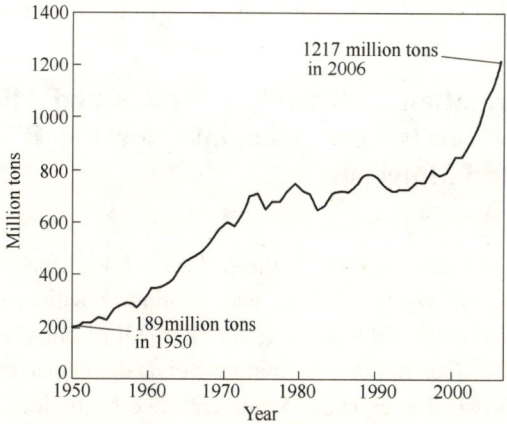

Figure 1.6 World output of crude steel since the time of LD converter invention

If mechanical properties and application properties are largely increased at low cost, traditional steel materials can be developed into advanced structural materials. Our effort is to do research and development work on new generation steel materials. General goal is to change the steel materials from traditional materials into advanced materials through creative and innovative work. The specific requirements for the new generation steel materials are described as follows:

1. In accordance with the requirement of sustainable development, natural resources and energy resources should be saved in production of materials. Moreover, in accordance with the principles of social development, production processing should be completed while meeting the requirement of recycling economy (3R).

2. Well-balanced properties are required including strength, toughness, and service performances.

3. No increase of production cost, in some cases it should be some what reduced.

When above-mentioned 3 conditions are fulfilled, new steel materials featuring in ultra fined microstructure, in high cleanness, and in high homogeneity and possessing double strength level and double service lifetime are classified as "New generation steel materials".

The R & D work has been concentrated in obtaining ultra fine grains concerning physical metallurgy and mechanical metallurgy, in obtaining high cleanness concerning chemical metallurgy, and in high homogeneity concerning the solidification as key factors. The research results are described in the respective chapters as follows: Chapters 2~7 controlling technologies on the formation of ultra-fine microstructures of different kinds of steels; Chapter 8 Metallurgical technologies of high cleanness steels; Chapter 9 Solidification technologies on high homogeneity; Chapter 10 Welding techniques for ultra-fine grained steels which are important for ensuring service performance and safety.

1.3   The Formation of Ultra-fine Grains and Microstructural Refinement of Steels-Core Technique for the R & D of New Generation Steel Materials

The historical evolution procedure of the strength of steel materials started from the understanding of crystal defects and continued with the application of interaction of different crystal defects. In the first half of previous century, before the maturation of dislocation theory, complete crystal was pursued doing a lot of work in preparing whisker crystals. At the end, due to the increasing volume of materials, various crystal defects could not be removed. Thus, people were turning to the increase of dislocation density, to the actual use of dislocation interaction for strengthening. Figure 1.7 shows schematically the relationship of strength and defect density.

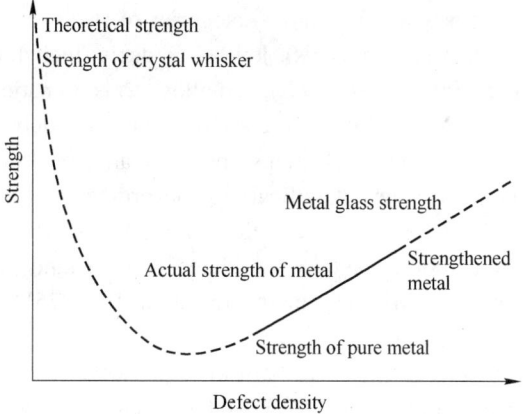

Figure 1.7　Relationship of strength and defect density

In steel materials, point defects (voids, interstitials, and substitutes) lead to the solid solution strengthening; increased linear defect (dislocation) density and defect interaction lead to dislocation strengthening; planar defects (grain boundaries) retarding dislocation movement and pinning grain boundaries (Interaction of precipitated phase and grain boundaries) lead to grain boundary strengthening; volume defects, e.g. secondary phase particles M (CN) and/or inter-metallic compounds) lead to the precipitation strengthening. These defects and their strengthening models are shown in Figure 1.8.

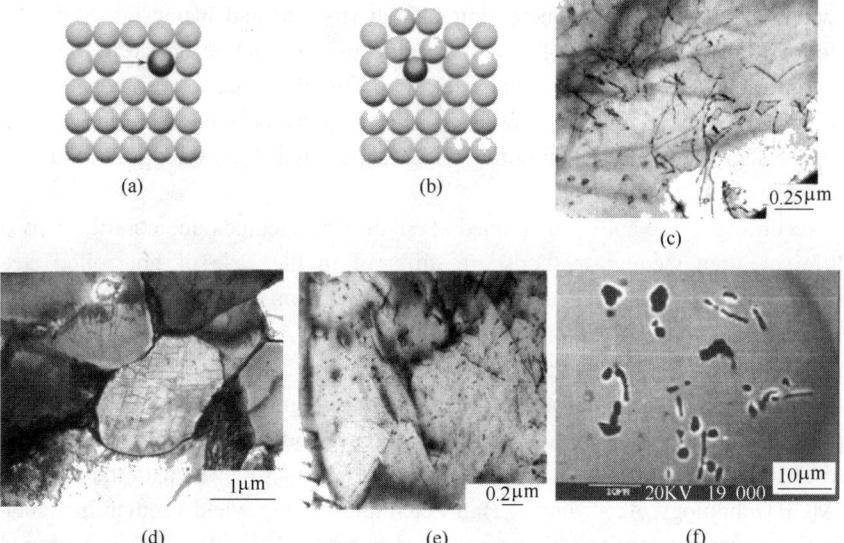

Figure 1.8　Various defects and their strengthening models in metal materials

(a) Point defects (void, substitution), solid solution; (b) Point defects (interstitial), solid solution; (c) Linear defects (dislocation), dislocation strengthening; (d) Planar defects (grain boundary), grain-boundary strenthening; (e) Volume defects (precipitate), precipitation strengthening; (f) Volume defects (inclusion Al_2O_3), material strengthening

Steel materials can be classified into 3 categories of steels, i.e. non-alloy steels (commonly called plain carbon steels), low alloy steels (including high strength low alloy steels and microalloyed steels), and alloy steels. In national standards of various countries, there are different classifications and definitions of steels according to the types of alloy elements and their amounts contained in steel. From the viewpoint of the classifications according to strength level in multi-national standards, it can be seen that over 50% of steel materials are of carbon steels. Low carbon steels are considered to be a kind of steels of yield strength level about 200 MPa (R_p in the range of 195~275MPa and they are composed of 10 designations).

Low alloy steels are considered to be a kind of steels of yield strength level about 400 MPa (R_p is in the range of 295~460MPa and they are composed of 20 designations). Alloy structural steels are classified according to their chemical compositions. However, these steels are at tensile strength level about 800 MPa not above 1000 MPa after quenching and tempering (Li X F, 1999). The research program of new generation steel materials in China is composed of three categories of steels with different objectives, i.e. to double the R_p strength level to 400 MPa for the steel category of R_p 200 MPa strength level, to double the R_p strength level to 700~800MPa for low alloy steel category of R_p 350~400MPa, and to raise the tensile strength level to 1500 MPa for alloy structural steels. For alloy structural steels of strength level above 1500 MPa, besides grain ultra-refinement, there exist problems of increasing resistance to delayed fracturing strength and of increasing fatigue strength and increasing of fatigue lifetime. For this category of steels, the objective of double service lifetime can not be reached simply by ultra grain refining. Therefore, the work is concentrated in the techniques of improvement of resistance against delayed fracturing strength and of increasing service lifetime under super-high cycles fatigue conditions (number of circles $\geq 10^8$).

According to the above-mentioned strengthening methods, the contributions of different strengthening methods are different in the case of hot rolled steel products with double strength level, (R_p increased from 200 MPa to 400 MPa and R_p increased from 350~400 MPa to 700~800 MPa). As it is shown in Figure 1.9, matrix strength is a basic value and solid solution, dislocation, precipitation, all three strengthening methods, contribute to the strength of material. For example, grain size of low carbon fine grain steel under industrial condition can reach ASTM GSN 8~9 corresponding to grain size 20~14 μm which is the result of TMCP technology. According to Hall-Petch relationship, yield strength increment from grain refinement for this type of steel is $kd^{-1/2}$=131~148 MPa. The strength contribution from grain refinement occupies 60%~70%. As it is shown in Figure 1.9, as the strength of steel increases, the grain refinement strengthening contribution increases. It can be concluded that the predominant method for the improvement of steel strength and toughness is the grain refining technology.

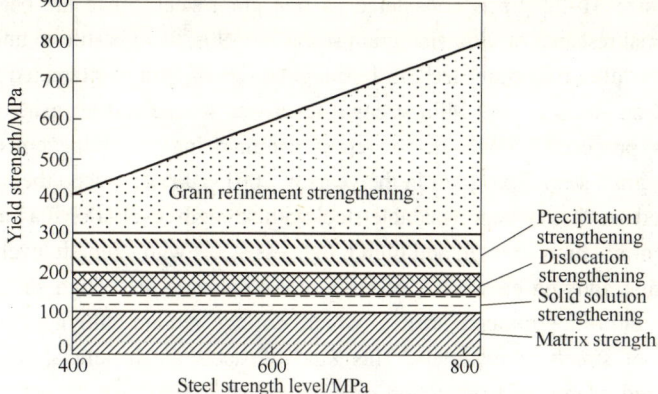

Figure 1.9 Scheme of various strengthening effects

It is different from other strengthening methods that grain refinement strengthening not only increases strength but also keeps the toughness level basically not to decrease. The other strengthening measures decrease toughness while increasing strength. That means grain refinement strengthening provides better safety. In accordance with Petch's relationship of low temperature brittleness transition temperature, $T_c = a - bd^{-1/2}$, fine grain steel shows high resistance to low temperature brittle fracturing. Figure 1.10 shows the curves of toughness versus impact testing temperature for reinforcing bar steel(20MnSi) with various grain size. This illustrates that steel applied for low temperature structures can be fine grained steel in stead of Ni and other element alloy steel.

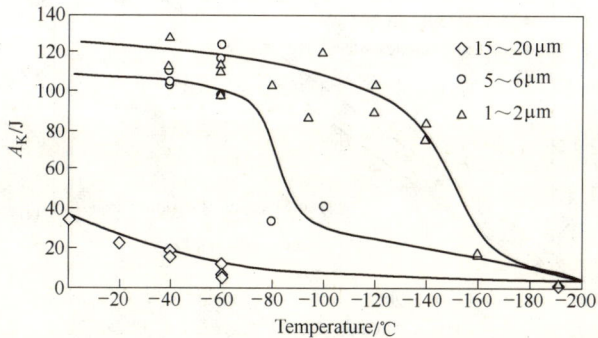

Figure 1.10 Low temperature impact toughness of trial-produced rebar steel 20MnSi with various ferrite grain size

It is necessary to give an explanation on the concept of "ultra-fine grain". The traditional concept of fine grain steels used in industry in many countries in the world is as follows: In accordance with ASTM GSN evaluation specification, the steel of GSN 1-3(grain size 250~150 μm) is considered as coarse grain steel; the steel of GSN

4~6(gain size 88~44 μm)is considered as medium grain size steel; the steel of GSN 7~8(grain size 31~22 μm)is considered as fine grain steel. Since the beginning of multi-national research of ultra-fine grain steels in 1990s, there is still no unified clear definition of "ultra-fine grain size". In Japan, grain size of 1μm was targeted at when R & D work on steels of 800 MPa strength level was started and no exact grain size range was proposed. NIMS in its report summarizing the achievements of its "Ultra-fine grain steels" program in the years of 2001~2005 described their work was concentrated on "heavy gage weldable steel with strength level 400MPa" and on the development of "high strength and high toughness steels with strength level 800 MPa without using alloying elements". NIMS's report declared that "high strength steels (alloy-free ultra-fine grained steels), which do not require alloying, are a new generation of structural materials. This kind of steels are beneficial to saving of resources and energy and protection of environment". Here, we do not see clearly common concept of ultra-fined grain steels either. "ultra-fine grain steels" and "double strength level" are of different conceptual categories but they were put forward at the same time and interrelated. Through ultra-grain refinement double strength level can be reached that is their relationship. The question now is how fine the grain size is sufficient for double strength level.

In 1997, Y. Kimura and S. Takaki published their laboratory experimental results on the relationship of yield strength with grain size, see Figure 1.11. In the figure, the results on austenitic stainless steel by Hayashi are also included (Kimura Y, Takaki S, 1997). It is shown that whether the material is of bcc lattice structure or of fcc lattice structure and whether grain size is of micron scale or of sub-micron scale, the Hall-Petch formulae works. It is seen from Figure 1.11 that if we want to

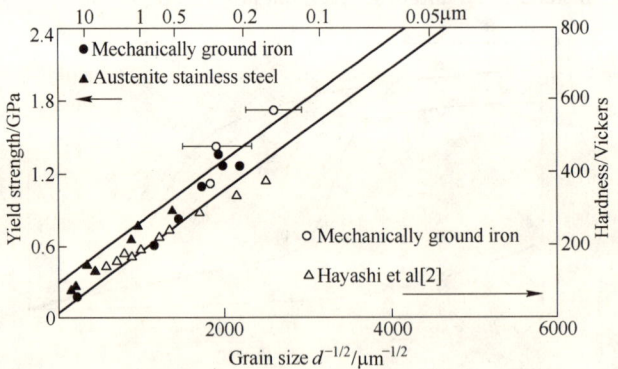

Figure 1.11   Relationships of yield strength with grain size

double the strength level of low carbon steels now with yield strength 200 MPa, which are used in very large quantity, refining of ferrite grain size to several microns will work in this concern. In Japan, the target at doubling strength level of carbon steels now with 400 MPa (No clear definition whether it is tensile strength or yield strength in Japan) can be achieved accordingly by refining grain size to

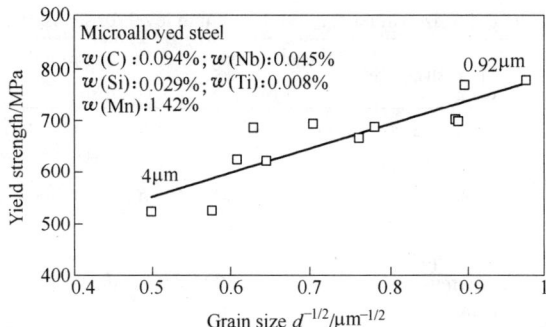

Figure 1.12 Relationship of fatigue strength and grain size for a microalloyed steel

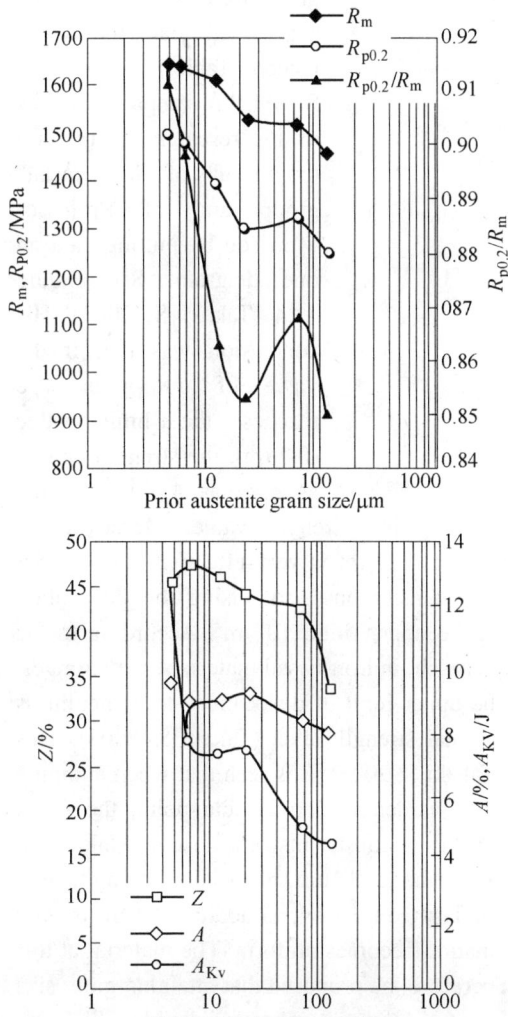

1μm. Figure 1.12 shows the experimental results of grain size and yield strength of microalloyed pipeline steel X65 (Weng Y Q, 2003). Figure 1.13 shows the experimental results of austenite grain size and mechanical properties of structural alloy steel 42CrMo (Weng Y Q, 2003). A conclusion can be reached by generalizing above-mentioned results as follows: under the conditions that chemical composition, and microstructure of original material remain unchanged, by grain refinement strengthening, the steel reaches double strength level while the refined grain size attains a certain value. This respective grain size value means the basic value of ultra-fine grain size of the material. According to this conclusion, the ultra-fine grain size values for ensuring double strength level for steels of various categories being concerned in this book are listed in Table 1.3.

Table 1.3   Ultra-fine grain size values for double strength level for steels of various categories

Steel category	Microstructure	Present strength / MPa	Target strength / MPa	Grain size /μm
Low carbon steels	Ferrite-pearlite	R_{eL} about 200	R_{eL} about 400	about 5 (α)
Low (micro-) alloy steels	Low carbon bainite or acicular ferrite	R_{eL} about 400	R_{eL} about 800	1~2 (α)
Alloy structural steels	Tempered martensite or bainite or both	R_m about 800	R_m about 1500	about 5 (γ)

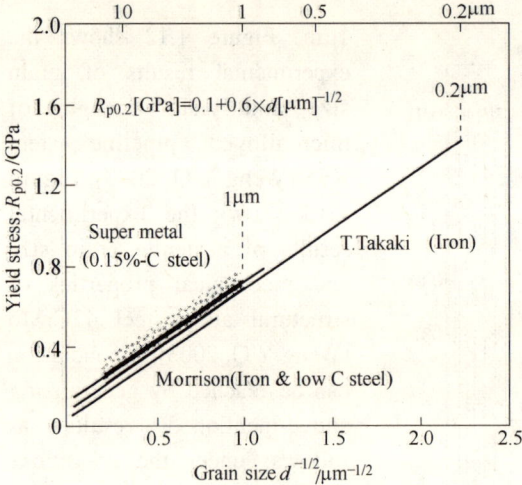

Figure 1.14   Hall-Petch relations in bulky iron & steels

What will be the result if grain size can be refined to a size finer than the value listed in Table 1-3? Professor S. Takaki compared results of his research group with those results of "Super metal" group and of Professor Morrison by putting data on one diagram, See Figure 1.14 (Takaki S, 2003). His conclusion was that if the value of ultra-grain size reaches the limit value (0.2μm), the strength can be as high as 4 times of the traditional strength value instead of double strength value. Moreover, he concluded that "Ultra grain refinement to 0.25μm is very effective not only for promoting the increase of dislocation density but also raising the dislocation density." Dislocation density reaches the upper limit, $10^{16}/m^2$. According to the linear relationship formula of Bailey-Hirsch, in iron-based materials, the strongest dislocation strengthening effect or the upper limit of dislocation strengthening is about 1.14GPa, i.e. 4 times of traditional strength level (Takaki S, 2003). This estimation is shown in Figure 1.15 (Takaki S, 2003). It is seen that when attaining the strength upper limit through work hardening above yield point, the finest ferrite grain size is 0.33μm. This result is in consistent with those of Maki et al. Maki considered that if grain size is as fine as 0.1μm, dislocation strengthening disappears and there is no grain boundary conception; in addition, there is very small stress concentration and deformation becomes uniform. The material at this stage is close to an ideal material. Therefore, he proposed that attaining grain size 0.1μm is the goal of microstructural control for structural materials (Maki T, 1996).

In consequence of this analysis, ultra-fine grain refinement has its limitation. The maximal grain refinement effect is about 4 times of the present strength of fine grain materials. The finest grain size would be about 0.25μm and 0.1μm grain size is the limit value for ideal structural materials.

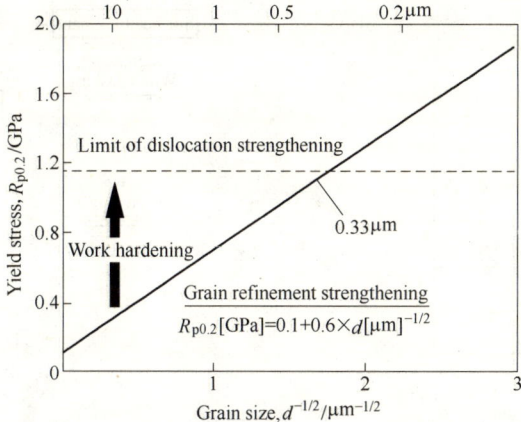

Figure 1.15   Illustration showing the shift of strengthening mechanism with ultra grain refinement

For attaining the finest grain size 0.25 μ m or for attaining the limit grain size 0.1 μm, there is so far no such production technology yet. Scientist in materials area are working with severe plastic deformation methods, e.g. ECAP(equal channel angular process), ARB (additive roll bonding), MAF(Multi-axes forging), SMAT, HPT and so on. Figure 1.16 schematically shows their working concepts. By using these methods, it is possible to obtain small pieces of samples with ultra-fine grain microstructures of sub-micrometer or nanometer scale. However, there is no economical and large-scale (above 10 thousand tons/a) production to be seen in the future. In order to make it possible for industrial application within 5~10 years, our research work has been relying on the modern iron and steel production processes, i.e. on the bases of clean steel metallurgy, homogeneous solidification and applying rolling process to form steel products and at the same time to obtain ultra-fine grain materials. In another words, the technical innovation and creation in R & D of the formation theory and controlling technology of ultra-fine grain structures are pursued on the basis of TMCP technology.

In 2001, Nükura briefly introduced new methods to obtain ultra-fine grain steels based on TMCP technology (Nükura M et al, 2001). Three methods are applied which are basically under specific conditions and can result in grain size in micron scale and in double strength level of new steel products. See Figure 1.17. However, up till now, all the laboratory results have not been approved in industry. The theory and technology of ultra-fine grain steels are with background of industrial production and application. Up till now, there have been about 10 million tons of steel products produced by using the technology as introduced in this book. Some methods which are proved effective in laboratories but not yet applied in large-scale production will not been introduced in the book.

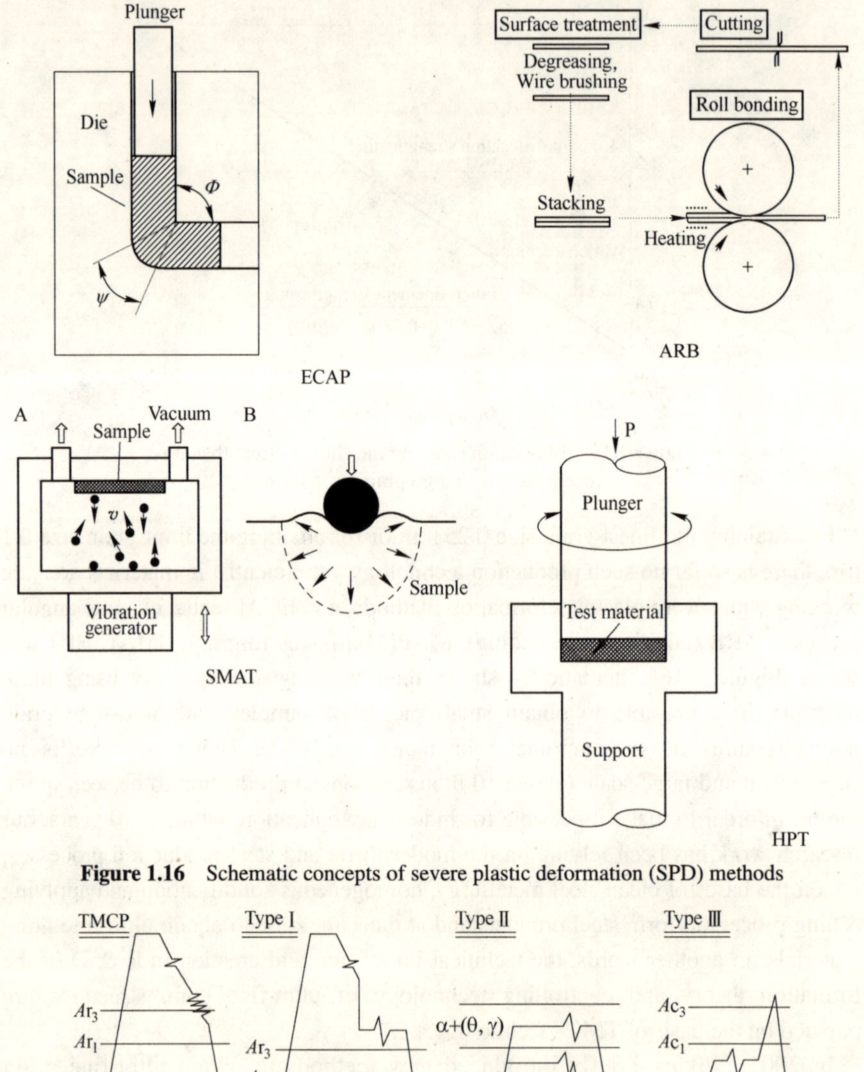

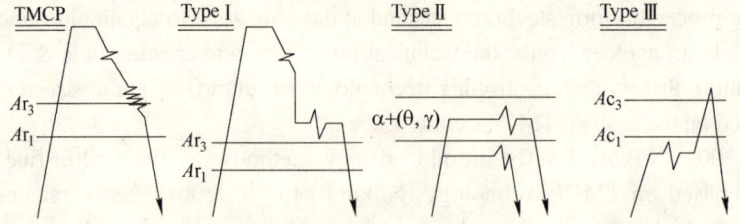

Figure 1.16 Schematic concepts of severe plastic deformation (SPD) methods

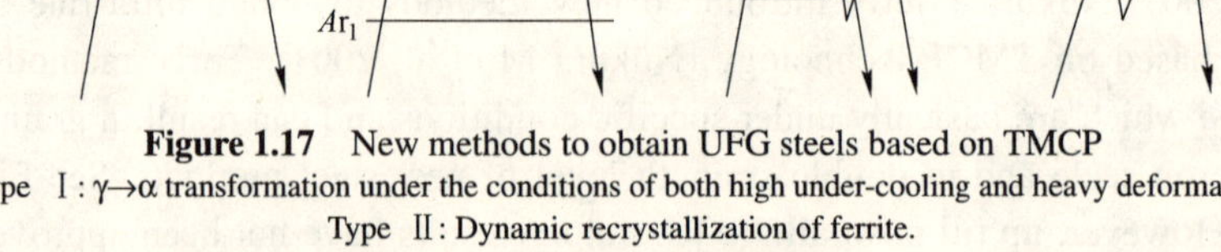

Figure 1.17 New methods to obtain UFG steels based on TMCP
Type Ⅰ: γ→α transformation under the conditions of both high under-cooling and heavy deformation.
Type Ⅱ: Dynamic recrystallization of ferrite.
Type Ⅲ: Spontaneous reverse transformation

1.4 Theory and Technology on Ultra-fine Grains

Chapters 2~7 introduce six types of ultra-fine grain formation theories and corresponding technologies. They are concerning different microstructures, different strength levels, and different application properties. For those who do not have much time in reading the whole book, Section 1-4 gives its summary.

1.4.1 The state change and microstructure refinement of austenite during hot deformation

The refinement of austenite microstructure by making use of dynamic recrystallization has been proved to be effective by the work done by Maki in 1980s and the recent work by Nagai. See Figure 1.18 (Nagai K, 2002). Here, we consider that austenite refinement is related to a parameter of strain rate compensated with temperature Z (Zener- Hollomon parameter) (Nagai K, 2002). That means whether austenite grain refinement is taking place or not depends on occurrence of dynamic recrystallization. The expression of Z is as follows:

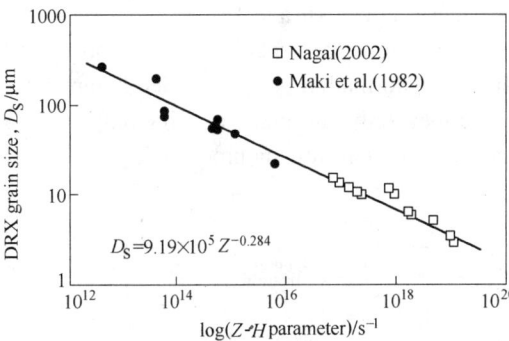

Figure 1.18 DRX grain size is a function of Z-H parameter under a wide range of process conditions

$$Z = \dot{\varepsilon}\exp(Q/RT) = A\sigma_p^n \qquad (1.1)$$

where, $\dot{\varepsilon}$ is strain rate; Q is deformation activation energy; R is gas constant; T is absolute temperature; A, n are constants; σ_p is first flow stress peak value. From formula (1.1), it can be seen that if we want to obtain refined austenite grain size to several microns, the strain rate should be fairly high and deformation temperature fairly low. Usually, when the strain rate at hot rolling is $\dot{\varepsilon} = 10^{-4}\text{s}^{-1}$, dynamic recrystallization takes place. However, it can also seen from Figure 1.18 that if we want to refine the austenite grain size from several tenths μm to several μm, Z-value should be increased to 10^4~10^5, i.e. strain rate be increased by 4~5 magnitudes and it is impossible in hot rolling practice. In addition, Z-H parameter is correlated to strain value and high strain rate leads also to the increase of peak flow stress ($\varepsilon_{99\%} = AZ_c^\gamma$, where $\varepsilon_{99\%}$ means how much strain was needed for completing the 99% DRX). Therefore, simple application of high strain, high strain rate, and low deformation temperature and use of dynamic recrystallization is not an effective way for obtaining ultra fine grain size. Nevertheless, it tells us that proper control of ε, $\dot{\varepsilon}$, and T(strain ε, strain rate $\dot{\varepsilon}$, and deformation temperature T) may lead to austenite grain refinement due to dynamic recrystallization during roughing process and at the same time, to the preparation for the later finishing process for deformation induced ferrite transformation due to accumulation of deformation. Take the modern bar rolling mill as an example, rolling temperature can be controlled between 1250~700℃, strain rate ($\dot{\varepsilon}$)between 0.5~200s^{-1} , inter-pass time between 0.1~10s, and deformation can be as high as above 30%. These conditions provide big room for the research of austenite dynamic recrystallization behavior. By applying intensified cooling, austenite is under under-cooling condition leading to high nucleation rate of ferrite during γ→α transformation. Due to enhanced γ→α transformation, it is beneficial to the ultra- fine grain refinement of austenite and then transformed ferrite.

Ultra fine grain formation during hot rolling process is a systematic change. It is not a simple physical procedure. The process includes deformation and under-cooling of austenite, dynamic recrystallization and also includes recovery, static, continuous and un-continuous phenomena depending deformation and temperature conditions, and the phase transformation procedure. See Figure 1.19. The first chapter of this book describes only austenite conditioning at high temperatures that is the preparation stage for the following procedures.

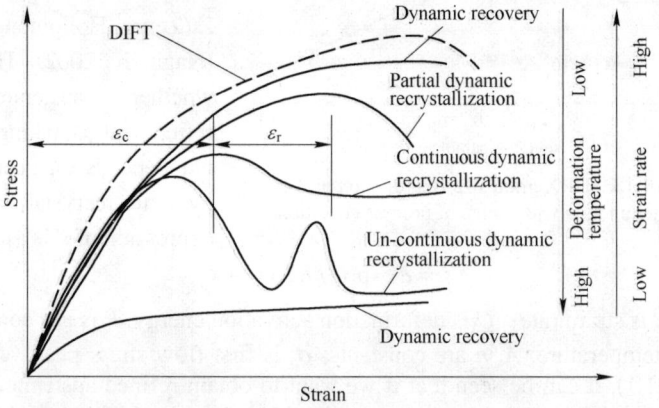

Figure 1.19   Schema of true stress-true strain curves in relations
with deformation temperature and strain rate

1.4.2   *Deformation induced ferrite transformation (DIFT)*

In 1981, R. Priestner reported that it had been found that γ→α phase transformation taking place in low carbon steel within roll gap during hot rolling and he called it strain-induced transformation to ferrite (Priestner R, 1981; Priestner R, Ali L, 1993) In 1983, Yada et al (1983a; 1983b) obtained fine ferrite grain size of 2~3 μm of C-Mn steel during experimental rolling on laboratory rolling mill. They proposed deformation induced concept. Later on, in 1987 (Matsumura Y, Yada H, 1987) a combination of DIT with ferrite dynamic recrystallization was further proposed. Thus, the direction of obtaining ultra-fine grains through hot rolling has been established. In 1990s, P. D. Hodgson et al (Beyon J H, 1992; Hodgson P D et al, 1999; Hickson M R et al, 2002), Lee et al (1995), and W. Y. Choo (2002; 2001; 2000) consecutively reported similar results. Although the names of the concepts were different among different workers and their research methods were different, there are two essential implications which are the same.

1. γ→α phase transformation is happening during the procedure of deformation rather than being happening during the cooling. Therefore, this kind of phase transformation is a dynamic one.
2. By using this kind of phase transformation, ultra fine grains can be obtained. The chapter 2 of the book introduces this kind of phase transformation. Although it takes place under the condition of necessary amount of accumulative strains (critical strain), the chemical composition, original condition after solidification, stress, strain, strain rate, inter-stand cooling and inter-pass time, rolling temperature schedule, after-rolling cooling, and coiling, all of these, are related to this phenomenon. It is a combination result of multi-variations and multi-factors. Concerning ferrite/pearlite steels, it is called deformation induced ferrite transformation and will be introduced in detail.

1.4.2.1 Thermodynamic consideration of deformation induced ferrite transformation (DIFT)

The difference between DIFT and the phase transformation during conventional controlled rolling and controlled cooling (TMCP) relies on that the transformation (γ→α+P in low carbon steels) takes place during rolling process rather than during after-rolling cooling process.

Commonly, the whole procedure of rolling takes place in austenite zone, see Figure 1.20(a). People are concerned with deformation amount, temperature, rolling force, rolling speed, and the final shape and dimensions, and their precision of the rolled product. The conditions for phase transformation to take place during rolling are less concerned and pursued. When phase transformation is studied, we have to bear in mind that for phase transformation to take place the necessary thermodynamic conditions should be fulfilled. The direction for phase transformation going on should be that direction which leads to the lowering of free energy of the system, i.e. $\Delta G < 0$. The expression of free energy change is as follows:

$$\Delta G = -V(\Delta G_V - \Delta G_E) + \Delta G_S \tag{1.2}$$

where, ΔG is the change of total free energy of the system, ΔG_V is the change of chemical free energy (V means volume), ΔG_E is elastic free energy change and ΔG_S is the change of surface free energy for the formation of new phase.

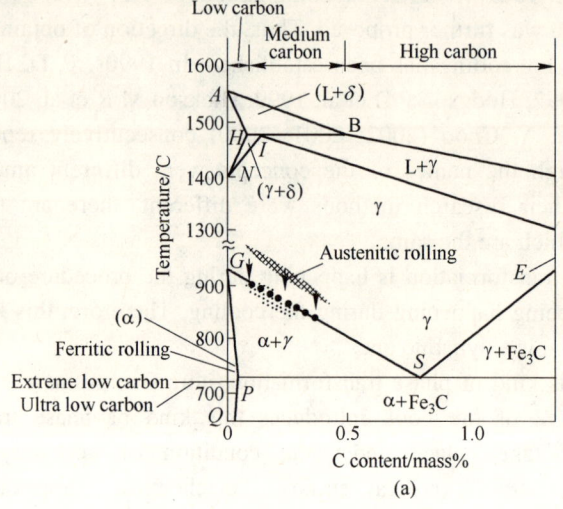

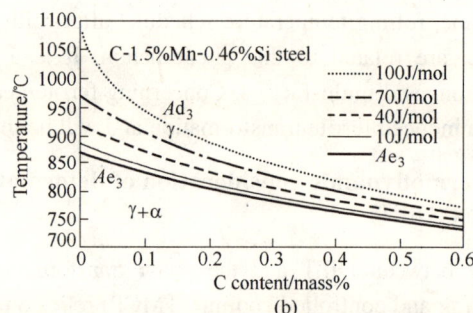

Figure 1.20   Fe-C phase diagram (a) and Ae_3 curve and its change after deformation (b)

Expression 1.2 indicates that reduction of chemical driving force of phase transforming system has to overcome elastic energy increase and surface energy increase of the newly formed phase of the system. Expression usually works under isobaric condition (commonly one atmospheric pressure).

If the stress-train procedure during rolling is considered, plastic deformation in steel in the process of rolling inevitably leads to un-releasing of part deformation energy and/or to heat relaxation in the system. Especially, in modern high speed rolling, a part of energy is kept in the deformed steel. Our work shows that 5%~10% deformation energy is stored in the steel. This part of deformation energy causes change of the system free energy that in turn transfers into phase transformation driving force, i.e. lowers free energy of the system. If we define this change as ΔG_D, then the expression 1.2 can be modified as follows:

$$\Delta G = -V(\Delta G_V - \Delta G_E) + \Delta G_S - \Delta G_D \qquad (1.3)$$

Due to the change of the system free energy, the critical point Ae_3 of the deformed steel changes. Ae_3, at which temperature α-phase starts its appearance under equilibrium state, increases to the point of Ad_3 (d means "deformation") due to the effect of ΔG_D. Calculation (See Figure 1.20(b)) shows that the large the stored deformation energy, the more Ad_3 increases. During the finish rolling, deformation taking place at the temperature close to Ae_3, the steel may enter into the inter-critical zone ($\gamma + \alpha$). The newly formed phase α is called as deformation induced ferrite. Normally, DIFT working zone is between $Ae_3 \sim Ar_3$. In the case of microalloyed steels and under large strain rate, it is possible that Ad_3 may be higher than Ae_3.

1.4.2.2 DIFT phase transformation and characters of transformed products

The research work done on DIFT indicates that the transformation characters are found to be different than those understood in the past. They are described as follows:

1. DIFT is a kind of dynamic phase transformation. The stored energy due to deformation increases the driving force for phase transformation. Phase transformation occurs mainly during deformation, which is different from that during TMCP. The latter phase transformation mainly occurs after deformation cooling.

   Since it is a dynamic phase transformation and under non-equilibrium condition, there is a possibility of reverse transformation and formation of meta-stable phase under certain conditions.

2. It is a kind of phase transformation by nucleation. α phase nucleates at the original γ grain boundaries where is of high level of distortion energy.

   Nuclei of new phase which are larger than critical size (r^*) form in the high distortion area on front lines of α / γ grain boundaries. When the local strain (micro-strain ε) is large enough, nuclei form repeatedly in distortion area. When strain (ε) is further increased, nuclei also form within grain in the high distortion areas (deformation bands, slip bands, twin-zones, sub-grain boundaries, and interfaces with second phase) continuously. This repeated nucleation process is an unsaturated process. It is different from "nucleation saturation mechanism" proposed by Cahn concerning the kinetics of thermal deformation transformation of under cooled austenite and can not be described by first phase J-M-A formula.

3. It possesses fast phase transformation feature. According to our research on crystallographic relations between parent phase and new phase including research on various textures, and the feature of phase transformation driven by chemical potential, DIFT has been proved to be diffusive phase transformation. Carbon diffuses upslope. When temperature is comparatively high, pearlite

forms at the final zone of trigonal grain boundaries. When the temperature is lower enough, divorced pearlite or cementite particles form in the area of high distortion (high dislocation density) inside grains.

Due to the hot deformation, dislocation density continuously increases. Diffusion of carbon is going on through channels, i. e. along grain boundaries or along dislocations. Therefore, DIFT is of a kind of fast diffusion process. Our calculation result shows that it happens in a time of several microseconds that means it is in accordance with the essence of dynamic phase transformation.

4. DIFT leads to the formation of ultra-fine grains. Calculation shows that DIFT phase transformation features smaller critical nuclei size (r^*) compared to traditional γ-α transformation. If ΔG_D=50 J / mol, r^*= 0.064 μm. See Figure 1.21. Considering that DIFT is fast dynamic phase transformation which mainly relies on nucleation rather on grain growth, the newly formed α phase is of ultra-fine grains. Especially in microalloyed steels, due to the existence of M (CN) phase, α phase is easy to nucleate at the vicinity of precipitates and is not easy to grow. Therefore, grain size of ultra-fine ferrite is generally finer than that in low carbon steels. This is the basis of "double strength level" of microalloyed steels with already higher strength compared to low carbon steels.

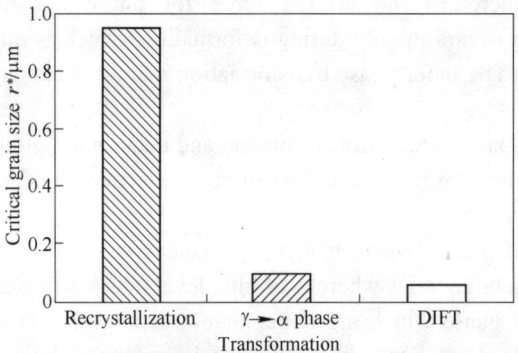

Figure 1.21   Critical grain size (r^*) for various procedures

5. DIFT is accompanied by dynamic recrystallization of ferrite. Through dynamic recrystallization of ferrite (α-DRX), ultra-fine grain equiaxed ferrite forms. Hence, high strength and high toughness and basic isotropic are guaranteed. DIFT and α-DRX are two stages but they are taking place consecutively and alternatively. This is the important start-point for process control.

6. The influence of steel composition on the process and characters of DIFT is described in respective chapters and paragraphs. The influences of carbon, manganese, niobium, vanadium etc are introduced. Except low carbon steel that is composed of ferrite and pearlite, due to different chemical compositions, the second structural constituent may be bainite. The carbides

of bainite are formed either as lamellar or as granular. Relative parts of this book introduce rules of microstructural evolution under different conditions. Due to different microstructural compositions, the strength, toughness, yield ratio, formability, and weldability are different, thus creating favorable conditions for the specific industrial applications in the down-stream.

7. In the process control, under-cooling (ΔT), strain (ε), strain rate ($\dot{\varepsilon}$), etc can be varied in considerable ranges. Increasing under-cooling is a major aspect in deformation intensified phase transformation. Due to the high strain rates of modern rolling mills i.e. $\dot{\varepsilon} > 100$ s^{-1} for hot strip rolling mill and $\dot{\varepsilon} > 30$ s^{-1} for wire rod rolling mill, the phenomena which could not be observed by Yada, Hodgson et al in their works have been observed in this present work and they are described in the book. Through this work, new understanding has been gained about dynamic recrystallization of austenite and the behavior of austenite under high strain rate deformation.

8. DIFT leads to the change of steel mechanical properties. Experiments proved that well-balanced high strength and high toughness, good cold bending property, high r-value, low FATT of ultra-fine grain steels indicate that ultra-fine grain steels possess outstanding service properties. As results of these merits of DIFT, ultra-fine grain steels possess the same level of properties as high strength low alloy steels do. Many iron & steel companies in China are continuing work on second development and on R & D of new steel products. In this field at present, China is a country in the world that industrial trials are underway in large scale including trial-production and industrial application. Further research and industrial application are still needed in order to deepen the understanding of the essence of DIFT.

In the research work of DIFT, some authors of the book held that DIFT is a process of massive ferrite transformation without long distance diffusion (especially for carbon diffusion). Its evidence has been identified in the ultra low carbon steel or under high strain rate deformation. Therefore, it is believed that DIFT is a kind of diffusionless civilian transformation implying that it is an interface controlled phase transformation. Hence, further research on the essence of DIFT and interfacial controlled phenomena is the direction of our future work. From the observation and analysis of DIFT kinetics, it is known that in microalloyed steels, mainly dynamic recovery takes place and dynamic recrystallization does not. Under the rolling temperature and deformation parameters, whether carbon steels undergo accompanied dynamic recrystallization has become the point of argument. Whether Ad_3 is always lower than Ae_3, there were different experimental observations supporting different points of view. All these arguments tell us that the theory of DIFT needs further work.

1.4.3   *Deformation induced precipitation and medium temperature phase transformation control*

The yield strength level of low carbon ferrite-pearlite unalloyed steel can be increased from 200 MPa to 400 MPa through ultra-fine grain processing. When the steel strength is further increased, e.g. yield strength reaches 500 MPa or even more, the ferrite-pearlite steel is facing a series of problems. Strength increase requires increase of carbon content in steel leading to the deterioration of weldability, plasticity, toughness, cold and hot workability, simultaneously leading to the decrease of low temperature toughness and unfavorable fracture toughness. Although high strength low alloy steels are improved by adding microalloying elements to obtain precipitation strengthening and hence avoiding increase of carbon content, the combined propertied of ferrite-pearlite steels with strength level higher than 400~500 MPa are inferior to those of acicular bainite steels or bainite-martensite multi-phase steels. For example, strength level of ferrite-pearlite steels is lower than that of low carbon bainite or bainite-martensite steels. Taking acicular bainitic steels as an example, Table 1.4 shows the comparison of mechanical properties of pipeline steels X65 and X70 (both with the same chemical composition but processed in to two kinds of different microstructures). Figure 1.22 shows the comparison of toughness (in terms of CVN, CTOD, And DWTT) of two X70 steels with different microstructures. It can be seen from Table 1.4 and Figure 1.22 that at yield strength level of 400~600MPa, acicular bainitic steel possesses clear superiority in toughness properties over ferrite-pearlite steel. And when at yield strength level above 600 MPa, low carbon bainite and ultra-low carbon bainite-martensite multi-phase steels show even stronger superiority.

Table 1.4   Comparison of mechanical properties of pipeline steels with the same composition but with different microstructures

Pipeline steels	Microstructure	R_{eL}/MPa	R_m/MPa	Yield ratio	A/%	Z/%	Charpy energy/J
	Ultra-fine grain ferrite	477	625	0.76	27.0	72.6	-
X65	Acicular ferrite	529	595	0.89	27.7	85.3	320(room t.)
	Ferrite+pearlite	523	579	0.90	32.6	75.7	202(room t.)
X70	Ferrite+pearlite	545	640	0.85	42	-	161(-20℃)
	Acicular ferrite	552	628	0.88	42	-	320(-20℃)
X80	Acicular ferrite	596	720	0.83	40	-	285(-20℃)

The similarity of the work in Chapter 4 and that of Chapter 3 is how to obtain ultra-refinement of microstructures of acicular ferrite and low carbon bainite steels under conditions of deformation.

The work focus on this kind of steels is how to control and make use of the microstructural evolution during rolling deformation and after deformation for the purpose of ultra refinement of lath bainite and acicular ferrite. At first, the solid solution and precipitation behaviors and the formation of carbonitrides [M(C, N)] have to be considered that. Part of M(C, N) precipitates are formed during solidification (especially titanium related carbonitriding); and more of them are

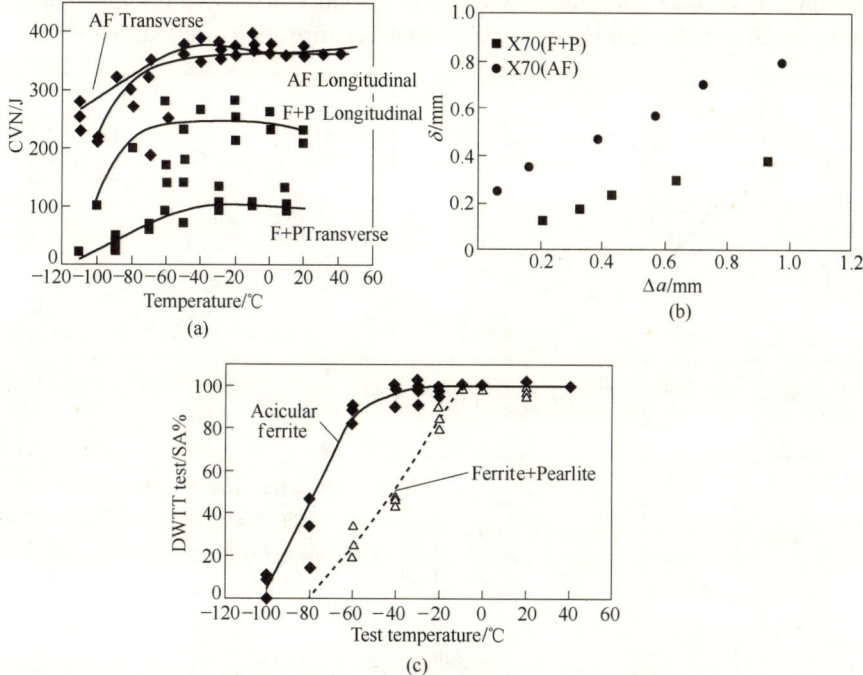

Figure 1.22 Comparison of mechanical properties of pipeline steels with different microstructures

(a) CVN comparison; (b) CTOD comparison;(c) DWTT comparison

formed during hot rolling (especially carbonitrides of Nb and V). In consequence of M(C,N) precipitation, recrystallization controlled rolling process becomes available. During hot rolling of slabs, recrystallization and deformation induced precipitation take place. Moreover , this two procedures interact. Kinetics of crystallization depends on strain (ε), strain rate ($\dot{\varepsilon}$) while precipitation driving force depends on under-cooling degree (difference between equilibrium precipitation temperature and actual precipitation temperature). Figure 1.23 is a scheme of these two mutual restricting factors (Maki T, 1996). Figure 1.23(a) and (b) show starting point of recrystallization (R_s) and precipitation starting point (P_s), and that under deformation induced condition precipitation starting point shifts to p_s'. This is a single process scheme of deformation induced precipitation. Figure

1.23(c) is the result of these two mutual restricting factors. By detail analyzing, it can be divided into 3 zones. These 3 zones are as follows: In zone ①, there exists austenite recrystallization controlled rolling; in zone ②, recrystallization of γ takes place at first, then precipitation starts at the recrystallized grain boundaries; in zone ③, precipitation takes place at first, then recrystallization being retarded and non-recrystallization controlled rolling can be conducted. It tells us that deformation induced precipitation in zone ② and zone ③ should be paid special attention to. It is the basis of the existence of deformation induced precipitation p_s' curve. In chapter 4 of this book, its experimental confirmation is introduced.

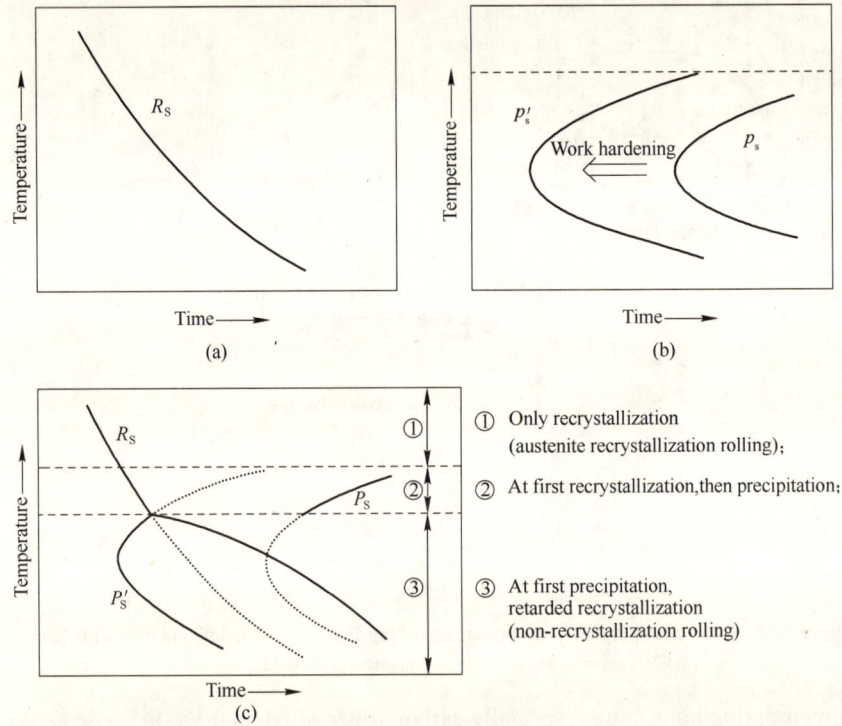

Figure 1.23   Schema of interaction of recrystallization and precipitation of M (C,N)

Due to the high speed of modern rolling mill, especially of the finishing train of hot strip rolling mill, in the actual non-recrystallization rolling of HSLA steels, neither dynamic precipitation, nor γ recrystallization takes place. The matrix remains to be austenite with high density of dislocation. The medium temperature phase transformed low carbon bainite and/or acicular ferrite are both microstructures with high density of dislocation. It indicates that in the deformed austenite before transformation there exist high accumulation of strain and high density of dislocation. Therefore, to have a comprehensive control of the M (CN) precipitation and relaxation of dislocation and to form Relaxation－Precipitation－

Controlling technology i.e. RPC technology has become one of the implications of the present book. The essence of RPC technology is to have the effect of intra-granular acicular ferrite intersecting the deformed austenite; to have cell structure with certain orientation difference in deformed austenite grains before transformation to bainite which exerting restricting effect on the growth of transformed bainite; and to have the stabilizing effect of strain induced M (CN) precipitates on the sub-structures. Under combined function of these 3 effects, ultra refined bainitic matrix with micrometer and sub-micrometer scale is obtained. This kind of microstructures exhibits outstanding combined properties. Among these, the cell structure forms at proper temperature (for example, 850 ℃) and after short time of air-cooling and then followed by water-cooling. The short time air-cooling control is needed for relaxation of high dense dislocations and the formation of cell structures. Figure 1.24 shows the microstructural evolution of a low C (0.06)-Nb-Ti steel during the processing by using RPC technology. By this way, the material strength (R_{eL}) has been increased from 600 MPa to 800 MPa.

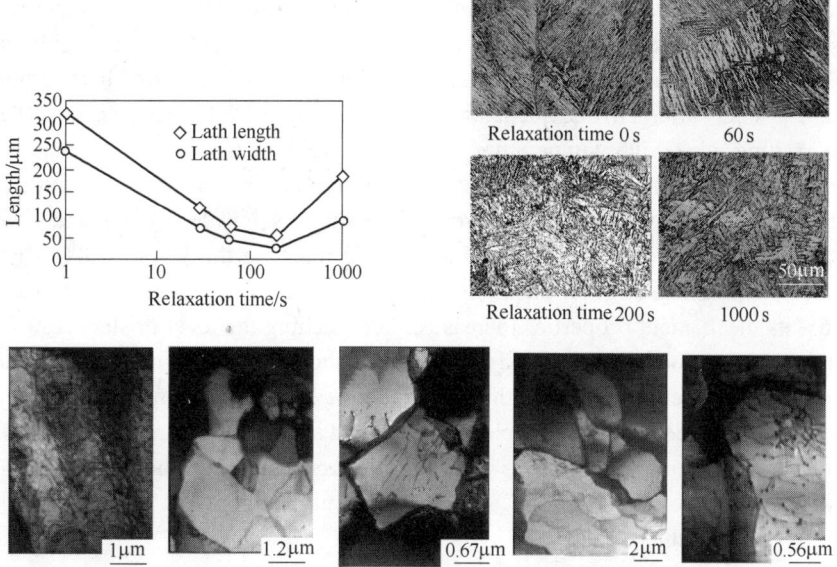

Figure 1.24 Microstructural evolution of low carbon bainitic steel during RPC processing

One of the development tendency of high strength microalloyed steels in 21st century is low carbon microalloyed acicular ferritic (or granular bainitic) steels. The influence of hot deformation on the microstructural changes has been studied. Hot deformation can promote the phase transformation at medium temperature. Dynamical CCT diagram shows that the medium transformation zones have the tendency to move towards left and up direction. This benefits the refinement of acicular ferrite and the refinement of "island" microstructure (Shan Yiyin, Xiao Furen et al, 2001). In order to obtain fine acicular ferrite microstructure, it is necessary to start from the roughing stage and to systematically control the rolling temperature, cooling after rolling according to the requirement of ultra refinement. The requirements for alloy elements and purity should be taken into account. For example, molybdenum can retard the precipitation of M (C,N) from austenite and promote the precipitation hardening of ferrite. Deformation leads to the formation of defects and activate the grain boundaries. In order to develop the high strength hot rolled microalloyed steels, further work is needed.

For the two types of steels of microstructures (LCB/ULCB or A.F/B-M), "tempering" process of controlled rolled steels has been developed in our work, i.e. high temperature (about 600℃) tempering, was conducted for TMCP rolled steels. The tempering not only refines microstructure and makes properties more stable; but what is more important is that tempering also promotes the further precipitation of M(C,N). Although RPC is applying the same concept, experiment shows that the precipitation is more complete after tempering; especially, for precipitation of V (C,N) that can be realized thoroughly at 500~600℃ tempering. Table 1.5 lists the mechanical properties of low carbon bainitic steels after TMPC, quenching and tempering, RPC hot rolling, and RPC hot rolling plus high temperature tempering. Table 1.6 lists the mechanical properties of acicular ferrite steels after two different kinds of processing. It can be seen that after two kinds of different processing, the tensile strength and yield strength of the two steels increased apparently reaching the level of 800 MPa, while maintaining original plasticity (A%). In the case of acicular ferrite steel X65, its mechanical properties increase either reaching the level of steel X80. In acicular ferrite steel, precipitated carbonitrides and the pined up dislocations can work as hydrogen traps. Thus, they provide new locations for mobile hydrogen to re-distribute contributing in releasing the local stress not to surpass the critical stress for micro-cracking. It is believed that by this way the resistance to hydrogen induce cracking (HIC) of the steel can be improved. Chapter 3 will deal with this subject.

Table 1.5　Mechanical properties of low carbon bainitic steels after four different processes

Chemical composition/%		0.05%C-1.6%Mn-0.3%Si-0.04%Nb-0.25%Mo-0.4%Cu-0.2%Ni		
Properties		R_{eL}/ MPa	R_m/ MPa	A_5/%
Process	TMCP	565	800	20
	Q+T	619	655	19
	RPC rolling	690	869	18
	RPC+T	816	851	17

Table 1.6 Mechanical properties of low carbon acicular steels after two different processes

Chemical composition/%		0.037%C-0.24%Si-1.58%Mn-0.052%Nb-0.03%V-0.018%Ti-0.02%Cr-0.22%Cu-0.13%Ni -0.033%Al-0.0007%S-0.0032%O-0.0028%N		
Properties		R_{eL}/ MPa	R_m/ MPa	Charpy energy/J	A_5/%
Process	Rolled	540~570	630~670	300~330	23~27
	Tempered	680~710	730~780	280~300	22~26

1.4.4 *The influence of nanometer size precipitates on ultra fine grain steel*

Since the establishment of nanometer science and technology (Nano-ST), materials community has been paying considerable attention to and it becomes the focus of science and technology. Generally speaking, nanometer size is defined to be within 1~100 nm. We have done a research on the precipitated phase of nanometer size in the carbon steel produced by using thin slab casting and rolling (TSCR). It was found that phase of nanometer size plays a favorable role in the ultra fine grain refinement. Its details are introduced in Chapter 5 of the book.

From the viewpoint of materials science, there are noticeable different features between thin slab continuous casting and rolling and traditional hot strip rolling. The first feature is that the thickness of thin slabs is in the range of 50~70 mm (CSP), while traditional thick slabs are in the range of 200~250 mm. As a consequence, the solidification cooling rate has been increased by 1~2 order of magnitude (See Figure 1.25). Fast solidification leads to the reduction of secondary arm-spacing reaching the level of sub-micrometer. See Table 1.7 as follows.

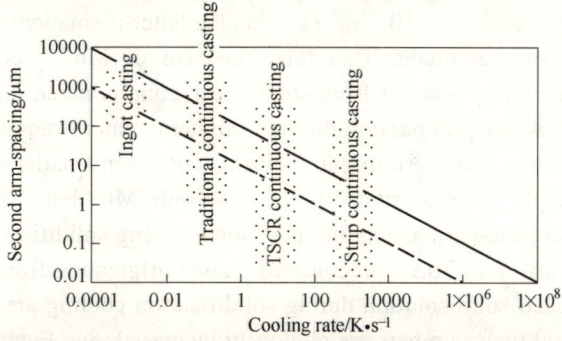

Figure 1.25 Secondary arm-spacing size verse cooling rate

Table 1.7   Comparison of process parameters of traditional thick slabs and thin slabs of TSCR process

Process	Traditional slab (250 mm thick)	Thin slab (50 mm thick)
Solidification time/min	10~15	1
Cooling rate (1560~1400℃)/K $\cdot$ s^{-1}	0.15	2
Secondary arm-spacing/μm	10~200	1~10

Since the casting process of TSCR is a fast solidifying procedure, low carbon steel goes fast from L phase (liquid phase)to (L+δ)zone, then cooled into (δ+γ) zone or to γ phase. See Figure 1.26. At this time, in the process of

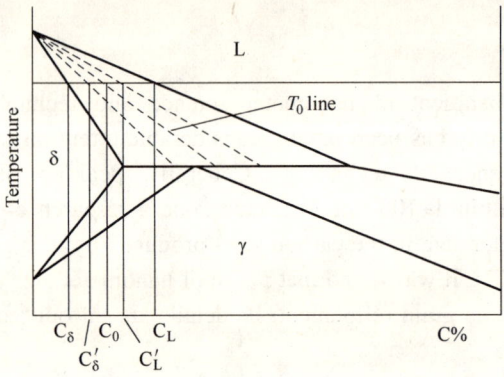

Figure 1.26   Scheme of TSCR slab solidification process in phase diagram (thermodynamics of MnS precipitation)

MnS inclusion formation, one has to bear in mind that the diffusion coefficients of Mn and S in δ phase are different than those in γ phase, the diffusion coefficient of Mn in δ-ferrite is $4.0×10^{-11}$m^2 $\cdot$ s^{-1} while that in γ-phase is $4.2×10^{-13}$m^2 $\cdot$ s^{-1}, i.e. the latter is smaller than the former by two orders of magnitude; and the diffusion coefficient of S in δ phase is $1.6×10^{-10}$m^2 $\cdot$ s^{-1}, while that in γ phase is $3.9×10^{-11}$m^2 $\cdot$s^{-1}, i.e. the latter is smaller than the former by one order of magnitude. Therefore, the size of MnS precipitated from solid-liquid two phase zone or from solid phase zone is much different. In the case of TSCR, when slab passing through this temperature range, MnS mainly precipitates from γ phase resulting in inclusions of much smaller size. Based on the same principle, the precipitated phases (not only MnS but also Fe$_x$O$_y$, AlN and so on, conventional nonmetallic inclusions) during solidification procedure are of smaller size too. Those precipitated phases originating from precipitation of super-saturated solid solution during solidification cooling are of nanometer scale in size and their numbers are obviously increased. See Figure 1.27. Detail description will be included in Chapter 4. The second feature of TSCR is the direct rolling of slabs. As it is shown in Figure 1.28, it is dissimilar to the conventional hot strip rolling, thin slabs after equalized at 1100 ℃ are rolled

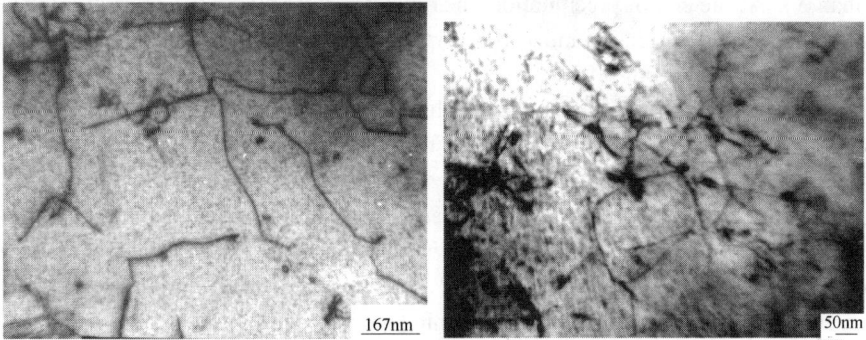

Figure 1.27 TEM evidence of precipitated phase of nanometer scale in TSCR steel

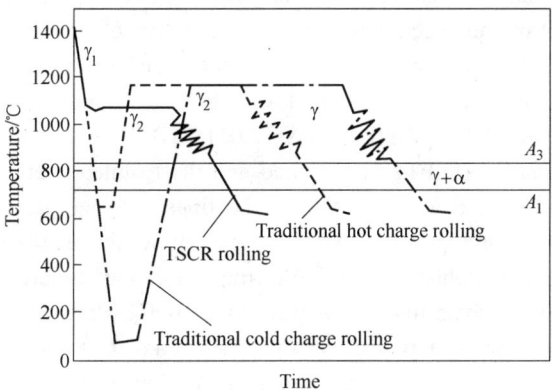

Figure 1.28 Scheme of comparison of TSCR and traditional hot strip rolling

directly. In conventional rolling, slabs are slowly cooled down. During cooling, phase transformation $\gamma \rightarrow \alpha + P$ takes place. Before rolling, cool slabs enter to the reheating furnace being reheated. During reheating, phase transformation of $\alpha + P \rightarrow \gamma$ takes place. On one hand, there are no transformations taking place during thin slab casting and continuous rolling. On the other hand, due to the cleanness of liquid steel in TSCR production, e.g. in China Zhujiang Steel the analyses of 20000 tons of steel shows average S content being $53 \times 10^{-4}\%$, O content being below $30 \times 10^{-4}\%$, low C content being about 0.05%C and low Mn content, solubility product $c_{[Mn]} \cdot c_{[S]}$ is low that makes the highest precipitation temperature of MnS lower than the liquidus of steel. Moreover, FeO mainly precipitates during continuous rolling. Therefore, the quantity sulphides and oxides with nanometer scale increased.

The finishing pass temperature of direct rolling coincides with the temperature of AlN precipitation. It is known that from the TEM observation and the calculation result of kinetics modeling of AlN precipitation that AlN precipitates at the finishing stage and the time for the whole process of precipitation is shorter than 3 s. At the end of precipitation, the diameter of AlN is about 2 nm. It implies that there is a deformation induced precipitation (speeding up precipitation) going on during direct rolling.

Since the scrape of row materials in China Zhujiang Steel Works contains copper (about 0.2%), deformation also promotes the precipitation of phases which is rich in copper. These nanometer size precipitates hinder the growth of ferrite grains after rolling and also provide precipitation strengthening. As it is resulted that the grain size of the final microstructure is between 3~5μm (depending on the product thickness) and the strength is almost doubled. The related grain refinement strengthening and precipitation strengthening are introduced in Chapter 5.

From the function of nanometer phases in the thin slab casting and rolling technology, it can be seen that for the steel materials containing precipitated phases, to control the precipitation process and try to obtain large amount of nanometer precipitates is an effective way to realize ultra fine grain refinement strengthening. In the R&D of ultra low carbon microalloyed steel (0.003%C-0.22%Si-1.12%Mn-0.052%Nb-0.011%Ti), the deformation induced ferrite transformation (DIFT) was applied and the resulted average grain size of ferrite has been refined to 0.89μm. It is the finest average grain size of ferrite obtained in our research program. TEM analysis shows that there exists nanometer size level precipitated phase containing ferrous oxide (see Figure 1.29). The final yield strength of the experimental steel reached 1000 MPa and is multiply higher than that of traditional low carbon steel. It means that the improvement of processing and application of new technologies can change the sulphides and oxides,

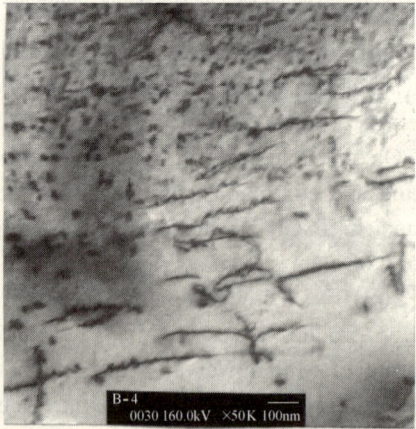

Figure 1.29   Secondary phase nanometer size precipitates of low alloy steel after rolling with deformation induced ferrite transformation

which are usually considered detrimental inclusions, into nanometer size particles. This approach is under certain circumstance which is more economical and more effective than the improvement of steel quality by simply lowering the quantity of sulphur, oxygen, nitrogen and other tramp elements. There has been put forward a new concept of steel purifying that to refine the inclusions into nanometer size "beneficial" precipitated phases and in turn to greatly increase steel strength. In this aspect, a lot of further work is needed.

1.4.5   *Ultra grain refinement of alloy structural steels and the way of increasing the resistance against delayed fracturing*

Alloy structural steels are mostly medium carbon alloy steels and are used under the quenching and tempering condition. This group of steels is of multiple microstructures (high or medium temperature tempered martensite +carbide or bainite+martensite). Through the ultra fine grain refinement of austenite before quenching, the mechanical properties can be further increased. The previous Figure 1.13 shows the relations of austenite grain refinement and the major mechanical properties (R_m, R_p, R_A, E_L and Charpy energy) of commercial steel 42CrMo (SCM440/AISI4140). It is seen that the properties have been all-round improved by austenite grain refinement.

In order to double the strength level from 800~1000 MPa to 1500 MPa, the grain refinement alone is not enough. Two factors should been considered as follows:

1. Many measures can be taken in order to increase the strength of alloy structural steels, i.e. lowering tempering temperature, increasing carbon content and contents of alloy elements, fast quenching and so on. The existing works (Matsuoka, 2004) indicate that when the tensile strength exceeds 1200 MPa, almost all alloy structural steels suffer the reduction of resistance against delayed fracturing and have no improvement of their fatigue properties; hence they are losing application value. Therefore, the resistance against delayed fracturing must be considered together when the ultra fine grain refinement is applied. Chapter 6 of this book introduces the relationship among ultra fine grain refinement, tensile strength, and resistance against delayed fracturing (expressed by apparent ratio of resistance against delayed fracturing) of alloy structural steel ADF1 (see Figure 1.31). It is seen that when the austenite grain size ensured below 4 μm, there exist well balanced tensile strength and resistance against delayed fracturing and when the grain size becoming finer, there is no beneficial influence on the comprehensive properties of the steel at strength level of 1500 MPa.

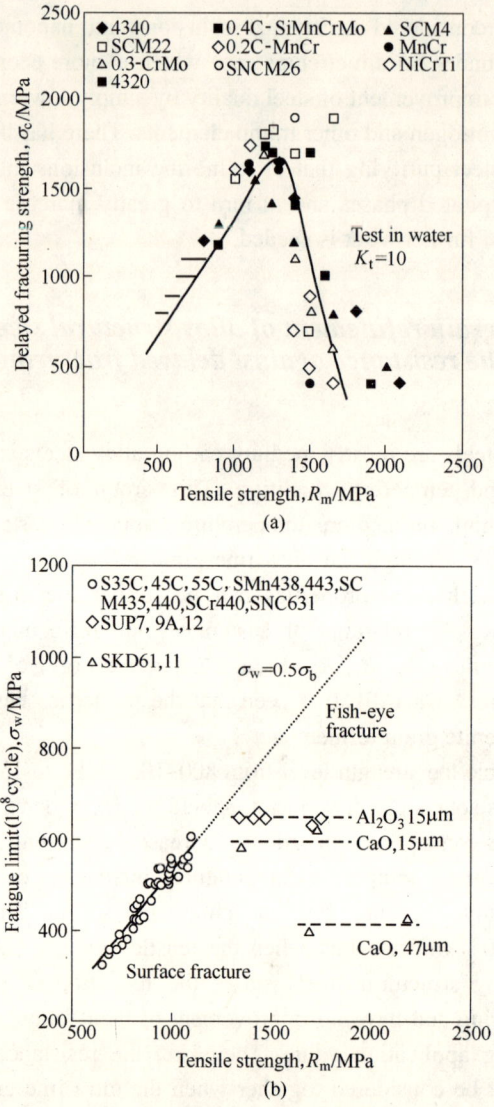

Figure 1.30　Comparison of delayed cracking strength and fatigue strength of different steel grades

(a) Delayed fracturing;(b) Fatigue limit

2. The type, size, shape, and distribution of carbides are very important to increase the properties of alloy structural steels besides the refinement of the matrix microstructure. In order to comprehensively fulfill the R&D of new material with high resistance against delayed fracturing and with strength level 1500 MPa (It is the common new goal of China, Japan, and Korea etc.), the following approaches have been adopted:

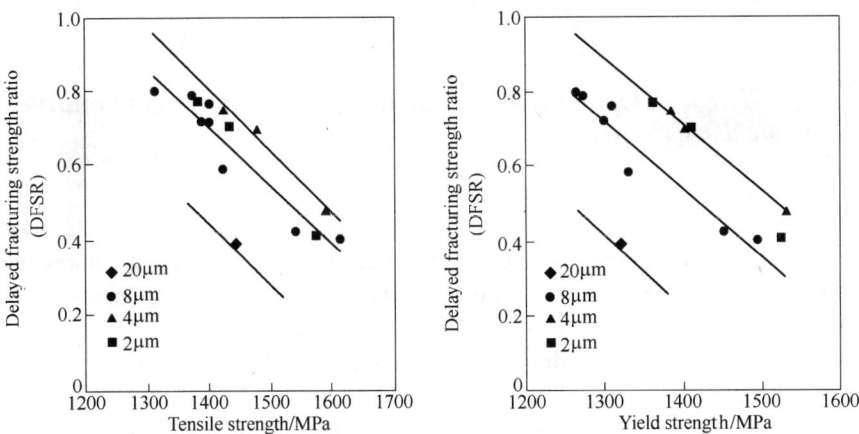

Figure 1.31 Relationship of ultra fine grain size, tensile strength, and resistance against delayed fracturing of an alloy structural steel (ADF1)

1) By applying secondary hardening to obtain higher strength of the steel after high temperature tempering, Mo_2C and VC precipitation controlled processing has been adopted.

2) By applying the grain refinement effects of Nb and V, the fine γ grain size is guaranteed during heat treatment.

3) Considering that the cause of delayed fracturing is hydrogen absorption eading to hydrogen induced inter-granular fracturing, molybdenum is applied to strengthen the grain boundaries. The grain boundary segregation of molybdenum eliminates temper brittleness and negative effect of deteriorated elements (such as P, S, N) segregation. Related content is introduced in Part VI of the book.

4) Considering that inclusions, especially oxide inclusions are easy to function as fatigue cracking origin leading to low fatigue life, high purity steel melting technology is applied.

5) As the final manufacturing procedure of the steel products is done in the machinery, it is necessary to apply fast electric heating technology in order to ensure ultra fine grain γ.

6) Application of favorable chemical composition and appropriate tempering parameters lead to the beneficial distribution of carbides, good strength & toughness balance, and formation of hydrogen traps. Hence, the intergranular fracturing of delayed fracturing is replaced by plastic transgranular fracturing.

In our research program, in consequence of application of above mentioned approaches, the developed new steel grade has been already applied in automotive industry in batch quantity. It is estimated that the new steel grade will become an excellent new steel for international high strength fasteners market. Related content is introduced in Chapter 6 of the book.

1.4.6   *The development of carbide-free bainite/martensite multiple phase steels (CFB/M)*

By applying new alloy design and microstructure design, the steels with carbide-free bainite/martensite and thin film retained austenite microstructures can be produced. Carbide-free bainite microstructure is beneficial to the improvement of toughness. Thin film retained austenite is beneficial to the increase of resistance against delayed fracturing. There are two features of this kind of steels which are described as follows:

1. The steel contains certain amount of silicon. As a non-carbide forming element, silicon hinders carbide precipitation at the bainitic phase transformation and promotes the formation of carbon-rich austenite along the lath boundaries of low bainite and martensite. During the following cooling, retained austenite films form at the original austenite grain boundaries, at the lath boundaries of low bainite and martensite, and at sub-lath boundaries.

2. Film shape retained austenite not only eliminates the precipitation of detrimental intergranular carbides leading to blunt the tip of fatigue crack, but also dramatically increases resistance against delayed fracturing. The hydrogen absorptivity of austenite is about one order of magnitude larger than that of ferrite and austenite is a strong hydrogen trap (see Figure 1.32).

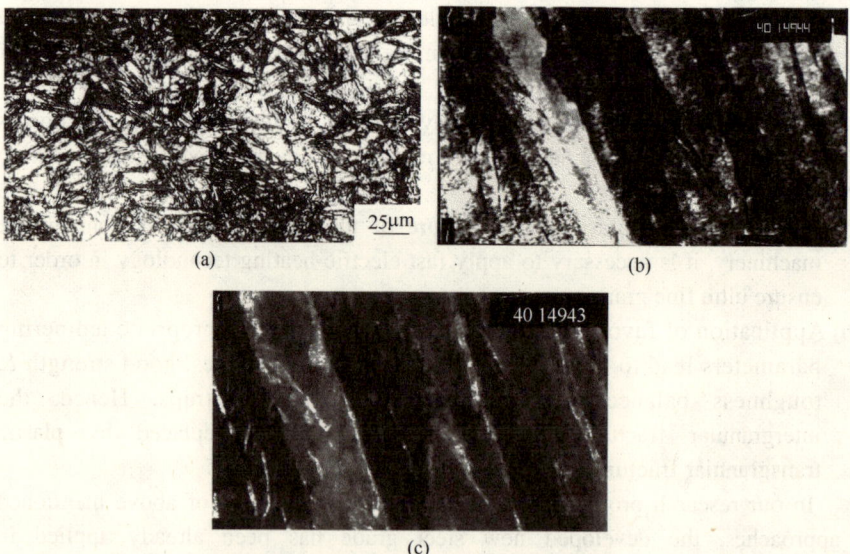

Figure 1.32   Typical distribution of retained austenite of new steel grade
(See details in Chapter 7)
(a) Optical micrograph; (b) TEM bright field; (c) TEM dark field

3. When austenitized multi-phase B/M steel is cooled from high temperature, at first, a certain amount of carbide-free low bainite is precipitated inside austenitic grains and segmenting grains. Then, the later formed martensite laths are refined resulting in high strength and toughness of the steel.

4. The steel contains silicon leading to the higher tempering resistance. After medium temperature tempering, the steel possesses good balanced properties.

The new steel product developed by applying the above-mentioned approaches is ensured to have tensile strength at 1500 MPa level after 350℃ tempering. The steel under this condition shows better impact toughness (see Figure 1.33) and better fracture toughness (see Table 1.8) compared with martensitic steel tempered at the same temperature. When heat treated to the same strength level as 30CrMnSi ultra high strength low alloy steel (R_m=1510 MPa),stress corrosion cracking test showed that K_{ISCC} increased 40%, crack propagation rate da/dt decreased more than 50%. The details can be found in Figure 1.34 and in Table 1.9.

Table 1.8 Fracture toughness comparison for steels with different microstructures (M; CFB/M)

Steel grade	Microstructure	Property	Tempering temperature	
			280℃	350℃
U25AB	M	K_{IC} / MPa • m$^{1/2}$	104.2	93.7
	CFB/M	K_Q / MPa • m$^{1/2}$	103	117.5
		K_{max} / MPa • m$^{1/2}$	170	179
U20Si	M	K_{IC} / MPa • m$^{1/2}$	—	98
	CFB/M	K_Q / MPa • m$^{1/2}$	112	123
		K_{max} / MPa • m$^{1/2}$	150	188.5

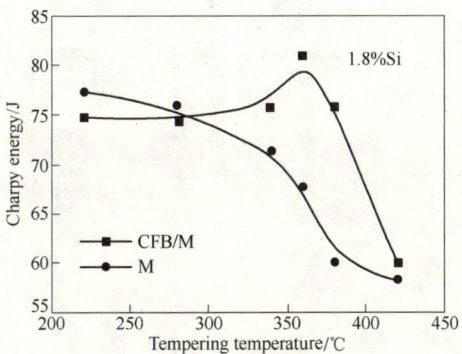

Figure 1.33 Charpy energy comparison of steels with two different microstructures

Fatigue S-N curves and da/dN-ΔK curves of a steel with carbide-free bainite-martensite multiphase and of the same steel with martensite microstructure (Here FM—steel with martensite microstructure, CFB/M — steel with carbide-free bainite-martensite multi phase).

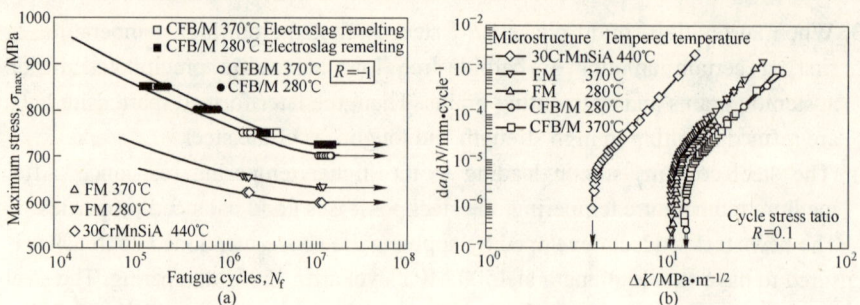

Figure 1.34   Fatigue S-N curves (a) and da/dN-ΔK curves (b)

Table 1.9   Mechanical properties of carbide-free bainite-martensite multi phase steel and steel 30CrMnSiA

Mechanical properties	R_m/MPa	K_{ISCC}/MPa $\cdot$ m$^{1/2}$	da/d$t \times 10^{-5}$/mm $\cdot$ s^{-1}
30CrMnSiA	1510	36.2	3.2
CFB/M	1520	54.5	1.2

The large decrease of fatigue crack propagation rate da/dt is originated from the stable retained austenite *in* CFB/M steel. In the process of crack propagation, this austenite makes the crack tip blunt, branched, and diversified in direction. Hence, energy required for crack propagating is increased, crack propagation rate reduced, and fatigue life increased. See Figure 1.35.

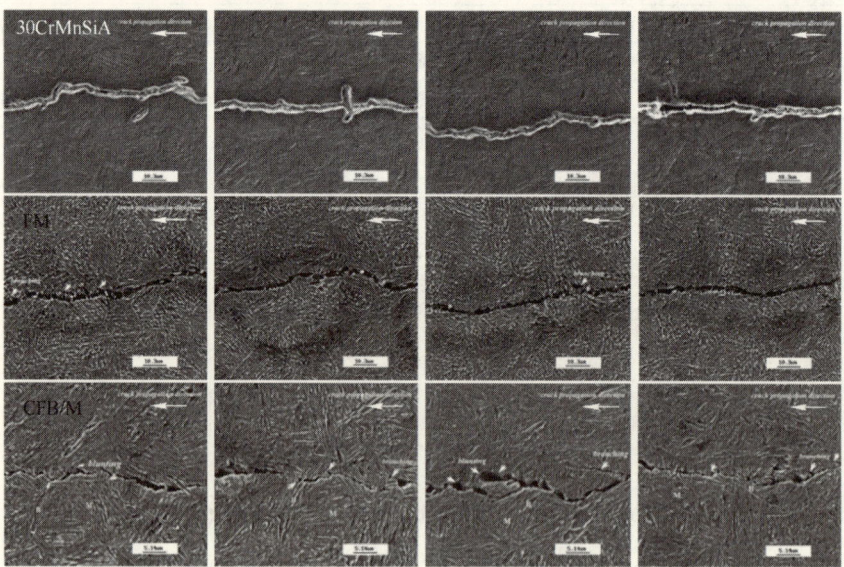

Figure 1.35   Fatigue crack propagating paths of ultra high strength materials with different microstructures

In order to develop this kind of steels, the important points that have to be paid attention to are as follows:

1. If the low or medium temperature tempering at around 350℃ is applied, resistance against first type temper brittleness must be dealt with, and properly designed and tempering process well controlled. The start temperature of first type tempering brittleness has to be lowered. Increase of silicon content can lead to the increase of higher tempering resistance and to the prevention of precipitation of carbides in the B/M microstructures.

2. Considering the low toughness of medium and/or low tempered steels, theoretically, CFB/M+ retained austenite (γ_r) can be applied to greatly increase impact toughness and fracture toughness. However, in practice, the steel must be of high cleanness. The theoretical approach comes from the physical metallurgy and should be guaranteed by the steel cleanness that is an approach of chemical metallurgy. Hence, it is possible to have good plasticity, good toughness, and eliminated first type temper brittleness.

3. By applying carbon-rich retained austenite films, both the resistance against hydrogen induced fracturing and the toughness can be improved. However, the thermal stability (No phase transformation takes place at lower temperature.) and mechanical stability (No phase transformation takes place like TRIP steels under stress condition.) must be ensured. Related content is introduced in Chapter 7 of the book.

4. Further increase of the homogeneous distribution of retained austenite films and the refinement of grain size during austenitization are problems to be solved for the further improvement of the type of alloy steels.

At present, this type of steel materials has been trial-used in some areas. The large size fasteners of 14.9 class ($R_m \geqslant 1400$ MPa, $R_{eL}/R_s \geqslant 0.9$) for the cranes of landing stage of the newly built Hongkong wharf No. 9 have been decided to use this type of material through international biding.

1.5 Several Key Technologies Concerning the Development of Ultra Fine Grain Steels

As the development of high strength and high toughness steels by applying ultra fine grain refinement technology, there must be corresponding development of production technologies. In order to guarantee the property consistency, increase of steel cleanness and maintaining high homogeneity of chemical composition throughout the macroscopic sections of steel materials are the two most important aspects. Chapter 8 of the book, The chemical metallurgical principles of ultra fine grain steels, introduces the technological progress of clean ultra fine grain steels. Chapter 9, Theoretical basis of solidification homogenization of cast slabs, introduces some theoretical concepts and technological development of chemical composition homogenization throughout the macroscopic sections.

In practical applications of ultra fine grain steels, many practical performances of the materials have to be considered. For example, deep drawing ability, weldability, and tendencies of plasticity to brittleness transition due to temperature change during service process need to be paid attention to. If detail descriptions are needed, property anisotropy caused by texture, service safety of welded structures, plasticity to brittleness transition behavior, and aging sensitivity of material at long time service have to be dealt with at spending a lot of pages. Our work group has done some R & D work on the above-mentioned aspects. However, since they are of too many in contents, it is not suitable for a short description. Therefore, in this book, the subject of welding which is of great concern is introduced in Chapter 10.

1.5.1   *Steel cleanness*

As the strength of steel materials increasing, the sensibility of steel materials to internal cracking increases. Inclusions behave as origins of internal cracking leading to the fracturing during service process. Figure 1.36 shows the relationship of fatigue life versus inclusion size for alloy structural steel of strength level 1500 MPa. Authors of this book have done systematical analysis of the literature on the influence of steel cleanness on the properties and at the same time, have done laboratory study determining the necessary lowest cleanness levels under different contents of S, P, O, and N for various steel types of various strength levels including R_p=400 MPa, 800 MPa, and R_m=1500MPa. Suggestions are summarized into Table 1.10.

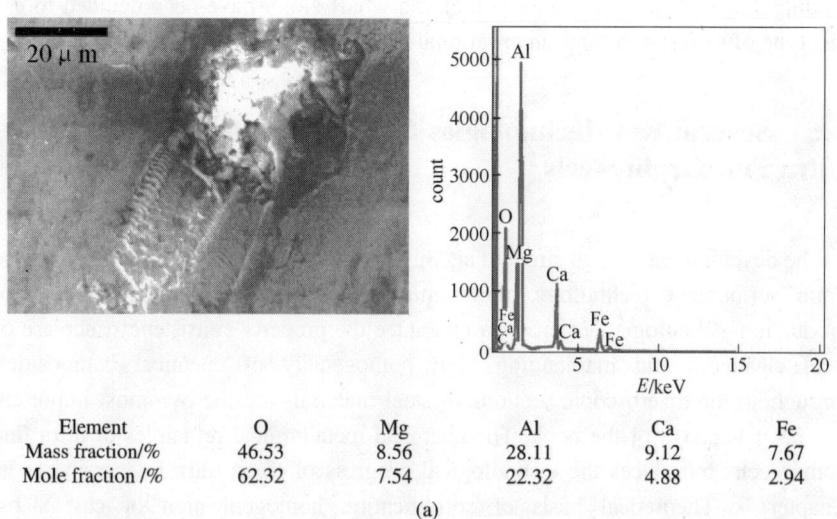

Element	O	Mg	Al	Ca	Fe
Mass fraction/%	46.53	8.56	28.11	9.12	7.67
Mole fraction /%	62.32	7.54	22.32	4.88	2.94

(a)

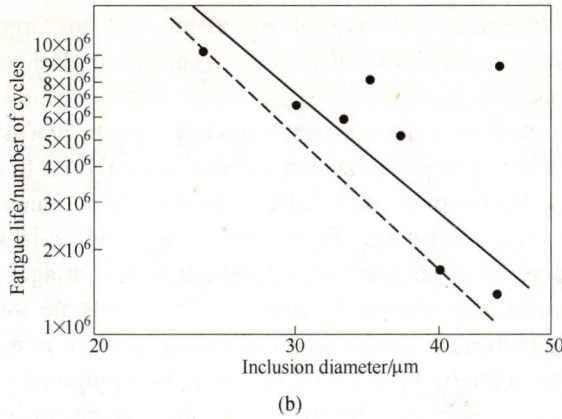

(b)

Figure 1.36 The relationship of fatigue life versus inclusion size for alloy structural steel of 1500MPa strength level

(a) SEM micrograph and compositional analysis of an inclusion at the surface of fatigue specimen;
(b) Relationship of fatigue life and size of inclusion close to surface as fatigue crack origin

Table 1.10 Suggested necessary cleanness levels for new generation steel materials

Steel type	Type of material	w (P)/%	w (N)/%	[O]/%	w(N)/%
400 MPa level	Long products	≤0.030	≤0.025	≤0.004	≤0.007
	Flat products	≤0.030	≤0.010	≤0.004	≤0.007
800 MPa level	Flat products	≤0.015	≤0.005	≤0.004	≤0.005
	Pipeline steels resistant to HIC	≤0.005	≤0.0005	≤0.003	≤0.004
1500 MPa level	Long products	≤0.015	≤0.015	≤0.003	≤0.005

It is necessary to give an expression of steel cleanness. IISI Committee on Technology (TECHCO) published in 2004 a paper "State of the Art and Process Technology in Clean Steel-making" giving a definition as follows: "Any specific definition of clean steel must include its product requirements. It should be recognized that these requirements become more severe as the applied product thickness is reduced and therefore, one definition could be as follows: 'when non-metallic inclusions are responsible, either directly or indirectly, for lowering fabrication capacity or in-service properties or requirements, then the steel is not clean but when there is no such effect, then the steel can be considered to be clean, irrespective of the number, type, size or distribution of non-metallic inclusions'".

According to the above definition, it is not pursued for "purified steel" but for "clean steel". If it is in accordance with some metallurgists, the total amount of the six elements, i.e. C, S, P, O, N, H should be less than 60 ppm or 80 ppm. This requirement may be necessary for some high strength steels but not for conventional steels used in large quantity. Otherwise, it may lead to extreme difficulties in chemical metallurgical processing and to large increase of production cost. Therefore, we call it as an "Economical cleanness" instead of "Ultimate cleanness".

The focus of clean steel development should be " the treatment into harmless inclusions" in addition to deoxidization and degassing (N, H) to extreme clean level. As it is well-known, under the fatigue loading condition, cracking originates either from the surface of steel material or from internal inclusions. We have done analyses of 12 different steels. 100 fatigue fracturing specimens from 14 steel companies were statistically analyzed. The results are shown in Figure 1.37. From Figure 1.37, it can be seen that fatigue strength is measured at the fatigue life demand for 10^7 cycles, 61% fatigue cracking originates from surface; while fatigue life is required for 10^9 cycles, 71% fatigue cracking originates from inclusions (See right part of Figure 1.37), only 23% fatigue cracking from surface. It implies that under condition of ultra high cycles ($>10^7$cycles), internal defect, namely inclusion induced fatigue cracking probability increases. Therefore, when the service condition is mainly fatigue loading, it is necessary to develop "inclusion engineering" by using secondary metallurgy (ladle refining) and lowering the 6 important elements.

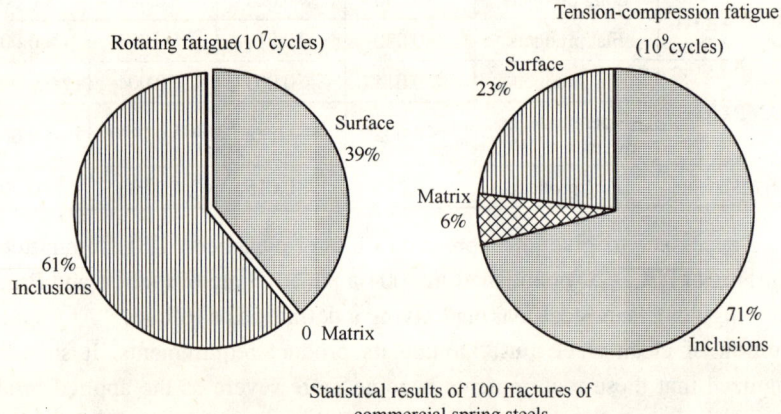

Statistical results of 100 fractures of
commercial spring steels

Figure 1.37   Statistical results of 100 fatigue fractures of 12 different commercial spring steels

Considering both production cost and cleanness requirement, there are two alternative ways to reduce the harmfulness of inclusions. One way is to reduce big size and brittle inclusions by applying an adequate metallurgical technology. The target is to control the size of the biggest inclusion to be smaller than the critical inclusion size, i.e. to avoid the occurrence of inclusion of maximal size that does lead to fatigue cracking. The related calculation result shows the critical inclusion size depends on the strength of material, defined loading conditions, and other internal conditions. The dotted line in Figure 1.36(b) is pattern of treatment. The relation of minimal fatigue life (FL_{min})and inclusion size resulted from regression analysis in this figure is as follows:

$$FL_{min} = \frac{2.279 \times 10^{12}}{d^{3.827}}$$

If we define FL_{min} by increasing number of fatigue cycles from 10^7 to 10^8, the maximal safe inclusion size should be controlled under 13.8 μm.

The other way is to apply inclusion modification. Chapter 7 of this book introduces controlling technology of plastic nonmetallic inclusions in Si-Mn deoxidized high carbon steel. The plastic inclusion compositional ranges of SiO_2-MnO-Al_2O_3 and CaO-MgO-Al_2O_3 systems have been determined. By controlling slag basicity, Al_2O_3 content, and acid soluble aluminum content, brittle inclusions can be modified into plastic inclusions. Of course, these technologies are extremely sophisticated for practice and of commercial know-hows. This book only introduces principles and practical results.

1.5.2　Refinement and homogenization of solidification structure

As the solidification structure of traditional cast ingot or thick slab concerned, it is composed of fine grain zone, columnar dendrite zone, and equiaxed grain zone in accordance of solidification sequence. In the process of gradual solidification, at the front of solidified metal, there is gradual concentration of elements of low melting point. Thus a center-line segregation appears in the center area of ingot or slab where final solidification takes place. Figure 1.38 (a) shows schematically the segregation of ingot and Figure 1.38(b) shows a macrograph of serious center-line

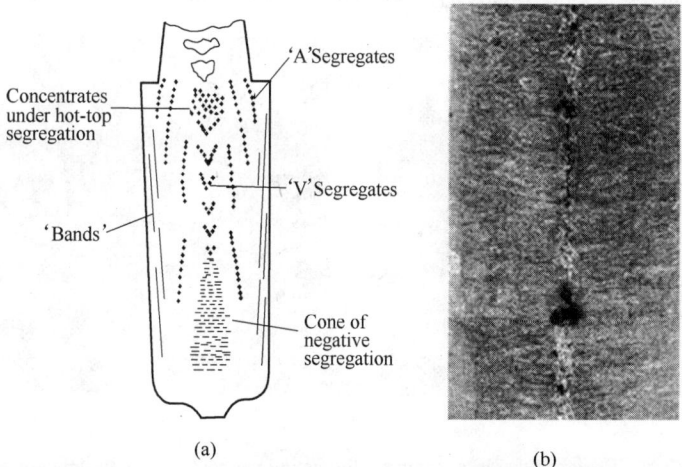

(a)   (b)

Figure 1.38　Segregation scheme of a solidified traditional ingot and a thin slab

segregation of a continuously cast thin slab (CSP slab). In the case of thin slab, due to fast solidification, well developed columnar dendrite zone leads to serious center-line segregation. In consequence of center-line segregation, there exists inhomogeneous distribution of chemical elements, especially, C, Mn, S, P and other light or segregation sensitive elements leading to macroscopic segregation. The macroscopic segregation causes inhomogeneous mechanical properties and inconstant properties of material. This problem leads to quality accidents for high performance steel materials.

In order to increase the compositional homogeneity of steel materials and to reduce macroscopic center-line segregation, the authors of this book raised a concept of increasing the fraction of equiaxed dendrite zone and changing the sequent solidification into homogeneous solidification, i.e. changing into fully equiaxed dendrite structure in order to eliminate center-line macro-segregation. For example, in case of silicon steel with major contents of C, Si, and S, when different solidification parameters (including overheat, temperature gradient, and cooling rate in casting mould) are applied, well-developed columnar dendrite structure or well-developed equiaxed dendrite structure may be obtained. Figure 1.39 (a) shows the well-developed columnar dendrite structure of silicon steel and (b) shows its well-developed equiaxed dendrite structure. The results of chemical analysis across the sections show that the frequency of chemical composition meeting its specification has been largely increased and the largest segregation degree has also been obviously decreased. See Table 1.11.

Chapter 9 of this book introduces the theory and key technologies for increasing homogeneity and obtaining fully equiaxed dendrite solidification structure.

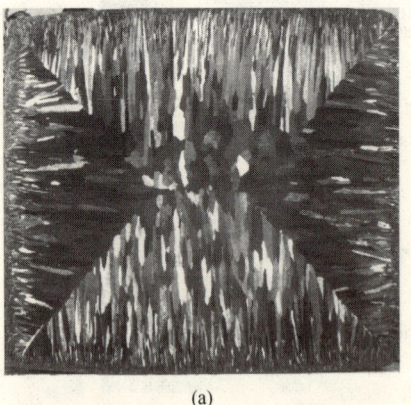 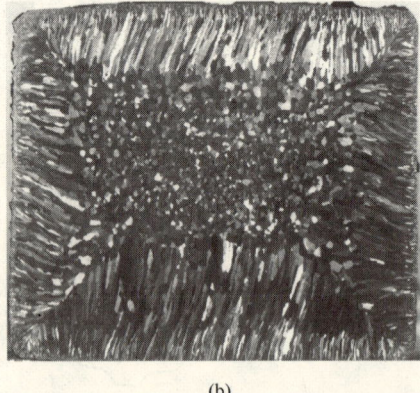

(a) (b)

Figure 1.39 Equiaxed dendrite structure eliminating macroscopic center-line segregation
(a) Well-developed columnar dendrite; (b) Well-developed equiaxed dendrite

Table 1.11 Chemical analysis across section of silicon steel with
well-developed equiaxed dendrite structure

Chemical analysis	w (C)/%		w(Si)/%		w(S)/%	
	Columnar (A)	Equiaxed (B)	Columnar (A)	Equiaxed (B)	Columnar (A)	Equiaxed (B)
Composition ranges between	0.031 ~0.071	0.043~ 0.083	2.23~ 2.63	2.26~ 2.66	0.014 ~ 0.022	0.011~ 0.019
Frequency/%[1]	81.29	90.21	42.51	71.34	22.91	55.98
Max. segregation ratio	1.89	1.67	1.31	1.26	1.73	1.72

[1]The frequency of chemical composition meeting its specification.

1.5.3 Brief introduction of welding technique and economy of ultra fine grain steels

Many countries in the world pay great attention to relative welding technique when developing ultra fine grain steels in order to avoid grain coarsening in welding zone that might retard the application future of ultra fine grain steels. The core work here is that the chemical composition, microstructure, and properties of weld metal and heat affected zone (HAZ) should be compatible with the ultra fine grain state of matrix metal. Our work has shown that if the traditional welding method is applied to the ultra fine grain steel, the problem of grain coarsening in HAZ becomes more serious than that of traditional steels. In the aspect of plain carbon steel of strength level 400 MPa, minor change of chemical composition of weld materials, low energy input welding, fast cooling after welding (easier to realize for strip welding), and the development of new types of welding consumables and other measures have been taken resulting in proper control of microstructure and properties of weld metal and HAZ. If there are not such control measures, there would be negative influence in application of ultra fine grain steels. Concerning the welding of plain carbon ultra fine grain strip steels, by selecting and controlling welding parameters, electric arc welding (including manual welding and automatic welding) and argon arc welding or CO_2 gas shield welding can be used for industrial welding of steel structures. Welding with cored wires and laser welding providing better welding results were trial-used in automotive plants and are normally applied after evaluation and certification. Concerning ultra fine grain plain carbon steel long products (reinforcing bars-rebars), butt flash welding including direct current resistance flash welding and electric welding are applied and the fracturing under loading of welded joint is controlled within matrix metal (see Figure 1.40(a)). At the same time, bending test

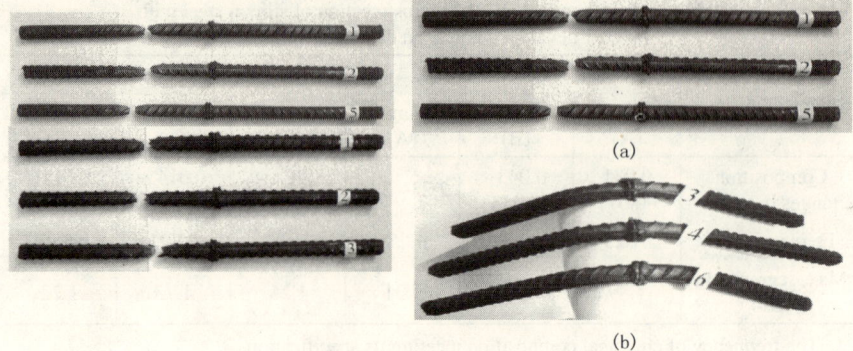

(a)

(b)

Figure 1.40   Weld specimens of ultra fine grain rebar steels
(a) Tensile specimens of flash butt welds of rebar steel;
(b) Bending specimens of flash butt welds of rebar steels

results are all satisfactory (see Figure 1.40(b)). When assistant bar welding, overlap welding, melting pond bar welding, and groove welding were applied, results showed that strength and fatigue strength of weld joints meet the requirements of engineering specifications. See Figure 1.41.

Assistant bar weld

Lap weld

Melting pond bar weld

Groove weld

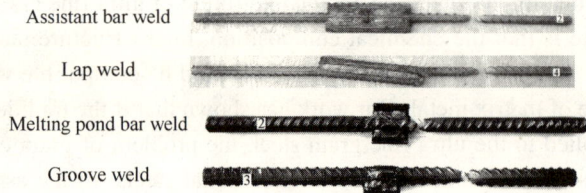

Figure 1.41   Tensile specimens of different welds of ultra fine grain steels

Concerning microalloyed ultra fine grain steels, gas shield welding wire made of ultra-low carbon high strength steel has been developed for ultra fine bainitic steel of 800 MPa strength level. With this welding wire, there is no preheat needed. Strength and low temperature toughness are excellent. We have developed welding wire for submerged arc welding of high toughness corrosion resistant pipeline steel, which is an acicular ferrite high strength pipeline steel. Testing and evaluation of X80 pipeline steel welds made by using submerged arc welding proved that their quality reached the level of actual longitudinal welded pipes manufactured by Europipe. Since our development of weld wire started from the requirements of practical welding, the speed of development was comparatively higher compared to the similar work done by Japanese and Koreans. Their work on the development of welding wire for X80 pipeline steel started from new concepts and from laboratory experiments.

Finally, the economy of production and application of ultra-fine grain steels will be briefly introduced. Under the preconditions of ensuring technological advancement, high strength and toughness, and double service life-time, the increase of ratio of property to cost and sustainable development as strategic goals are also considered. K. Nagai (Nagai K, 2000) compared at the conference of "THERMEC2000" that which way is better? Whether the yield strength increase ($\Delta R_{0.2}$) is obtained through application of alloy elements or through intensified rolling? See Figure 1.42. For low carbon steel of 0.7%Mn-0.2%Si -0.005%N and ferrite grain size 10 μm, if above-mentioned two measures are taken, $R_{0.2}$ can be increased to double level. Production practice of Shougang Steel, Sanming Steel and Huaiying Steel and other steel companies in China have proved that by applying DIFT processing while no addition of alloy elements or a bit increase of Mn, Si etc, the production cost per ton of steel reduced by 2%~4%. Rebar steels produced by these steel companies on the basis of carbon steels possess properties of II class rebar steel. If the steel is sold at price of II class rebar steel (20MnSi), the enterprise benefit (profit) will increase by 20%. If it is sold at the price of III class rebar steel, it will increase by 30%. Although low temperature rolling leads to the increase of energy consumption and the roller consumption, due to lowering of reheating temperature and decreasing of scale loss, the practice based on production line producing 220000t long products by using low temperature rolling in Sweden shows that production cost has been decreased by 3 USD/ton of steel. See Table 1.12.

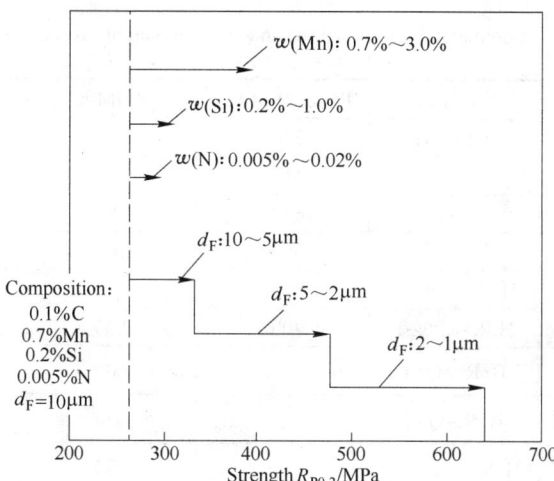

Figure 1.42 Economical comparison of strength increase by using ultra-fine grain steels and by using alloy elements

In the aspect of microalloyed steels, a relaxation-precipitation-control technology (RPC) is applied to the ultra-fine grain steels resulting equal property level compared to that of quenched and tempered steels. For example, compared to the case of steels Welton 80-100 or CF80, the RPC steel applies less alloy elements (including microalloying elements but Mn is not accounted as alloy element), i.e. total amount of alloy elements has been reduced by 1/2~2/3. In addition, the RPC steel does not undergo quenching treatment. The selling price of RPC ultra-fine grain steel in 2001 when the market price level was low, was about 100 USD/t lower than that of Q+T steels of same strength level. See Table 1.13.

Table 1.12 Economical benefits brought by low temperature rolling

Item	Reheating temperature /℃		
	1150	950	750
Oil consumption of reheating furnace /L·t^{-1}	40.1	31.7	22.1
Oil fee/USD	180×10^4	143×10^4	98×10^4
Metal loss/%	1.3	0.4	0.2
Cost for oil/ USD	62×10^4	19×10^4	9.6×10^4
Electricity consumption /kW·h·t^{-1}	90	110	120
Electricity fee/USD	60×10^4	73×10^4	79×10^4
Total cost/USD	301×10^4	234×10^4	187×10^4
Cost saving per ton of steel /USD		3	5.2

Table 1.13 Commercially selling price and alloy amount of several HSLA steels (Or microalloyed steels)

Grade	Processing	Price[1]/Yuan·t^{-1}	R_{eL}/MPa	Alloy amount[2]/%
16Mn	Hot rolled	2400	350	0
HG70	Q+T	4100	600	0.8
HG80	Q+T	4400	685	1.7
CF80	Q+T	5500	700	2.3
DB685	H. R.+RPC+T	3850	590	0.9
DB800	H.R.+RPC+T	4000	800	1.0
A710	H. R. +Q+T		600	3.5
DB bridge plate	H. R.+Q+T		690	2.5
DB bridge plate	H. R.+ direct Q		750	3.0

[1]China internal market price in 2001; [2]Mn is not included as alloy element.

In the field of alloy structural steels, cost of steel with carbon-free bainite and martensite combined phase microstructure (CFB / M) is lower than that of 30CrMnSiA, a low alloy ultra high strength steel of the same strength level. Moreover, the toughness of the former steel is higher than that of the latter steel by 50%. If steels of ADF series, which was introduced in Chapter 5, are applied for high strength fasteners, product size is reduced; weight reduced by 30%; and manufacturing cost increased by 30%; but total production cost remains unchanged. Nevertheless, when 13.9~14.9 class materials are used, the weight of automotive engine system reduces. This gives rise to the obvious increase of economic efficiency. From the viewpoint of sustainable development, all the ultra-fine grain steels do not contain alloy elements or contain less alloy elements. At the same time, process pollution is lowered, emission of CO_2 is reduced (because of low temperature rolling). The development procedure of ultra-fine grain steels indicates that this kind of steels possesses strong market competitiveness and is environment friendly, and meeting the strategy of sustainable development. The production and application of this kind of steels is welcomed by many enterprises and sees bright future.

At present, the development and trial-production of new generation steel materials has been vigorously expanding. Except those dozen large and medium iron and steel companies being already involved, a group of Chinese iron and steel enterprises is joining in this work. About 50% of large and medium iron and steel companies are interested in this work. It is hoped that through the efforts of science and technology workers and managers of enterprises, the tempo of application engineering of ultra-fine grain steels will speed up.

References

Akira Sato Tekkoh Kai, (1997), (12):14

Beynon J H, Hodgson P D (1992) Mater. Forum, 16:37-42

Choo W Y (2002) Proceedings of first international conference on advanced structural steels, Tsukuba, Japan, 19

Choo W Y (2001) Present developing status of high performance steel in Korea (HIPER-21 project), workshop on new generation steel, The Chinese Society for Metals, Beijing, 11

Choo W Y,Lee J S, Lee C S,et al(2000) CAMP-ISIJ, 13:1144

Dong T (1999) Microalloying and mechanisms of strengthening and toughening of steels, Teaching text for the training class of " Product variety and structure adjustment" organized by CSM

Glover G, Sellors C M (1973) Metall. Trans., 4: 765-775

Gray J.M, Yeo R.B (1968) Trans. ASM 61, 255

Hickson M R, et al(2002) The production of ultrafine ferrite in low-carbon steel by strain-induced transformation, Metall. Mater. Trans. A., 33A:1019-1026

Hiroyuki Kajioka (1997) Ladle Refining (Chinese version, 2002.6 , Metallurgical Publishing House)

Hodgson P D, Hickson M R, Gibbs R K (1999) Scripta Mater., 40:1179

Kimura Y, Takaki S (1997) CAMP-ISIJ, 10.541

Lee S, et al.(1995) Metall. Mater. Trans. A., 26A: 1093-1100

Li X F (1999) Handbook of comparative world steel standards (2nd edition), Beijing Winmedia Electronic Pub. House, China

M. Nükura, et al (2001) Journal of Meter. Proc. Tech., 117:341-346

Maki T (1996) Microstructural contral by machanical and heat treatment, "Japan Nishiyama memorial technical seminar, No.161,162", 11

Maki T, et al (1997) CAMP-ISIJ, 10:540

Matsumura Y, Yada H (1987) Evolution of ultrafine-grained ferrite in hot successive deformation, Trans. ISIJ, 27:492-498

Matsuoka (2004) FFEMS, 27:159-167

Nagai K (2002) Proceedings of the 4th workshop on HIPERS-21, pp.17-25, Pohang, Korea, Jan. 17-19

Nagai K (2000) Electronic Proc. of the Conf. on Thermomechanical processing of steels and other Materials THERMEC 2000, Las Vegas. Dec, 4-8

Priestner R(1981) Processing of an International Conference on the Thermomechanical Processing of Microalloyed Austenite, Metallurgical Society of AIME, Edited by A.J.DeArdo, G.A.Ratz, P.J. Wray, 455

Priestner R(1993) Ali. L, Mater. Sci. Tech., 9:135-141

Shan Yiyin, Xiao Furen, et al(2001) Proceedings on new generation steels (in Chinese), The Chinese Society for Metals, Beijing, Nov. 348

Takaki S. Materials Science Forum, 426-432, 215-222

Weng Y Q (2003) Microstructure Refinement of Structural Steel in China, ISIJ International, Vol.43(2003) No.11. pp.1675-1682

Weng Y Q (2006) High Technology Development Report, www.sciencep.com, p.38

Weng Y Q, et al (2003) "Ultra-fine Grained Steel—Microstructure Refinement Theory and Controlled Technology" (in Chinese), Metallurgical Industry Press, pp.18, Beijing

Yada H,et al (1983) Collected Abstracts of the 1983 Autumn Meeting of Japan Inst. Metals, JIM, Sendai, 190

Yada H,et al(1983) Tetsu-Hagane (Japan), 69:1459

2
Refinement of Austenitic Microstructure and Its Influence on $\gamma \rightarrow \alpha$ Transformation

The metallurgy research in physical-metallurgy and rolling process for austenitic grain refinement is presented in the first part of this chapter. And the influence of austenitic grain refinement on $\gamma \rightarrow \alpha$ transformation is introduced in the second part. It is as follows:

1. Thermomechanical control process and refinement of austenitic microstructure.
2. Influence of austenitic grain variety on subsequently transformed grain size. In the first part, the thermomechanical control process (TMCP) and basic theoretics of austenite grain refinement are discussed, which includes description of austenite dynamic recrystallization (DRX), metadynamic recrystallization (MDRX), static recrystallization (SRX) and non-recrystallization (NRX). Meanwhile, it was deal with microalloying technology and control rolling process in the austenite temperature region and under-cooled temperature region. Also control process of accelerated cooling (AC) and austenite grain refinement are considered.

In the second part, the influence of recrystallized, partially recrystallized and non-recrystallized austenite on subsequently transformed grain size was discussed. Meanwhile, the affect of different austenite phenomenon occurring during deformation on deformation induced ferrite transformation (DIFT) are reflected.

2.1 Thermomechanical Control Process and Refinement of Austenitic Microstructure

Thermomechanical process (TMCP) consists of controlled rolling (CR) and accelerated cooling (AC) processes, which can be used solely and be assembled.

Either of them can effectively refine the final microstructure, improving the strength and low-temperature toughness. Controlled rolling technique has been applied in the industrial production for more than 40 years. The steels produced by CR exhibit better mechanical properties than that with the same compositions produced by normalizing or quenching-and-tempering process because this technique can refine grain size very effectively. Accelerated cooling means that the hot materials are rapidly cooled by the rate of around 10℃ to go through the temperature range of 750～500℃, in which ferrite transformation is generally expected to happen. Now this technology has been broadly used in different steel productions.

Influence of hot deformation and the subsequent cooling on the decomposition of austenite was studied at the beginning of the 20th century(Stattman, 1892; Oberhoffer, 1913; Haneman, 1925). The CR technique was industrialized in Europe after World War Ⅱ（Vandrbeck,1958）, on which the rolling temperature was relatively high because the rolling facilities were not capable of high work load at low rolling temperature. In 1960s, Nb-microalloyed steels were widely produced. In order that low-temperature toughness of Nb microalloyed steels can be improved, much work was conducted in North America and Australia to introduce CR into production of large-diameter linepipe steels. Rolling at recrystallization temperature region and above Ac_3 was actually implemented for this objective(Grange, 1964). In the middle of 1960s, fundamental researches on CR were conducted in the western countries, particularly on the CR processes for V or Nb-microalloyed steels and for small-diameter bar on the pilot roller(Duckworth 1964; 1965; Philips, 1966). A lot of efforts were also put to understand suppression on austenitic recrystallization by the addition of Nb, and appearance of bimodal grain size distribution in the Nb-microalloyed products. All contributed to the subsequent application of CR to massive industrial productions(Irani, 1967; Jones, 1968; Pristner, 1968). In 1970s, CR at the non-recrystallization region was studied for production of microalloyed steels.

In 1980s, the first on-line accelerated cooling (AC) was established in Japan(Tsukada, 1982). This integrated process to combine CR and AC techniques is a milestone for the modern thermomechanical process. In order to refine grains in the plate rolling line with a small work load, CR at recrystallization temperature region was developed by addition of microalloying Ti element (<0.02%). Presence of Ti can lead to precipitation of TiN to prevent the growth of austenite grains(Weng etal,2003); consequently ferrite grains are refined. Such process, unfortunately, was not extensively adopted in the applications. Now, TMP is widely applied in the production of bars, strips and plates.

In summery, development of CR and AC is associated with development of HSLA steels, whose compositions are similar to C-Mn steels but microalloyed for refined microstructure. The mechanism for grain refinement by the microalloying of Nb, V and Ti elements has been extensively studied since 1960s.

Nb, V and Ti microalloying elements can be dissolved in matrix or combine with C or N to precipitate as compounds. When they are in solution, they can prevent grain growth due to the solute drag effect; when they precipitate at low temperature, they can prevent recrystallization and grain growth due to pinning by precipitates so that the transformation from the non-recrystallized austenite is much enhanced. In addition, Nb and V can precipitate in the transformed ferrite so that precipitation hardening is expected.

Nb-microalloying is the best choice for CR performed at the non-recrystallized region since both the solute Nb and strain induced Nb-precipitates can suppress recovery and recrystallization due to the solute drag and grain boundary pinning respectively, and the latter shows much stronger suppression on boundary migration than the former. Furthermore, presence of Nb can suppress the grain growth after recrystallization. When Nb is added into the C-Mn steel, the critical strain for dynamic recrystallization and the incubation time for onset of static recrystallization both increase, and the critical strain and minimum temperature for static recrystallization are both raised, leading to the expanded temperature region for non-recrystallization. Microalloying by Nb can result in finer recrystallized grain size than the steel without Nb. However, a bimodal grain size distribution is sometimes observed in the cast or rolled Nb-microalloyed steel, which may be caused by strain induced grain boundary migration, compositional segregation, heterogeneous temperature/strain field in the bulk.

V behaves similar to Nb, but with a much weaker suppression on recrystallization because more V can be dissolved in austenite than Nb. Therefore, austenite grain refinement by V has no industrial application. V has slight influence on strain induced ferrite transformation. When V-N alloy is added into C-Mn steel, the solution temperature for V carbonitrides is raised so that austenite grain growth is suppressed.

Ti can form TiN, the most stable compound among the microalloying precipitates, to suppress the austenite grain growth at high temperature. In the modern bar-rolling line, the bulk is transported in a high speed between stands so that CR is conducted at high temperature. In this case, Ti is a necessary element to produce ferrite grains as fine as in the conventional rolling at low temperature. TiN can precipitate just below the solidus temperature with relatively small size if contents of Ti and N are suitable. TiN particles grow very slowly at high temperature and can suppress austenite grain growth during the reheating.

Successful development in modern HSLA steels is to combine microalloying elements and thermomechanical process, which is one of the most influential achievements in 20th century. Developing recyclable steels with the least expense of nature resources and energy will be a trend in future.

In this chapter, the development of thermomechanical process for a plain carbon steel, Q235, is presented and the mechanism behind it is discussed.

2.1.1   *Rolling at the austenite-recrystallization temperature region (RARTR)*

Hot rolling at the austenitic phase generally consists of four different stages with the decreasing temperature. Firstly, the conventional hot rolling above 1000℃ results in coarse grains after austenitic recrystallization; Secondly, hot rolling below 1000℃ is conducted and it includes three different cases, as shown in Figure 2.1(a) A significant grain growth after complete recrystallization in the deformed austenite grains, (b) Recrystallized grains are fine and the subsequent grain growth is suppressed. (c) Recrystallization takes place just in the par of the deformed austenite. Thirdly, hot rolling is conducted generally a bit above Ar_3, the austenite-to-ferrite transformation temperature so that no recrystallization can take place, which results in deformed austenite grains and they can transform to much finer ferrite grains during the subsequent cooling(Cohn M, 1984). Fourthly, hot rolling is carried out at the intercritical region, i.e., the dual-phase region of austenite plus ferrite, often results in deformed microstructure.

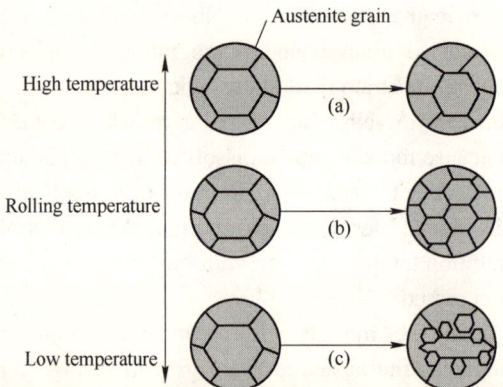

Figure 2.1   Rolling of austenite recrystallize region
(a) Normal rolling at high temperature; (b) Recrystallize control rolling; (c) Part recrystallize rolling

RARTR is illustrated in Figure 2.1 (b). Such process requires materials rolled above the $T_{95\%}$ temperature, at which 95% of the bulk has been recrystallized, see Figure 2.2. The austenite grains almost immediately start to recrystallize at the beginning of deformation and the recrystallized grains are subsequently deformed and then recrystallized again, such phenomenon is repeated during deformation. This leads to refinement of austenite grains if the grain growth, which may happen during the period of interpass or between finish rolling and transformation during cooling, can be prevented. Therefore, application of RARTR in industry requires: a wide temperature region for recrystallization when the steel is hot rolled; and suppression of recrystallized austenite grains. Fine austenite grains achieved by recrystallization can lead to finer ferrite and pearlite if cooling rate is high enough. The plain carbon steel without microalloying and solute alloying elements generally has a very wide temperature region, in which the critical temperature for onset of recrystallization is close to the transformation temperature. Even if this steel is lack of precipitate pinning or solute drag, fine ferrite grains can still be achieved by RARTR if thermomechanical process can suppress the growth of recrystallized grains.

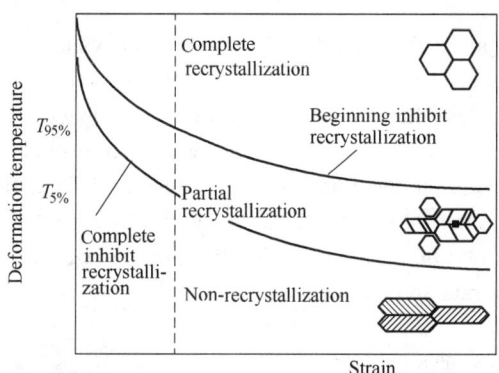

Figure 2.2   Austenite under different deformation condition

In the most industrial productions, static recrystallization (SRX) is a dominant softening mechanism, particularly for microalloyed steels. Static recrystallization kinetics, grain size and grain growth during the period of interpass and compositional influence on recrystallization are all important issues that have receive wide attention in the past decades. Recent researches have shown that dynamic recrystallization can occur in the bar or wire rolling production, in which the strain can be accumulated due to very short interpass time(Pussegoda, 1990; Yue, 1995). Moreover the occurrence of dynamic recrystallization leads to metadynamic recrystallization after deformation(Hodgson, 1992; Roucoules, 1994). Therefore, RARTR includes three mechanisms: static, dynamic and metadynamic recrystallization, each of which can be realized by the different TMP parameters.

Dynamic recrystallization(DRX) plays a significant role on thermomechanical processing of metals because of the improvement in mechanical properties through enhanced grain refinement(Sakai, 1996, Roucoules,1994). Dynamic recrystallization affects grain refinement both during and aften deformatio; in the latter case this can be static recrystallization and metadynamic recrystallization(Roberts, 1979, Jonas, 1969). Onset of DRX depends on deformation and temperature that can be described by Zener-Hollomon parameter(Sellars, 1966) with the following equation:

$$Z = \dot{\varepsilon}\exp(\frac{Q_{def}}{RT}) = A(\sin h(\alpha\sigma_{p}))^{n} \qquad (2.1)$$

where $\dot{\varepsilon}$ is strain rate, Q_{def} is active energy for deformation, T is absolute temperature, R is gas constant, and A, α and n are all constants.

It is generally accepted that progress of dynamic recrystallization follows(JMAK)Avrami equation(Cabrera, 2003, Hernandez1996):

$$X = 1 - \exp(-Bt^{n}) \qquad (2.2)$$

where X is the volume fration of the material recrystallized, t is time and B and n are constants.

It has been found that there exists a critical value of Z for dynamic recrystallization, Zc. Austenite grains are prolonged and subject to dynamic recovery when Z is less than Zc; while they are recrystallized when Z is more than Zc, and can be completely recrystallized when strain increases. Figure 2.3 illustrates the evolution of microstructure during deformation: initial work hardening and then partial recrystallization and finally complete recrystallization. Therefore, occurrence of dynamic recrystallization can be predicted by Equation 2.1 based on strain rate and temperature.

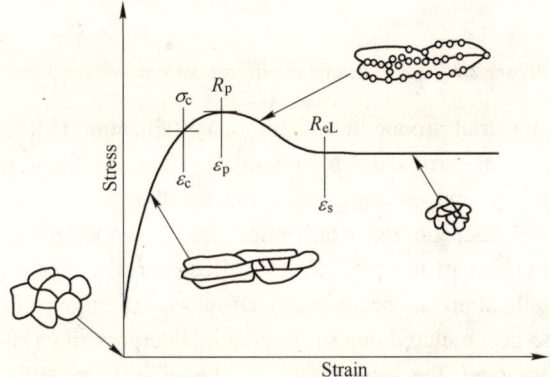

Figure 2.3   Austenite hot deformation true stress-strain and the microstructure change

In the past, DRX was studied at higher temperatures (Cahn R W, 1983; Sakai, 1984)or with low strain rates of $10^{-1}\sim10^{-5}$(Himmel, 1963; Sakuil, 1977; Weiss, 1983). Thanks to the development of modern rolling facilities, high strain rate and low finish rolling temperature are possible now. For example, a modern bar and wire rolling mill in China is characterized by rolling temperature ranging from 1200℃ to 700℃, strain rate from 0.5/s to 200/s, interpass period between stands from 0.1s to 10s and deformation increasing by 30% more than the conventional one. Therefore, physical phenomena happening in the modern bar and wire high-speed rolling line are definitely worth of extensive studying and deep insights into them are valuable for commercial production.

The true stress-strain curves for a plain carbon steel, whose composition is

0.18%C-0.60%Mn-0.21%Si-0.016%P-0.020%S-0.0082%Al and equilibrium transformation temperature Ae_3 is around 840℃(Wang, 2006a), were measured by hot compression tests and shown in Figure 2.4. The specimen was firstly heated to 1100℃ for isothermal holding and cooled to the test temperatures in the range of 1100~750℃ by the rate of 3℃/s, and then deformed to a true strain of 0.9 by various rates of 0.1~60s^{-1}. Phase diagram for DRX, partial DRX and non-recrystallization as function of deformation temperature and strain rate is shown in Figure 2.5. When strain is fixed, the regions for DRX, partial DRX and no DRX can be clearly distinguished in the diagram. When both strain and strain rate are fixed, the deformed austenite can experience at decreasing temperature: dynamic recovery (DRV) plus DRX at the beginning, then followed by mere DRV and finally dynamic transformation. With increasing strain rate, the dynamic softening mechanism of deformed austenite changes from DRV+DRX to a mere DRV, i.e. DRX only occurs at relatively high deformation temperature with low strain rate.

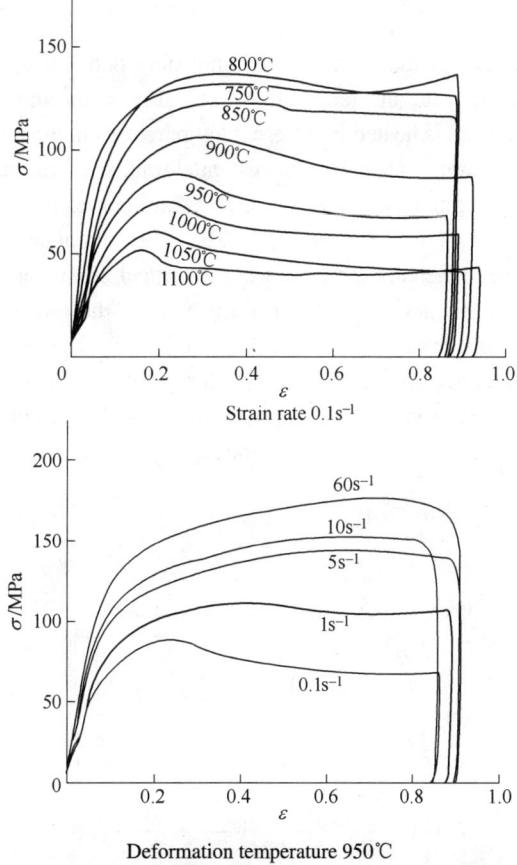

Figure 2.4 The true stress-strain curve under different deformation condition

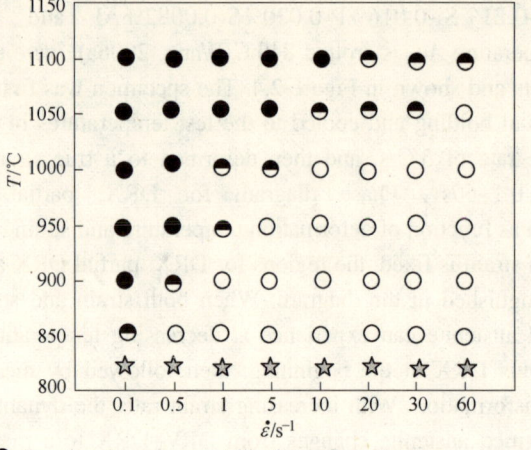

Figure 2.5   Physics metallurgy process of carbon steel Q235 under different deformation conditions

It should be noted that the onset of DRX not only depends on the Z parameter (combination of strain rate and temperature) but also on the initial grain size and strain. When Q235 steel is heated to different temperatures in the range of 900~1300 ℃ for isothermal holding to achieve the austenite grain sizes varying from 30μm to 400μm, influence of initial grain size on stress-strain curves at 900℃ at the strain rate of 0.1s^{-1} can be given in Figure 2.6. The finer initial austenite grain size, resulting from lower reheating temperature, the critical strain for onset of DRX is reduced, i.e. fine grains are easy to recrystallize when the process parameter Z is fixed. In other words, the range for DRX is expanded with the finer initial austenite grains since Zc increases. At the austenization temperature of 1300℃, a very coarse austenite grains can be produced, leading to mere DRV during deformation without DRX observed at 900℃ at the same strain rate.

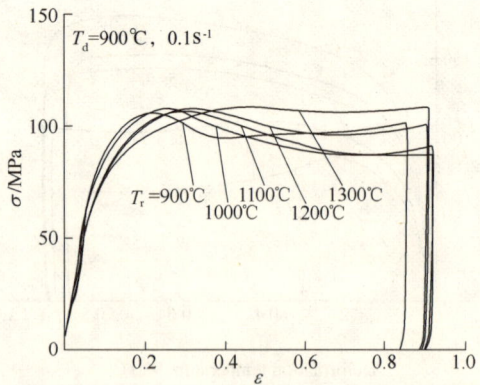

Figure 2.6   The true stress-strain curves under different heat temperatures
with the same deformation condition

Zc can vary with strain, as it is revealed by hot torsion tests and shown in Figure 2.7, in which true stress - true strain curves are measured for the 0.085%C-0.29%Si-0.95%Mn-0.045%Nb steel(CHO, 2001). Even though presence of Nb can strongly suppress recrystallization, DRX can be observed at 850℃ with the strain rate of 1/s and at 950℃ with strain rate 5/s, and the corresponding critical strain for onset of DRX is also raised, which is difficult to be observed in the hot compression tests due to the limited strain achieved. It can be known that an increase in strain leads to raised Zc for onset of DRX, i.e. DRX can happen even when Z is large. Therefore, onset of DRX is dependent on both Z and strain.

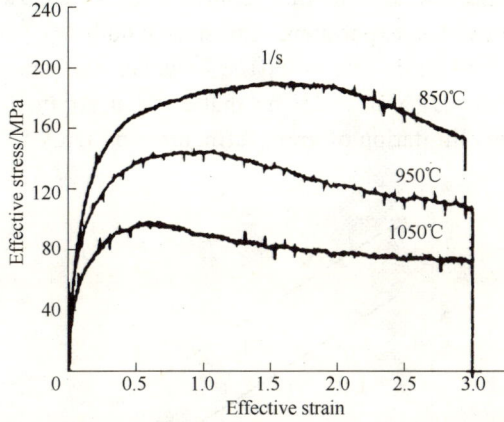

Figure 2.7   In hot torsion tests, true stress - true strain curves are measured for the 0.085%C-0.29%Si-0.95%Mn-0.045%Nb steel

The dynamically recrystallized grain size (DRGS) is determined only by thermomechanical process parameter Z, which can be described by the following equation:

$$d_{drx} = a_1 Z^{b_1}$$
(2.3)

where a_1 and b_1 are both constants. Thus, an increase in Z can lead to refinement of recrystallized grain size. Meanwhile, DRX occurs only when Z is less than Zc, therefore, the value of Zc has to be raised. Increased strain and reduced initial austenite grain size can both effectively raise Zc, resulting in the onset of DRX at higher value of Z, consequently, dynamically recrystallized grains are refined. Relationship between process parameter Z and DRGS is shown in Figure 2.8, where d_{mdx} is metadynamically recrystallized grain size and discussed in the following relevant section. Salvatori et al. conducted the uniaxial compression tests on SUS304L stainless steel with various strain rates at relatively low temperature and found the similar dependence between them(Nagai, 2002). When our experimental data are compared with Maki et al's data, it can be shown in Figure 2.9. It can be seen that the two sets of data agree very well, and indicating DRX can further refine grain size down to several micrometers. The finest grain size achieved by DRX is 4~5μm when log$Z$ is 10^{19} s^{-1}. However, it should be noted that such extension of grain refinement by DRX in Figure 2.9 may not be applied to other steel grades. The strain-Z region for complete DRX, partical DRX and no DRX are shown respectively in Figure 2.10(Nagai, 2002), where ε_c is the critical strain for onset of DRX and $\varepsilon_{99\%}$ is the strain necessary for completion of 99% DRX. It can be seen that large strain is required for onset of DRX when the value of Z is high, i.e. high strain rate and low deformation temperature. At 1023K, the maximum strain of 3.1 employed in experiments can satisfy both ε_c and $\varepsilon_{99\%}$ for the complete DRX when strain rate is 0.01/s; however, the strain of 3.1 can not ensure the complete DRX at 872K no matter what strain rate is employed. The latter indicates limitation of grain refinement by DRX.

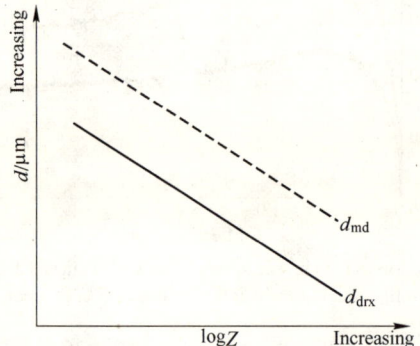

Figure 2.8   The relationship between austenitic dynamically recrystallized grains size d_{drx}, metadynamically recrystallized grain size and value Z

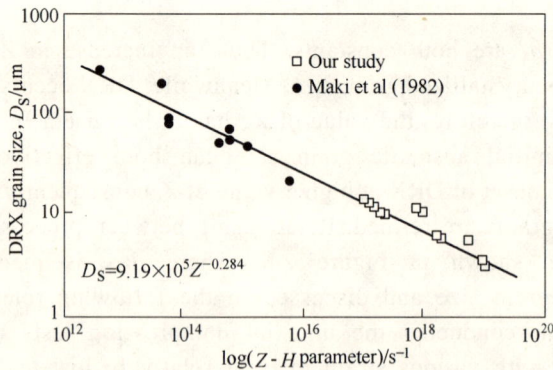

Figure 2.9   The ferrite grain size obtained under high Z value(Nagai, 2002)

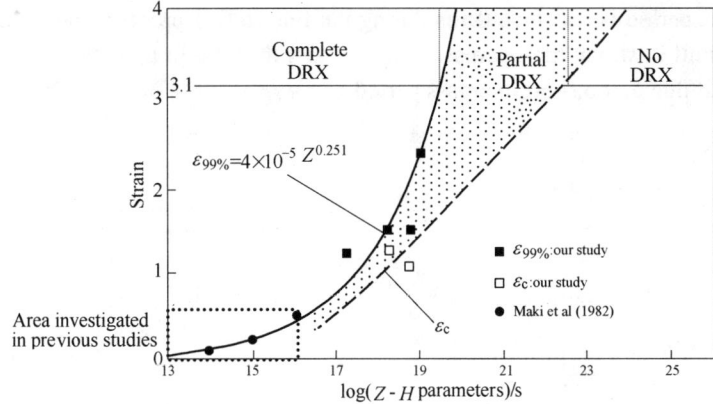

Figure 2.10   The distribution of parameter ε —Z-H dynamically recrystallization(Nagai, 2002)

Due to the need for large number of experimental examinations can be on the occurrence of dynamic recrystallization and volume fraction (or area fraction) of recrystallized grains make a judgment, it is now a scholar has put forward new research methods (Saden,2005). This approach utilises the stress–strain curve of the material to quantify the progress of dynamic softening. The outcome of this method showed a good agreement with experimental results for alloys of this study.

2.1.1.1   Metadynamic recrystallization (MDRX)

If DRX occurs during deformation, the nuclei for recrystallization has been formed and can continue to grow by boundary migration after deformation without incubation period observed, which is termed as metadynamic recrystallization. In the classical theory it is commonly believed that MDRX kinetics depends on strain rate and deformation temperature, but not on strain and the initial austenitic microstructure. However, recent researches proved that MDRX kinetics could be dependent on strain when strain is located in the range of $\varepsilon_c < \varepsilon < \varepsilon_T$, where ε_T (CHO,2001; Zahiri,2004; Uranga P, 2003) is another critical strain beyond which strain has no influence on MDRX. i.e. strain-independent softening. Within this range, strain can influence MDRX kinetics because there are just a few DRX nuclei formed and static recrystallization can occur after deformation, leading to mixed mechanism of static recrystallization and MDRX.

Studies on MDRX kinetics have revealed that it strongly depends on strain rate(Hodgson, 1992; Liang, 2006), as shown in Figure 2.12. It can be seen that the higher stain rate leads to MDRX completed in a shorter time. This indicates that MDRX might play a dominant role in the bar and wire rolling mill, in which interpass period is less than 0.15s during the fine rolling process, and in the strip rolling mill in which the interpass period is less than 1s. In both cases, SRX may not occur due to too short interpass period.

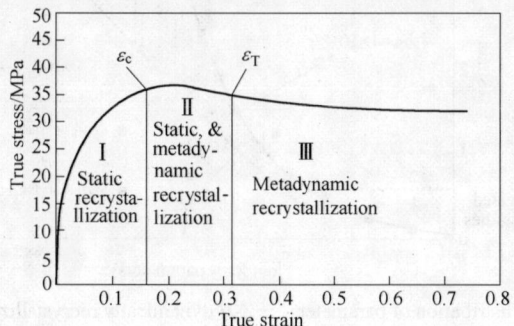

Figure 2.11   The influence to intenerate mechanism by strain after deformation

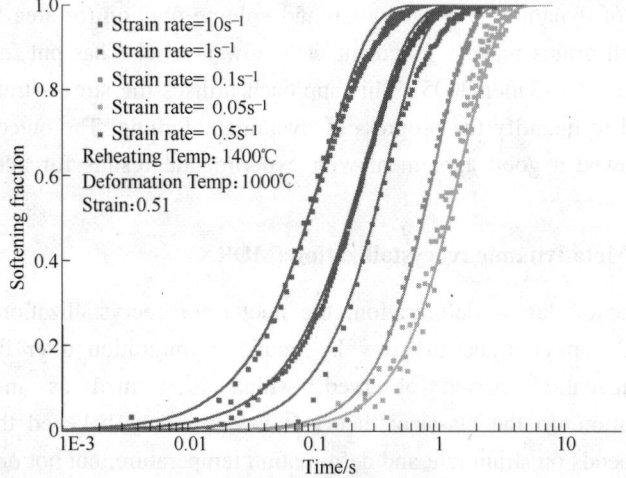

Figure 2.12   Strain rate influence on MDRX kinetics (Liang, 2006)
（Steel components mass%: 0.06C-0.02Si-0.2Mn-0.03Al）

Similar to DRX, metadynamically recrystallized grain size shows no dependence on initial austenite grain size and strain when strain is more than ε_T, but dependence on strain rate and deformation temperature by:

$$d_{md} = a_2 Z^{b_2} \tag{2.4}$$

where a_2 and b_2 are both constants. By this equation, a higher value of Z can result in finer metadynamically recrystallized grain size, shown in Figure 2.18. It is possible to adapt MDRX into rolling at relatively low temperature since MDRX is not so sensitive to deformation temperature(Hodgson, 1992). The low rolling temperature should be coupled with high strain rate, which can ensure a high value of Z for austenite grain refinement.

2.1.1.2   Static recrystallization (SRX)

Static recrystallization means that recrystallization takes place in the deformed austenite after deformation, for examples. during the period of interpass, or during the cooling after rolling. Cold-deformed materials can recrystallize during annealing, which is also a kind of SRX but will not be discussed here since it is not relevant to thermomechanical process. SRX generally requires incubation time for the onset of recrystallization, which is different from MDRX. SRX kinetics not only depends on deformation temperature and strain rate but also strongly depends on strain and initial austenite grain size (IAGS). An increasing strain and decreasing IAGS both significantly accelerate SRX and reduce the statically recrystallized grain size. Therefore, SRX is related to both deformation and the microstructure after deformation.

SRX has a very important role on grain refinement. During the hot deformation, the evolution of austenitic microstructure includes(Titchener, 1958; Bever,1973):

1. Various defects are introduced into crystalline lattice, such as dislocations, vacancies and stack faults. At the initial stage of deformation there is an increase in both the flow stress and the stored energy as dislocations interact and multiply. Higher dislocation density, generated by further deformation, leads to work-hardening rate, flow stress and stored energy all increased. 80%~90% of deformation energy is stored in the deformed material through dislocations multiplication.
2. Grains are deformed and fragmentized. Deformation applied in the austenite leads to dislocations to slip along a certain direction until cells and even subgrains are formed within grains, which divide grains into smaller parts.
3. Deformation texture appears during deformation. The orientation changes that take place during deformation are not random. They are a consequence of the fact deformation occurs on the most favorably oriented slip or twining systems and it follows that the deformed austenite acquires a preferred orientation or texture by grain rotation. Texture change can also company with phase transformation, recrystallization and magnetic transformation, which are now receiving more attention to understand the inherent mechanism.

All the above-stated phenomena are associated with deformation conditions, but the former two have particularly dominant influence on grain refinement by recrystallization.

1. Deformation mode. Different deformation modes can influence dislocations slip and consequently work hardening performance. Besides hot compression, other deformation modes developed for producing superfine microstructures include:
1) Hot torsion. Superfine ferrite grains around 1μm in the Si-Mn steel were developed by Hodgson et al (1992) with hot torsion at around Ar_3 temperature.
2) ARB（accumulative rolled bonding）technique, which can produce to very high strain for superfine microstructure (Tsuji N, 1999).

3) ECAP (equal channel angular processing), that refines microstructures by large shear deformation(Valiev, 2000).

All of these techniques have a promising future in the industrial application.

2. Strain. Strain can influence dislocation density and stored energy at the early stage. The stored energy and dislocation density increase with strain until they get saturated at a certain strain(Gorden, 1955). Therefore, the final dislocation density and stored energy may not be determined by strain.

3. Strain rate. Higher strain rate leads to more pronounced work hardening rate; consequently both dislocation density and stored energy get higher in the material. Strain rate, however, has little influence on the geometry of deformed grains.

4. Deformation temperature, which has similar influence on grain refinement as strain rate. Lower temperature leads to more pronounced work hardening rate, higher dislocation density and stored energy. It also has little influence on the geometry of deformed grains.

5. Initial grain size. Metals with fine sizes show more pronounced work hardening than those with coarse sizes. It has been found that dislocation density generated by deformation is inversely proportional to grain size(Himmel, 1963).

6. Solute atoms. They can have a significant drag force on dislocation, which leads to higher work hardening rate and consequently dislocation density and stored energy both raised.

7. Second phase particles. Only non-deformable particles can increase work hardening rate.

Factors of $1 \sim 4$ are decisive parameters of deformation and factors of $5 \sim 7$ are inherent parameters for the material itself. From the viewpoint of grain refinement, grain fragmentation is more important than geometries of deformed grains. Deformed metals experience recovery, recrystallization and grain growth during annealing. Influence of grain size on nucleation and growth of recrystallization and the mechanical properties have all been extensively studied since 1920s(Burke, 1952). Recovery generally takes place before recrystallization and do not involve formation and migration of large-angle boundaries. Recrystallization consists of nucleation and growth stages, whose kinetics is similar to phase transformation and widely described by so called JMA equation as firstly presented by Johnson, Mehl(1939)and Avrami(1939; 1940; 1941).In JMA theory, it is assumed that nuclei are formed at a rate I and grow into deformed material at a linear rate G. The fraction recrystallized Xv rises rapidly with time until the new grains impinge on each other. If nuclei randomly distributed in the material, the fraction of materials which would have recrystallized is known as the ***extended volume*** X_{VEX}, in which nuclei in the already recrystallized material are also included, and is given by

$$X_{VEX} = fIG^3 t^4 / 4 \qquad (2.5)$$

where f is shape factor and $4\pi/3$ for spheres. During a time interval dt, the extended volume increases by an amount dX_{VEX}. As the fraction of unrecrystallized material is $1-X_V$, it follows:

$$(1 - X_V)dX_{VEX} = dX_V \qquad (2.6)$$

Combining Equations 2.5 and 2. 6 leads to Johnson-Mehl equation:

$$X_V = 1 - \exp(-fIG^3 t^4 / 4) \qquad (2.7)$$

Or Avrami equation with more general form:

$$X_V = 1 - \exp(-Bt^n), \qquad (2.8)$$

where B depends on deformation temperature, activation energy for recrystallization and grain boundary energy, and n is in the range of $3 \sim 4$ for the three dimensional growth with a constant rate.

The deformation stored energy is the driving force for recrystallization. Therefore, factors affecting the stored energy can also influence recrystallization:

1. Deformation temperature. Higher deformation temperature will lower the stored energy, which is not beneficial to onset of recrystallization. However, both nucleation and growth rate increase exponentially with temperature, particularly the energy barrier for nucleation of recrystallization is significantly reduced with increasing temperature, therefore, raising temperature facilities onset of recrystallization and shortens recrystallization period, see Figure 2.13 (Hoogendorrn, 1977).

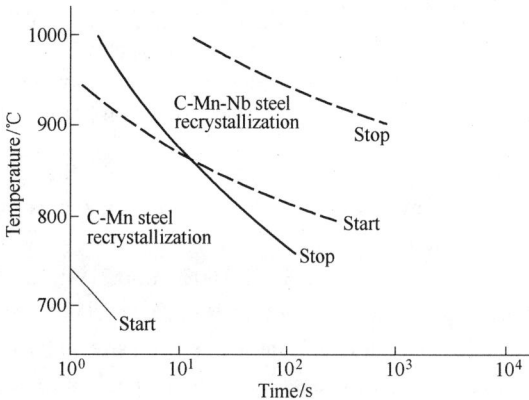

Figure 2.13   The curve of recrystallization-temperature-time of C-Mn steel and C-Mn-Nb steel after 50% reduction Nb steel components C 0.10%, Mn 0.99%, Nb 0.039%

2. Strain. An increase in the strain leads to expansion of temperature range for SRX due to increased stored energy and consequently increased nucleation rate. Increase in both strain and temperature can even lead to DRX during deformation. The conditions in which SRX or DRX can occur are generally described by strain-temperature diagram, as shown in Figure 2.14(Sekine,et

al,1982). This figure is obtained by the following experiment: a 0.1%C-0.25%Si-1.40%Mn steel was heated to 1250℃ and then cooled to rolling temperature, and then subject to single pass rolling followed by brine quenching after 1s. Recrystallization at specified different strains and temperatures are examined and recrystallized grain sizes are indicated by number in the circles. It can be seen that the minimum temperature for SRX decreases rapidly with increasing strain.

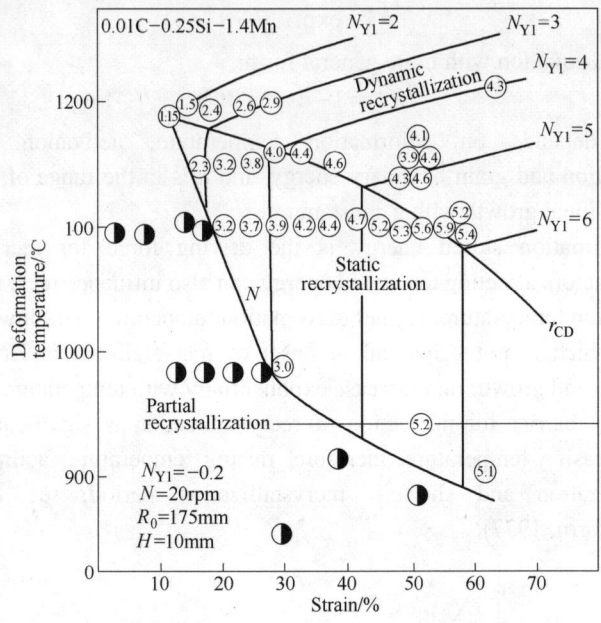

Figure 2.14   The diagram of C-Mn steel hot rolling Austenitic recrystallization r_{CD} - fully dynamic recrystallization reduction; r_{cs}' - Completely static recrystallization reduction

3. Strain rate. A rise in strain rate can significantly raise the rate of dislocation generation during deformation, which leads to higher stored energy and facilitating recrystallization.

SRX in Q235 carbon steel (0.18%C-0.60%Mn-0.21%Si-0.016%P-0.020%S-0.0082%Al) was investigated and reported in Ref(Wang, 2006b). It was found that deformation temperature, strain and initial austenite grain size all have strong influence on SRX kinetics. In addition, an increase in strain rate could also accelerate SRX, as shown in Figure 2.15. Such static recrystallization could complete in a very short time, particularly after a large strain. For example, after 70% reduction at 850℃ with strain rate of 10/s, SRX is completed within 1.3s after deformation.

Influence of process parameters on SRXed grain size in the Q235 steel has been also studied. When the steel was cooled from the austenization temperature to the deformation temperature 800~850℃ (above Ar_3) and deformed to true strain 0.7~1.2

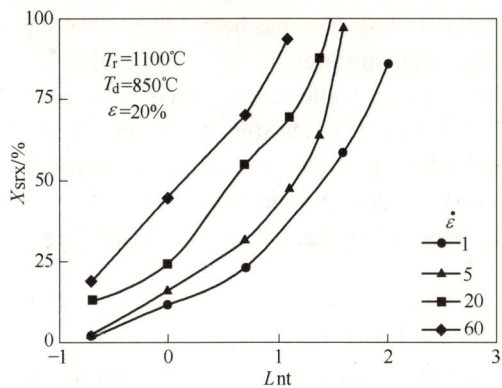

with strain rate $10\text{--}60\text{s}^{-1}$, the austenite grain size after SRX can be refined to $10\text{--}20\mu m$. Figure 2.16 shows microstructures after two typical deformation processes, both lead to completely recrystallized grains. When cooling rate is 20℃/s or even higher, ferrite grains are $4\sim6\mu m$ or finer (Wang, 2004). By comparison of the two process and the corresponding microstructures, it can be found that high strain rate and deformation at low temperature lead to strong

Figure 2.15   Strain rate influence on recrystallization kinetics

T_r —Heating temperature;T_d—Deformation temperature,

ε—Deformation; $\dot{\varepsilon}$ —Deformation rate;

fragmentation of austenite grains.

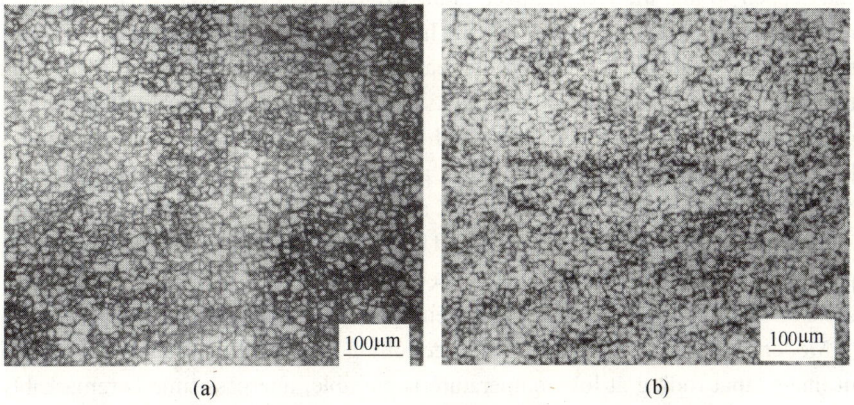

Figure 2.16   Austenite microstructure of plain Carbon Steel Q235
under different deformation conditions

(a)Reheating at 1100℃,Cooling rate 10℃/s,deformation at 850℃, true strain 0.9, strain rate10s^{-1};
(b)Reheating at 900℃, Cooling rate 30℃/s, deformation at 800℃, true strain 1.2, strain rate 30s^{-1} After
the deformation sepals are direct water quenched and delay time before that is about 0.5~1.5s

4. Initial austenite grain size (IAGS), solute atoms, second phase particles (SPP).

Finer initial austenite grain size leads a denser dislocation generated during deformation and higher stored energy, leading to accelerated recrystallization. In addition, the minimum temperature and strain for recrystallization both decrease with finer IAGS as reported(Sekine, 1982; Sellars, 1980).

Presence of solute atoms and non-deformable second phase particles(SPP) can raise stored energy during deformation; but can suppress recrystallization due to solute drag and pinning by SPPs. In particular, microalloying element, Nb, can significantly raise the minimum temperature for recrystallization, and expand the temperature range for non-recrystallization rolling. This has been adapted into the modern thermomechanical process in the steel industries.

Factors to influence recrystallized grain size after deformation have been extensively studied(Krchynsky, 1977; Balance, 1976; DeArdo, 1982). In general, some empirical equations were presented to quantify the relationship between various factors and recrystallized grain size, as discussed in (Sllars, 1980).

The recrystallized grain size D_{SRX} depends on nucleation rate I and linear growth rate G by:

$$D_{SRX} = k(G/I)^m \qquad (2.9)$$

where k is constant and m is between 1/4 and 1/6.

It can be summarized now that large deformation at the low temperature of austenitic region, coupled with a certain interpass time and rapid cooling after finish rolling, can lead to significant refinement of ferrite grains. If low-temperature rolling, high strain rate and short interpass time are all employed, this may lead to significant strain accumulation at the subsequent rolling pass. Consequently, DRX or MDRX can happen so that the recrystallized grain size can get even finer. Therefore, grain refinement by SRX or DRX in the hot rolling line depends on the rolling temperatures, reduction at each rolling pass and interpass time determined by bulk transporting speed. Since SRX in Q235 steel is quite fast and recrystallized grains grows rapidly, this determines that the hot rolling process of Q235 steel requires low-temperature rolling, high strain rate and high transporting speed so that strain can be accumulated for the onset of DRX and MDRX.

Since rolling temperature, reduction and interpass time all vary with different rolling passes; microstructural evolution, such as occurrence of DRX or SRX or deformation/ shear bands or grain growth, can be different from rough rolling to fine rolling.

Modern hot rolling facilities offer large rolling load and high transporting speed in line so that rolling at low temperature is possible, interpass time is remarkably shorten and strain rate is getting higher. Those lead to strain accumulation for DRX or MDRX at low temperature and suppress the grain growth during the interpass period. If accelerated cooling is introduced after rolling, the refined ferrite grains in Q235 steel can then be achieved in the modern hot rolling line even if there are no precipitates such as TiN or NbC and solute drag in this plain carbon steel to prevent grain growth.

2.1.2 *Rolling in austenite non-recrystallization temperature region (RANRTR)*

RANRTR has been industrialized for the commercial production of Nb, V and Ti microalloyed steels. When austenite grains are deformed below T_{nr} as shown in Figure 2.2, the pancake geometry of grains is achieved after deformation and lots of defects are introduced into matrix, see Figure 2.17. Boundary surface area per unit volume S_v can be approximated as grain size, and it consists of prior austenite grain boundaries, deformation bands and discontinuous twin boundaries. Increasing strain can lead to more defects introduced but deformation temperature and strain rate are key parameters to determine the quantity of deformation bands. Figure 2.18 gives the relation between strain and the equivalent austenite grain boundary surface. Uniform distribution of deformation bands due to RANRTR is necessary for homogeneous ferrite microstructure, otherwise a bimodal ferrite grain size distribution can be observed. This requires larger reduction at rolling passes and lower rolling temperature, which leads to higher resistance force and brings difficulty to the real production. Microalloying addition can raise the Tnr so that RANRTR can be performed at high temperature, which has been successfully implemented in the commercial production. When RANRTR is followed by accelerated cooling, the ferrite grains can be refined significantly.

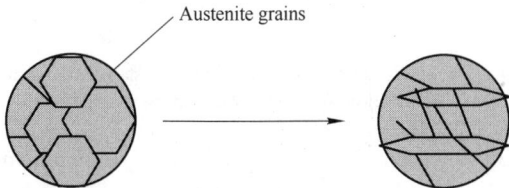

Figure 2.17   The sketch map of austenite non-recrystallization control rolling

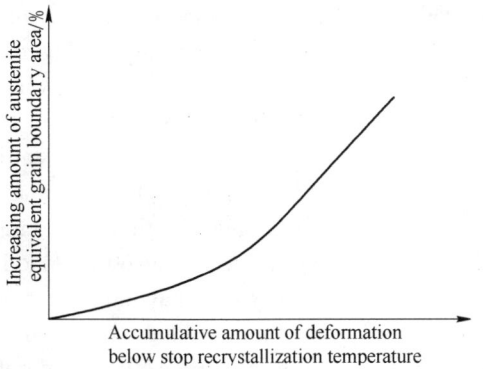

Figure 2.18   The correlation between amount of deformation and increase of austenite equivalent grain boundary area amount below stop recrystalliation temperature

Microalloying elements play twofold influences: on the one hand, they can facilitate austenite recrystallization and grain refinement by the pinning of precipitates on boundaries and raised stored energy; on the other hand, recrystallization can be suppressed by solute drag of microalloying elements and reduced stored energy due to strain-induced precipitation. Figure 2.19(Cuddy,

1984) shows that suppression on recrystallization in 0.075%C-1.40% Mn-0.25%Si varies with concentrations of microalloying solutes. It can found that Nb has the strongest suppression on recrystallization so that Tnr is significantly raised and the non-recrystallization temperature range is expanded.

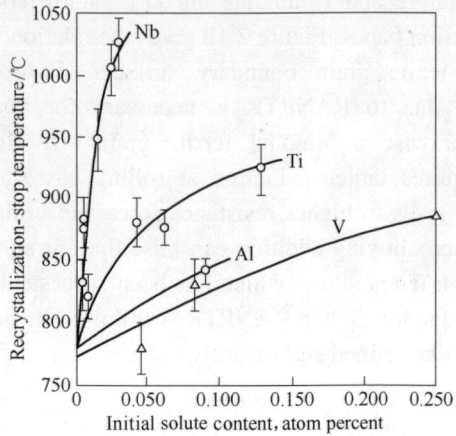

Figure 2.19   The effect of solute elements on recrystallization temperature in C-Mn Microalloying steel, per reduction is 10%~15%

It was generally believed that RANRTR would be much more difficult for plain carbon steels because both DRX and SRX can easily happen during deformation or during the period of interpass respectively. Whilst the modern high-speed rolling line offers the high strain rate and short interpass time, which both facilitate RANRTR for plain carbon steels. Figure 2.20 shows the dependences of recrystallized fraction on strain and deformation temperature at strain rates of 0.1/s and 0.5/s, indicating that an increase in strain rate can raise both Tnr and the minimum strain for recrystallization so that non-recrystallization temperature region is expanded. In addition, increasing strain can lower the Tnr. Figure 2.21 gives the time for completion of different recrystallization fraction in the Q235 steel after 60% reduction with 0.1/s and 0.5/s. Compared with Figure 2.13, SRX may not occur when deformation temperature is around 800℃ and interpass time is less than 1s as shown in Figure 2.5. This constructs a solid basis for RANRTR and deformation induced ferrite transformation implemented in hot rolling production. It is well know that interpass time is less 1s in the modern rod and wire rolling line. Therefore, the final microstructure can be refined by the suitable controlled rolling and accelerated cooling in the modern rolling production line.

In graph the 0.1, 0.5 are deformation rate and 20%, 50%, 90% are fraction of recrystallization grains respectively.

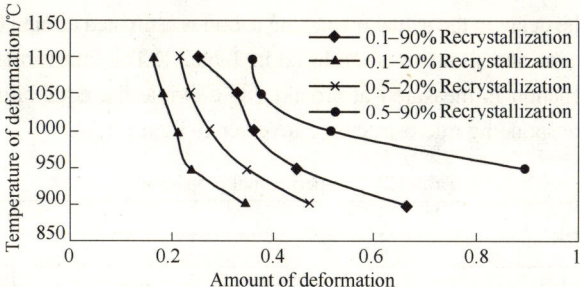

Figure 2.20   Static recrystallization and non-recrystallization curves of plain
low carbon Steel Q235, deformation rate 0.1 and $0.5s^{-1}$

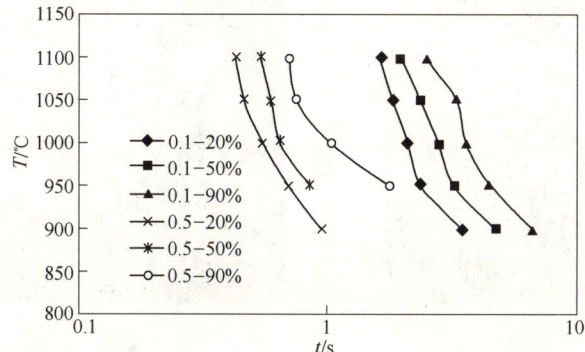

Figure 2.21   Transiting time of static recrystallization under different
deformation rate in plain low carbon steel after 60% reduction

2.1.3   *Rolling at the uder-cooled astenite (RCA)*

Microstructure refinement by RCA has been studied extensively as well(Hodgson, 1998; Yada, 1988; Weng, 2003). The concept of RCA is to implement large strain (>50%) at temperature around Ar_3 with relatively high strain rate so that ferrite grains can be refined by deformation induced ferrite transformation (DIFT)(Qi, 2002a; 2002b; 2002c; Yang W, 2001; Yang P, 2001). However, the austenite in the plain carbon steel is easy to recrystallize both statically or dynamically, so that the deformation stored energy can be reduced by the proceeding recrystallization, consequently, there is no enough driving force left for DIFT(Yang, 2000a; 2000b; Yang, 2001). The number of deformation/shear bands produced by deformation at Ar_3 with relatively high strain rate is proportional to deformation stored energy. It is shown in Figure 2.4 and Figure 2.5 that the minimum temperature for DRX is 800℃ when strain rate is 0.1/s, whilst it is 950℃ when strain rate is 10/s. Deformed austenitic microstructure after under cooling was simulated by Gleeble thermomechanical simulator according to the following process: specimens were firstly heated to 950℃ for 2min isothermal holding and then cooled to deformation temperature, subject to 60% compression and then immediately quenched by water jets (the delay in the actual quenching action is estimated around 0.5~1.5s), the investigated strains and strain rates are listed in Table2.1. The transformation point Ar_3 after the deformation is measured at around 780℃ while the equilibrium one Ae_3 is 840℃. The corresponding microstructures are given in Figure 2.22.

Table 2.1 Experimental programme

Strain rate/s^{-1}	40	0.1
	770	770
Temperature/℃	785	782
	790	790

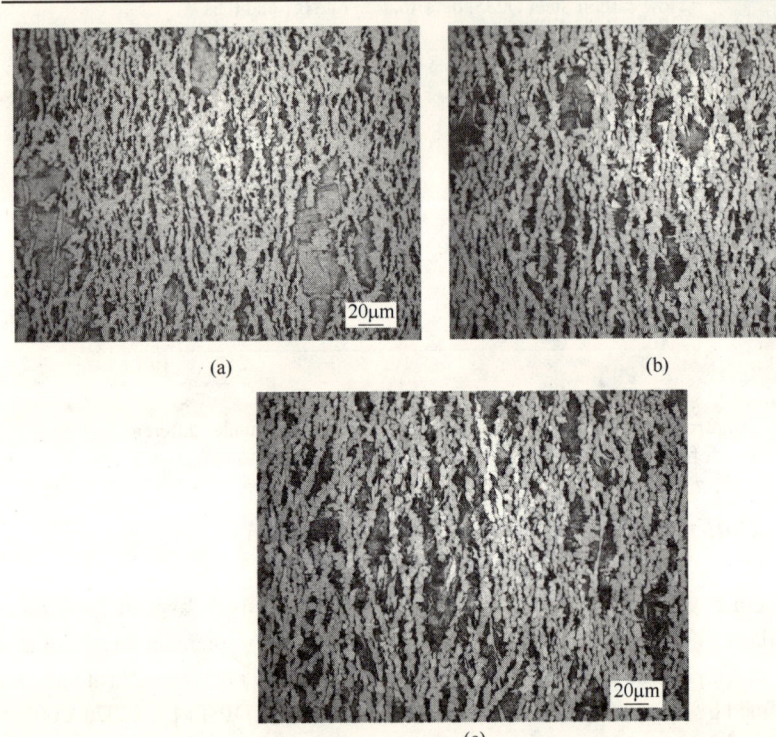

(a)   (b)

(c)

Figure 2.22   The microstructure of plain low carbon steel after deformation with strain 60% and strain rate 0.1s^{-1} at different temperature

(a) 770℃; (b)782℃; (c)790℃

In Figure 2.22, non-recrystallized microstructures were observed. Ferrite was formed in a morphology like necklace and martensite was prolonged, resulting from the pancaked austenite grains. That is, austenite can not recrystallized either dynamically or statically when temperature is 770~790℃ and strain is 60% at the strain rate of 0.1/s. Prolonged austenite grains, companying with dynamic recovery during deformation, then transform to martensitic band structure as observed. When strain rate increases to 40/s, the strongly deformed microstructure, with more fragments but without any recrystallization, is observed. It is surprising to notice that the refined ferrite and martensite are both equaxial, suggesting the prior austenite grains should be equaxial as well, as shown in Figure 2.23. Author studied influence of various strains on microstructure and observed the similar phenomena. Stress-strain curves at 0.1/s and 40/s are shown in Figure 2.24. By comparison of Figure 2.22 and Figure 2.23, the possible mechanisms behind this phenomenon are discussed below:

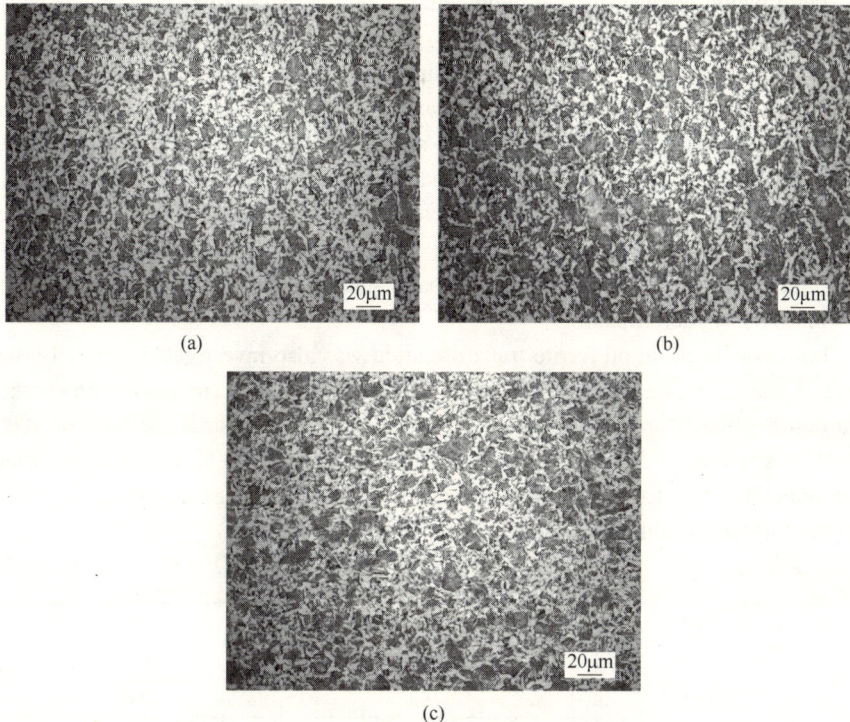

(a)   (b)

(c)

Figure 2.23   The microstructure of plain low carbon steel after deformation with 60%
and strain rate 40s⁻¹ at different temperature
(a)770℃; (b)785℃; (c)790℃

1. SRX mechanism. SRX might occur during the quenching. High strain-rate deformation leads to formation of dense deformation bands and much increased S_v, resulting in SRV inevitably taking place in this very unstable austenite even during quenching. Consequently, equaxial microstructure can be observed. However, SRX generally requires incubation time for nucleation and nuclei distribute heterogeneously, therefore, some martensitic band structure, inheriting from prolonged austenite grains, should be observed in the quenched specimens, which is contradict to the observation. Therefore, the appearance of SRX during quenching seems not justified.
2. Transformation mechanism. Ferrites in Figure 2.22 and 2.23 look different.

Ferrite in Figure 2.22 seems pro-eutectoid one whilst that in Figure 2.22 seems a strain-induced ferrite at grain boundaries. Both have been investigated from the viewpoints of deformation texture and grain boundary angle in Refs.51~55. In Figure 2.22, the deformation lasts for 6s so that the under cooling has less influence on austenite-to-ferrite transformation kinetics because a dual phase of austenite plus ferrite may have been achieved during deformation. Meanwhile, austenite grains did not recrystallize both dynamically or statically so that the pancaked geometry could remain. Both lead to pro-eutectoid ferrite plus band martensite as shown in Figure 2.22. In Figure 2.23, a large amount of ferrite was formed during deformation lasting for 0.015s, which might be strain induced ferrite. Stress-strain curves exhibit typical characteristics of dynamic recovery. It is postulated that strain induced ferrite at grain boundaries could reduce stored energy and prevent dislocation multi-slip within grains; consequently, the rest austenite could still be equaxial. This generally requires high strain rate and large strain to make sure that ferrite transformation takes place during deformation.

Influence of strain on ferrite transformation was also investigated to clarify the real mechanism. Specimens were firstly heated to 950℃ for 2min and then cooled to deformation temperature by 10℃/s, and then subject to strain of 30% or 40% with strain rate of $30s^{-1}$, and finally quenched by water jets immediately after deformation. The detailed process parameters adopted in the experiments are listed in the following Table 2.2.

Table 2.2　Experimental programme

Strain/%	40	30
Temperature/℃	790	770
	780	760
	770	750

Deformation is 30% in the dual phase region of austenite plus ferrite; and 40% in the region for both dual phase and under cooled austenite. Comparison of corresponding microstructures can conclude: intercritical deformation leads to prolonged microstructure and necklaced pro-eutectoid ferrite; whiles under-cooled deformation leads to equaxial microstructure and its stress-strain curves have identical characteristics with curves in Figure 2.24. Such characteristics can be repeated well when strain is increased. The difference between temperature for intercritical deformation and that for under-cooled deformation is just 10~20℃ whilst the former seems no influence on grain refinement but the latter does, the real reason why a small temperature variation can lead to such big difference is absolutely worthy of further studies.

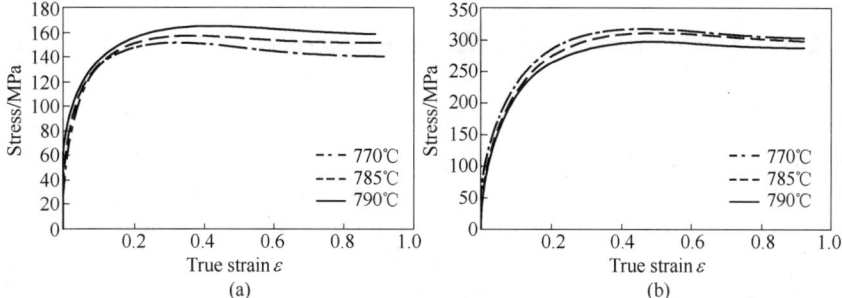

Figure 2.24   The stress strain curve at different strain rate:0.1s⁻¹and 40s⁻¹

(a)Strain rate 0.1s⁻¹;(b)Strain rate 40s⁻¹

The experimental results stated above indicate that fine equaxial microstructure can be achieved only if the controlled rolling is performed in the under-cooled austenitic region in the high speed rolling line.

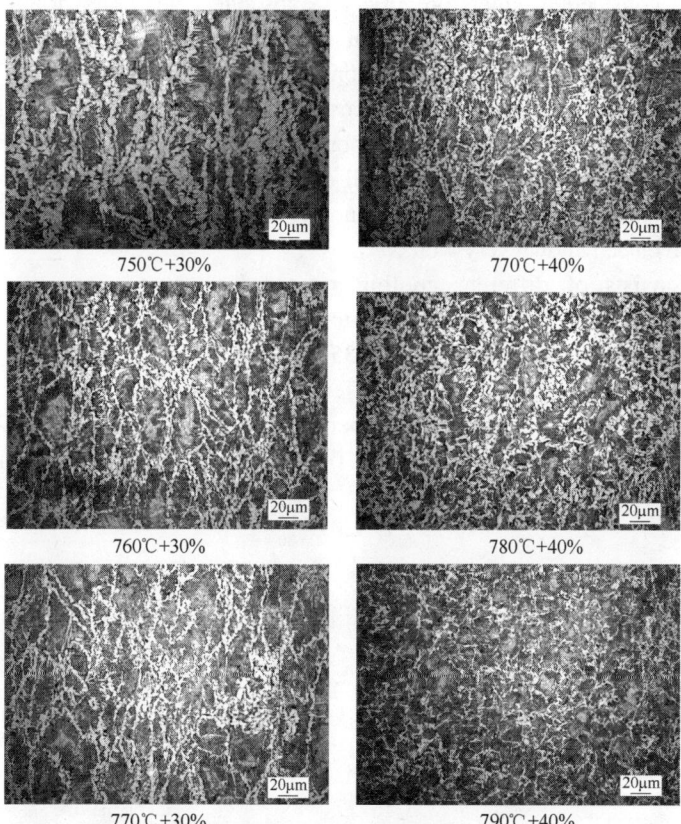

Figure 2.25   The microstructure of low carbon steel when
Strain is 30% and 40% repectively

2.1.4   *Accelerated cooling (AC) and microstructural refinement*

Accelerated cooling after rolling, an important part of TMP, can prevent the grain growth during cooling to refine microstructure for better mechanic properties. This technique has been extensively used in the commercial production of low carbon steels, HSLA steels and microalloyed steels. Rapid cooling adopted in AC can lower Ar_3 and suppress the recovery in austenite so that ferrite can nucleate at deformation/shear bands within the deformed austenite grains; consequently, ferrite grains are refined (Amin, 1982). Rolling at high-temperature recrystallization region and at low-temperature non-recrystallization region both result in refinement of austenite grains and an increase in grain boundary surface area, consequently, Ar_3 is raised so that the deformed austenite is easy to transform to ferrite after deformation. If the cooling is slow, the transformed ferrite grains can grow considerably, therefore, AC is a absolutely necessary. Rapid cooling after low-temperature deformation can result in divorced pearlite in the low carbon steels because ferrite nucleation at grain boundaries requires enough diffusion of carbon; in addition, rapid cooling can prevent precipitation of coarse carbides at boundaries in the high carbon steels, and reduce the size of pearlite domain and space between lamellas, all of which benefit mechanical properties. AC is now just a common process technology since CCT curves for various steel grades have been known very well.

AC consists of different cooling rates achieved at continuous stages, generally classified by different microstructural transformation finishing temperatures. For example, when Q235 steel is deformed by 50% at various temperatures and then subject to different cooling rates, the corresponding microstructures and mechanical properties are shown in Figure 2.26. It is clearly that high cooling rate leads to finer ferrite grain size and higher yield strength.

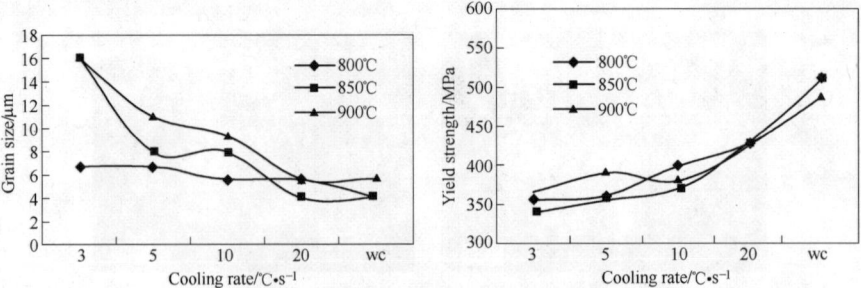

Figure 2.26   The ferrite grain size and yield strength
of plain low carbon steel at different cooling
rate after rolling (WQ, water quenching)

2.2   Influence of Austenitic Recrystallization on Subsequently Transformed Grain Size

Rough rolling generally starts at 1200°C. With the decreasing rolling temperature, austenite will be dynamically recrystallized, dynamically recovered and work-hardened during deformation. Influence of recrystallized and non-recrystallized austenite on ferrite/pearlite phase transformation has been systematically studied; combination of AC and AC has been extensively applied in the commercial production of microalloyed steel. Grain refinement by DIFT, however, is still at its initial stage. The effort for refinement of ferrite and pearlite in Q235 steel for better properties was just made in the last ten years. In the low carbon steels, influence of deformation applied in austenite on the subsequent transformation kinetics is often ignored because the minimum temperature for recrystallization is very close to Ar_3 and deformed austenite can recrystallized very easily. Since deformation stored energy is eliminated by the proceeding recrystallization, whether there is enough deformation stored energy left as driving force for the subsequent phase transformation has received a wide discussion. As discussed before, to lower rolling temperature and raise strain rate make rolling without recrystallization possible, then enough driving force is available for DIFT.

2.2.1   *Influence of recrystallized or deformed austenite on ferrite transformation*

2.2.1.1   Influence of recrystallized austenite on ferrite transformation

Generally, fine recrystallized austenite grains can transform to even finer ferrite grains. The ratio of the transformed ferrite grain size to the prior austenite grain size (PAGS) is around 0.3 when PAGS is ASTM 3~5 grade; and around 0.7(Sekine, 1982)when PAGS is around ASTM 8~10. The transformed ferrite grain size is close to the prior austenite grain size when the latter is fine, this is because fine austenite grain size can lead to CCT curve shift to left and raise Ar_3 and reduce the under cooling. Besides, when grain boundary area is increased with the finer austenite grain size, more nucleation sites are available so that even a small driving force can make austenite-to-ferrite transformation possible. Dynamically or metadynamically recrystallized grain size is not dependent on PAGS but on the deformation temperature and strain rate; whilst statically recrystallized grain size is determined by both initial austenite grain size and strain. Therefore, to understand both dynamical and static recrystallization kinetics is important for ferrite grain refinement. An increase in strain could be an effective method to refine ferrite grains since recrystallization or DIFT from deformed austenite can be completed across the entire section of deformed bulk at high strain, which leads to homogeneously refined ferrite grains.

Ferrite nucleation in the recrystallized austenite during the cooling can be classified into two categories: nucleation within grains or at boundaries. Rapid cooling has a limited enhancement on intragrain nucleation because ferrite prefers to nucleate at boundaries of recrystallized grains. In this case, only boundary-nucleated ferrite and acicular ferrite extruding into grains can be observed. The coarse austenite grains have a strong tendency to transform to Widmanstatten ferrite. An increase in strain can refine austenite grain and then results in homogeneous ferrite grain size distribution. Increases in both strain and cooling rate can avoid the formation of Widmanstatten microstructure, whilst rolling temperature seems to have little influence on it. Therefore, even finer ferrite grains require rolling performed in austenite non-recrystallization temperature region.

2.2.1.2　Influence of partially recrystallized austenite on ferrite transformation

Partial recrystallization (PR) can frequently occur when plain carbon steel is subject to rolling at low temperature. Recrystallized austenite grains result in fine ferrite grains, whilst ferrite grains transformed from non-recrystallized austenite may have necklace morphology with relatively coarser size, and pearlite transformed from such austenite is not spherical but rod-like. Thus, partial recrystallization in austenite can lead to bimodal ferrite grain size distribution, which has little influence on strength but generally impairs toughness. Recrystallization in plain carbon steel is easily completed at high temperature; however, bimodal grain size could appear in the final microstructure if rolling temperature is at 850~750℃ and strain, strain rate and cooling rate are not in the expected range.

2.2.1.3　Influence of non-recrystallized austenite on ferrite transformation

Tnr is key parameter to know whether steel subject to rolling at non-recrystallization temperature is feasible in industrial production. Since Tnr in plain carbon steel is close to Ar_3, it was believed in the past that rolling at non-recrystallization temperature was not possible. However, the temperature range for non-recrystallization is dependent on strain rate, as shown in Figure 2.5. Therefore, when high strain rate （$1\sim250s^{-1}$）, short interpass time (0.1~1s) and rolling at low temperature (700~800℃)are all realized in the modern high-speed rolling line, the process of rolling at non-recrystallization temperature followed by DIFT during cooling can achieve superfine ferrite grains. Deformation at austenite non-recrystallization range leads to formation of lots of deformation bands that act as nucleation sites. Density of deformation bands increases with strain, but it strongly depends on deformation temperature. An increase in strain rate reduce the time to achieve a certain density of deformation bands but often leads to heterogeneous deformation, thus, high strain rate is usually coupled with large strain. In a continuous rolling line, it is important to ensure that temperatures at several rolling passes, not just at the final rolling pass, are located in the non-recrystallization range. When more nucleation sites are available in the austenite because of formation of deformation bands, the transformed ferrite grains get refined remarkably.

It can be summarized that rolling at non-recrystallization temperature range is often followed by deformation induced ferrite transformation, which is the mechanism for effective refinement of ferrite grains.

2.2.2 Influence of recrystallization in the austenite on DIFT

The temperature for DIFT is around Ar_3(Hodgson, 1998; Yada, 1988; Weng, 2003) and onset of DIFT requires large strain or large accumulative strain （>50%）. Either dynamical Recrystallization or statical one can easily happen during hot deformation in the plain carbon steel, which can compete for DIFT to consume deformation stored energy. Therefore, a deep insight into phenomena happening around Ar_3 after large deformation is necessary. DIFT generally starts between Ae_3 and Ar_3 because deformation stored energy raises the free energy of austenite, i.e. higher driving force for ferrite transformation. In addition, highly dense dislocations are introduced into austenite after large strain so that Ar_3 transformation point can be raised due to much more nucleation sites available, which can be also responsible for the ferrite transformation to start above Ar_3. Which of thermodynamical or kinetical contribution is greater is still unknown and more efforts should be put in future. Thermodynamical calculation indicates that Ae_3 can be raised when part of deformation stored energy is added to the austenite free energy, such analysis is still undergoing on for clarification. There is a dispute on influence of prior austenite grain size. One is that large PAGS facilitates DIFT(Mintz, 1997) and the other(Kaspar, 1994) is that fine PAGS facilitates DIFT due to more grain boundary surface as nucleation sites for DIFT. There are different opinions about influence of cooling rate and strain rate on DIFT too.

DRX, DRV and DIFT are three fundamental physical phenomena during the hot rolling process in steels. Defects like dislocation introduced by hot deformation are basis for understating the three phenomena. A lot of work has to be done for better understanding in the future. DRV may happen through the hot rolling process since it occurs before DRX and DIFT. DRX and DIFT are both nucleated at deformation bands, twin boundaries and grain boundaries. Therefore, the local dislocation density in the bulk together with deformation period, not the average dislocation density, determines onset of DRX and DIFT. Higher strain rate results in higher dislocation-generated rate and then a very heterogeneous dislocation distribution, which might be responsible for the onset of DIFT. Heterogeneity of strain distribution in the material resulting from plastic deformation with high strain rate can be reduced by large strain.

The critical parameter for onset of DRX and DIFT is deformation temperature, or the critical dislocation density. Strain rate determines the generation rate of dislocations and the percentage of local dislocations whose density is more than critical one. Low strain rate does not favor accumulation of dislocation during deformation, and long deformation time can suppress growth of recrystallized nuclei and nucleation of ferrite. Onset of DRX and DIFT requires different strain rates coupled with a certain strain. In addition, the dislocation density calculated from flow stress generally differ from the actual one with several orders of magnitude, thus, predication of onset of DIFT by the calculated dislocation density is not feasible.

Large prior austenite grain size is difficult to dynamically recrystallize, thus stored energy can be raised, which benefits DIFT. Moreover, strain is more heterogeneous in the materials with large grain size, which may lead to some local highly dense dislocations that facilitates DIFT too. However, larger PAGS leads to lower transformation point Ar_3 at the same cooling rate, thus, larger under cooling is required to overcome energy barrier for nucleation. Therefore, too large and too small austenite grain size do not favor onset of DIFT.

The present knowledge on DIFT is still at its initial stage. A deeper insight into this unique phenomenon may be achieved by analyzing energy variation of atoms and electrons from the view point of condensed physics. This novel subject is definitely worthy of further efforts in future.

References

Amin R K, Pickering F B (1982) In: DeArdo A. J. (ed) Thermomechanical Processing of Microalloyed Austenite, Warrendale: TMS-AIME

Avrami M, Chem I Phys (1941) (9): 177

Avrami M, Chem I Phys (1940) (8): 212

Avrami M, Chem I Phys (1939) (7) ; 103

Balance J B (ed) (1976) The Hot Deformation of austenite, TMS – AIME, New York

Bever M B, Holt D L and Titchener A L (1973)   Prog. in metal Science, (17)   Pergamon Press, Oxford

Burke J E, Turnbull D (1952)   Progress in Metal Physics, (3) : 220

Cabrera J M, Ponce J, Prado J M (2003) Mater Process Technol, 143–144:403

Cahn R W (1983) Recovery and Recrystallization. In: Cahn R W, Hasen P (ed) Physical

Metallurgy, 3rd Ed. Armsterdam: North-Holland Physics Publishing

CHO Sang-Hyun, KANG Ki-Bong and JONAS J, (2001) ISIJ International, Vol.41(1): 63-69

Cohn M, et al (1984) Micro-alloying and Controlled Rolling of Steel, paper analects, CNMIP, 4

Cuddy L J (1984) The Effect of Microalloy Concentration on the Recrystallization of Austenite During Hot Deformation, Thermomechanical Processing of Microalloyed Austenite, Warrendale, PA: TMS-AIME: 129-140

Deardo A J (ed) (1982) Thermomechanical Procrssing of Microalloyed Austenite, Warrendale: TMS-AIME,

Duckworth W E, Philips R, Chapman J A (1965) Iron Steel Inst. London, 203: 1108-1114

Duckworth W E(1964)Iron and Steel, 37: 585-588

Gorden P (1955) Trans AIME, 203: 1043

Grange R A (1964) In: Backofen W (Eds) Fundamentals of Deformation Processing. Syracuse: Univ. Press: 299-317

Haneman H, Lucke F (1925) Stahl und Eisen 45: 1117-1122

Hernandez C A, Medina S F, Ruiz J (1996) Acta Mater;(44)1:155

Himmel L (ed) (1963) Recovery and Recrystallization of metals. New York, Interscience Publishers

Hodgson P D, Hickson M R, et al (1998) The Production and Mechanical Properties of Ultrafine Ferrite. Mater. Sci. Forum, 281-1-2086: 63

Hodgson P D, Gibbs R K (1992) ISIJ International, Vol.32 No.12: 1329-1338

Hoogendoorn T M, Spanraft M J (1977) In: M. Korchynsky (ed).Conf. Microalloying 75, Union Carbide Corp., New York

Irani J J, Burton D, Jones J D, Rothwell A B (1967) ISI Publication, 104: 110-122

Johnson W A, Mehl R F (1939) Trans AIME, 135: 416

Jonas J J, Sellars C M, McG Tegart W J (1969) Metall Rev, 14:1

Jones J D, Rothwell A B (1968)ISI Publication, 108: 78-82

Kaspar R, Lotter U, Biegus C (1994)The Influence of Thermomechanical Treatment on Transformation Behavior of Steel, Steel Research, , 65(6): 242

Korchynsky M (ed) (1984) HSLA' 83, ASM, Ohio

Korchynsky M (ed) (1977)Conf. Microalloying 75,. Union Carbide Corp., New York

Liang Xiaokai(2006)The Microstructure Evolution Study of Carbon Steel by Thin Slab Continuous Casting and Rolling, doctoral thesis，CISIR

Mintz B, Lewis J, Jonas J J (1997)Importance of Deformation Induced Ferrite and Factors Which Control Its Formation, Mater. Sci. Technol. 13(5): 379

Nagai K (2002) Grain Refinement Through Heavy Deformation, Conf. The Development of High Performance Structural Steels for 21st Century, Pohang,Korea, POSCO: 17-25

Oberhoffer P (1913) Stahl und Eisen, 33: 1507-1513, 1564-1568

Philips R, Chapman J A (1966) JISI, 204: 615-622

Pristner R, Early C C (1968)Randall J. H., JISI, 206: 1252-1262

Pussegoda L N, Yue S, and Jonas J J (1990) Metall. Trans. A, 21A: 153

Qi Junjie,Yang Wangyue,Sun Zuqing (2002)Microstructure and Microtexture Change During Deformation of Undercooled Austenite In A Low Carbon Steel.Acta Metallurgica Sinica 38(6):629-634

Qi Junjie,Yang Wangyue, Sun Zuqing (2002)Mechanisms of Microstructure Evolution during Deformation of Undercooled Austenite in a Low Carbon Steel. Journal of University of Science and Technology Beijing 24(2): 97

Qi Junjie,Yang Wangyue,Sun Zuqing (2002)Ultra-fine ferrite formation during deformation of undercooled austenite in a low carbon steel, Acta Metallurgica Sinica，38 (9): 897

Roberts W, Boden H, Ahlblom B (1979) Metal Sci;13:195.

Rossard C (1973) Proc. Int. Conf. Met. Alloys, Cambrige, v.2: 175

Roucoules C, Hodgson P D, Yue S and Jonas J J (1994) Metall. Mater. Trans. A, 25A: 389-400

Saden H. Zahiri a, Chris H J Davies B, Peter D. Hodgson (2005)   Scripta Materialia 52: 299–304

Sakai T, Jones J J (1984) Acta metall, 32: 189-209

Sakai T, Miura H (1996) In: McQueen H J, Konopleva E V, Ryan N D, (eds). Hot workability of steels and light alloys-composites. Montreal: The Metallurgical Society of CIM: 161

Sakui S, Sakai T, Takeishi K (1977) Hot Deformation of Austenite In a Plain Carbon Steel, Transaction ISIJ, Vol. 17: 718-725

Sekine H., Maruyama T, Kageyama H, Kawashima Y (1982) In: DeArdo A J,(ed) Thermomechanical Processing of Microalloyed Austenite, Warrendale: TMS-AIME

Sellars C M, McG W J. Tagart W J (1966) Acta Metall, Vol. 14(11): 1136-1138

Sellars C M (1980) In: Sellars C M, Davies G J (eds) Hot Working and Forming Process, IMS, London: 3 Stattman A,(1892) Stahl und Eisen, 12: 550-558

Titchener A L, Bever M B (1958)Prog. in Metal Phys, (7): 247

Tsuji N, Saito Y, Ussunomiya H, et al (1999) Ultra-fine grained bulk steel produced by accumulative roll-bonding (ARB) process, Scr. Mater, 40(7):795-800

Tsukada K, Matsumoto, K, Hirabe K, Takeshige K (1982) IS&M 9,(7): 21-28

Uranga P, Fernandez A I, Lopez B, Rodriguez-Ibabe J M (2003) Materials Science and Engineering, A345:319-317

Valiev R Z, Alexandrov I V (2000) Bulk nanostructrued materials from severe plastic deformation, Progress in Materials,(45): 103-189

Vandrbeck RW (1958) Weld. J. 37: 114-116

Wang Ruizhen, Yang Zhongmin, Che Yanmin(2006) Dynamic Recrystallization and Dynamic Transformation of Austenite in Low Carbon Steel Q235,Journal of Iron and Steel Research，18, No.1: 28-33

Wang Ruizhen,Yang Zhongmin, Che Yanmin(2006) Static Recrystallization of Deformed Austenite in Low Carbon Steel Q235, Journal of Iron and Steel Research, 18, No.3: 33-37

Wang Ruizhen,Yang Zhongmin, Che Yanmin(2004) Grain Refinement of Hot-rolled Low Carbon Steel Rebar by Recrystallization Controlled Rolling and Controlled Cooling,Iron and Steel, 39,No.2: 47-50

Weiss I, Alvarrado P J, Fitzsimona G, Deardo A J(1983) Grain Refinement and Coarsening During Dynamic Recrystallization In Plain Carbon Steel , Vol. 17: 693-697

Weng Yuqing, et al (2003), Ultra-fine Grained Steel, Metallurgical industry press, China

Yada H, Matsumura Y, Senuma T (1988) In: Tamura I (ed) Proc. of Inst. Conf. On Phys. Metall. of Thermomechanical Processing of Steels and Other Met. (Thermec' 88), ISIJ, Tokyo, 20

Yang Ping, Fu Yunyi, Cui Feng'e, Sun Zuqing (2001) Haracteristics of Strain Enhanced Transformation and Its Influencing Factors in Q235 Plain Carbon Steel, Acta Metallurgica Sinica, (37) 6: 592

Yang Wangyue, Hu Anmin,Qi Junjie, Sun Zuqing(2001) Microstructure Refinement of Deformation-enhanced Transformation in Low Carbon Steel, Chinese Journal of Material Research, (15)2 :171

Yang Zhongmin, Zhao Yan, Wang Ruizhen, Chen Qi'an, Che Yanmin, Qi Changfa, Du Mingshan(2001) Intercritical Austenite Control Rolling Process For Ultra-Fine Grain Structure of Plan Low Carbon Steel, Steel, 8: 43

Yang Zhongmin, Zhao Yan, Wang Ruizhen, Che Yanmin, (2000) The Formation of Ultra-fine Ferrite Grains in Low Carbon Steel Through Low Temperature Heavy Deformatio, Acta Metallurgica Sinica, 10:1061

Yang Zhongmin,Zhao Yan, Wang Ruizhen, Che Yanmin (2000) Formation Mechanism of Deformation Induced Ferrite, Acta Metallurgica Sinica, 8: 818

Yue S, Roucoules C, Maccagno T M and Jonas J J (1995) 37th Mechanical Working and Steel Processing Conf. Proc., ISS, Hamilton, Ontario, Canada :651

Zahiri S H, Hodgson P D (2004)Materials Science and technology, (20) 4: 458-464

3
Deformation Induced Ferrite Transformation

DIFT Processing is a new promising technology for ferrite grain refinement. In terms of thermodynamics, a prominent feature of DIFT distinguished from static transformation without deformation is the addition of deformation stored energy into the transformation driving force, which leads to an increase in the Ae_3 temperature or/and greatly accelerates the transformation at a temperature between Ae_3 and Ar_3. In terms of kinetics, DIFT is a nucleation dominant process; on the contrary, the continuous cooling transformation or isothermal transformation without deformation is a grain growth dominant process. The mechanism of DIFT is still ambiguous. Our recent study shows that DIFT possibly has a unique mechanism which could involve limited diffusion of carbon that is different from both massive transformation and pro-eutectoid ferrite transformation. Based on DIFT theory, new TMCP procedures have been developed to produce ultrafine grained plain low carbon steel and microalloyed steel.

3.1   Introduction

Deformation and transformation (or heat treatment) are two basic means of solid state processing of steels. Originally, deformation and transformation were thought to be independent of each other, so they were separately utilized to acquire the desired shape and properties of steels respectively. In the late of 1950s, it began to be recognized that deformation could have an influence on the subsequent transformation, which resulted in the occurrence of the famous Thermo-mechanical Controlled Processing (TMCP) technology in 1960s(Tamura, 1988). In 1980s, it was found that $\gamma \rightarrow \alpha$ transformation could even be dynamically induced by deformation in low carbon steels, and the grain size of the dynamically transformed ferrite was much finer than that produced by conventional hot rolling (Matsumura, 1987; Priestner, 1981). As an economic and simple means to produce ultrafine grained ferrite, the dynamic $\gamma \rightarrow \alpha$ transformation has been extensively studied since 1990s though the names that different researchers called were different(Choi, 2003; Sun, 2002; Yada, 2000). In 1981, R. Priestner et al indicated that $\gamma \rightarrow \alpha$ transformation could occur in roll gap during rolling and called it "Strain Induced Transformation to Ferrite" (Priestner, 1981). In 1987, Y. Matsumura and H. Yada reported that the ferrite grain of plain C-Mn steel could be refined to 1~3μm through multi-pass deformation at 1073K, in which the grain refinement mechanisms were considered as the combination of both "Deformation Induced Transformation" and ferrite dynamic recrystallization (Matsumura, 1987). Hereafter, P.D.Hodgson et al (1992; 1998), S. Lee et al (1995)and W.Y.Choo et al (2000) reported this kind of transformation in succession, and they named it "Strain Induced Transformation" and "Strain Induced Dynamic Transformation" respectively. Although the names that different researchers used are different, this kind of transformation possesses two common characteristics. First, the $\gamma \rightarrow \alpha$ transformation occurs during deformation rather than during cooling after deformation. Second, ultrafine ferrite grains could be obtained through the transformation. The work of ours shows that the transformation is induced through the increase of both austenite free energy and nucleation site density caused by deformation applied, so each of deformation variables, as well as strain, strain rate, temperature or deformation manner could have an effect on the transformation. Thus, we named this kind of transformation as "Deformation Induced Ferrite Transformation" (abbreviated as DIFT) (Dong, 2005; Weng, 2005; Dong, 2003). DIFT was applied by the authors to refine ferrite grains to 3μm in plain low carbon steels and 1μm in microalloyed steels, with yield strength to be increased to the level of 400MPa and 800MPa respectively (Dong, 2005; Weng, 2005; Dong, 2003).

Figure3.1 illustrates the difference between DIFT and the conventional TMCP. DIFT occurs at lower temperatures in the non-recrystallization region of austenite ($Ar_3 < T_{DIFT} < Ad_3$), where Ad_3 is the upper limit temperature for DIFT. It can be seen that DIFT Processing is quite close to TMCP, so it could be realized in the existing industrial production facilities or in the modified ones. This is the advantage over other grain ultra-refinement methods. Therefore, DIFT Processing is expected to have an attractive future for application.

In this chapter, the theory and application of DIFT are briefly reviewed, where six aspects are addressed: evidence and study methods of DIFT, thermodynamics, kinetics, transformation mechanisms, factors influencing DIFT and the applications of DIFT in production of ultrafine grained steel.

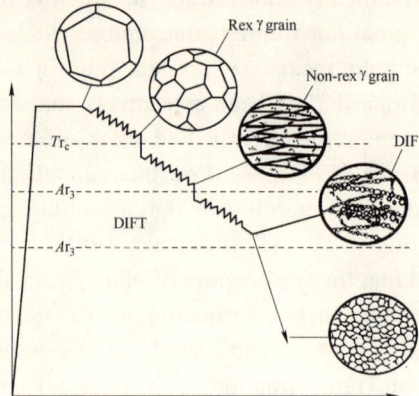

Figure 3.1   Schematic illustration of the difference between DIFT and conventional TMCP

3.2   Experimental Confirmation and Study Method of DIFT

DIFT is a kind of dynamic transformation process that occurs during deformation, not during the cooling after deformation. This has been confirmed by several experimental means including microstructure observation on the quenched sample, mechanical behavior measurements, dilatometry measurement and *in-situ* X-ray diffraction.

3.2.1   *Microstructure observation on the quenched sample*

The earliest evidence of DIFT was obtained by the microstructure observation on the sample quenched immediately after deformation. The role of quenching was to preserve the ferrite dynamically transformed during deformation. A typical example was shown as follows. A low carbon microalloyed steel (0.094C -0.29Si -1.42Mn -0.045Nb) was soaked at 1453K for 3 minutes, followed by cooling at rate of 5K/s to 1039K (higher than Ar_3) and then water quenched immediately. The microstructure obtained is fully martensite, as shown in Figure3.2 (a). If the steel specimen was compressed with strain of 0.92 at 1039K and at the strain rate of $1s^{-1}$, followed by water quenching immediately, the microstructure obtained is the equiaxed ferrite and martensite, as shown in Figure3.2 (b). The equiaxed ferrite was thought to be the dynamically transformed one. Now the microstructure characterization on the quenched sample has become the most popular method to study DIFT. However, the microstructure dynamically formed during deformation is very easy to change during the quenching because of the very low stability of deformed low carbon austenite. Thus, when the above mentioned method is used, the quenching procedures should be carefully designed to ensure that the ooling rate is rapid enough to preserve the microstructure formed during deformation. L.X. Du et al(Du, 2002) determined the critical cooling rate to prevent pro-eutectoid formation from deformed austenite during cooling in plain low carbon steel (0.057C-0.35Si-0.91Mn) to be about 673K/s.

(a)   (b)

Figure 3.2   Optical micrographs of 0.094C-0.29Si-1.42Mn-0.045Nb steel obtained by direct water quenching at 1039K (a) and by water quenching after deformation at 1039K (b)

3.2.2   *Mechanical behavior measurement*

The mechanical behaviors are the macroscopic reflection of the microstructure change in steels, so DIFT can be reflected by the mechanical behaviors to some extent. S.C. Hong et al (2003) compared the measured flow stress with the calculated one of 0.14C-1.50Mn-0.79Si steel at 1008K, and found that the former was lower than the latter. The difference was considered to be due to the formation of soft phase α during deformation, i.e. deformation induced ferrite. H. Yada et al (2000) measured the flow stress of 0.096C-5.98Ni steel as a function of temperature (Figure3.3(a)), and observed that the stress at lower temperatures deviated from the tendency at higher temperatures due to DIFT. B. Mintz et al (Mintz, 1994) measured the peak stress of 0.1C-0.31Si-1.43Mn steel as a function of temperature at different strain rates (Figure 3.3(b)), and also observed the deviation of flow stress at lower temperature. J.-K. Choi et al (2003) measured the critical strain of a low carbon steel during high temperature deformation, as shown in Figure 3.3 (c). It is observed that in the higher temperature region, the critical strain increases with decreasing temperature, which is due to dynamic recrystallization of austenite; in the lower temperature region, however, the critical strain decreases with decreasing temperature, which is due to DIFT.

3.2.3   *Dilatometry measurement*

Dilatometry is an effective method to study the transformation in steels, and some researchers have used it to prove the existence of DIFT. W.Y. Choo measured the dilatation curve of a low carbon steel during heating and cooling after deformation at 923K(Choo, 2000), as shown in Figure 3.4 (a). During the second heating, inflection in the dilatational curve was observed due to DIFT. Z.M. Yang measured the dilatation curves of a plain low carbon steel during continuous cooling after deformation at different temperatures(Yang, 2003) (Figure 3.4 (b)). It could be seen that at 1103K, the first inflection point indicating the formation of pro-eutectoid ferrite became unobvious, and at 1073K, the inflection point disappeared, which indicated that ferrite had been induced during deformation. Y. Matsumura et al measured the dilatation curves of 0.11C-1.0Mn steel during holding after deformation at different temperatures (Matsumura,1987), as shown in Figure3.4(c). It was observed that the dilatation decreased during holding at 1098K and 1123K, which indicated that ferrite with volume fraction higher than the equilibrium one, had been induced during deformation. On the other hand, the dilatation increased during holding at temperatures below 1098K, which meant that the volume fraction of DIF had not reached the equilibrium fraction.

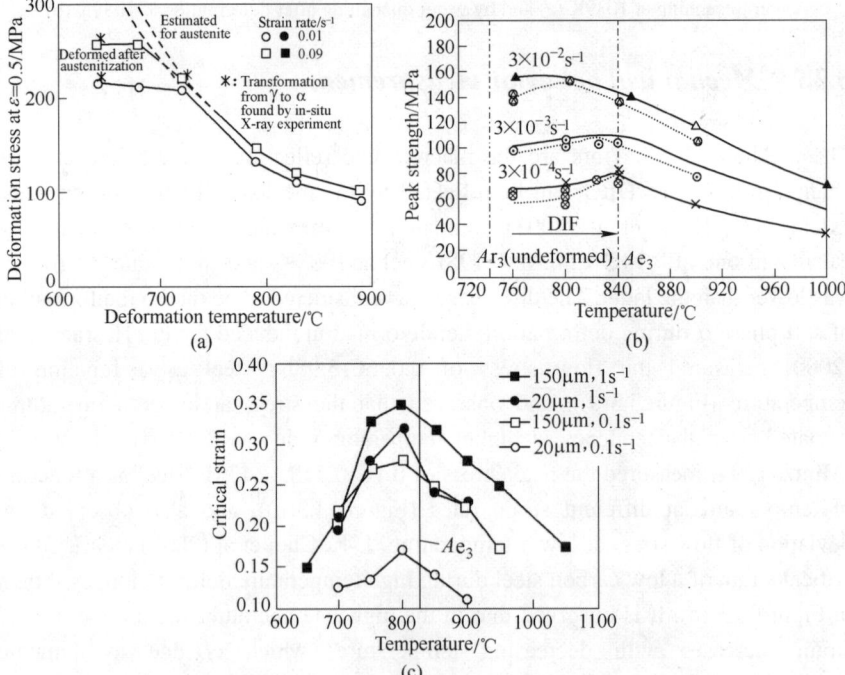

Figure 3.3   Influence of DIFT on mechanical behaviors of austenite

(a) Deformation stress as a function of temperature; (b) Peak stress as a function of temperature;
(c) Critical strain for DIFT or DRX as a function of temperature

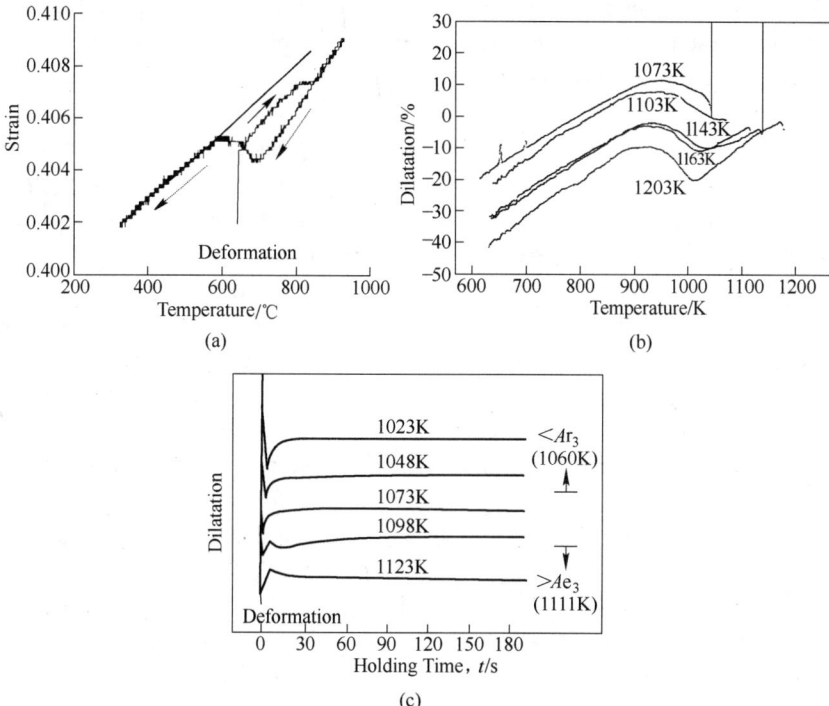

Figure 3.4 Dilitation-temperature (or holding time) curves after deformation of austenite
(a) Dilatation during heating and cooling after deformation at 923K; (b) Dilatation during
cooling after deformation at different temperatures; (c) Dilatation during holding
after deformation at different temperature

The authors have developed a new method, which is based on combination of quantitative dilatometry measurements and optical microstructural characterization after deformation, to infer the ferrite fraction formed during deformation in low carbon steel (Sun, 2007). The key points are as follows:

1. An isothermal holding experiment is conducted immediately after DIFT, and dilatometric data are measured during the holding, as shown in Figure3.5.

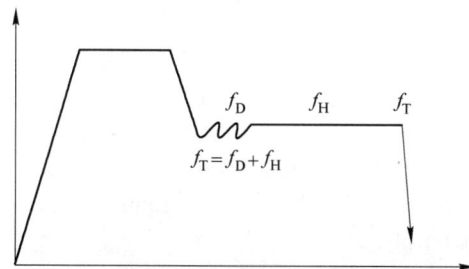

Figure 3.5 Schematic diagram of the new method to measure the DIF quantitatively

2. The DIF volume fraction (f_D) can be calculated by the expression $f_T = f_D + f_H$, where f_T is the final volume fraction of ferrite after the holding, and f_H is the volume fraction of ferrite formed during the holding. f_T can be measured through quantitative metallography on the quenched specimen. Because the deformed austenite in this low carbon steel can be completely recrystallized after the isothermal holding with a relatively long period, and because the austenite will be gradually enriched with carbon with the proceeding $\gamma \rightarrow \alpha$ transformation during the isothermal holding, the stability of remained austenite is greatly improved. Thus, the austenite will be much easier to completely transform to martensite or bainite rather than ferrite during quenching, which can ensure that the measurements on the quenched specimens subject to prolonged isothermal holding is much more reliable than that on the immediately quenched specimens. f_H can be converted from of the dilatometric measurement.

The DIF volume fraction measured by the new method was compared with that obtained by the water quenching method. It was found that the DIF volume fraction measured by the new method was less than that obtained by the water quenching method.

3.2.4   *In-situ X-ray diffraction*

H. Yada et al presented a direct evidence of DIFT by using *in-situ* X-ray diffraction(Yada, 2000; Li, 1999; Li, 1998), as shown in Figure3.6. The specimen was exposed to the X-ray beam during torsional deformation period. X-ray lines were recorded on a film in a flat camera shielded from heat with thin aluminum foils. It was shown from Figure3.6 that there appeared a line corresponding to $(110)_\alpha$ together with $(111)_\gamma$ line. This clearly showed that $\gamma \rightarrow \alpha$ transformation occurred during deformation. Through this method, it was proved that DIFT could occur in a wide range of temperatures including those higher than para-equilibrium transformation temperature, A_3^p in Fe-6Ni-(0.0008~0.29) C alloys. However, quantitative study on DIFT by using in-situ X-ray diffraction is almost impossible presently because of the low intensity of X-ray beam.

In summary, DIFT has been recognized by researchers through several experimental techniques. However, because DIFT is a kind of transformation during deformation, there are really some difficulties to observe the phenomenon directly and measure transformation variables accurately. It is necessary to develop better method to study DIFT in the future in order to understand the transformation more deeply.

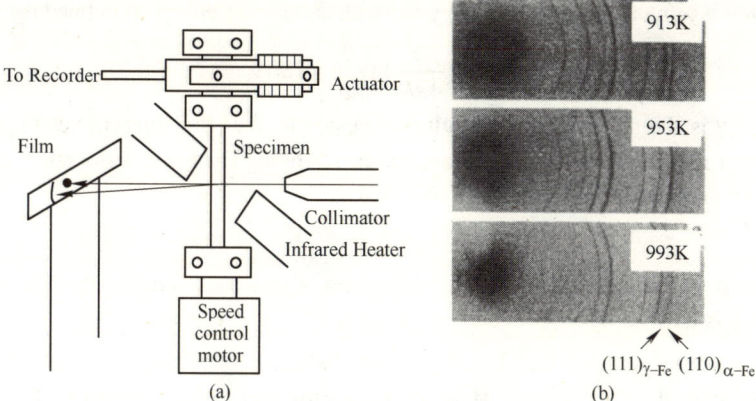

Figure 3.6 Evidence of DIFT obtained by using *in-situ* X-ray diffraction
(Yada, Li, Yamagata, 2000; 1999; 1998)

(a)A schematic diagram of the in-situ X-ray diffraction experiment setup; (b) Typical X-ray diffraction
patterns of the sample deformed at various temperature

3.3 Thermodynamics of DIFT

The most significant difference in thermodynamics between DIFT and static
transformation without deformation is that the deformation stored energy is
introduced into the transformation driving force for DIFT. Therefore, it is
important to obtain the value of deformation stored energy quantitatively and to
study its influence on DIFT.

3.3.1 *Deformation stored energy*

The deformation stored energy of austenite is thought maily consist of mainly two
parts: grain boundary energy change and dislocation energy change. The increase
of grain boundary energy during deformation is dependent on two factors. First,
the deformation elongates austenite grains and increases the grain boundary areas.
Second, the deformation enhances the disorder of grain boundary structure, which
leads to an increase in the grain boundary energy per unit area, $\sigma_{\gamma/\gamma}$(increased by
approximately 10%). Assuming the initial austenite grain is cubic with size of D_0
and the deformation mode is plane strain compression, the grain boundary energy
per unit mole, ΔG_{gb} as a function of strain can be expressed by

$$\Delta G_{gb} = \left[\exp(\varepsilon) + \exp(-\varepsilon) + 1\right] \cdot \sigma_{\gamma/\gamma} \cdot V_\gamma / D_0 \qquad (3.1)$$

where $\sigma_{\gamma/\gamma}$ is equal to 0.8J/m^2, V_γ is the molecular volume of austenite (=7.1×
10^{-6}m^3/mol) and ε is the strain.

According to the dislocation theory, the total energy of dislocation per unit length, E, which is a sum of elastic strain energy and dislocation core energy, is defined by

$$E = \frac{\mu b^2}{4\pi K} \ln \frac{R}{\lambda b} = k\mu b^2 \tag{3.2}$$

where μ is the shear elastic modulus of austenite, b is the Burgers vector, k is a constant ranging from 0.5 to 1.0 and takes 1.0 here. Then, the dislocation energy of austenite per unit mole ΔG_{dis} is obtained as

$$\Delta G_{dis} = \mu \rho b^2 V_\gamma \tag{3.3}$$

where ρ is the dislocation density. The flow stress as a function of dislocation density is defined by

$$\sigma = M \alpha \mu b \rho^{1/2} \tag{3.4}$$

where σ is the flow stress, M is Taylor factor and α is a constant. Then, the dislocation energy per unit mole as a function of flow stress is obtained as

$$\Delta G_{dis} = \frac{\sigma^2 V_\gamma}{M^2 \alpha^2 \mu^2} \tag{3.5}$$

Figure 3.7 shows the grain boundary energy of austenite as a function of strain calculated from Equation 3.1. Figure 3.8 shows the dislocation energy of austenite as a function of flow stress calculated from equation (3.5), where μ is taken as $7.9 \times 10^{10} \text{N/m}^2$, $M=3.11$ for fcc metals and α is taken as 0.15. Generally, the flow stress during hot rolling of low carbon steels ranges from 150MPa to 300MPa, so the dislocation energy ranges from 10J/mol to 40J/mol. It can be seen from Figure3.7 that the grain boundary energy does not increase significantly until the strain is relatively large. For example, for the austenite grain of 50μm in size, although the strain over which the grain boundary energy increases remarkably is as larger as 2.5, grain boundary energy is one order smaller than dislocation energy. Thus, in general, the contribution of grain boundary energy to the deformation stored energy could be ignored.

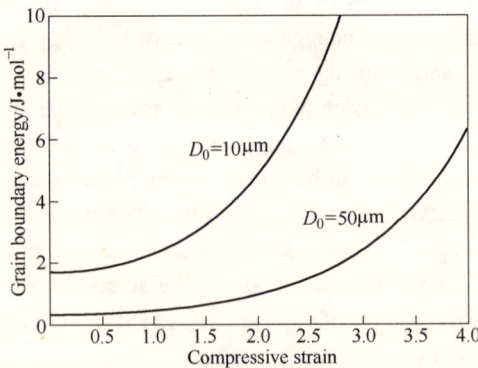

Figure 3.7   Austenite grain boundary energy as a function
of compressive strain

It is necessary to obtain the relationship between deformation stored energy and deformation variables. The method is described as follows. First, the relationship between flow tress and deformation variables can be described through the constitutive equation of hot deformation as follows:

$$\dot{\varepsilon} = A\{\sin h(\alpha\sigma)\}^n \exp(-Q/RT) \tag{3.6}$$

where the undetermined constants A, n and deformation activation energy Q can be obtained through experiments. Then, the relationship between deformation stored energy and deformation variables can be achieved through equation (3.5).

Based on the method mentioned above, we have obtained the relationship between deformation stored energy and deformation variables for a low carbon microalloyed steel (0.11C-0.25Si-1.48Mn-0.048Nb).

$$\Delta G_D = 77.5 - 13.5(\log Z) + 0.57(\log Z)^2 \text{ (J/mol)} \tag{3.7}$$

where ΔG_D is the deformation stored energy and Z is the Zener-Hollomon parameter

$$Z = \dot{\varepsilon}\exp(Q/RT) \tag{3.8}$$

The deformation stored energy is plotted as a function of both temperature and strain rate, as shown in Figure3.9. This figure shows that the deformation stored energy increases with decreasing temperature and increasing strain rate.

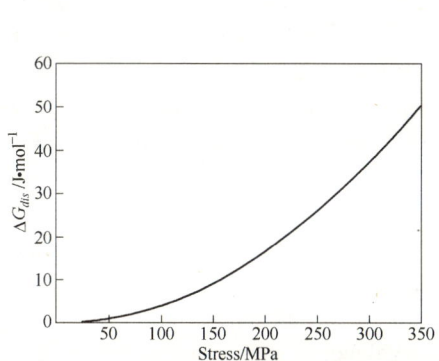

Figure 3.8 Dislocation energy as a function of flow stress

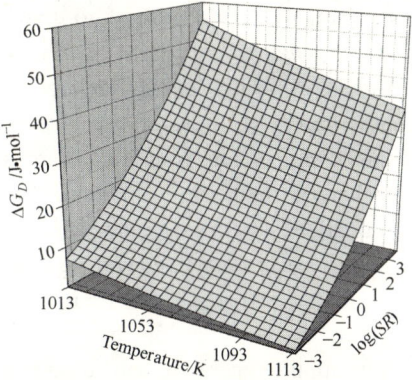

Figure 3.9 Deformation stored energy as a function of temperature and strain rate (ε=0.6)

3.3.2 *Transformation driving force*

The free energy change of $\gamma\rightarrow\alpha$ transformation without deformation can be expressed by

$$\Delta G = -V\Delta G_{chem} + A\sigma_{\gamma/\alpha} + V\Delta G_s \tag{3.9}$$

If austenite is deformed, part of the deformation mechanical energy could be stored in the austenite if dynamic recrystallization does not occur. Then, equation (3.9) is rewritten as

$$\Delta G = -V\Delta G_{chem} + A\sigma_{\gamma/\alpha} + V\Delta G_s - V\Delta G_D$$
$$= -V(\Delta G_{chem} + \Delta G_D - \Delta G_s) + A\sigma_{\gamma/\alpha} \qquad (3.10)$$

where ΔG_{chem} is the chemical driving force, ΔG_D is the deformation stored energy, ΔG_s is the volume strain energy, and $G_{\gamma/\alpha}$ is the γ/α boundary energy. It is clear that the total driving force under deformation condition consists of two parts: one is the chemical free energy ΔG_{chem}, and the other is the deformation stored energy ΔG_D. ΔG_{chem} could be calculated by Thermo-Calc. Figure3.10 illustrates both the chemical driving force and the deformation stored energy as a function of temperature for the steel 0.11C-0.25Si-1.48Mn-0.048Nb. Figure3.11 represents the total driving force ($\Delta G_D+\Delta G_{chem}$) as a function of temperature. As shown in Figure3.11, the driving force for DIFT is associated with both temperature and strain rate at a certain strain.

3.3.3   Ad₃ versus deformation stored energy

The addition of deformation stored energy can change the equilibrium $\gamma\rightarrow\alpha$ transformation temperature. Figure3.12 shows the effect of deformation stored energy on the equilibrium $\gamma\rightarrow\alpha$ transformation temperature for 1.48Mn-0.25Si-0.048Nb steel, as calculated by Thermo-Calc. It is clear that the introducing of deformation stored energy enlarges ($\gamma+\alpha$) two phase region and raises the equilibrium $\gamma\rightarrow\alpha$ transformation temperatures to higher temperature. The new dynamic temperature is called the upper limit transformation temperature for DIFT at a certain deforming condition, Ad_3. Figure3.13 shows Ad_3 as a function of deformation stored energy for 0.11C-1.48Mn-0.25Si-0.048Nb steel. The data in Figure3.13 is linearly fitted and the following regression equation could be obtained

$$Ad_3 = 1096.8 + 0.87(\Delta G_D) \text{ (K)} \qquad (3.11)$$

Then, the relationship between Ad_3 and deformation variables, such as deformation temperature and strain rate is obtained, as shown in Figure3.14. It is shown that Ad_3 increases with the increase of strain rate or the decrease of deformation temperature.

It should be mentioned that the distribution of deformation stored energy is inhomogeneous due to inhomogeneity of strain distribution in austenite. In other words, the energy at some local locations could be much higher than the average energy. Thus, the local increase in Ae_3 temperature should be greater than that described in Figure3.12. Further works are needed to quantitatively calculate the distribution of deformation stored energy within austenite.

In summary, the deformation stored energy could induce $\gamma\rightarrow\alpha$ transformation at a temperature above Ae_3, or greatly accelerate the transformation at a temperature between Ae_3 and Ar_3 due to the increase of the total transformation driving force.

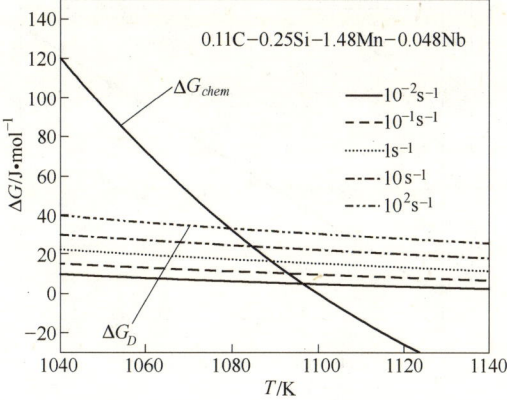

Figure 3.10 Deformation stored energy and chemical driving force as a function of temperature

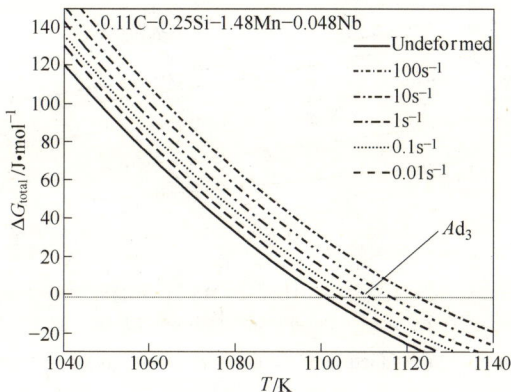

Figure 3.11 Total driving force as a function of temperature

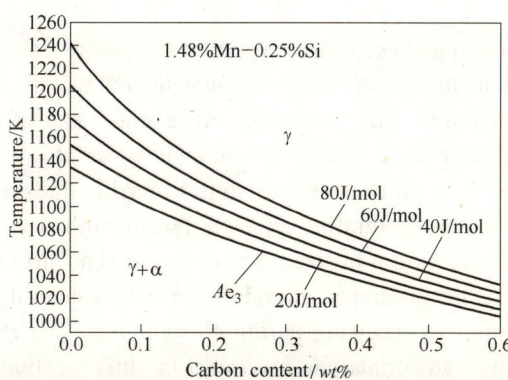

Figure 3.12 Influence of deformation stored energy on equilibrium γ→α transformation temperature

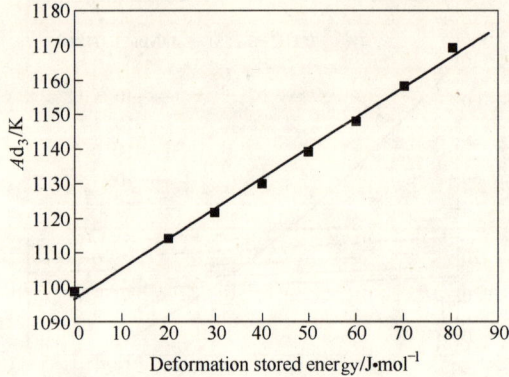

Figure 3.13 Ad_3 as a function of deformation stored energy

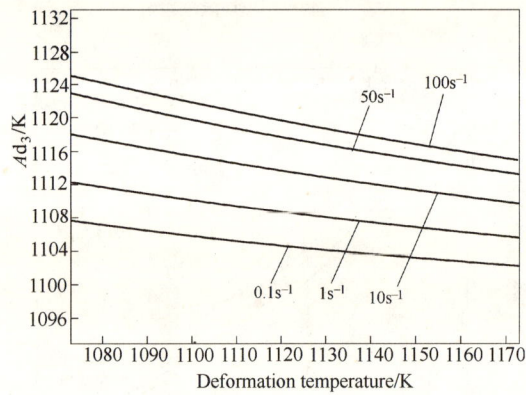

Figure 3.14 Ad_3 as a function of temperature at various strain rates (ε =0.6)

3.4   Kinetics of DIFT

The transformation kinetics from austenite to ferrite is of fundamental significance since it directly controls the final microstructure and property of steels. It has been found that a limiting ferrite grain size of about 5μm for microalloyed steel and about 10μm for plain low carbon steel exist for the conventional TMCP in which the austenite-to-ferrite transformation occurs cooling. during However, ultrafine grained ferrite with 1~2μm in size for microalloyed steel and 3~5μm in size for plain low carbon steel can be obtained by DIFT. Obviously, the difference of grain refinement capability between DIFT and static transformation occurring during conventional TMCP is attributed to the difference in transformation kinetics. In this section, the kinetics characteristics of DIFT is depicted, and compared with that of static transformation.

3.4.1 *Microstructural evolution and nucleation sites*

Figure 3.15 shows the microstructural evolution of a niobium-containing steel: 0.087C- 0.25Si- 0.51Mn- 0.017Nb (mass%) during DIFT. The microstructures were obtained by water quenching subsequent to compression at 1053K (higher than Ar_3 but lower than Ae_3) and at a strain rate of 15s^{-1} to various strains. It can be seen that the deformation induced ferrite (DIF) grains firstly nucleate at the prior-austenite grain boundaries (Figure3.15(a)), and then they occupy most of the prior-austenite grain boundaries, forming a continuous net-like structure (Figure3.15(b)). With the increase of strain, the ferrite begins to nucleate within prior-austenite grains, which leads to a rapid increase of ferrite fraction (Figure3.15(c)). It is found that there are two types of intragranular nucleation site for DIF. One is the deformation band or twin band (Figure3.16(a)), and the other is the γ/α interface (Figure3.16(b)) The repeated nucleation of ferrite at the γ/α interface results in the advance of DIF into the region of untransformed austenite.

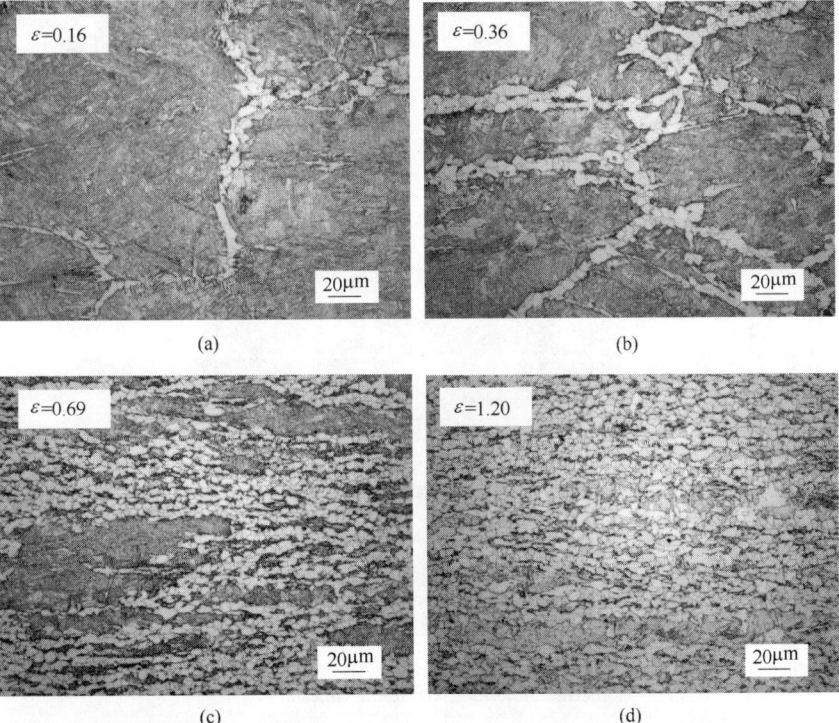

Figure 3.15 Microstructures obtained by deformation at 1053K and at a strain rate of 15s^{-1} to various strains for the 0.087C-0.25Si-0.51Mn-0.017Nb (mass%) steel

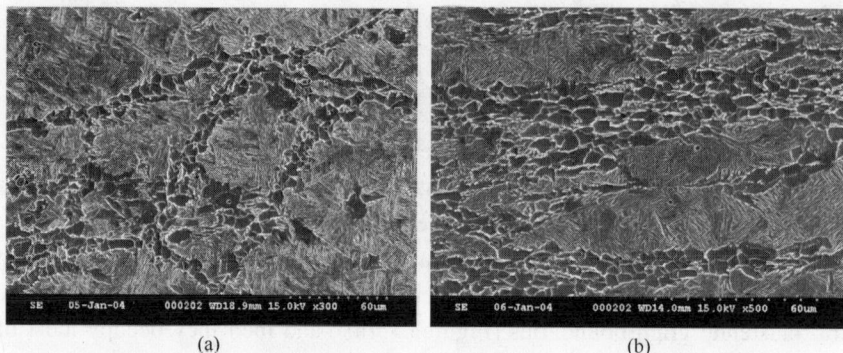

(a)   (b)

Figure 3.16   Intragranular nucleation of DIF at (a) deformation bands
or twin bands and (b) γ/αinterfaces

Figure 3.17 shows the microstructural evolution during isothermal holding at 1013K for a plain low carbon steel. It can be seen that the prior-austenite grain boundaries are the only nucleation sites. Furthermore, the ferrite grain grows up obviously during the isothermal holding.

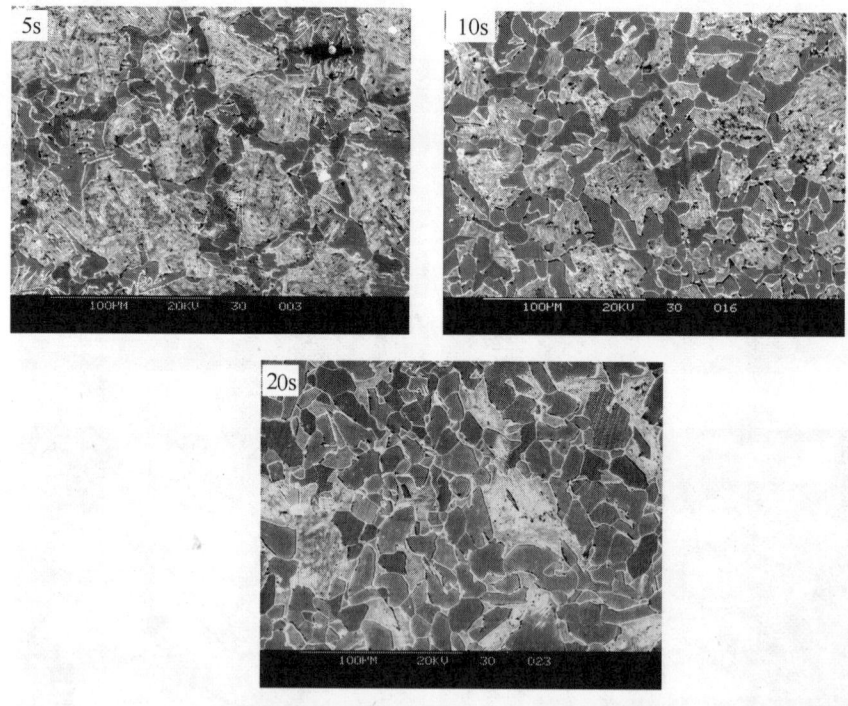

Figure 3.17   Microstructures of a plain low carbon steel obtained by water quenching after
isothermal holding for different times at 1013K

Figure 3.18 shows the microstructural evolution of a niobium-containing steel during continuous cooling at a rate of 5K/s after deformation at 1093K to the strain of 0.92. It can be seen from Figure 3.18 (a) that the microstructure obtained by water quenching immediately after deformation is a mixture of bainite and martensite, which is the transformation product of deformed austenite during water quenching, indicating that DIFT didn't occur during the high temperature deformation. During cooling after deformation, the ferrite grains nucleate at both austenite grain boundaries and deformation bands and subsequently grow up. Table 3.1 gives the volume fraction, mean grain size and grain number of ferrite at different temperature.

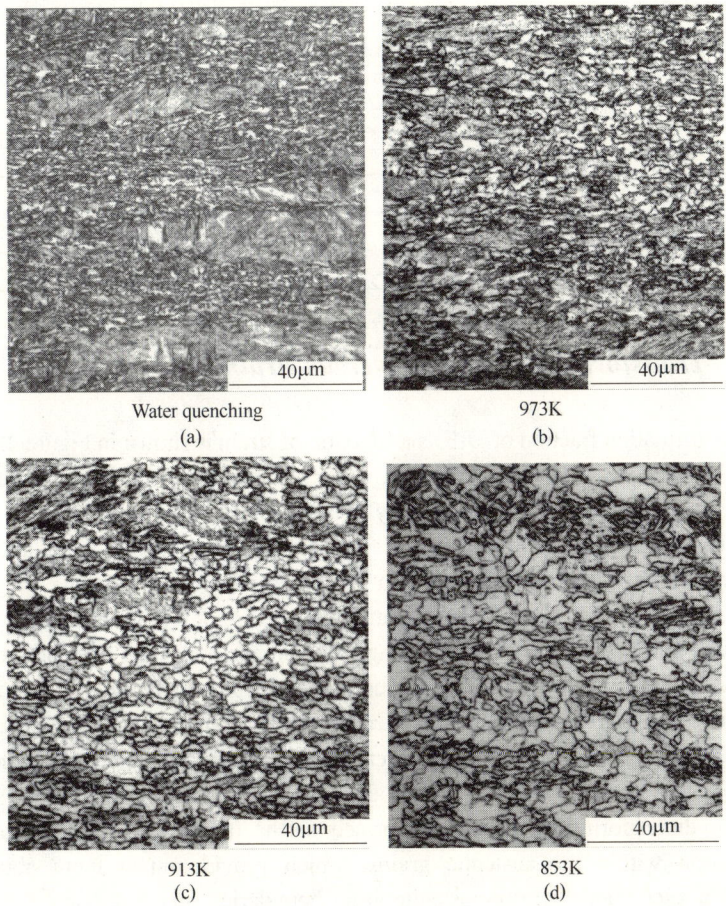

Figure 3.18   Microstructures of a Nb-microalloyed steel obtained by deformation at 1093K to a strain of 0.92 followed by cooling at 5K/s to various temperatures and then water quenching

It can be seen from Table 3.1 that the volume fraction of ferrite increase from 973K to 913K, but it changes very little from 913K to 853K. This indicates that the γ→α transformation is nearly finished at 913K. The ferrite grain size increases continuously during the whole transformation process. The increase of grain size from 913K to 853K is evidently resulted from grain coarsening because the transformation is nearly finished at 913K. It should be noted that the ferrite grain number per unit area decreases with $\gamma \rightarrow \alpha$ transformation. This indicates that the nucleation of ferrite conforms to the so-called site saturation mechanism(Christian, 2002).In other words, the nucleation process is finished at the initial stage of transformation, and during the subsequent transformation, grain growth and coarsening are dominant. Similar results were also reported in the study of continuous cooling transformation of C-Mn-Nb steel in the literature(Enomoto, 1994).

Table 3.1   Ferrite volume fraction (f_α), mean grain size (d_α) and ferrite grain number per unit area (N_A) of the Nb-microalloyed steel deformed at 1093K to a strain of 0.92 followed by cooling at the rate of 5K/s to various temperatures

Temperature /K	f_α /%	d_α /μm	N_A /mm^{-2}
973	23.1	2.88	20401
913	61.5	5.7	16925
853	63.0	7.5	15651

3.4.2   *Transformation fraction versus strain*

The transformation fraction of DIF as a function of strain is shown in Figure 3.19 (a). It can be seen that the curve exhibits a sigmoid shape, which means that the transformation proceeds relatively slowly at both lower and higher strain levels and proceeds most rapidly at medium strain level. Figure 3.19 (b) shows the relationship between DIF grain number per unit area and strain, which also exhibits a sigmoid shape. Thus, it is considered that there are three stages for DIFT, i.e. the first stage with lower nucleation rate, the second stage with higher nucleation rate and the third stage with lower nucleation rate. Because the DIF grains firstly nucleate at the prior-austenite grain boundaries, and because the nucleation sites provided by the prior-austenite grain boundaries are very limited, the nucleation rate and the transformation rate are relatively low at the first stage. With the increase of strain, however, the deformation bands are formed or the twin bands are activated by deformation within the austenite grains, which provide much more abundant nucleation sites than the prior-austenite grain boundaries, and furthermore, the γ/α interfaces also become potential nucleation sites. These lead to high nucleation rate and transformation rate at the second stage. At the final stage of transformation, the volume fraction of DIFT approaches the equilibrium state gradually, leading to the decrease of the nucleation rate and transformation rate. Figure 3.20 schematically illustrates the three-stage microstructure evolution during DIFT.

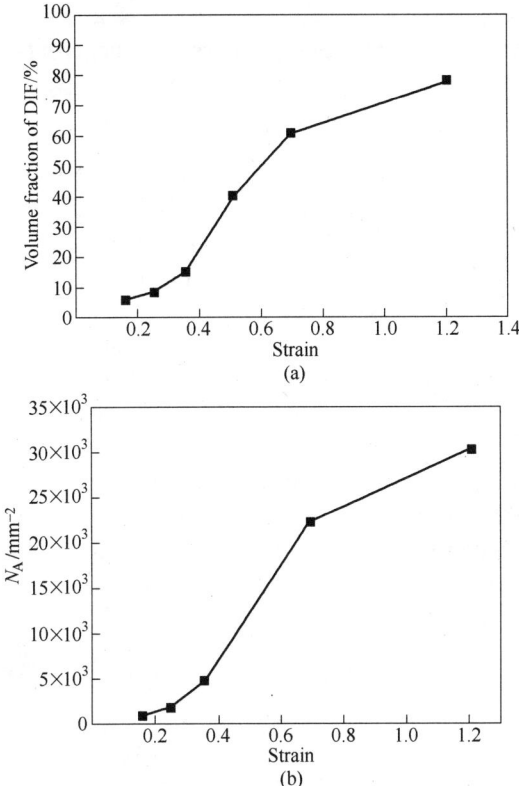

Figure 3.19　Volume fraction of DIF
(a) and ferrite grain numbers per unit area; (b) as a function of strain

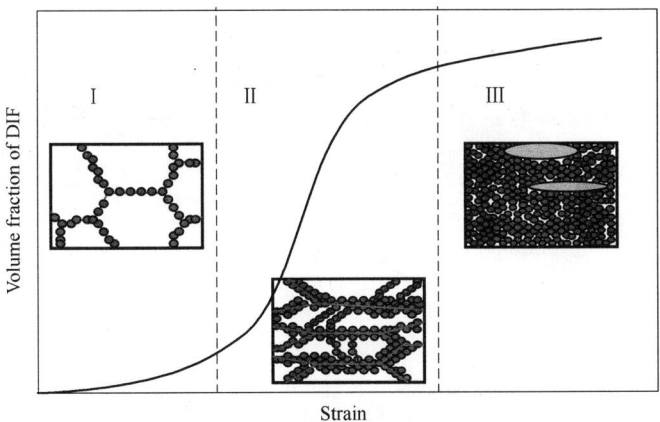

Figure 3.20　Schematic illustration of three-stage
microstructural evolution for DIFT

3.4.3   *Ferrite grain number and grain size versus transformation fraction*

Figure 3.21 shows the change of ferrite grain number per unit area with ferrite volume fraction during DIFT and continuous cooling transformation for Nb-microalloyed steel (a) and during DIFT and isothermal transformation without deformation for a plain low carbon steel (b). It can be seen that the ferrite grain number increases continuously during DIFT, but it decreases during continuous cooling transformation in Nb-microalloycd stccl, or only slightly increases during isothermal transformation in a plain low carbon steel(Yang, 2001). Therefore, DIFT is a nucleation dominant process, i.e, the transformation is mainly accomplished through the continuous nucleation process, whereas the static transformation is a grain growth dominant process. The growth of ferrite grain is inhibited to a great extent during DIFT due to a rapid and repeated nucleation of ferrite grain at γ/α interface, which results in a final finer grains than those obtained through static transformation without deformation or TMCP, as shown in Figure 3.22(Yang, 2004).

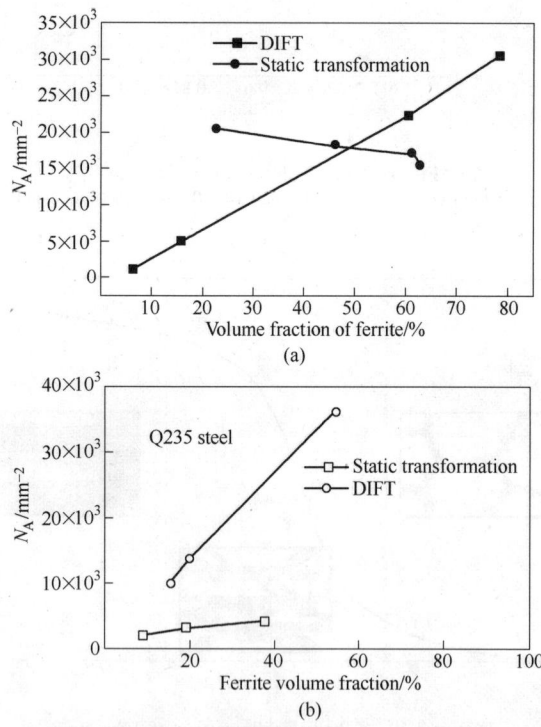

Figure 3.21   Change of ferrite grain number per unit area with ferrite volume fraction
(a) during DIFT and continuous cooling transformation for Nb-microalloyed steel; (b) during DIFT and isothermal transformation without deformation for a plain low carbon steel

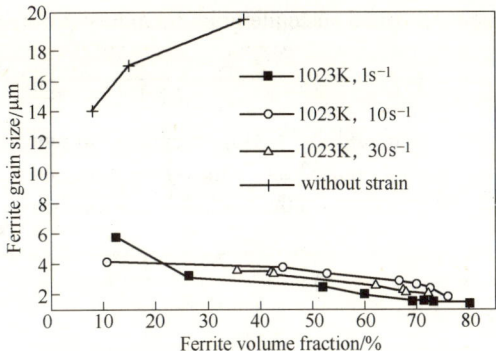

Figure 3.22   Change of ferrite grain size with ferrite volume fraction during DIFT and isothermal transformation for a plain low carbon steel

3.4.4   *Theoretical analysis*

3.4.4.1   Ferrite nucleation rate and deformation stored energy

Assuming ferrite nucleates along austenite grain boundaries, at the early stage of nucleation, the ferrite nucleus should be as coherent with one austenite grain as possible and be incoherent with another austenite grain. Assuming the shape of the nucleus is a spherical cap and its bottom surface lies on the austenite grain boundary, the free energy change for formation of such a nucleus is expressed as

$$\Delta G = \frac{2}{3}\pi r^{3}(\Delta G_{chem} + \Delta G_{D}) + 2\pi r^{2}\sigma_{\gamma/\alpha} \qquad (3.12)$$

The free energy change for formation of a nucleus of the critical size i.e. critical nucleation work is obtained by differentiating *r* in equation (3.12).

$$\Delta G_{GB}^{*} = \frac{8\pi\sigma_{\gamma/\alpha}^{3}}{3(\Delta G_{chem} + \Delta G_{D})^{2}} \qquad (3.13)$$

The critical nucleation work of ferrite for 0.11C-0.25Si-1.48Mn-0.048Nb steel is calculated according to Equation.3.13, as shown in Figure 3.23, Here, the coherent γ/α boundary energy is approximately equal to 0.07J/m^{2}; $\Delta G_{chem.}$ and ΔG_{D} are obtained from Figure3.10. It can be seen in Figure 3.23 that the addition of deformation stored energy reduces the critical nucleation work of ferrite, and the reduction is more significant at higher temperature.

According to the solid state transformation theory, the nucleation rate of ferrite is defined as

$$I = K_{v}\exp(-\frac{\Delta G^{*}}{kT})\exp(-\frac{Q}{kT}) \qquad (3.14)$$

where K_{v} is a constant related to the fraction of nucleation site, Q is the self-diffusion activation energy of iron atom in γ phase, which changes hardly with temperature, and k is the Boltzmann constant. The ratio between the rate of ferrite nucleation along deformed austenite grain boundary and the rate of ferrite nucleation along non-deformed austenite grain boundary is obtained as

$$\frac{I_{Deform}}{I_{Undeform}} = \exp(\frac{\Delta G^{*}_{Undeform} - \Delta G^{*}_{Deform}}{kT}) \tag{3.15}$$

The ratio can be calculated by taking the data shown in Figure3.23 into Equation3.15, as shown in Figure3.24. This figure suggests that the addition of deformation stored energy increases the nucleation rate of ferrite remarkably.

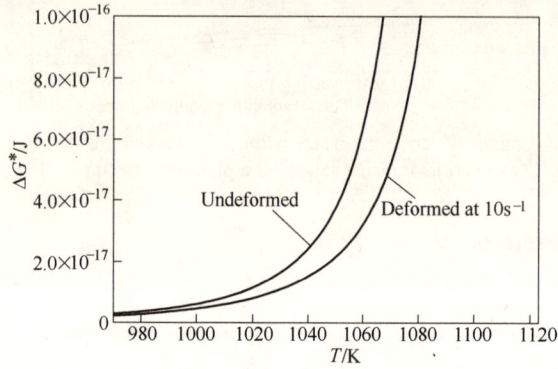

Figure 3.23   Influence of deformation on free energy change for formation of a ferrite nucleus of the critical size at various temperatures

3.4.4.2   Ferrite grain growth and deformation stored energy

For the diffusive $\gamma \rightarrow \alpha$ transformation, the relationship between the thickness of ferrite grain S and the transformation time t is expressed by

$$S = \alpha \cdot t^{1/2} \tag{3.16}$$

where α is the parabolic rate constant which is defined by

$$\alpha = \sqrt{\frac{D(C_{\gamma} - C_{0})^{2}}{(C_{0} - C_{\alpha})(C_{\gamma} - C_{\alpha})}} \tag{3.17}$$

where C_{γ} is the carbon content of austenite in the vicinity of γ/α boundary, C_{α} is the carbon content of ferrite, C_{0} is the carbon content of austenite matrix, and D is the volume diffusion coefficient of carbon atom in austenite. The addition of deformation stored energy presents an influence on the values of C_{γ} and C_{α}, which can be calculated using Thermo-Calc. The diffusion coefficient D is obtained from the following equation

$$D = 0.5\exp(-30C_{\gamma})\exp\left[-\frac{38300 - 190000 + 5.5 \times 10^{5} C_{\gamma}^{2}}{RT}\right] \tag{3.18}$$

The calculating results of the parabolic rate constant for 0.11C-1.48Mn-0.25Si-0.048Nb steel are shown in Figure 3.25 and Figure 3.26. The value rise of α is related to temperature decrease and increase of deformation stored energy. At 1053K, the value of α increases by 0.14μm/s$^{1/2}$ with deformation stored energy increased by 10J/mol. Therefore, the effect of deformation stored energy on α is less significant.

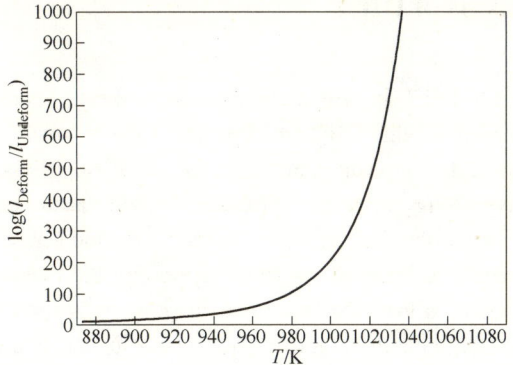

Figure 3.24 Influence of deformation on nucleation rate of ferrite at various temperatures

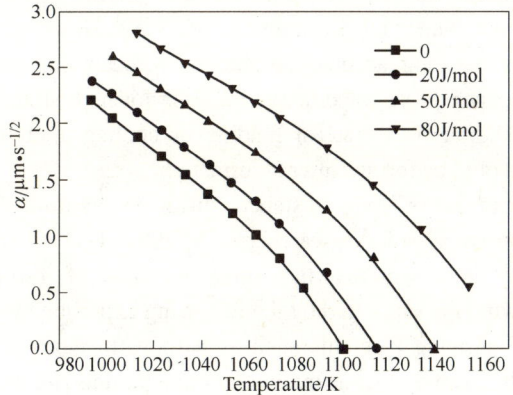

Figure 3.25 Influence of temperature and accumulative deformation energy on parabolic rate constant

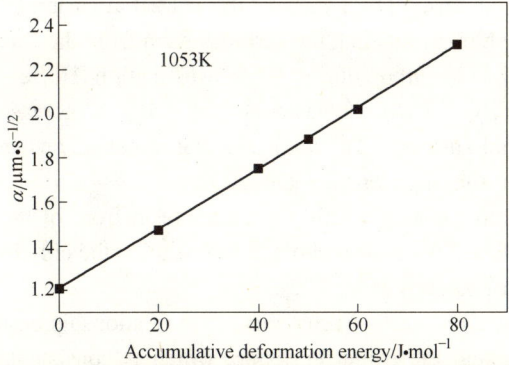

Figure 3.26 Parabolic rate constant α as a function of accumulative deformation energy at 1053K

3.5   Mechanisms of DIFT

The mechanism for DIFT is still ambiguous at present. There are two typical opinions with regard to the DIFT mechanism. One is massive transformation mechanism proposed by H. Yada et al (2000; Li, 1999; Li, 1998). This mechanism does not involve long distance diffusion within austenite. Actually, the transformation is only controlled by short distance diffusion across γ/α boundary. H. Yada et al presented two kinds of evidence supporting the massive transformation mechanism proposed. First, the micro-beam ion mass-spectrometric analysis indicated no measurable distribution of carbon across the γ/α boundary. Second, the rate of transformation seemed too large compared with that of pro-eutectoid ferrite transformation since the deformation induced ferrite could be formed in considerable amount even at a high strain rate of $250s^{-1}$. However, H. Yada et al did not present the measuring accuracy of the micro-beam ion mass-spectrometric analysis in their paper. More importantly, the time for high strain rate deformation could be much shorter than that for holding or cooling after deformation, so a portion of ferrite could be formed after deformation.

The other opinion is long distance diffusion controlled transformation mechanism proposed by some researchers (Qi, 2002; Du, 2002; Hurleg, 2001a). This mechanism is essentially the same as that of pro-eutectoid ferrite transformation, which is supported by the following experimental facts.

1. The effect of alloying elements such as carbon, manganese and niobium in solution on DIFT is the same as that on pro-eutectoid ferrite transformation, that is, the increase in the contents of C, Mn and Nb in solution can retard both kinds of transformation.
2. Carbides formed during DIFT are mainly located at austenite grain boundaries and at edges, which means that the carbides form from the final austenite which has been enriched in carbon during the transformation (Hurley, 2001).
3. The hardenability of remained austenite after DIFT is increased compared with that of the initial austenite. This indicates that remained austenite is enriched in carbon or other alloying elements (Du, 2002).
4. A transition zone existing within the austenite in front of the γ/α boundary is observed by SEM. This zone is thought to be due to the enrichment of carbon in front of the γ/α boundary (Qi, 2002).
5. There exists the Kurdjumov-Sachs orientation relationship between deformation induced ferrite and the parent austenite, which is consistent with the case of pro-eutectoid ferrite transformation (Hurley, 2001). For the massive transformation, however, the ferrite is randomly oriented with the parent

austenite.

More recently, we have observed the substructure within ferrite induced by deformation using TEM (Weng, 2005). It is frequently observed that there are a large amount of Fe_3C precipitates with less than 20nm in diameter within DIF, Figure3.27. This strongly indicates that carbon in DIF is initially supersaturated, which results in precipitation of Fe_3C after deformation. In other words, the diffusion of carbon during DIFT is quite insufficient and far from the equilibrium state. Therefore, it is speculated that DIFT is possibly a new kind of transformation different from both massive transformation and pro-eutectoid ferrite transformation. In addition, it is found in Figure3.27 (a) and Figure3.27 (c) that the dislocation density within DIF is low, and some dislocations are being rearranged to form a low angle grain boundary. This indicates that dynamic recovery of DIF occurs during deformation. More efforts are asked to be paid to study the transformation mechanism of DIFT.

3.6 Factors Influencing DIFT

The factors that have influences on DIFT include deformation variables, chemical composition of steel, prior-austenite grain size, etc. There have been numerous works on this topic up to now. In this section, the influence of deformation variables, chemical composition of steel and prior-austenite grain size on DIFT will be reviewed with emphasis on the works of the authors.

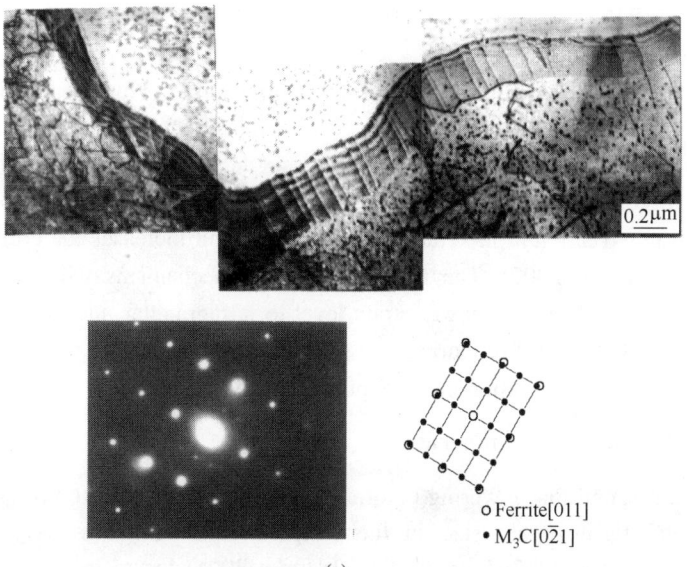

o Ferrite[011]
• $M_3C[0\bar{2}1]$

(a)

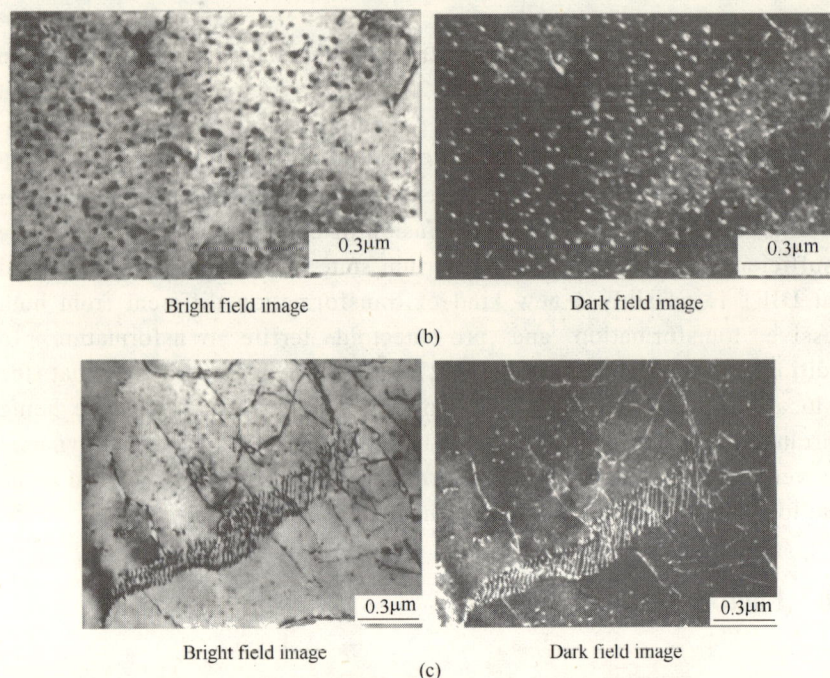

Bright field image   Dark field image

(b)

Bright field image   Dark field image

(c)

Figure 3.27   TEM images of DIF in low carbon steels
(a) 0.09C-0.25Si-0.51Mn-0.017Nb (mass%) steel; (b) and (c) 0.12C-0.34Mn-0.22Si (mass %) steel

3.6.1 *Deformation variables*

3.6.1.1 Strain

There is a critical strain required for DIFT to happen, which is related to the deformation conditions and chemical compositions. The critical strain becomes smaller as deformation temperature decrease due to increased transformation driving force (Hong, 2003; Choi, 2002). The increase in the contents of carbon, manganese and niobium in solution retards DIFT and increases the critical strain (Dong, 2003; Qi, 2002). The ferrite nucleation mechanisms will change from intergranular nucleation at lower strain level to intragranular nucleation at higher strain level (Dong, 2003). During this process, the ferrite grain numbers and the transformed volume fraction increase progressively.

3.6.1.2 Deformation temperature

It has been found that lowering deformation temperature will promote DIFT and reduce the ferrite grain size in the temperature range above Ar_3 (Dong et al,2003;Choi et al,2002;Hong et al,2003;Hurley,2001) due to the increase in the driving force for the transformation. An example is shown as follows.

Figure3.28 shows the microstructures of the 0.09C-0.25Si-0.51Mn-0.017Nb (mass%) steel which was obtained by water quenching subsequent to compression to the true strain of 0.69 at $15s^{-1}$ and at different temperatures. It can be seen that the microstructures were martensite and bainite at deformation temperatures above 1173K, indicating that DIFT didn't occur at above 1173K. When the temperature decreased to 1143K, however, the DIF was found to appear at the prior-austenite grain boundaries and the deformation bands. In addition, the fraction of DIF increased with decreasing the temperature.

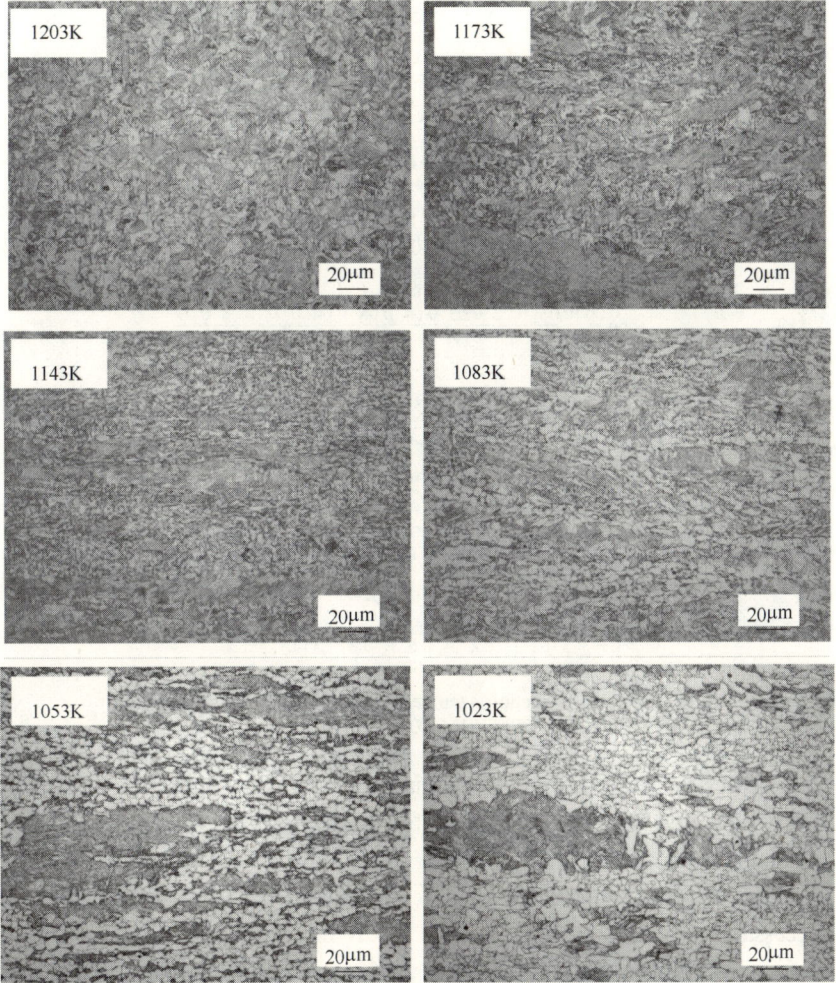

Figure 3.28   Microstructures of the 0.09C-0.25Si-0.51Mn-0.017Nb (mass %) steel which was obtained by water quenching subsequent to compression to the true strain of 0.69 at $15s^{-1}$ and at different temperatures

Figure3.29 shows the volume fraction change of DIF with temperature at different strains. It is clear that lowering deformation temperature can promote DIFT indeed. According to Figure3.29, the DIF fraction – temperature – strain (time) diagram is plotted, as shown in Figure3.30. It can be found that:

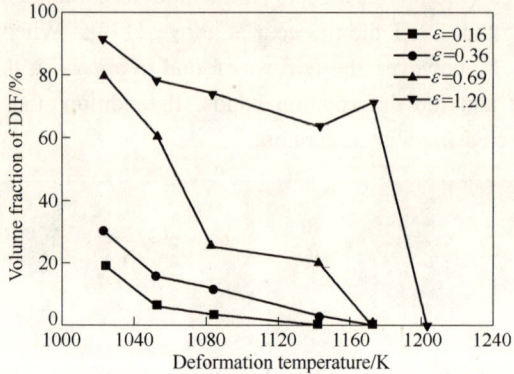

Figure 3.29   Volume fraction change of DIF with deformation temperature for the 0.09C-0.25Si-0.51Mn-0.017Nb (mass %) steel

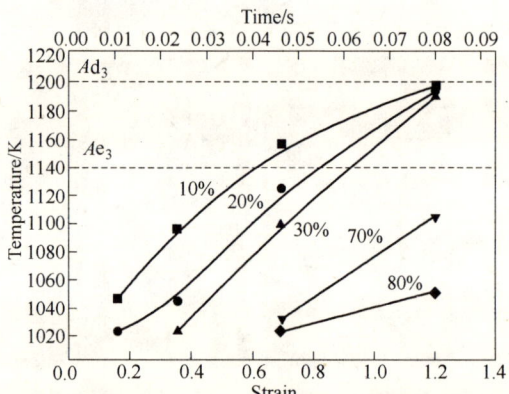

Figure 3.30   DIF fraction – temperature - train (time) diagram of the 0.09C-0.25Si-0.51Mn-0.017Nb (mass %) steel

1. The lower the deformation temperature is, the smaller the critical strain for DIFT is and the more rapidly the transformation proceeds.
2. The curves move to the right bottom corner with the increase of transformed amount, which suggests that low temperature and heavy deformation are necessary for obtaining a large amount of DIF in single pass deformation.

Compared with the static TTT diagram of low carbon steels, this diagram has the following unique features. First, the upper limiting temperature for DIFT (Ad_3) is higher than Ae_3 of the steel. Second, the incubation time for the transformation is in the order of magnitude of $10^{-2}s^{-1}$, which is much shorter than that of static transformation (from several seconds to several hundred seconds for low carbon steels). This means that deformation could enhance the $\gamma \rightarrow \alpha$ transformation amazingly.

Figure3.31 shows the DIF grain size as a function of deformation temperature for 0.09C-0.25Si-0.51Mn-0.017Nb steel. It can be seen that the DIF grain size decreases with the decrease of deformation temperature.

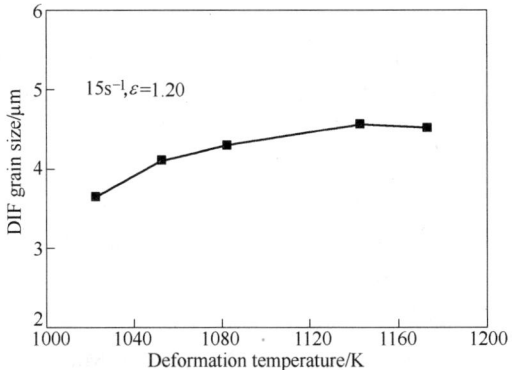

Figure 3.31   DIF grain size as a function of deformation temperature for
0.09C-0.25Si-0.51Mn-0.017Nb (mass %) steel

If the deformation temperature is decreased to below the Ar_3 temperature, however, DIFT will be inhibited to some extent due to the preferential formation of pro-eutectoid ferrite (Hurley, 2001b). The deformation temperature also has an influence on the ferrite nucleation site, and the decrease of deformation temperature will enhance intragranular nucleation (Hong, 2003).

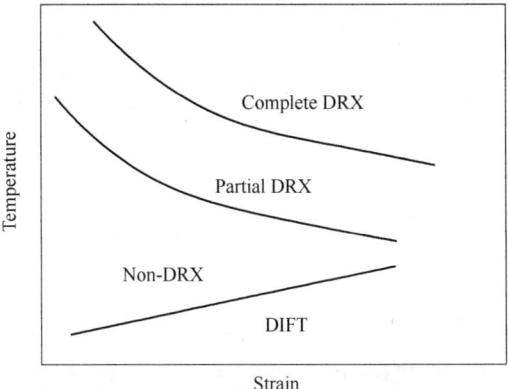

Figure 3.32   Schematic diagram showing the effect of deformation temperature on the
microstructure change of austenite(Dong et al,2003)

The free energy of austenite can be raised by deformation, and the accumulative deformation energy could be released by two competitive ways: dynamic recrystallization (DRX) of austenite and DIFT. With decreasing deformation temperature at a certain strain, the microstructure change of austenite during deformation might undergo four stages in succession: complete DRX, partial DRX, work hardening (or non-DRX) and DIFT (Dong, 2003), as shown in Figure3.32. The upper curve in this figure represents the critical strain for completion of DRX, the middle curve represents the critical strain for onset of DRX and the lower one represents the critical strain for DIFT as a function of temperature.

3.6.1.3   Strain rate

There exist different opinions with the effect of strain rate on DIFT. B. Mintz et al reported that the transformed amount of deformation induced ferrite (DIF) decreased with increasing strain rate at a certain strain in C-Mn steels (Mintz, 1994). However, H. Yada et al(Yada, 2000) and S.C. Hong et al(Hong, 2002) reported the result opposite to that of B. Mintz et al(Mintz, 1994)　in Fe-Ni-C alloy and C-Si-Mn-Nb-V steel respectively. P. Yang et al(Yang, 2004) and P.J. Hurley et al(Hurley, 2001b) reported that strain rate had little influence on the amount of DIF at a certain strain, but affected the morphology of DIF: lower strain rates could lead to the non-uniformity of the DIF grain size and extensive polygonization of the DIF.

The authors have systematically investigated the effect of strain rate on DIFT at different temperatures for the 0.11C-1.48Mn-0.25Si-0.048Nb steel (Dong, 2003). The main conclusion is that the effect of strain rate is closely related to the deformation temperature: at higher temperature (1073K), DIF fraction declines with increasing strain rate at a certain strain, as shown in Figure3.33 (a); at lower temperatures (1033K), however, DIF fraction declines firstly then rises with increasing strain rate, as shown in Figure3.33 (b). DIF grain size decreases with increasing strain rate and reach a limiting value finally, as shown in Figure3.33.

The effect of increasing strain rate on DIFT has two aspects. On one hand, increasing the strain rate will retard DRX of austenite and increase the accumulative deformation energy, and thus promote DIFT. On the other hand, increasing the strain rate means that the deformation duration is reduced, but the transformation is a time dependant process. This is unfavorable for DIFT. The combined effect could account for the above-mentioned differences about the effect of strain rate on DIFT.

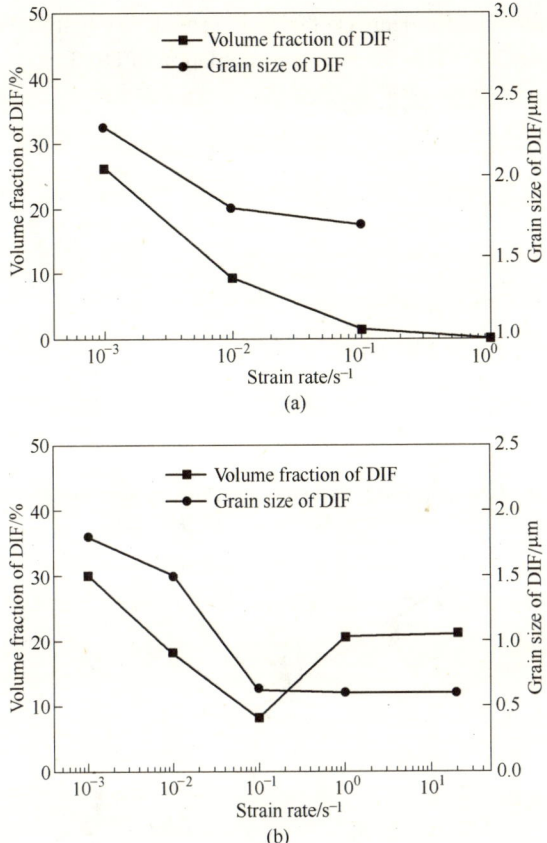

Figure 3.33 Effect of strain rate on the volume fraction and grain size of DIF
(a) 1073K; (b) 1043K

3.6.2 *Chemical compositions*

3.6.2.1 **Effect of carbon and manganese**

Figure3.34 illustrates the effect of carbon content on DIF volume fraction (a) and grain size (b) for the Nb-microalloyed steels deformed to the true strain of 0.92 at $1s^{-1}$ and at 1073K. It can be seen that both the volume fraction and grain size of DIF decrease with increasing carbon content. A similar trend with respect to the effect of manganese content can be seen in Figure3.35. In summary, the increase in the contents of both carbon and manganese can retard DIFT, but it is favorable for grain refinement.

Thermodynamics analysis indicates that the increase in the contents of both carbon and manganese reduces the transformation driving force, as shown in Figure3.36. The decrease in the transformation driving force can not only lower the nucleation rate but also decrease the grain growth rate (parabolic rate constant), as shown in Figure3.37. This leads to the retardation of DIFT.

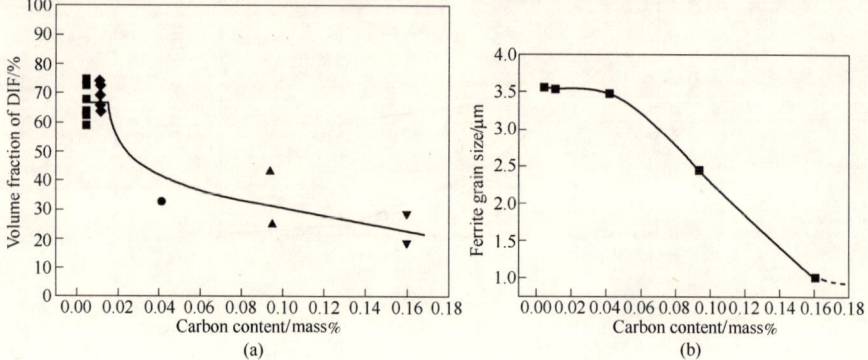

Figure 3.34 Influence of carbon content on the volume fraction (a) and grain size (b) of DIF ($\varepsilon=0.92$)

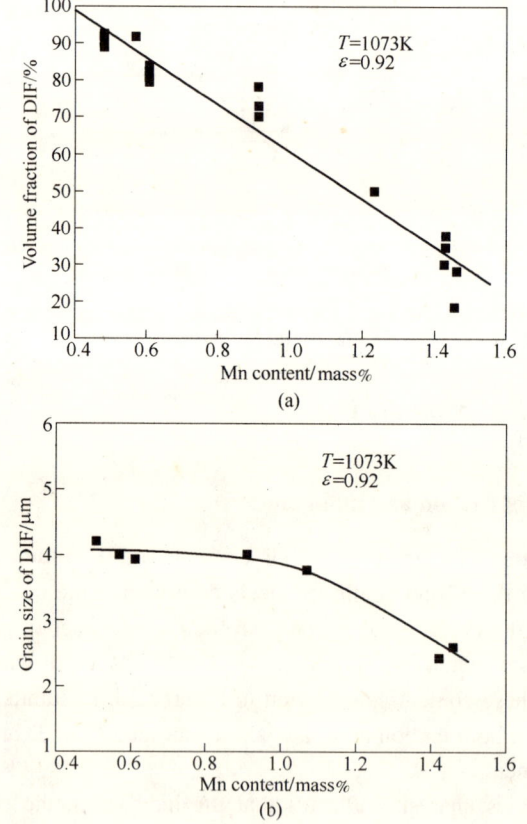

Figure 3.35 Influence of Mn content on the volume fraction(a) and grain size (b) of DIF

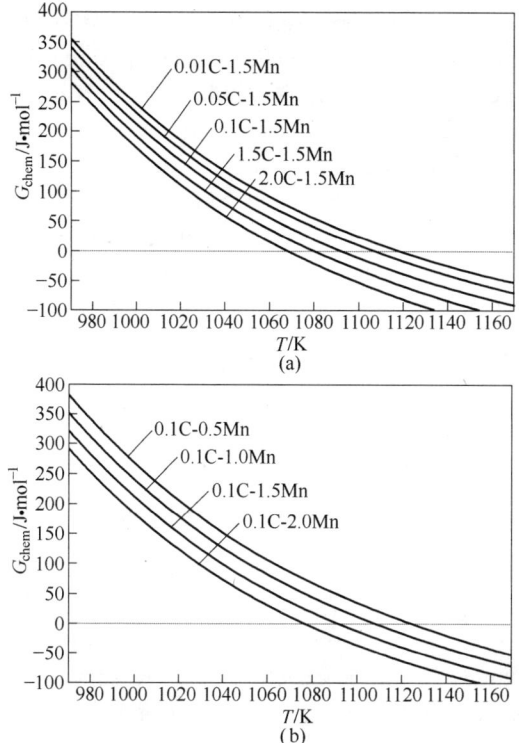

Figure 3.36 Influence of C (a) and Mn (b) content on the transformation driving force

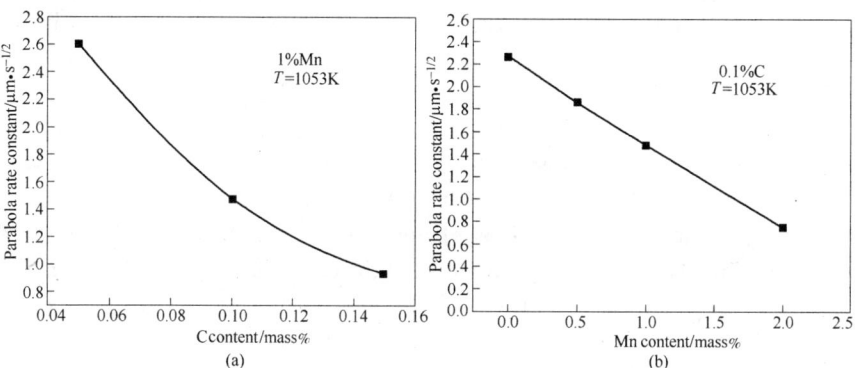

Figure 3.37 Influence of C (a) and Mn (b) content on the parabolic rate constant

3.6.2.2 Effect of niobium and vanadium

There are two existing states of microalloying elements in austenite: one is the dissolution state, and the other is the precipitation state. They have different influences on DIFT.

(A) Effect of dissolved niobium and vanadium on DIFT

Five experimental steels were used to investigate the effect of dissolved niobium and vanadium on DIFT. The chemical compositions of the tested steels are shown in Table 3.2. Steel A and B are ultra-low carbon steels with different niobium contents, and Steel C, D and E are plain low carbon steel, Nb-containing steel and Nb-V steel respectively. The samples were firstly soaked at 1453K for 5min to dissolve niobium into austenite completely, then cooled at 20K/s to different temperatures (above Ar_3). Hereafter, the samples were compressed at a strain rate of $1s^{-1}$ to the true strain of 0.92, followed by water quenching to preserve the microstructures at high temperature.

Table 3.2   Chemical compositions of the tested steels (mass%)

Number	C	Si	Mn	Nb	V	Ti	N
A	0.003	0.22	1.12	0.052	—	0.0110	0.0012
B	0.003	0.19	1.10	0.110	—	0.016	0.0014
C	0.086	0.16	0.57	—	—	—	—
D	0.091	0.18	0.56	—	0.064	—	—
E	0.088	0.17	0.55	0.027	0.070	—	—

The microstructures of the quenched sample are shown in Figure 3.38 and Figure3.39. It can be seen that the microstructure of Steel A is composed of fine polygonal ferrite induced by deformation and large quasi-polygonal ferrite formed during water quenching. It is noted that the austenite untransformed during deformation transforms into quasi-polygonal ferrite rather than martensite as commonly observed in low carbon steel due to the ultra-low carbon content of the tested steels. Furthermore, it can be seen from Figure3.39 that more fine polygonal ferrites, i.e. deformation induced ferrites are formed at lower deformation temperatures. For Steel B, however, the microstructure is almost composed of very large and elongated ferrite with length up to several hundred microns and with width larger than 10 microns. It is obvious that this kind of ferrite should be formed during water quenching, and it is not the deformation induced ferrite. The addition of 0.11%Nb can completely inhibit the formation of DIF in a wide range of temperature and strain. Thus, it can be concluded by comparing Figure3.38 and Figure3.39 that the dissolved niobium can retard DIFT.

Figure3.40 shows the microstructures of Steel C, D and E obtained by water quenching immediately after deformation to various true strains at 1033K and at the strain rate of $70s^{-1}$. It can be seen that at the strain of 0.36, a large amount of DIF have formed in Steel C and D, but DIF hasn't formed in Steel E. With increasing the strain to 0.51, the volume fraction of DIF increases in Steel C and D, and DIF just begins to appear in Steel E. The results of quantitative metallography measurement are shown in Figure 3.41. It is clear that vanadium has little influence on DIFT, and niobium can retard DIFT significantly although only 0.027%Nb was added.

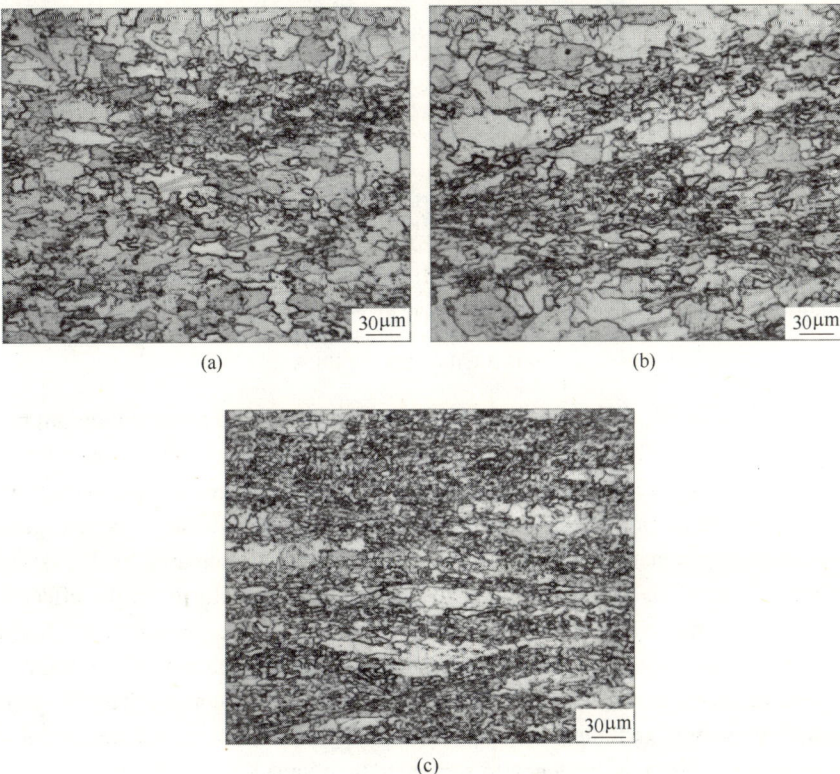

(a)

(b)

(c)

Figure 3.38 Microstructures of Steel A obtained by deformation to the true strain of 0.92 at various temperatures and following water quenching

(a) 1153K; (b) 1121K; (c) 1073K

(a)

(b)

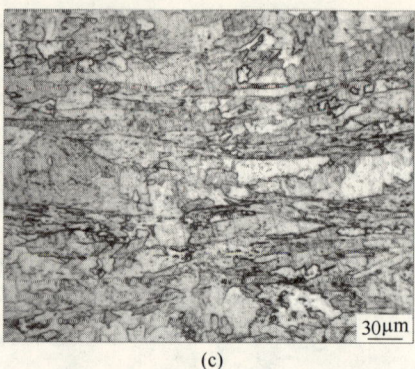

(c)

Figure 3.39   Microstructures of Steel B obtained by water quenching following deformation to the true strain of 0.92 at various temperatures
(a) 1145K; (b) 1115K; (c) 1095K

The works of M. Enomoto et al (1994) showed that the dissolved niobium had great influence on the pro-eutectoid ferrite nucleation rate in low carbon steel, as illustrated in Figure3.42. It can be seen that the dissolved niobium can reduce the nucleation rate of pre-eutectoid ferrite at both the grain boundary face and grain boundary edge remarkably, with the nucleation rate being decreased by 2~3 orders of magnitude when 0.089% Nb was added into the steel. However, the effect of vanadium is much less than the effect of niobium. The reduction of ferrite nucleation rate was thought to be related to the segregation of niobium or vanadium atoms at the austenite grain boundaries, which could lower the grain boundary energy and thus increase the nucleation energy of ferrite. Because niobium has a stronger tendency to segregate than vanadium, niobium can reduce the nucleation rate more notably than vanadium , as shown in Figure3.42. Since DIF nucleates preferentially at austenite grain boundary just same as the pre-eutectoid ferrite, it is easy to understand that niobium also delays the DIF nucleation. Furthermore, niobium can decrease the ferrite grain growth rate by the solute drag effect on the γ/α boundary migration, as will described in the following text. In summary, both the nucleation rate and grain growth rate during DIFT will be decreased by the dissolved niobium, and eventually lead to the retardation of DIFT.

(B) The effect of Nb (C, N) precipitation on DIFT

In order to investigate the effect of Nb (C, N) precipitation on DIFT, the thermo-mechanical simulation schedules were designed as follows. The samples with the chemical composition: 0.094C-0.29Si-1.42Mn-0.045Nb-0.008Ti-0.0038N (mass%) were firstly soaked at 1473K for 5min, then cooled at 10K/s, followed by a two-pass compression. The first pass compression was conducted at 1153K with the true strain of 0.51, followed by isothermal holding for different times. The second pass compression was carried out at 1053K with the true strain of 0.69, followed by water quenching. It should be mentioned that DIFT can't occur during the first pass deformation as the deformation temperature is so high.

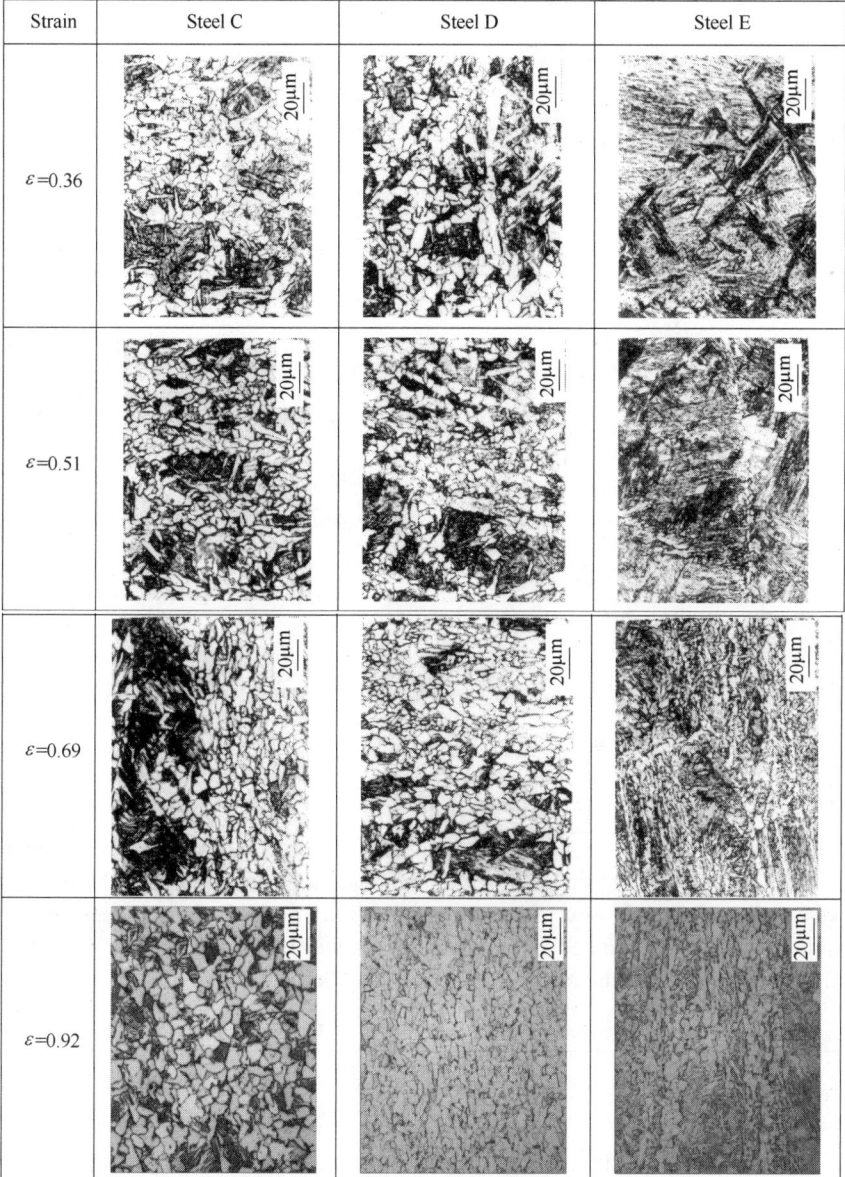

Figure 3.40 Microstructures of Steel C, D and E obtained by water quenching immediately after deformation to various true strains at 1033K and at the strain rate of 70s^{-1}

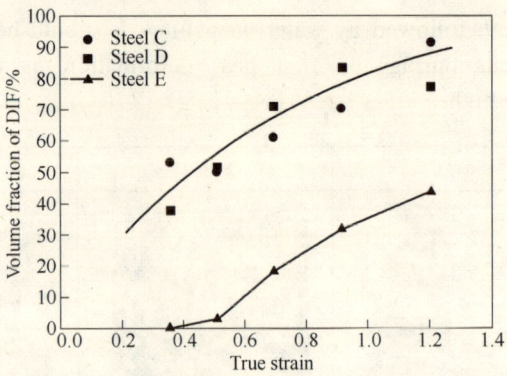

Figure 3.41　Volume fraction of DIF in Steel C, D and E as a function of true strain

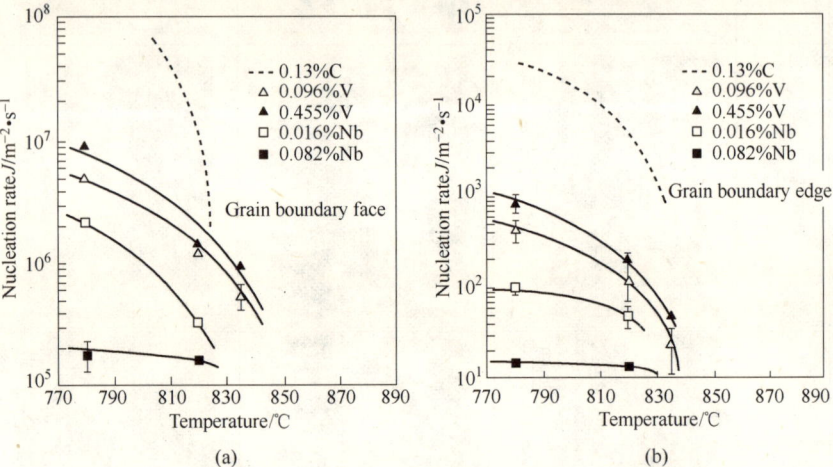

Figure 3.42　The effect of Nb and V on the nucleation rate of ferrite at grain boundary face
(or ledge) in 0.1%C steel

During the holding after the first pass deformation, strain induced precipitation of Nb (C,N) can occur. Table 3.3 shows the content of precipitated niobium which was measured by the physical-chemical phase analysis. It can be seen that the amount of the precipitated niobium increases with the holding time prolonged. Figure3.43 illustrates the Nb (C,N) particle morphology observed by TEM.

Table 3.3　The contents of the precipitated niobium with the holding time

Holding time /s	3	10	32	100
Precipitated Nb /mass%	0.0065	0.0077	0.0097	0.0164

Figure3.44 shows the microstructures of the tested steel subject to two-pass deformation with different holding time. The quantitative metallography results are shown in Figure3.45. It can be seen that when the holding time is shorter than 10s, the volume fraction of DIF is increased with increasing holding time; however, a reversed trend is shown when the holding time is longer than 10s.

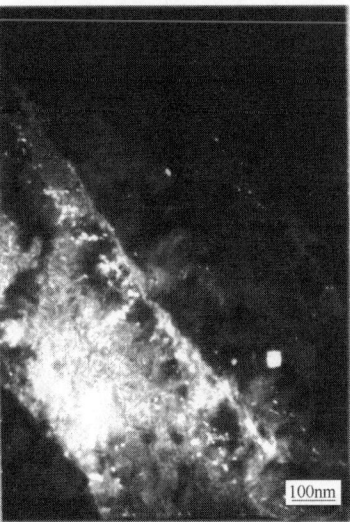

Figure 3.43 TEM image showing the morphology of Nb (C, N) particles in the sample subject to 100s holding after deformation at 880℃

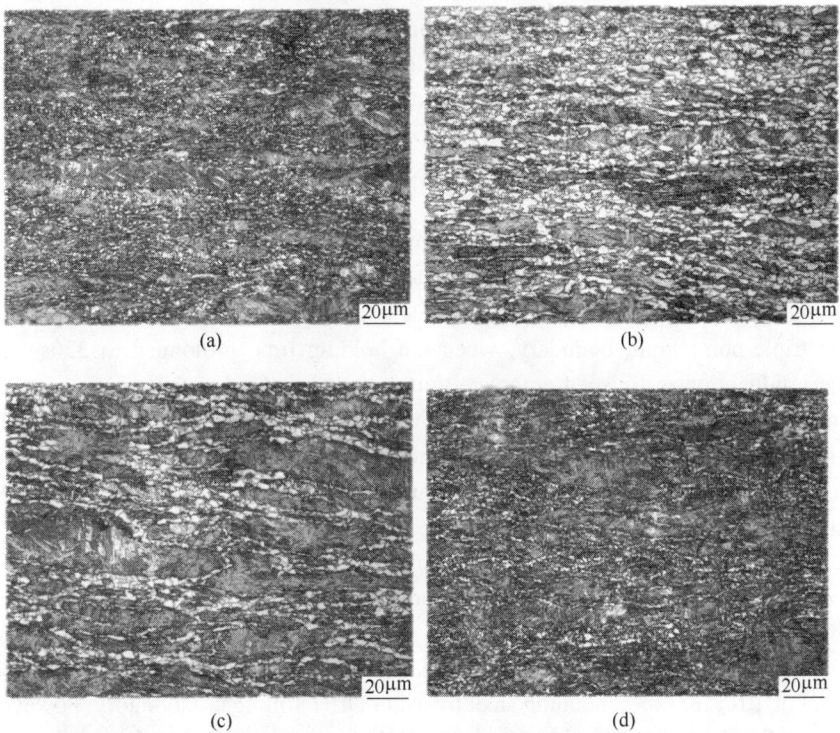

(a)

(b)

(c)

(d)

Figure 3.44 Microstructures of the tested steel subject to two-stage deformation with different holding times

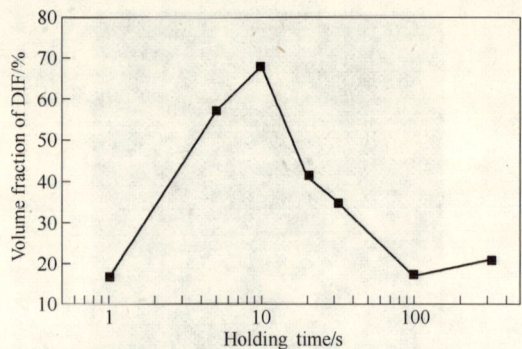

Figure 3.45 Volume fraction of DIF as a function of the holding time

It is believed that the increase of DIF fraction with holding time at the initial stage is related to the precipitation of Nb (C,N). Three possible mechanisms have been proposed to explain the phenomenon. First, the precipitation of Nb (C,N) decreases the content of the dissolved niobium, and thus enhances DIFT. Second, the niobium and carbon depleted zone formed around the Nb (C,N) particles can provide higher driving force for ferrite nucleation, and thus promote the formation of DIF. Third, those Nb (C,N) particles in size comparable to the critical nucleus size of ferrite could act as the favorable sites for heterogeneous nucleation of ferrite within austenite grains (also called as intragranular ferrite nucleation), and as a consequence, the nucleation rate of DIF can be raised. However, further experimental and theoretical works are needed to confirm the mechanisms mentioned above.

In order to make clear the reason why DIF fraction decreases after a longer holding, the austenite microstructures after the holding were observed, as shown in Figure 3.46. After 10s holding, fine recrystallization grains begin to appear at the triple-point grain boundary; when the holding time prolonged to 320s, the recrystallization is finished completely. It is well known that deformation stored energy plays an important role in inducing ferrite formation during deformation. If the recrystallization occurs, the energy stored in austenite will be released, which is definitely unfavorable for DIFT and thus leads to the decrease of DIF fraction at longer holding time.

(C) Effect of Nb on grain refinement in DIFT

It has been commonly observed that the DIF grain size in Nb-containing steel is much smaller than that in plain low carbon (PLC) steel under the same deformation conditions. For example, the ferrite grain size can be refined to the level of 1μm for Nb-containing steel by using DIFT rolling at laboratory; however, it can only be refined to about 3μm for plain low carbon steel. It is well known that the final grain size is dependant on both the nucleation rate and grain growth rate, and the grain size is finer at higher nucleation rate and lower growth rate. As

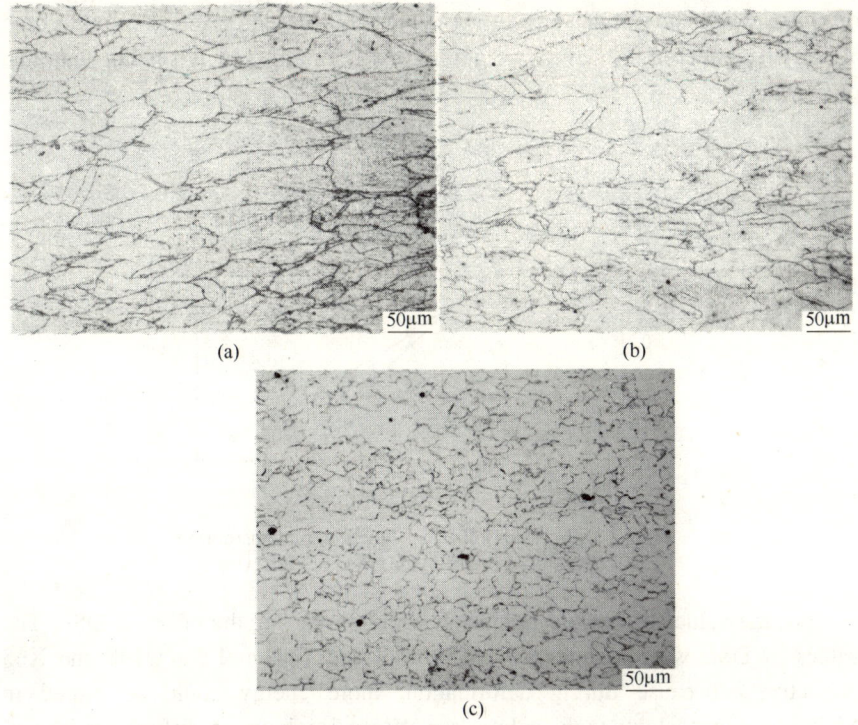

Figure 3.46   Austenite microstructure after different holding time
(a) 3s; (b) 10s; (c) 320s

mentioned above, the nucleation rate of ferrite during DIFT is greatly reduced by the dissolved niobium, so the more obvious grain refinement in Nb-containing steel than in PLC steel during DIFT can only be attributed to the lower grain growth rate. Actually, it has been well documented that the dissolved niobium can slow down γ/α boundary migration rate by the solute drag effect. In the following, an attempt will be made to estimate quantitatively the influence of niobium on the grain growth rate of ferrite.

K.J. Lee et al (Lee, 1999) have taken into account the solute drag effect of niobium by modifying the diffusion coefficient of carbon:

$$D=D_c\exp(-5000X_{Nb}(2750/T-1.85)) \tag{3.19}$$

Where D_c is the diffusion coefficient without considering the effect of solute drag, which is given by Equation3.18; X_{Nb} is the atom fraction of niobium and T is the absolute temperature. According to Equation 3.17, the parabolic growth rate constant, α can be obtained.

Two commercial steels, PLC steel Q195 and Nb-containing steel X65, were selected for the present calculation. Firstly, the values of α were calculated without considering the effect of deformation stored energy (DSE), as shown in Figure 3.47. It can be seen that the grain growth rate of X65 is equivalent to that of Q195 when the solute drag effect is not considered; when the solute drag effect is considered, however, the grain growth rate of X65 is smaller than that of Q195.

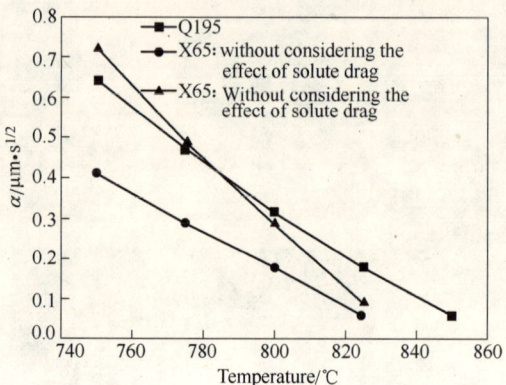

Figure 3.47   Values of α as a function of temperature
(without considering the effect of DSE)

Next, the values of α were calculated with considering the effect of DSE. The values of DSE were assumed to be 50J/mol and 100J/mol for Q195 and X65 respectively because during deformation, more energy could be stored in Nb-containing steel due to the solute drag effect of niobium on dislocation motion. The calculation results are given in Figure 3.48. It can be seen that the grain growth rate of X65 is smaller than that of Q195 even though much more DSE is assumed for X65 than Q195, and the difference of the α values in the two steels becomes larger at lower temperature.

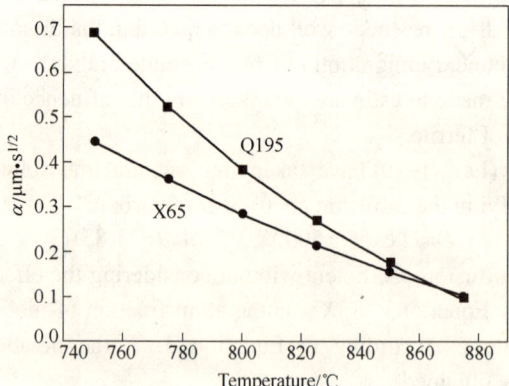

Figure 3.48   Values of α as a function of temperature
(considering the effect of DSE)

In summary, the calculation results show that the dissolved niobium can indeed decrease the grain growth rate during DIFT. This is the reason why much finer gain size is easy to be obtained in Nb-containing than in PLC steel during DIFT.

3.6.3   Prior austenite grain size

Most researches have shown that the reduction of austenite grain size can lead to an increase in the amount of DIF at the same strain. In other words, finer austenite grain size is more advantageous to DIFT.

However, Beynon et al found that a coarse austenite grain size appeared to be more favorable for DIFT under the condition of single pass rolling(Beynon, 1992). The explanation for this is that a coarse austenite grain size is able to prevent the formation of pro-eutectoid and provide large undercooling, which enhances intragranular nucleation and leads to rapid formation of a large amount of DIF.

3.7   Applications of DIFT

3.7.1   Applications of DIFT in plain low carbon steel

Based on the study of DIFT and recrystallization of austenite, the authors have developed a new TMCP procedure to produce fine grained plain low carbon steel. The largest difference between the new TMCP and the conventional one is that the former makes full use of DIFT on the basis of a sound controlling of austenite state. First, the austenite is deformed at a relative higher Zener-Holoman parameter in order to refine the austenite grain by dynamic or static recrystallization more efficiently. The fine grained austenite obtained is favorable for DIFT and ensure the homogeneity of the final microstructure. Second, the fine grained austenite is deformed in the non-recrystallization temperature region, which is not only the necessary prerequisite of DIFT but also helpful for the ferrite grain refinement during cooling. It was thought before that the recrystallization of plain low carbon steel was very easy to occur and therefore there did not exist usually a so-called non-recrystallization region in practice. However, the previous study showed that under the condition of relatively lower deformation temperature and shorter interpass period, it was possible that the deformed austenite would not recrystallized or only partially recrystallized, which creates the suitable condition for DIFT. Third, fine grained ferrite is induced by deformation during rolling at a relative lower temperature. Finally, the retained austenite that has been divided into small segments by DIF transforms into fine ferrite during cooling.

The new TMCP based on DIFT rolling has been adopted by some steel plants in China to produce fine grained plain low carbon steel rebar and strip though the processing procedure could be different at different plants.

3.7.1.1   Plain low carbon steel rebar

Steel rebar has been of the major steel product for building construction in China. At present, almost all of the steel rebar produced is of HRB335 (20MnSi) steel rebar (yield strength over 355MPa). Steel saving to 14 percent in weight and safety increasing for buildings are the advantages when HRB355 steel rebar is replaced by HRB400 (yield strength over 400MPa) steel rebar. The establishment of design requirement for concrete structure GB50010—2002 in China enhances the production and applications of HRB400 steel rebar. Microalloyed steel is usually used to replace HRB355 steel as HRB400 steel rebar, while it increases the cost by the addition of microalloying elements. Grain refining in plain low carbon steel to micron scale shows a potential for the steel as HRB400 steel rebar at lower cost.

The cooling devices were installed between rolling stands to control rolling temperature within adequate range for grain refinement. The chemical compositions were adjusted to meet requirement for HRB400 steel rebar: 0.15%~0.24%C, 0.50%~0.90%Mn, 0.17%~0.57%Si, P≤0.04%, S≤0.04%. Industrial trials at Capital Iron and Steel Corporation shows that yield strength of steel rebar is over 400MPa combined with good ductility and required R_m/R_p ratio, Figure3.49. Ferrite grain at the core of steel rebar was refined to 9μm in size, Figure3.50. Up to now, thousands of plain low carbon steel rebar of 25mm in diameter have been produced at the revamped continuous rolling stands.

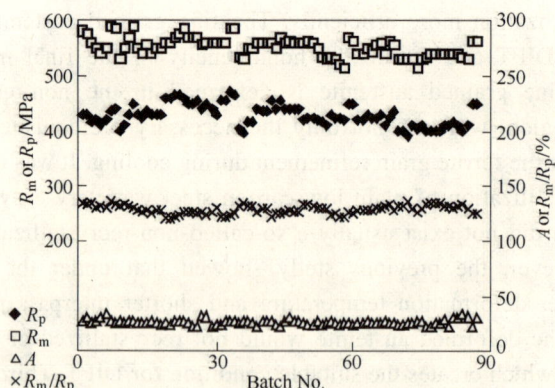

Figure 3.49   Mechanical property tolerance of PLC steel rebar produced in Capital Steel

Figure 3.50   Microstructure at the core of PLC steel rebar

Mean ferrite grains from 4.0 to 16.0μm in plain low carbon steel can be obtained through hot deforming simulations. It is showed by the result from tension test that strength increases and ductility decreases with grain refinement. When grain size is smaller than 5.0μm, yield strength of plain low carbon steel is over 400MPa. When grains are refined, both uniform plastic strain and strain hardening exponent are reduced, and the ratio of yield strength to ultimate tensile strength is raised.

Industry trials in plain low carbon rebar shows that lowering start rolling temperature (corresponding to lower finish rolling temperature) results in grain refining and strength raising. Comparing with 20MnSi steel rebar, yield strength of plain low carbon steel rebar with fine grains is higher, but ultimate tensile strength is lower. The ratio of yield strength to ultimate tensile strength is about 0.80 in fine grain steel, which is higher than those of conventional ferrite-pearlite steels. Lower ductility and higher ratio of yield strength to ultimate tensile strength are the important characteristics in plain low carbon steels with fine grains.

3.7.1.2 Plain low carbon steel strip

The typical steel grades of plain low carbon steel strips produced and applied in China are of Q195 – 295 series with yield strength from 195MPa to 295MPa respectively. The grain sizes of steel strips of this Q series plain low carbon steel are of dozens or scores microns, which could meet yield strength level the standard required.

According to the demand from automakers, the new steel needs to meet the requirement shown in Table 3.4 instead of microalloyed steel to manufacture truck beams. We applied the new grain refinement technology into the field production trials in both 1700 tandem rolling mill at Wuhan Iron and Steel Corporation (WISCO) and 1450 tandem rolling mill at Panzhihua Iron and Steel Corporation (Pan Steel). The plain low carbon steel strips produced in WISCO and Pan Steel were designated as WCX355 and SP52 respectively. Converter steelmaking and continuous casting were as same as those for Q235 steel production, while carbon contents in ultrafine grained plain low carbon steel were decreased, shown in Table 3.5. The start and finish tandem rolling temperature were in the ranges of 1223~1143K and 1093~1053K respectively. In order to lower the strip temperature, water cooling were applied into the hot strips between the rolling passes. The strips were coiled in the temperature range of 873~827K.

Table 3.4　Tension property of requirement for truck beams and commercial Q235 steel grade

Tension property	R_p /MPa	R_m /MPa	A/%	YR/%
Requirement	≥355	≥510	≥24	
Q235 (PanSteel)	275~360	400~450	30~40	69~80
Mean value of Q235	320	425	35	75
SP52	425	525	34	81
Q235 (WISCO)	279 (min).	413 (min).	32 (min)	68
Mean value of Q235	299	437	38	68
WCX355	425	525	28	81

Table 3.5　Chemical compositions of plain low carbon steel strips produced in WISCO and PanSteel

	Dimension	C	Si	Mn	P	S	Cu	Al$_s$
WCX355	3.5mm×1150mm	0.14	0.20	0.78	0.013	0.008	0.038	0.023
SP52	5.0mm×1000mm	0.14	0.22	0.61	0.014	0.009	—	—

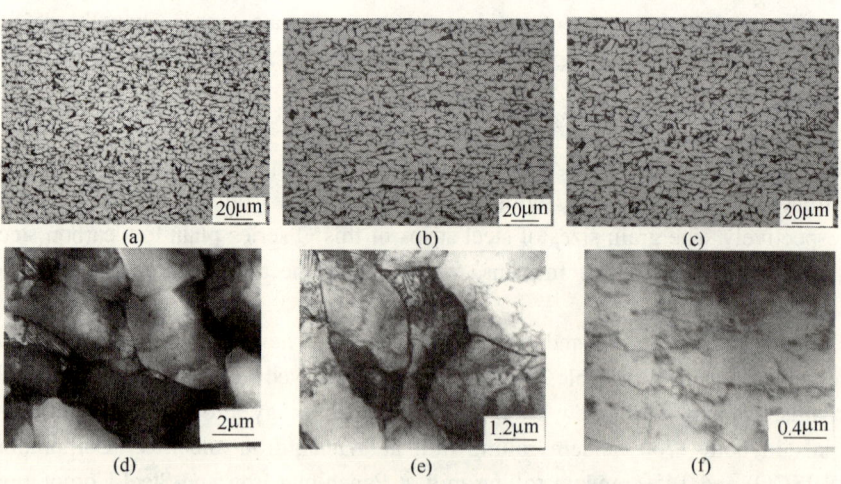

Figure 3.51　Microstructures of WCX355 steel strips of 4mm in thickness
(a) Near surface; (b) At 1/4; (c) At center; (d) Ferrite grain;
(e) Ferrite grain; (f) Dislocations within grain

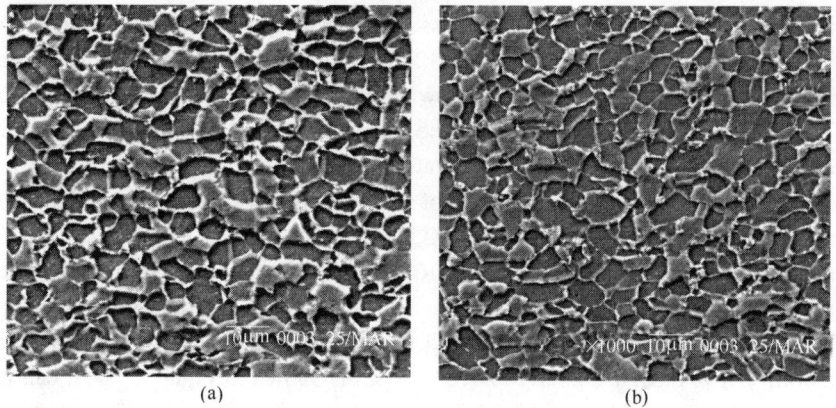

(a)　　　　　　　　　　　　　　　　(b)

Figure 3.52　Microstructures of SP52 steel strips
(a) *t*=3.0mm; (b) *t*=5.0mm

The mean grain size of ferrite in WCX355 steel strip is of 4.2 μ μ m. It is shown in Figure3.51 that microstructure of the strip consists of ferrite and pearlite with good uniformity across section of the strip. Equiaxed ferrite and diluted pearlite is of the main characteristics of the microstructure. It was observed that higher dislocation density was presented within these equiaxed ferrite grains. PanSteel produced SP52 steel strips in thickness from 3.0mm to 7.0mm. Similar microstructure characteristics were observed in SP52 steel strips in thickness of both 3.0mm and 5.0mm, Figure 3.52. More polygonal morphology is shown in SP52 steel strips compared with WCX355. The mean ferrite grain size of SP52 steel strips is in the range of 4~5 μ m. Both WCX355 and SP52 steel strips can meet the requirement for truck beams, Table 3.4. Yield strength of strips is over 400MPa and ultimate tensile strength is over 510MPa with small reduction in total elongation. The steel strips passed cold bending test and were affordable to cold forming and welding. Both WXC355 and SP52 steel strips were used to manufacture truck beams at Dongfeng Automobile Works.

3.7.2　Applications of DIFT in microalloyed steel

3.7.2.1　Laboratory trial production of 700MPa grade ultrafine grained steel

As mentioned in Section 3.6, the dissolved niobium can retard DIFT but the precipitation of Nb will enhance DIFT provided that no recrystallization of austenite occurs. The role of niobium in DIFT should be taken into consideration in the development of DIFT rolling procedure of niobium-containing steels. We have developed a new TMCP for the production of ultrafine grained Nb-microall-oyed steel in laboratory. A typical processing schedule is shown in

Figure3.53. A steel plate with thickness 30mm was firstly soaked at 1473K for 30min, followed by five pass rolling to a final thickness of 3mm, then cooled at 20K/s to 823K and finally cooled slowly in a furnace to room temperature to simulate coiling process of the strip. The role of the first pass rolling at 1273K is to refine austenite grains by recrystallization considering that fine austenite grains will be beneficial to DIFT. The role of the second pass rolling at 1223K is to promote the precipitation of (Nb,V) (C,N), which can help to accelerate DIFT kinetics. The final three pass rolling at 1093K is DIFT rolling as confirmed by the microstructural observation on water quenched samples. The final microstructure obtained in the experimental steel with chemical compositions 0.094C- 0.47Si- 1.38Mn- 0.1V- 0.04Nb- 0.02Al -0.018N (*wt%*) is shown in Figure 3.54. It can be seen that ultrafine ferrite grains of 1.5 μ m in mean size is obtained. The grains are much smaller than those produced by conventional TMCP (≥5 μ m). The yield strength of the experimental steel is over 700MPa.

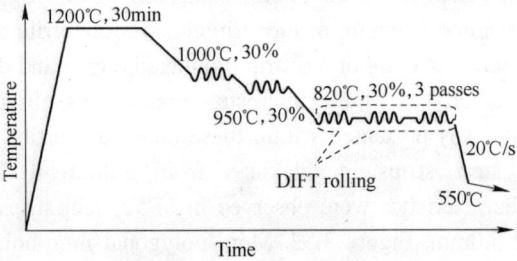

Figure 3.53   Laboratory rolling schedule for the production of ultrafine grained microalloyed steel

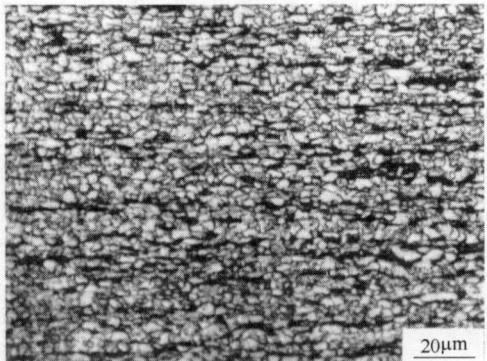

Figure 3.54   Microstructure of ultrafine grained V-Nb-N microalloyed steel produced by DIFT rolling

3.7.2.2   Industrial production of high strength Cu-P-Cr-Ni weathering resistance steel

There exists a steady demand of high strength for weathering resistance steel.

Based on SPA-H steel, chemical compositions and/or processing variables were modified in order to obtain finer grains through DIFT rolling: one was to modify tandem rolling processing variables for the steels with chemical compositions of conventional SPA-H steel, another one was to apply DIFT rolling to steels microalloyed with niobium. Five heats were melted in convert furnace, of which two heats were steels microalloyed with niobium, Table 3.6.

Table 3.6   Chemical compositions of weathering resistance steel in industrial trials,mass%

Heat No.	C	Si	Mn	P	S	Al$_s$	Ni	Cr	Cu	Nb
33132	0.09	0.31	0.41	0.085	0.010	0.03	0.17	0.50	0.29	—
18161	0.10	0.35	0.44	0.086	0.018	0.03	0.14	0.51	0.29	—
24081	0.08	0.28	0.40	0.075	0.007	0.02	0.50	0.14	0.29	—
24324	0.09	0.34	0.43	0.080	0.014	0.04	0.18	0.52	0.28	0.03
14245	0.09	0.28	0.41	0.078	0.009	0.03	0.48	0.13	0.28	0.03

For conventional SPA-H steel rolled at low temperature, the mean yield strength and ultimate tensile strength are 430MPa and 540MPa respectively, comparing with R_p=400MPa and R_m=510MPa of commercial SPA-H steel, Table 3.7. As DIFT rolling was applied to microalloyed steel, the mean yield strength and ultimate tensile strength were increased to 510MPa and 605MPa respectively. The strength increment is mainly due to grain refinement from commercial SPA-H of 10 microns to microalloyed steel of 4 microns with good uniformity across section, Figure3.55.

Table 3.7   Tension property of conventional steel (SPA-H) subject to low temperature rolling and Nb microalloyed steel subject to DIFT rolling

Heat No.	Batch No.	R_p/MPa	R_m/MPa	A/%
33132	0729	475	590	31
18161	02861J	415	525	29
	02871J	450	550	27
24081	0538P	390	510	31
	05941J	425	525	29
24324 (Nb microalloyed)	02801J	490	600	28
	02821J	530	625	23
	02831J	535	625	23
	02841J	505	590	24
	02851J	510	615	23
14245 (Nb microalloyed)	0595P	490	585	25
	05961P	495	585	26

Figure 3.55   Microstructures of weathering resistance steels
(a) Conventional SPA-H steel; (b) Microalloyed with Nb

References

Beynon J H, Gloss R, Hodgson P D (1992) The production of ultrafine equiaxed ferrite in a low carbon microalloyed steel by thermomechanical treatment. Mater. Forum 16: 37-42

Choi J K, Seo D H, Lee J S, et al (2003) Formation of ultrafine ferrite by strain-induced dynamic transformation in plain low carbon steel. ISIJ Int. 43(5):746-754.

Choi J K, Seo D H, Lee J S, et al (2002) Effect of processing parameters of strain induced dynamic transformation on the microstructures and mechanical properties of ultrafine grained low carbon steels. In: Proceedings of First International Conference on Advanced Structural Steels (ICASS 2002), The Iron and Steel Institute of Japan, Tsukuba, 22-24 May 2002

Choo W Y, Lee J S, Lee C S, et al (2000) Strain induced dynamic transformation of austenite to fine ferrite and it's characteristics. CAMP-ISIJ 13: 1144

Christian J W (eds) (2002) The theory of transformation in metals and alloys. Elservier Science Ltd, Netherlands

Dong H, Sun X J (2005) Deformation induced ferrite transformation in low carbon steels. Curr. Opin. Solid State Mater. Sci. 9: 269-276

Dong H, Sun X J, Liu Q Y, et al (2003) Deformation induced ferrite transformation: phenomena and theory. Iron Steel 38 (10): 56-67 (in Chinese)

Du L X, Zhang C B, Ding H, et al (2002) Determination of upper limit temperature of strain induced transformation of low carbon steels. ISIJ Int. 42(10): 1119-1124

Enomoto M, Nojirl N, Sato Y (1994) Effects of Vanadium and Niobium on the nucleation kinetics of proeutectoid ferrite at austenite grain boundaries in Fe-C and Fe-C-Mn alloys. Mater. Trans. 35(12): 859-867

Hodgson P D, Hickson M R, Gibbs R K (1998) The production and mechanical properties of ultrafine ferrite. Mater. Sci. Forum 284-286: 63-72

Hong S C, Lee K S (2002) Influence of deformation induced ferrite transformation on grain refinement of dual phase steel. Mater. Sci. Eng. A323:148-159

Hong S C, Lim S H, Lee K J, et al (2003) Effect of undercooling of austenite on strain induced ferrite transformation behavior. ISIJ Int. 43(3): 394-399

Hurley P J, Hodgson P D (2001a) Formation of ultra-fine ferrite in hot rolled strip: potential mechanisms for grain refinement. Mater. Sci. Eng. A302: 206-214

Hurley P J,Hodgson P D (2001b) Effect of process variables on formation of dynamic strain induced ultrafine ferrite during hot torsion testing. Mater. Sci. Tech. 17: 1360-1367.

Lee K J, Lee K J (1999) Modeling of γ/α transformation in niobium-containing microalloyed steels. Scr. Mater. 40(7): 831-836

Lee S, Kwon D, Lee Y K, et al (1995) Transformation strengthening by thermomechanical treatments in C-Mn-Ni-Nb steels. Metall. Mater. Trans. A. 26A: 1093-1100

Li C M, Yada H, Yamagata H (1999) An In-situ X-ray diffraction study of $\gamma\rightarrow\alpha$ transformation during hot deformation in Fe-6mass%Ni-0.0008~0.29mass%C alloys. ISIJ Int. 39(2): 209-211

Li C M, Yada H, Yamagata H (1998) In situ observation of $\gamma\rightarrow\alpha$ transformation during hot deformation in an Fe-Ni alloy by an X-ray diffraction method. Scr. Mater. 39(7): 963-967

Matsumura Y, Yada H (1987) Evolution of ultrafine-grained ferrite in hot successive deformation. Trans. ISIJ 27: 492-498

Mintz B, Jonas J J (1994) Influence of strain rate on production of deformation induced ferrite and hot ductility of steels. Mater. Sci. Tech. 10: 721-727

Priestner R (1981) Strain induced $\gamma\rightarrow\alpha$ transformation in the roll gap in carbon and microalloyed steel. In: DeArdo A J, Ratz G A and Way P J (ed) Proceedings of an International Conference on the Thermomechanical Processing of Microalloyed Austenite, Metallurgical Society of AIME, p 455

Qi J J, Yang W Y and Sun Z Q (2002) Ultrafine ferrite formation during deformation of undercooled austenite in a low carbon steel. Acta Metall. Sinica 38(9): 897-902 (in Chinses)

Sun X J, Dong H, Liu Q Y, et al (2007) Dynamically transformed ferrite fraction inferred from dilatometry measurement after deformation, Mater. Sci. Eng. A doi: 10.1016/ j.msea.2007.09.065.

Sun Z Q, Yang W Y, Qi J J, et al (2002) Deformation enhanced transformation and dynamic recrystallization of ferrite in a low carbon steel during multipass deformation, Mater. Sci. Eng. A334: 201-206

Tamura I, Ouchi C, Tanaka T, et al (eds) (1988) Thermomechanical processing of high strength low alloy steels. Butterworth & Co,Ltd., Belfast

Weng Y Q, Sun X J, Dong H (2005) Overview on Deformation Induced Ferrite Transformation. Iron Steel 40(suppl.): 9-15

Yada H, Li C M and Yamagata H (2000) Dynamic $\gamma\rightarrow\alpha$ transformation during hot deformation in Iron-Nickel-Carbon alloys. ISIJ Int. 40(2): 200-206

Yang Z M and Wang R Z (2003) Formation of ultra-fine grain structure of plain low carbon steel through deformation induced ferrite transformation. ISIJ Int. 43(5): 761-766.

Yang P, Cui F E, Fu Y Y, et al (2001) Dynamic aspects of strain enhanced transformation in Q235 plain carbon steel. Acta Metall. Sinica 37(6): 617-624 (in Chinese)

Yang W Y, Qi J J, Sun Z Q, et al (2004) Characteristics of deformation enhanced transformation in low carbon steel. Acta Metall. Sinica 40(2): 135-140 (in Chinese)

4
Microstructure Refinement of Steels by TSCR Technology

In this chapter, the microstructure and properties of low carbon steel produced by TSCR (Thin Slab Casting and Rolling) technology are studied, and compared with that of traditional process. The microstructure refinement and austenite recrystallization of low carbon steel produced by TSCR technology are presented. The characteristic and the mechanism of AlN precipitation in the steel are discussed based experimental results. The dynamics and corresponding model of precipitation during the heating and rolling are discussed also. The influences of AlN particles on the precipitation action in austenite region and on the ferrite transformation are analyzed. In addition, the softening mechanisms of low carbon steel for cold rolling by TSCR are explained. These include the property requirements of cold-rolled drawing sheets to hot strip, softening methods, grain coursing and softening mechanisms of B added low-carbon steel, the effects of the hot rolling and cooling technology on the softening of low carbon steel as well as the influences of different softening technology on the formability of cold-rolled 08Al steels. On the other hand, the sulfide and oxide dispersive precipitates, other nanometer precipitates in the CSP low carbon steels, the carbides and carbonitrides in Ti containing steels, are introduced also in this chapter.

4.1 Microstructure Refinement Process and Austenite Recrystallization of Low Carbon Steels Produced by TSCR Technology

4.1.1 Contrast between TSCR technology and traditional technology

In the past few years, the processes used to control the rolling and cooling process continuously changes with the improvement in the technology of in the entire TSCR production line. Compared with the traditional technology, TSCR is similar in controlling of rolling and cooling process. However, it shows a special technology character and advantage by a systematic combination with the whole compact production line.

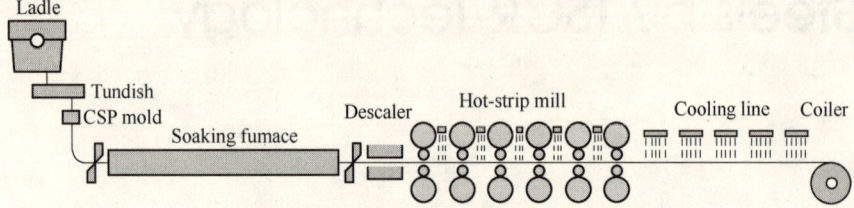

Figure 4.1   Disposal sketch of CSP equipment

More than 40 TSCR production lines have been built all over the world until 2006, CSP production lines count about 2/3 of those, while the others are FTSR, QSP, CONROLL, and so on. In CSP production line, the equipment is relatively simple, and the technological process is smooth. Besides, the production of CSP technology is very stable, and this technology is very perfect. The sketch of CSP equipment is shown in Figure 4.1. The thickness of casting thin slab in CSP line is usually between 50 and 70mm (when using dynamic soft reduction system, the thickness of casting slab, which is 90mm after mould, can be reduced to 65~70mm with the liquid core, or from 70mm to 55mm). The finishing mill group contains about 6~7 stands. Since the TSCR has its special technological constitution and characters, it is different from the traditional technology in the main segments, such as casting, rolling, and so on. The characters in rolling process of both the two technologies will be introduced as follows.

TSCR process is different from the traditional continuous casting and rolling mostly in the thermal histories. The contrast between them is shown in Figure 4.2. In TSCR process, from the smelting to the final strips, the slab experience a nonreversing phase transformation of $\gamma \rightarrow \alpha$ and from high to low temperature. However, in traditional process the thermal history of the slab is $\gamma_{(1)} \rightarrow \alpha$, $\alpha \rightarrow \gamma_{(2)}$, $\gamma_{(2)} \rightarrow \alpha$. Since the thermal histories, forming conditions and processes are different during continuous casting and rolling of thick and thin slabs, the conditions are different which determine recrystallization, phase transformation and the precipitates, including the precipitation process, status and factors. It takes about 2.5h for the liquid steel to be slabs in TSCR procedure, while the time is much longer in traditional ones. This will cause different influences on the microstructure and properties (Kang YL et al,2005).

At present, the key technique of CSP, continuous passing roller-hearth furnace is usually used to soak the slab, while laminar accelerate cooling system is used to cool the final strip. In CSP technology, the rollers are disposed in a different way from traditional production lines. The finishing mills engage closely with the soaking furnace. The great reduction and rolling with high rigidity are also

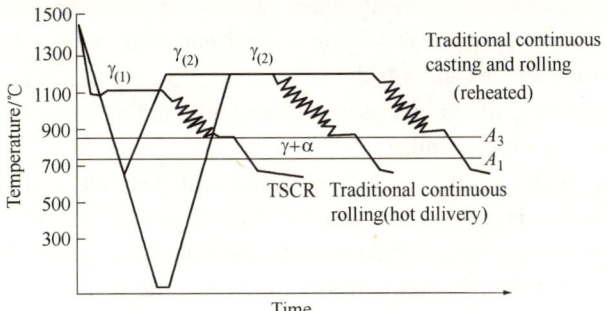

Figure 4.2   Comparison of heat histories between TSCR technology and traditional one

one of the technical characters of TSCR technology. The continuous passing roller-hearth furnace can guarantee that there is almost no difference in temperature of the slab from the head to the end. So there is no need to take some measures to modify and uniform the temperature, such as to heat the edge part, to speed up or to take a cooling technology between the inter-mills, which are always used in strip production. Laminar accelerate cooling can assurance the uniform temperature in the longitude and transverse directions, and constrain the solution status of microalloy elements. In this way,these precipitates of microalloy elements disperse orderly, which is beneficial for the phase-transformation refinement and microstructure strengthening (Guo L, 1999;Luis A et al,1997).

In the production of TSCR, grain refinement process has to be taken for several times so that the coarse original austenite grain can get refined. Besides, the grains must get a complete recrystallization. The recrystallization behavior of austenite grain can be improved by adding some microalloy elements.

Compared with the traditional technology, TSCR has a special microalloy elements behavior. This is because cooling rate is higher during the solidification of slab and the direct charging slab temperature is also much higher, which make the solution and precipitation behavior of the microalloy elements different from those of the traditional technologies. This can be explained by the different of the solution and precipitation strengthen effects of the carbides and nitrides. In TSCR technology, almost all of the microalloy elements solve in austenite, while in the traditional production technologies, they precipitate as the slab cool down. In this case, TSCR technology has an advantage of total microalloy elements, which do a great favor for the refinement of austenite grains and precipitation strengthening in the final microstructure. So it has an important influence on the properties of the final product. During the cooling process before reheating in traditional technologies, some of the microalloy elements have already precipitated in the form of carbides and nitrides. In the following limited reheating time and temperature, only part of the carbides and nitrides can dissolve. So some of the elements and precipitates are lost, which can refine the austenite grains and contribute to the final precipitation strengthening.

According to the main reasons above, wemust pay much attention to the procedure parameters, such as the casting, soaking, rolling schedule and cooling, because they have a direct relationship with the final microstructure and precipitates of TSCR technology. Only in this way, the final microstructure and properties of the steel can be understood and controlled better.

4.1.2　*The refinement process of microstructure during CSP hot continuous rolling*

In order to investigate the microstructure evolution of low carbon plates during the hot continuous rolling, ZJ330, a continuous casting low carbon slab was hot rolled for six passes on Zhujiang CSP line, and the samples were obtained in the required dimension from the rolling jamming slabs. The casting slab is 50mm in thick, while the thick of final strip is 1.9 mm. The locations where the samples were taken are shown as Figure 4.3, with the main chemical compositions in Table 4.1.

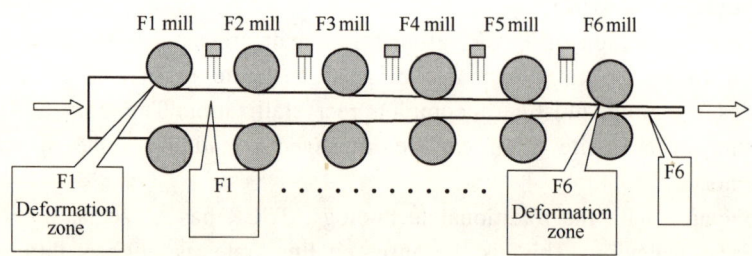

Figure 4.3　Sketch diagram to take samples

Table 4.1　Main chemical composition of hot continuous rolled low carbon strip ZJ330 (mass%)

C	Si	Mn	P	S	Al$_t$	Al$_s$
0.051	0.04	0.39	0.026	0.012	0.031	0.0306

Microscopic samples were taken from the casting slab and rolling block workpiece for six passes, and the microstructures in the rolling direction, transverse direction and the direction parallel to the surface of the strip were observed with optical microscope, so we can get a further analysis for the grain size, shape and rule of the distribution. The grain sizes were measured by using mean linear intercept method.

4.1.2.1 Variation of the grain size in rolling direction

The surface microstructures in rolling direction of F1~F6 passes are shown in Figure 4.4. In the first pass, under the condition of temperature 1090 ℃, deformation 55.4%,austenite can completely recrystallized,and the grain size changed from 85μm to 32μm. The grain size got a great refinement as a result of simulation of the reduction in the following passes. From the whole rolling process, the grain size reduced obviously in the first 5 passes, while the refinement effect is not so distinct in the last pass. After the first five passes, the grain size in the center change from 85μm to 6.5μm, and reach 5.6μm after the last pass.

The Figure 4.5 shows the evolution of the grain size in rolling direction in the passes. With the increase of cumulative deformation, the grain size got gradually refined. In the sixth pass, the grain sizes in the center and at the surface reached 5.4μm and 5.6μm respectively. The grain sizes varied in the different places from surface of the rolling block workpiece. The tendency is that the grain size increases gradually from the surface to the center, and this diversity decreases with the increase of deformation. In microstructures of pass five to six in the rolling direction, the grain size difference between center and surface is no more than 0.2μm, which is very helpful to gain a homogeneous microstructure and mechanical properties for ZJ330 strip.

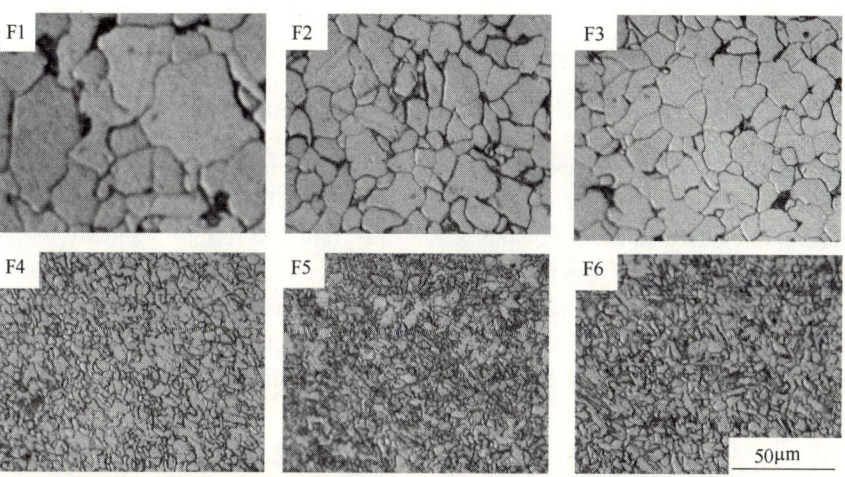

Figure 4.4　The central microstructure evolution in rolling direction in six passes

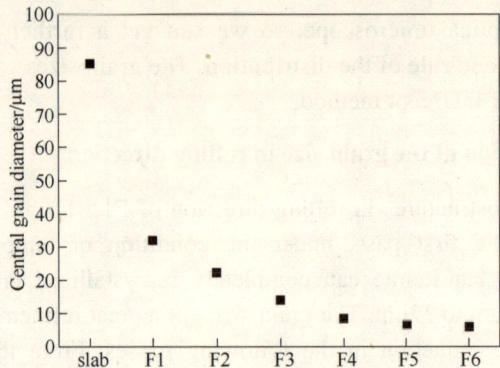

Figure 4.5   The central grain diameter evolution in rolling direction in six passes

4.1.2.2   Variation of grain size in rolling plane

The microstructures of surface in rolling plane from pass 1 to 6 are shown in the Figure 4.6. From this metallography, it can be seen that the grain size changes a

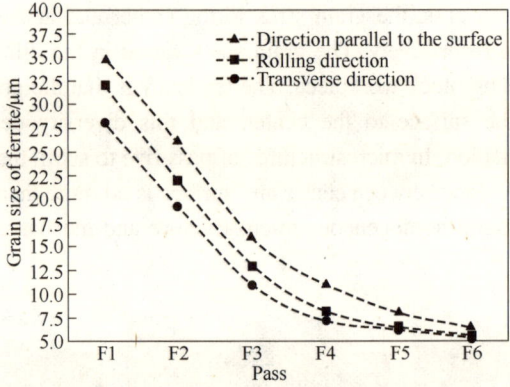

Figure 4.6   The grain diameter of ZJ330 in the center in different directions of pass 6

little in pass 1 and 2. However, it gets a great refinement in pass 3. That's because in the first pass, austeníte can get complete recrystallization, so the grain size refines obviously. In the following passes, the grain size refines gradually. In the whole rolling schedule, the refinement of grain focuses on the former 5 passes. In the last pass, the effect of refinement is not so obvious, which is coincident with the variation regularity in rolling and transverse direction. After the former five passes, the grain size in the central microstructure reaches 7.9μm, and most of them is equiaxial.

In different thickness area from the surface of rolling block workpiece, the grain sizes are different from each other. The variation regularity is that the grain size increases gradually from the surface to the center, and this difference vanished as the increment of cumulative deformation. In the microstructures of F5~F6 in the direction parallel to the surface, the grain size difference between surface and center is 1.0μm and 0.4μm, respectively, which is more obvious compared with the rolling and transverse direction.

4.1.2.3 Comparison of microstructure in transverse, rolling and surface direction of ZJ330 rolling block workpiece for different passes

The average grain size in central microstructure changes with passes in transverse, rolling direction and rolling plane. Compared the average grain size in rolling, transverse direction and direction parallel to the surface in different passes of ZJ330 low carbon steel 1.9mm, it can be found that in places of the same thickness, the variation of grain size is in this regulation: in rolling plane, the average grain size is the biggest, while it is the smallest in the transverse direction.

As the cumulative deformation increase, the difference of the microstructure can get a great improvement in the transverse direction, rolling direction, direction parallel to surface, and so does the uniformity in the same direction. Through the observation of microstructure of F6, it can be seen that the difference between different directions is not obvious. The grain size of surface has little difference with that of the center. Deviation of the grain sizes is around 0.2μm, in which the biggest is no more than 0.4μm. Microstructures of F6 in the transverse direction, rolling direction and rolling plane are shown in Figure 4.7.

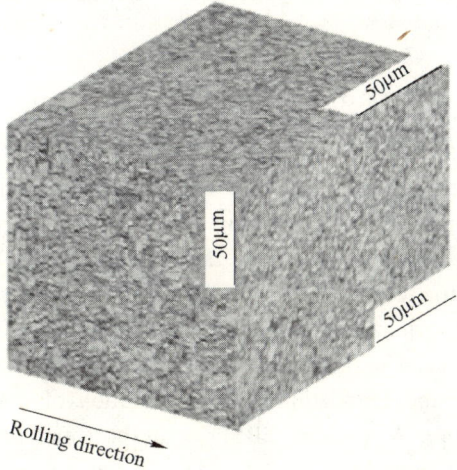

Figure 4.7　Microstructures in three directions after pass 6 of ZJ330

After rolling for several passes in recrystallization region, the dimension of austenite grains depends on the total deformation, as well as the deformation in each pass. Great deformation in each pass can promote the recrystallization of austenite and refine the grains. In the production of ZJ330 on Zhujiang CSP line, the start rolling temperature is usually between $1050 \sim 1100\,^{\circ}\text{C}$. The deformation is more than 50%, while the deformation rate is very low. The recrystallization occurs completely, so the grains get a great refinement. The first five passes are carried out above $950\,^{\circ}\text{C}$, and deformation of each pass is more than 30%. Analysis for this suggests that these are in recrystallization region. The austenite grain can get an obvious refinement through repeated deformation and crystallization. In this process, the austenite grain size mainly depends on deformation and temperature. In the last pass, the temperature is relatively lower, so the austenite grains are elongated along rolling direction, and deformation bands are created in the austenite grains. In the cooling process after rolling, ferrites can nucleate not only on the austenite boundaries, but also on the deformation bands, which helps austenite grain to get a further refinement. In the whole rolling process, austenite grain gets refined as a result of rolling in recrystallization region at the beginning. Rolling in the non-recrystallization region can increase nucleation points as well as driving force of phase transformation form $\gamma \rightarrow \alpha$, which settles the foundation for refined ferrite grains in the following accelerated cooling process. Through the observation of microstructure in final pass, the average ferrite grain size is about 5.3μm.

4.1.3   *The relationship between texture and the austenite and the ferrite*

4.1.3.1   **Texture analysis by EBSD**(Kang YL et al,2006)

The original austenite situation can be analyzed through the final microstructure of hot rolled low carbon steel by CSP. This analysis provides the evidence to discuss how the parameters of hot rolling affect the evolution of microstructure. EBSD technology, which is developed rapidly in recent years, becomes main analysis method for crystal in micro (sub-micron) level. Microstructures identified by micro-orientation can provide more details and information than direct microstructures. The direct relationship between microstructure and grain orientation provide the foundation for the evolution of microstructure in the view point of texture. At present, EBSD is the best method to investigate the characters of grain boundaries and to identify the proportion of high angle boundaries.

The samples were taken form the final product of low carbon plate rolled by CSP, 1.9mm thick. The experiment was carried out on the accessory of LEO-450 scanning electronic microscope. As is shown in Figure 4.8 and Figure 4.9, there is certain amount of subgrains of ferrite after phase transformation; however, most of the boundaries of ferrite are the kind of high angle (>15°). So in the continuous rolling process, austenite grains have recrystallized. During the recrystallization, the proportion of high angle boundaries increases, while those of low angle boundaries fall down. The reason is that the amount of subgrains that have similar orientation decreases with the recrystallization. The final microstructure of hot rolling is combination of deformed and recrystallized austenite grains, in which the recrystallized ones have a higher proportion.

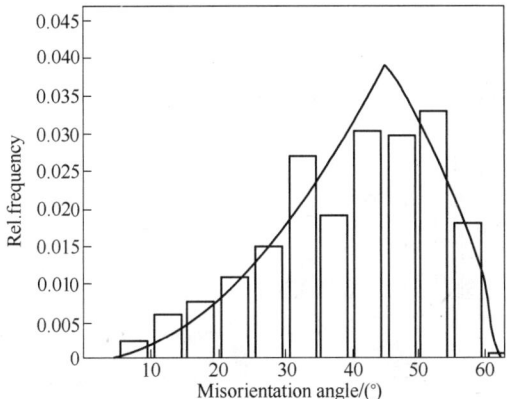

Figure 4.8 ODF for grain orientation for strip 1.9mm

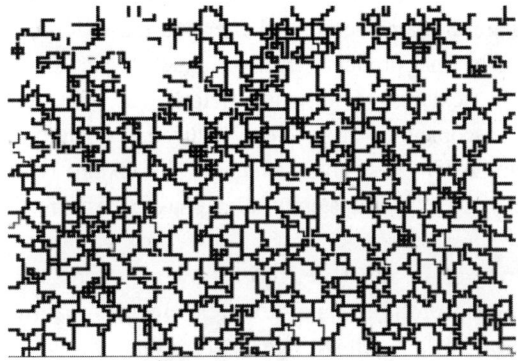

Figure 4.9 Microstructure graph of grain orientation for strip 1.9mm

Form Figure 4.9, it can also be found that most of the grains is not equiaxial, and most of the shapes are not regular. The included angle of grains is not 120° , which indicates that the grains are prone to continue growing. According to the diffraction patterns from EBSD, the orientations of grains are different. The dimensions of grains are different too, so this affects the properties of product to a certain degree.

Figure 4.10 shows the dimension distribution of ferrite grains according to disorientation. It can be concluded that there is a peak of property distribution of grain dimension less than 3µm. The distribution is not Gaussian or Γ pattern. This may be caused by smaller austenite grains because of the recrystallization, because EBSD technology can detect the ferrite grains that are gotten through phase transformation from refined recrystallized austenite grains.

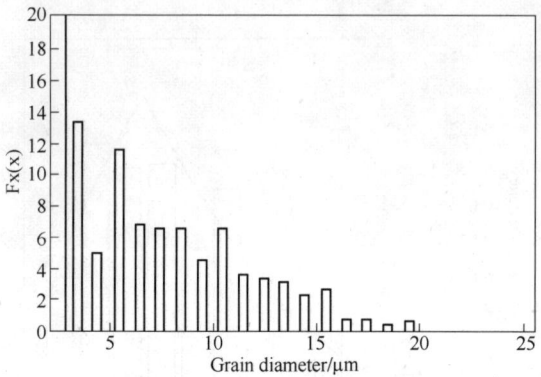

Figure 4.10   Scatter diagram of grain sizes

4.1.3.2   Orientation analysis by EBSD

Since the textures are the same before and after phase transformation, detection and research of texture in final product can investigate the status of original austenite microstructure. The textures of austenite before and after recrystallization are different. The microscopical texture of recrystallized austenite is weak, and can be thought of random. After phase transformation, the texture is weak and random, while the texture of deformed austenite after phase transformation is strong and concentrated.

If there are textures in austenite, the following microstructure after phase transformation is also prone to have textures. Besides, bainite and martensite after transformation has a much stronger texture than those of polygonal ferrite and perlite(Bevis et al, 1998). Austenite partly recrystallized, and ferrite grains nucleate on the boundaries of austenite. In this case, the texture of austenite was weakened to a certain degree. After the recrystallization, the strength of a certain texture depends on the grain size and amount that are related to it. When the amounts of grains are the same, the larger the dimension is, the stronger the texture becomes. As for recrystallized austenite, the grain is refined, and the texture is weak and random. As a result, the texture of ferrite after phase transformation is also weak and random. When deformed in non-recrystallization region, if there are lots of deformation bands inside the coarse austenite, most of the ferrite grains will nucleate on the deformation bands, or on the subgrain inside. Each of the new α nucleus follows the certain relationship of orientation with parent phase, so the texture is comparatively stronger.

In extremal graph, the texture is not random and it's much stronger if there are lots of points that converge to a certain place. If not, the texture is just the opposite. In Figure 4.11, the points scatter in an almost uniform way, and there is no obvious convergence. So the texture is weak and random, which means recrystallization occurred (Kang Y L et al,2006).

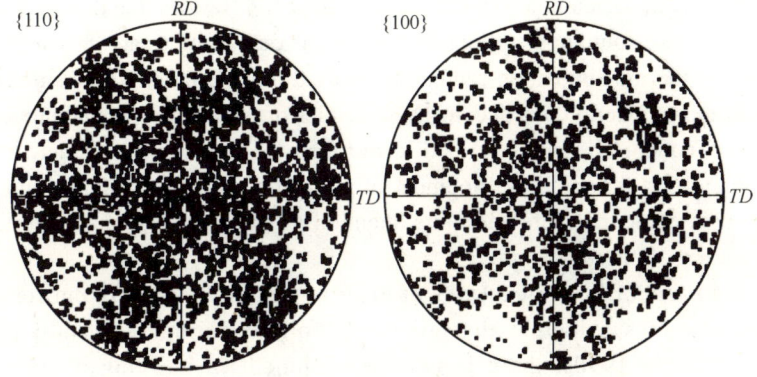

Figure 4.11 {110},{100} ODF for thin plate 1.9mm

The main rolling texture of body-centered cubic metal is {001}<011>. If the grains are not uniform, Goss texture, {110}<001>, is prone to forming. Form the ODF of thin slabs, it can be concluded that the main texture of hot rolled thin slab (1.9mm) is {110}<001>, which is in the adjacent of η fiber, which means the deformation during hot rolling is not uniform at all.

4.1.4 *Austenite recrystallization of low carbon steel during continuous hot rolling process*

Since CSP technology has its own special characters, it becomes key issues to work out whether the basic principles and models used for traditional hot rolling procedure can be used to investigate the microstructure evolution or not. As for the identification of parameters that influence microstructure evolution of CSP technology, it is significant to select and build up the model of microstructure evolution accurately, as well as to simulate the evolution of austenite during hot deformation.

4.1.4.1   Microstructure evolution model of austenite during hot continuous rolling for low carbon steel

During deformation, if the large austenite grains did not get refined effectively, they will become coarse ferrite grains. The more refined austenite grain is before phase transformation, the more refined ferrite grain is later. After rolling in the recrystallization region, the uniform refined austenite grains will keep the same for ferrite grains. The microstructures before and after phase transformation has transmissibility, so it is very important for microstructure and properties control for the final product to learn the variation and status of austenite during hot continuous rolling.

The slab is in austenite region all the time for CSP. Besides, the deformation is great during hot continuous rolling, as well as the deformation rate. So method of mechanical thermo-simulation can hardly be used in CSP. In long time simulation research and production practice, many principles of microstructure and properties have been concluded, and described in the form of mathematics model. At the same time, with the rapid development of computer and calculation technology, computer is attracting more and more attention as an assistant tool to investigate the evolution of microstructure.

On the basis of large quantities of experiment, Sellars firstly put forward the mathematics principle that all steels follow during recrystallization. From 1980s to 1990s, there is new development in building models and research on recrystallization and the following growth of grains. Some scholars have put forward the prediction models for different technologies. Although these models are in different forms, Kwon found that the prediction results for austenite grain size are mostly the same after cooperation of them. According to this, the models for simulation and prediction of austenite grains during CSP hot continuous rolling can be determined by the parameters such as the composition, partial technology and recrystallization parameters.

Now on the basis of CSP rolling schedule for rolling block workpiece of low carbon steel (C=0.05%), thickness 1.9mm, simulation calculation was carried out for the evolution of austenite microstructure in 6 passes continuous rolling. During deformation, according to the metallurgy behavior, chemical compositions and relative parameters, the models are chosen as follows (Medina S F and Mancila E, 1996; Majta J et al, 1996;Wang S R and Tseng AA,1995)

（A）Dynamic Recrystallization

To adjust whether dynamic recrystallization has occurred or not and the grain size after recrystallization, the formulas can be described as:

$$Z = \dot{\varepsilon} \exp\left(\frac{Q_{def}}{RT}\right) \tag{4.1}$$

$$\varepsilon_c = 1.3 \times 10^{-5} \exp(11500/T) \tag{4.2}$$

$$\varepsilon_{0.5} = 1.07 \times 10^{-2} d^{0.28} \dot{\varepsilon}^{0.03} \exp(2650/T) \tag{4.3}$$

$$X_{dyn} = 1.0 - \exp\left[-0.693\left(\frac{\varepsilon - \varepsilon_c}{\varepsilon_{0.5}}\right)^2\right] \tag{4.4}$$

$$d_{dyn} = 1.6 \times 10^4 Z^{-0.23} \tag{4.5}$$

where Z is Zener-Hollomon parameter, Q_{def} is dynamic recrystallization activation energy, ε_c is critical reduction for dynamic recrystallization, $\varepsilon_{0.5}$ is deformation for 50% recrystallization, X_{dyn} is proportion of dynamic recrystallization, d_{dyn} is the grain size when dynamic recrystallization finished.

After dynamic recrystallization, the growth of grains can be described as follows

$$d^2 = d_{dyn}^2 + 3.61 \times 10^{12}/T \exp\left(\frac{-194460}{RT}\right)t \tag{4.6}$$

where d is grain size after growth.

(B) Static Recrystallization

To adjust whether static recrystallization has occurred or not and the grain size after recrystallization, the formulas can be described as:

$$\varepsilon_a = \varepsilon_n + (1 - X)\varepsilon_{n-1} \tag{4.7}$$

$$(\varepsilon_a > \varepsilon_c), \quad t_{0.5} = 0.53Z^{-0.8} \exp\left(\frac{240000}{RT}\right) \tag{4.8}$$

$$(\varepsilon_a < \varepsilon_c), \quad t_{0.5} = 2.2 \times 10^{-12} S_v^{-0.5} \dot{\varepsilon}^{-0.2} \varepsilon^{-2} \exp(30000/T) \tag{4.9}$$

In the formula: $S_v = 24.0(0.4914e^{\varepsilon} + 0.155e^{-\varepsilon} + 0.1433e^{-3\varepsilon})/(\pi D_0)$

$$X = 1.0 - \exp\left[-0.693(t/t_{0.5})^2\right] \tag{4.10}$$

where $t_{0.5}$ is the time when proportion of recrystallization is 50%, X is proportion of recrystallization.

The grain size after static recrystallization d_{rex} can be calculated in the following formula:

$$d_{rex} = Md^r \varepsilon^{-m} Z^{-u} \tag{4.11}$$

In the formula: $M = 1 - ([\text{Nb}]\% + [\text{Ti}]\%)$, $r = 0.67$, $m = 0.67$, $u = 0$.

After static recrystallization, the growth of grains can be described as follows

$$d^2 = d_{rex}^2 + 4.27 \times 10^{12} \exp\left(\frac{-279720}{RT}\right)t \tag{4.12}$$

where d is grain size after growth.

(C)Deformation in Non-recrystallization Region

Deformation in non-recrystallization region can flatten austenite grains. The effective grain size of austenite after deformation can be calculated using the following formula.

$$d_{nr} = \overline{d} \exp(-\varepsilon/4) \qquad (4.13)$$

where $\overline{d}$ is the average diameter of austenite grains before deformation.

4.1.4.2 Simulation of microstructure evolution for austenite during hot continuous rolling of low carbon steel

During the process of hot continuous rolling, the mathematics formulas that were chosen to simulate the principle of austenite microstructure evolution are shown in table 4.2(Kang Y L et al, 2006). These models are fit for constant temperature process, while the real product practice is continuous cooling process. So the real product can be divided into lots of micro process, which is suggested to be constant temperature process. In this case, the simulation for the whole product practice can be achieved using iteration method. The relative data used in the calculation is shown in Table 4.3(Kang Y L et al, 2006).

As is shown in the results of calculation, the final microstructure of hot rolling consists of recrystallized and deformed austenite grains, which matches well with the experimental results. During the deformation of the first pass, dynamic recrystallization occurred for 99.31%; dynamic recrystallization occurred completely, so the grains got obviously refined. The grain size after recrystallization is about 47μm (the original one is about 80μm). During pass 2~5, static recrystallization occurred, so the grains got a further refinement. In pass 6, the time that proportion of static recrystallization reaches 50% is about 2.85 seconds. The slab quickly enters the cooling part, calculation shows that the proportion of static recrystallization is less than 5%. It can be considered that static recrystallization did not occur in austenite. The calculated effective austenite grain size is about 8.33μm. Generally, in the pass 1~4, austenite grain is coarse because of high deformation temperature, great deformation and relatively lower deformation rate. The effect of refinement is obvious. In the following passes, austenite grains got refined; the temperature is lower and deformation rate increases. The effect of refinement tends to be smooth. The calculated austenite grain size of each pass is shown in Figure 4.12 (Kang YL et al, 2006).

Table 4.2 Mathematic models for evolution of austenite grain during hot continuous rolling

	$Z = \dot{\varepsilon} \exp\left(\dfrac{Q_{def}}{RT}\right)$
	$\varepsilon_c = 1.3 \times 10^{-5} \exp(11500/T)$
	$\varepsilon_{0.5} = 1.07 \times 10^{-2} d^{0.28} \dot{\varepsilon}^{0.03} \exp(2650/T)$
Dynamic recrystallization	$X_{dyn} = 1.0 - \exp\left[-0.693\left(\dfrac{\varepsilon - \varepsilon_c}{\varepsilon_{0.5}}\right)^2\right]$
	$d_{dyn} = 1.6 \times 10^4 Z^{-0.23}$
	$d^2 = d_{dyn}^2 + 3.61 \times 10^{12}/T \exp\left(\dfrac{-194460}{RT}\right)t$
	$\varepsilon_a = \varepsilon_n + (1-X)\varepsilon_{n-1}$
	$(\varepsilon_a > \varepsilon_c), t_{0.5} = 0.53 Z^{-0.8} \exp\left(\dfrac{240000}{RT}\right)$
Static recrystallization	$(\varepsilon_a < \varepsilon_c), t_{0.5} = 2.2 \times 10^{-12} S_v^{-0.5} \dot{\varepsilon}^{-0.2} \varepsilon^{-2} \exp(30000/T)$
	$X = 1.0 - \exp\left[-0.693(t/t_{0.5})^2\right]$
	$d_{rex} = M d^r \varepsilon^{-m} Z^{-u}$
	$d^2 = d_{rex}^2 + 4.27 \times 10^{12} \exp\left(\dfrac{-279720}{RT}\right)t$
Non-recrystallization	$d_{nr} = \bar{d} \exp(-\varepsilon/4)$

From Figure 4.6 and Figure 4.12, it can be seen that the tendency that ferrite grains vary matches well with the tendency of austenite grains through calculation. The simulation results are coincident with literatures Michael and Stanislaw, 1998. It can be concluded that the simulation is rational from comparison of ferrite grain size and that of original austenite. It reflects the further effect of refinement by phase transformation and the following accelerate cooling from another aspect.

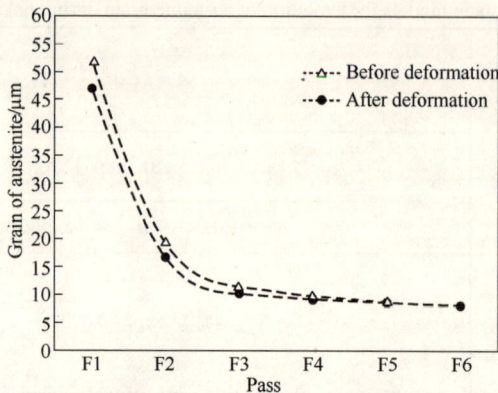

Figure 4.12   Calculated grain size and variation tendency after 6 passes

Table 4.3   Relative data used in calculation of austenite microstructure evolution during CSP hot continuous rolling for low carbon steel

Parameters	Finish mills					
	F1	F2	F3	F4	F5	F6
Entrance temperature/℃	1090.89	1051.88	1017.78	994.62	965.19	935.78
Exit temperature/℃	1071.16	1035.06	1010.34	980.21	948.43	895.94
Deformation	0.807	0.772	0.609	0.414	0.392	0.223
	55.4%	53.8%	45.6%	33.9%	32.4%	20.0%
Deformation rate/s^{-1}	5.5	15.7	37.8	75.8	128.5	147.3
Interval time between passes /s	7.33		3.72	1.99	1.24	0.87

During controlled rolling, enough deformation in the non-recrystallization before phase transformation is necessary so that the effect of grain refinement can be carried out completely. This requires a large range of temperature before phase transformation in order to accumulate the deformation by several passes. As for ZJ330 low carbon steel, the range of temperature in non-recrystallization is very narrow, about 100℃. It is hard to take several passes to accumulate the deformation effect. So recrystallization is the main way to refine the grains, rather than deformation refinement in non-recrystallization, which is coincident with the simulation results of austenite evolution during hot continuous rolling.

4.2 Microstructure and Properties of Low Carbon Steel Produced by Thin Slab Casting and Rolling(TSCR)

4.2.1 *Comparison on microstructure and properties of low carbon hot strip with different thermal histories*

4.2.1.1 Production comparison experiments of CSP and traditional technology in producing hot low carbon strip

As we know, the thermomechanical history, large reduction in pass and much high strain rate of CSP process are too difficult to be simulated by thermo-mechanical simulators or lab pilot mills, so the situation of practical production can't be truly simulated. Fortunately, from practical production line in Zhujiang Iron and Steel, we obtained the same specification finished strip from the same furnace produced by normal continuously casting thin slab and direct rolling and continuously casting thin slab-cold charging-tandem rolling. Using above finished strip, we investigated the influence to structure and performance of steel strip by the two processes (two different thermomechanical history), and provided theories for further study of relative mechanics, such as evolution, precipitation and strengthening of structure (Kang Y L et al, 2006).

The experimental materials are 4.0mm strips of low-carbon steel (marked as ZJ330), whose chemical composition is shown in table 4.4. Compared with the chemical composition of Q195 steel, the content of elements such as Si, P, S, Cu in ZJ330 low-carbon steel produced by CSP production line of Zhujiang Iron and Steel is lower.

Table 4.4   Chemical composition of the ZJ330 steels(mass%)

C	Si	Mn	P	S	Cu	Al
0.053	0.054	0.252	0.016	0.008	0.128	0.025

Using continuous casting thin slab of ZJ330 low carbon steel in one furnace, we produced 4.0mm slab of the same specification according to two different kinds of process. One of the processes was thin slab casting and direct rolling (CSP). In the other process, we didn't put the last one of the thin slabs into soaking furnace until it was cooled down to room temperature, then it was heated to the same temperature as CSP process and soaking (1150°C), after that, it was rolled, cooled and rolled up according to the rolling schedule of CSP, i.e. thin slab continuous casting—cold stock—continuous rolling process, and then named as TSP. The mainly difference between the above two kinds of process is that the TSP process contains one more phase change of $\gamma \rightarrow \alpha \rightarrow \gamma^*$ than the CSP one. The two processes are same except that, and their process drawings are shown in Figure 4.13.

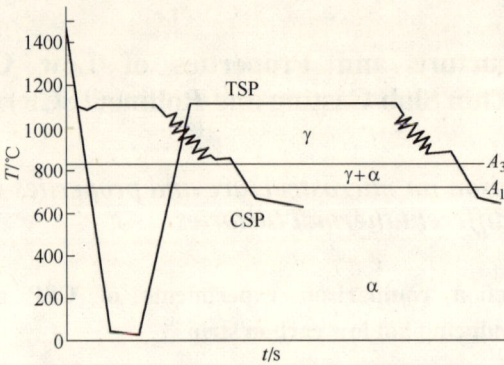

Figure 4.13   Process drawings of CSP and TSP

4.2.1.2   Comparison and analysis of mechanical properties and microstructure of strips produced by two kinds of process

(A) Mechanical Properties

The results show that there are great differences in mechanical properties between hot rolled plates of the same steel and the same specification produced by the two kinds of process. The yield strength of plate produced by CSP process is 30MPa higher than that of produced by TSP process, which are 359MPa and 328MPa, respectively. However, the extensions by the two processes are generally the same, which are 31% and 29%, respectively.

There would be grain growth coarsening, dissolving and growing of the second-phase during the thin slab was cooled down to room temperature and then reheated, which was related to the temperature and time of soaking. According to report (Yue et al., 1996), for C-Mn slabs with large original microstructure, there is little influence of strength and toughness by soaking because of no much phenomenon of grain growth coarsening without the function of microalloy precipitation, so the strength difference of plate produced by CSP and TSP is the result of phase processing and final microstructure, and no much connection of soaking.

(B) Optical Microscopic Structure

Microscopic structure is the internal decisive factor of mechanical properties. In order to investigate the relations between structure, property and rolling process, we compared and analyzed the microscopic structure of the two kinds of process as follows.

We can see from the microstructure photographs as shown in Figure 4.14 that the final microstructures of plate both are a number of ferrites and a few of pearlites produced by the two processes. In microstructure of plate produced by TSP process, the ferrite grains are more round and homogeneous, while in microstructure by CSP process, the shape of ferrite grains are irregular polygon, not so homogeneous, and the pearlites don't distribute in the grain boundary of ferrites like the former do. That's because the $\gamma \rightarrow \alpha \rightarrow \gamma^*$ phase change process which forces the interface energy of system move into lower direction makes the grain in TSP process more rounder than in CSP (Yu Y N, 2000), in addition, due to the heredity of structure after phase changing, the final structure of TSP process are better than the one of CSP process.

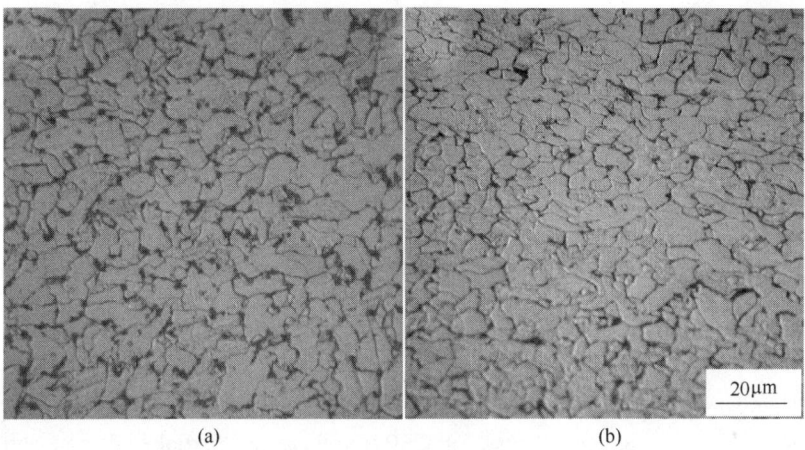

(a)　　　　　　　　　　　　　　　(b)

Figure 4.14　Optical microstructures in rolling direction of 4.0 mm plates
produced by different processes
(a) CSP; (b) TSP

The TSP microstructure is finer, while the strength is lower than the CSP ones. It's related to phase change as well as higher solution ability and higher precipitation efficiency of alloying agent for increasing the strength in CSP process, which increases the defects such as dislocation, deformation bands.

(C) Microstructure

Under 40000~50000 magnification times, we can see in the photos the pearlites in low-carbon steel produced by CSP consist of granular or clavate cementites and ferrites (Figure 4.15a), while the ones produced by TSP are typical flaky pearlites consisting of cementites and ferrites (Kang Y L,2004) (Figure 4.15b).

Grain boundaries as well as dislocations and deformation bands inside the grains are the vantage points of ferrites nucleation, where proeutectoid ferrites precipitate and separate the austenites for little parts. The higher the density of dislocations and deformation bands are, the more homogeneous and dispersive the little austenite parts are. The nucleating ferrites on grain boundaries grow towards the inner of the gains, and the ones in dislocations and deformation bands grow towards their periphery. There are zones that are abundant of C in the interfaces of ferrites and austenites. The zones are getting smaller with the decreasing of ferrites, then residulal austenites after precipitating ferrites is getting fewer, and C can't be diffused completely, so they are directly precipitated at the grain boundaries, dislocations and deformation bands where the deformation energy is high as the form of cementites (Sun et al, 2002).

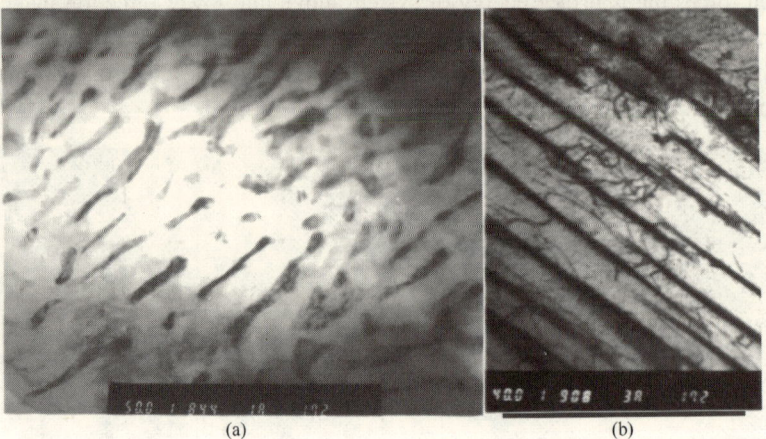

(a) (b)

Figure 4.15 Comparison on pearlites of low carbon sheet produced by CSP and TSP process (a) CSP; (b) TSP

There definitely is a fluctuation of the component of C because there is no $\gamma \to \alpha \to \gamma^*$ phase change process for CSP, i.e. there are partial high concentrate zones. The dislocations in deforming austenite grains are higher for CSP process, because its austenite grains before phase change process are bigger, and microalloy elements are more advantage in solution than the ones of TSP process. The nucleation of proeutectoid ferrites at or inside the grain boundaries is non-homogeneous, which results in the final cementite grains existing as form of short flakes and small graininesses. During the process of TSP, because of the $\gamma \to \alpha \to \gamma^*$ phase change process, the distribution of C diffusing through the grains is homogenous, the austenite grains is small, and the final dislocation density is low. Proeutectoid ferrites priority nucleation on the grain boundaries and grow towards the grains, and finally the microstructure of pearlite is formed. This is the main microstructure difference between CSP and TSP process, and it is also the important difference of different yield strengths.

4.2.2 Analysis of structure property in low carbon hot strip produced by CSP and traditional process

4.2.2.1 Comparison of structure and property of low carbon hot strip produced by CSP and traditional process

In order to further study the structure property of low-carbon hot strip of CSP, we compared the structure property of ZJ330 low-carbon strip (4.00mm) produced by CSP process and the same gauge Q195 strip produced by traditional process in specific steel work in this section.

There are great differences in mechanical property of the same gauge hot rolled strip between CSP process and traditional process. As for the samples in our experiments, the yield strength and tensile strength of strip produced by CSP process are both higher than the ones by traditional process. However, the yield ratio of CSP process is higher, and there is no much difference in elongation. The detailed illustration is shown in Figure 4.16 and Figure 4.17(Kang Y L et al, 2006).

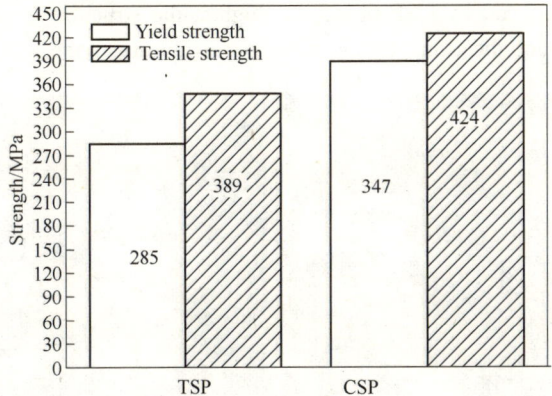

Figure 4.16   Yield strength and tensile strength of 4.0mm hot rolled strips produced by CSP and TSP process

(strips of CSP process:ZJ330; plates of TSP process:Q195)

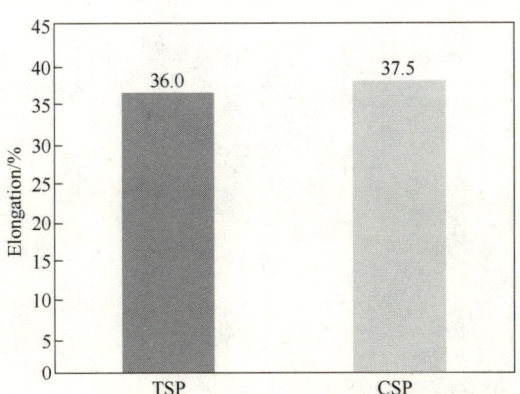

Figure 4.17   Elongation of 4.0mm hot rolled strips produced by CSP and TSP process (strips of CSP process:ZJ330; strips of TSP process:Q195)

As shown in Figure 4.18, we can see in the optical microscopic structure photos that the strip' structure of CSP process whose average grain size is under 10μm, is obviously finer than that of traditional process, while it's not as homogeneous as the traditional one. The heavy reduction and high rigidity rolling is the main characters of CSP rolling process. In order to investigate the influence to final microstructure and properties of strip by CSP process, the dislocation density of the two kinds of strip were tested using positron annihilation experiment. Its aim was to investigate the influence to dislocation density by rolling process. Figure 4.19 shows the dislocation comparison of the two kinds of strip. We can see in Figure 4.19, the dislocation density of CSP is higher, which is one of the reasons why its strength of strip is higher than the TSP ones (Kang Y L et al., 2006).

From mentioned above, compared to traditional process, the strength of hot rolled strip produced by CSP process is higher, the structure is finer but not so homogeneous, and the elongation is close to the traditional one.

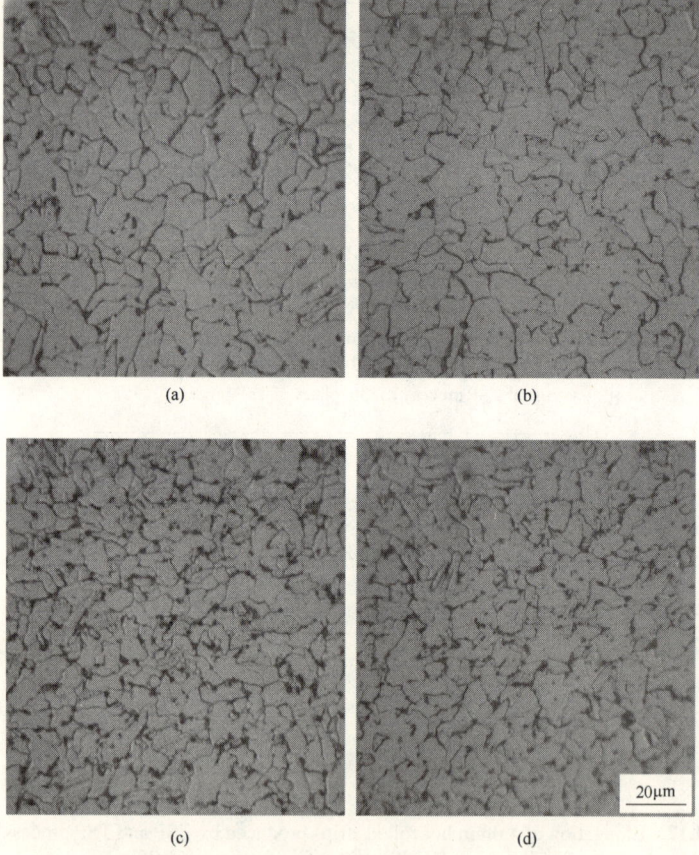

(a)   (b)

(c)   (d)

Figure 4.18　Microstructure in rolling direction of 4.0mm hot rolled strips produced by CSP process [(a),(b)] and TSP process[(c),(d)]
(a) edge;(b) center;(c) edge;(d) center
(strips of CSP process:ZJ330; strips of TSP process:Q195)

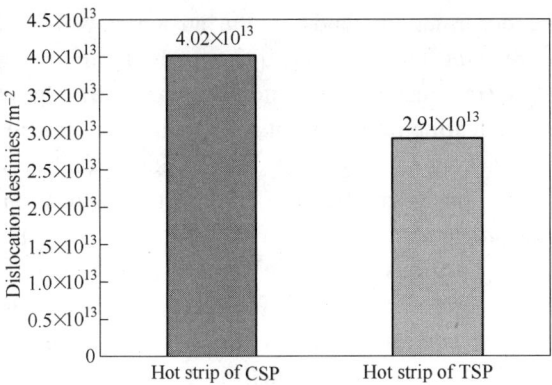

Figure 4.19 Dislocation destinies of 4.0mm hot rolled strips produced by CSP and TSP process (strips of CSP process:ZJ330; strips of TSP process:Q195)

4.2.2.2 Analysis of influencing factor on microstructure and properties of hot strip produced by CSP

We should pay more attention to the chemical composition which has great influence on structure and property of strips as an internal factor during product's property research. Because the contents of P, S and Si are all low in low-carbon steel, and the content of inclusions is low, too, the product's elongation is increased notably. Generally, nitrogen will increase the yield and tensile strength of steel, so the hardness value is increased. The free C and N atoms are the main reasons resulting the yield effect and strain aging because of Cottrell effect. The content of C is lower, while the yield effect is obvious, so the solid solution of N atom is considered in steel.

The finishing temperature is controlled below 900℃, and 20%~30% reduction in pass is given, which both are the powerful measures to increase the strength and refine the ferrite grains using "low temperature and heavy reduction" process in traditional. The finishing temperature of the 4 strips are all below 900℃, and the reduction in pass is about 20%, which is good for refining grains and increasing strength apparently.

The main reasons influencing grain fining are:

1. The effective diameters of austenite grains and the effective interfacial area of austenite grains before phase changing.

2. The cooling rate in two-phase region below the transformation point of Ar_3. In CSP process, 50mm casting slab whose cross-section microstructure with fine dendrites is rolled in large deformation, which provides the basic of refining the final ferrite grain in company with fine austenite grain.

By now, the main reason of grain refining is regarded as large quantity dislocations and deformation bands in the austenite which can create the recrystallization refining under the condition of high strain hugely increased the free energy, which make the ferrite gain large driving force of phase change and high nucleating rate. For hot rolled thin slabs of CSP, although the total compression ratio is not large, the deformation in each pass is relatively large. This creates the microstructure with high dislocation density and gathering dislocations in some place as well as the microstructure of subgrain that all the active positions of ferrite nucleation. During the subsequent cooling process, the ferrite grains are getting smaller with the driving force of phase change and the nucleation density are increased. The effective area of grains is increased, which creates the deformation bands, and the dislocation density is increased. Not only the deformation can increase the nucleation of ferrite, but it also can shorten the apparent distance of austenite, and increase the encounter opportunities of growing austenite grains that have been nucleated on the opposite boundaries. So the size of α ferrite grains in final microstructure is smaller.

In some sense, we can say the laminar cooling equipment is a powerful heat treatment system. $\gamma \rightarrow \alpha$ is a diffused phase change that is controlled by interface. The free enthalpy of $\gamma \rightarrow \alpha$ is increasing with cooling rate and degree of supercooling increasing. And it reduces the temperature of transformation point. As we know, the transformation point Ar_3 is decreasing and degree of supercooling is increasing with the cooling rate increasing. These not only accelerate the nucleation of new α grains, but also postpone the growth of α grains into γ base grains that have not been phase changed, so the percentage of α ferrites in final microstructure increases and the size of the grains is small(Flemming G and Hensger K E, 1998).

From the foregoing, the steel properties are decided by the final microstructure of materials, while the microstructure depends on the compositions, production lines and processing parameters of the steel and so on. "Chemical composition-processing technology-microstructure-property" all depends on each other. The production of hot rolled low carbon steel using CSP process complies with the above basic principle, so it is better for us to further study the refining and strengthening mechanisms of low carbon steel produced by CSP thin slab casting and rolling in aspects of chemical composition, production line and microstructure.

4.2.2.3 Microstructure and properties of C-Mn strips with high strength produced by CSP process

(A)Compositions and Properties of C-Mn High Strength Strips Produced by CSP Process

We can see from the chemical compositions of ZJ510L and ZJ550L low carbon high strength automobile strip produced by CSP process in Zhujiang Steel that there are no microalloy elements in compositions, and the yield strength, tensile strength and elongation are all higher(Table 4.5). There is a brand prospect for C-Mn steel which can replace partial microalloy steel using CSP grain refining process to increase the strength of the steel.

Table 4.5　Average properties of compositions of ZJ510L and ZJ550L
C-Mn steel produced by CSP process

Steel grade	C	Si	Mn	P	S	R_e/MPa	R_m/MPa	A/%	R_e/R_m
ZJ510L	0.17~0.20	<0.30	<0.60	<0.02	<0.010	438	583	29.7	0.75
ZJ550L	0.17~0.20	<0.40	<1.30	<0.025	<0.010	491	621	29.1	0.79

The strength of low carbon high strength automobile strip of different gauges produced by CSP process is higher, the plasticity is excellent, and the combination properties are good and homogenous.

(B)Fine-crystal Microstructure of C-Mn High Strength Steel Produced by CSP
　　Process
We will analysis the influence on microstructure and properties by relative factors on aspect of microstructure next. Low carbon high strength automobile steels of different gauges, ZJ510L and ZJ550L, were made into metallographic specimens, and observed under optical microscope and Scanning Electron Microscopy (SEM).

The optical microstructure photos in the surface of 4 different gauges ZJ510L low carbon high strength automobile strip are shown in Figure 4.20. We can see that there are a great deal of ferrites and some pearlites. The ferrites appear as irregular polygons, and the average size of ferrites is homogenous. The grain size is getting smaller and finer with the production thickness decreasing. The average ferrite grain size in the surface of 6.0mm automobile sheet is the smallest. It's about 5.5μm measured by mean linear intercept method. The average ferrite grain size of 10mm pilot production sheet is bigger, which is about 6.2μm.

The over-all mechanical properties of strips are decided by the homogenous level of the microstructure distribution and the size of the grains. High temperature and high deformation rate of continuous casting slabs are formed during the rolling process of F1 ~ F2 frameworks which make austenite recrystallized and produce small austenite grains, thus ferrite nucleate on austenite boundaries more easily, i.e. the average effective diameter of austenite grains before phase change is the main reason influencing the grain refining. For F3~F6 frameworks, the interval of passes is short, and the strain accumulates continuously. With the increasing of the entire deformation and the effective grain area, the deformation bands appear and the dislocation density increases which make the microstructure have high dislocation density, gathering dislocations in some place and subgrain microstructure. During the subsequent fast cooling process, the drive force of $\gamma \rightarrow \alpha$ phase change and the nucleation density increase, which make ferrite grains smaller.

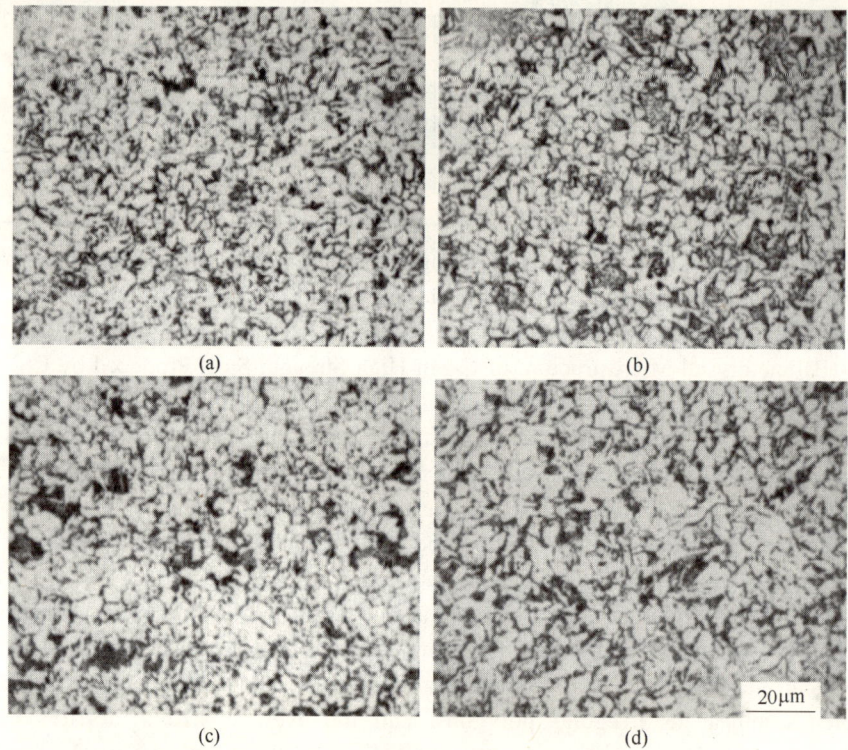

(a)   (b)

(c)   (d)

Figure 4.20   Optical microstructure photos in the surface of ZJ510L
low carbon high strength automobile sheet
(a) 6.0mm; (b) 7.9mm; (c) 8.0mm; (d) 10.0mm

Figure 4.21 shows the SEM microstructure in different positions of the samples of ZJ550L low carbon high strength automobile strip, from which we can see the microstructure of ZJ550L is finer than that of ZJ510L. The surface microstructure of ZJ550L is polygon ferrite, and the ones in transverse direction and longitudinal profile are finer ferrites with acicular shape and some diffusion distribution pearlites. The average grain size of ferrite is about 4.2~6.1μm measured by using mean linear intercept method, and the difference of average grain size between surface and center is little. We can see that the main reason of high strength of ZJ550L steel is that the ferrites are obviously refined (the size of some ferrite grains are under 3μm). During the rolling process, because of the low finishing temperature and low coiling temperature, the austenite residual strain in low temperature range and the storage energy of deformation increases, at the same time a great deal of dislocations and deformation bands are formed inside austenite grains, which increases the nucleation positions and the nucleation rate of ferrites, so the ferrite grains are refined greatly. The grains of low carbon high strength automobile strip produced by CSP process are fine and homogenous, according to Hall-Petch, so its yield strength is high.

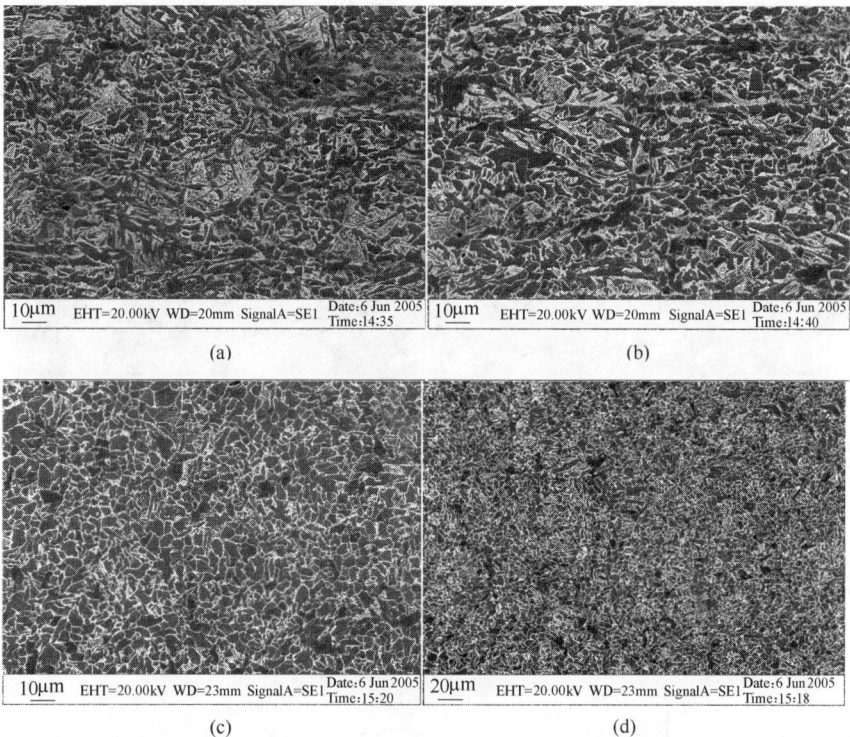

(a)

(b)

(c)

(d)

Figure 4.21　SEM microstructure of different parts in ZJ550L
low carbon high strength automobile sheet

(a)Transverse direction; (b) Longitudinal direction; (c)Rolling plane; (d)Rolling plane

The pearlites of etched samples of ZJ510L and ZJ550L low carbon high strength automobile strip were observed under SEM as shown in Figure 4.22. From which we can see that the pearlites of ZJ510L strip are not homogenous, the big ones like islands, a few parts are chain-like distributed, and the distance between two adjacent pearlites laminas is about 0.3μm. In the ZJ550L strip, the pearlite group is fine and its distribution is homogenous with the ferrite grains are refined, and the distance between two adjacent pearlites laminas is decreased

(about $0.1\sim0.3\mu m$). The pearlite nucleation rate increases, while the growth rate decreases, and the pearlite lamina distance is getting smaller with the temperature of pearlite transformation decreasing and the degree of supercooling increasing. In addition, the size of pearlite groups that are mainly formed at the grain boundaries decreases with the degree of supercooling increasing. The mechanical properties of flake pearlite is mainly decided by its microstructure (the size of pearlite group and distance of pearlite lamina, especially the pearlite lamina distance). The smaller the pearlite lamina distance is, the better the over-all mechanical properties of production are, its strength and toughness are both increasing. Some of the pearlite laminas have been broken, and distribute at the grain boundaries or inside the grains in the form of fine carbonide particles.

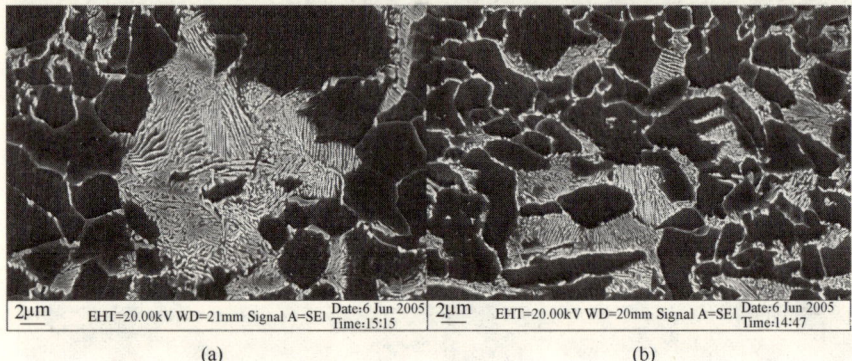

(a)　　　　　　　　　　　　　　　　　(b)

Figure 4.22　Pearlites of ZJ510L and ZJ550L steel
(a)ZJ510L；(b) ZJ550L

4.3　Mechanism and Precipitation Characteristic of AlN in Low Carbon Steel Produced by Thin Slab Casting and Rolling Technology

4.3.1　AlN *precipitation in low carbon steel of thin slab casting and rolling*

4.3.1.1　Experiment on precipitation of AlN during heating and rolling

It is well known that during the general process of producing low carbon steel (or Al-killed steel), AlN precipitates during the cooling process of the slab, but dissolve in the later high temperature reheating process. By the start rolling, end rolling at high temperature, and coiling at low temperature, AlN precipitation is restrained. This affects the performance of the steel not too much, but the AlN precipitation during the annealing process after cold rolling is important to the texture of the steel.

During the process of thin slab casting and rolling, the slab solidified at a high cooling speed(about 2℃/s). It is put in to the heating furnace at 950~1000℃, after heating for 20~30min it is taken out at 1150℃ and being rolled. The analysis on the sample show that the quality percent of AlN in slab before and after heating in the furnace is 0.004% and 0.003% respectively. The quantity of AlN after taken out of furnace is not changed, show as table 4.6 (Xu and Liu, 2005). This is distinctly different from the AlN precipitation during general routine, and will affect the growth of austenite recrystallization grain after heat rolling.

Table 4.6 The experiment result of AlN before and after heating and rolling in CSP

Sample	Before putting into furnace	taken out of furnace	F2	F3	F4	F5
AlN (mass%)	0.004	0.003	0.003	0.003	0.003	0.003

4.3.1.2 Experiment analysis on precipitation of AlN in hot rolled Strip by thin slab casting and rolling

A great deal of precipitation is found out by H-800 transmission electron microscope in the low carbon steel produced by CSP process. The content of AlN precipitated from the grain is small, and the size of it is about 30nm. There is no AlN along the grain boundary. Figure 4.23 shows the AlN precipitated in the ferrite grain, the size is about 50nm (Kang Y L et al, 2003).

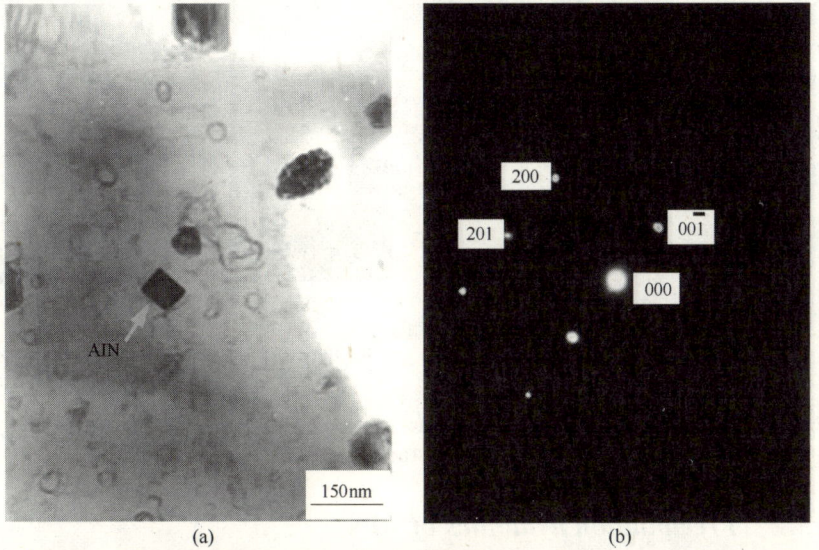

(a) (b)

Figure 4.23 Appearance and diffraction spot of AlN by TEM
(a)Appearance;(b)Diffraction spot

The size of AlN is about 40nm in extraction-replica sample by JEM-2010F transmission electron microscope. The grain less than 10nm is not found.

Reference (Rainforth W M et al, 2002; Palmiere E J et al, 1994; Dutta B and Sellars CM,1987) considered that the technique of electro-extraction chemical phase analysis is the most accurate and credible way among the test ways, such as thin slice TEM and extraction-replica, and so on. Using the X-ray diffraction pattern got from the deposition powder by electro-extraction, and according to the value of intensity line d and 2θ got from the ASTM(08-0262)card, it is confirmed that AlN exists in the precipitation and is hexangular crystal by analyzing the correlative data.

Put some deposition powder of AlN got from the chemical phase analysis into anhydrous ethanol, break up it adequately by ultrasonic oscillatory wave, and make it distribute equably amount the ethanol liquor. Gain some powder by copper net and observe it by H-800, it is found that the second-phase grain is very exiguous (shown in Figure 4.24(a)), and other second-phase grain is bigger than the former ones (shown in Figure 4.24(b)), of which the size is about 8nm. The electro-extraction chemical phase analysis shows that the component of the precipitation is mainly Al_2O_3、 MnS and AlN, and the quality percents of them are 0.00178%,0.011% and 0.0064% respectively (Kang Y L et al, 2003).

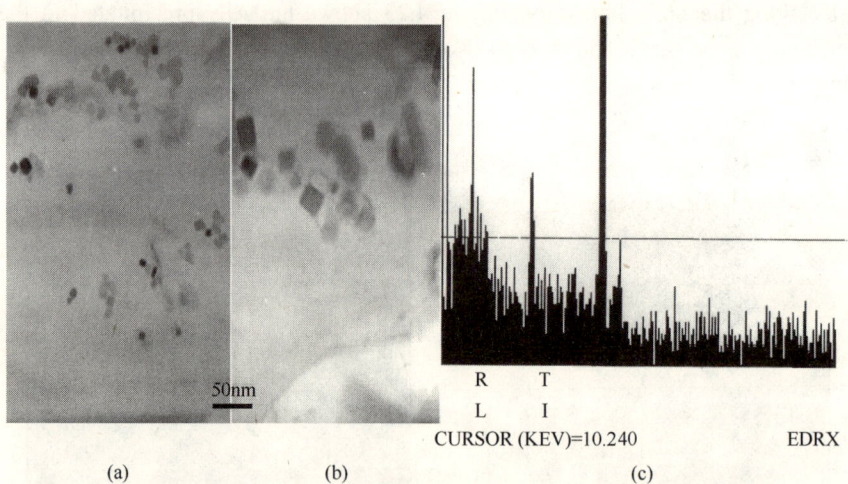

Figure 4.24   AlN in powder by chemical phase analysis (a,b) and EDAX energy spectrum(c)
(a) Small grain; (b) Bigger grain; (c) The EDAX spectrum of figure 4.24 (a)

4.3.2   *Precipitation dynamics of* AlN

During CSP process, the precipitation of oxide, sulfide and nitride is a spontaneous course, and whether it happen or not depends on the dynamics condition. In the process of hot rolling, technical parameters affect the grain boundary area and the defects in the grain, for example, dislocation. This improves the dynamics condition, accelerates the precipitation, that is, namely deformation induces the precipitation (Fu J et al, 2002). Base on the electro-extraction chemical phase analysis, in the precipitation, AlN possess biggish proportion. And so, control of the forming condition of AlN should be carried out to achieve a good effect on the structure and performance.

4.3.2.1 Dynamics model of AlN precipitation

(A) Nucleation Speed

According to the classical nucleation theory, during the constant temperature process, the relation of nucleation speed and precipitation time in unit volume is shown in the following formula (Zurob H S et al, 2001; Leno et al, 1999; Sun W P et al, 1993):

$$J = \frac{dN}{dt} = N_0 Z \beta' \exp\left(-\frac{\Delta G}{kT}\right) \exp\left(-\frac{\tau}{t}\right) \tag{4.14}$$

where N_0 is amount of supplying nucleation position in unit volume, Z is Zeldovich parameter, it is nearly independent of nucleation condition, k is Boltzmann constant, β' is atom amount impacting with the crystal nucleus in unit time, τ is nucleation gestation time.

The amount of supplying nucleation position in unit volume N_0 is always calculated in the following formula (Dutta B et al, 2001; Dutta B et al, 1992):

$$N_0 = 0.5 \rho^{1.5} \tag{4.15}$$

When the second phase precipitates along the dislocation line, N_0 can be expressed as the connection point in the dislocation net (dislocation entwist). ρ is the dislocation density at the beginning of precipitation, and its value is measured to be $2.80 \times 10^{13} \text{m/m}^3$ by positron annihilation technology according to the special condition under which the steel studied in this article was produced.

The product of $Z\beta'$ is often calculated as followss:

$$Z\beta' = \frac{D_{Al} X_{Al}}{a^2} \tag{4.16}$$

where D_{Al} is diffusion coefficient of Al atom in the austenite along the dislocation conduit. The defects, for example, dislocation, have higher energy than the austenitic matrix. Besides, the solute atom is prone to aggregating at these defects, and this is propitious to the precipitation in these places. Once the precipitation nucleus forms, it begins to grow up. To the second phase grain nucleate along the dislocation line, the diffusion speed of the solute atom along the dislocation conduit is much higher than other directions (Sun W P et al, 1992). As the diffusion speed of Al is much lower than N in the austenite, the diffusion of Al in austenite is considered as the main factor to the control of the precipitation. And because AlN precipitates along the dislocation line, the diffusion of Al along the dislocation conduit has a crucial effect on the precipitation and growth of AlN. So, D_{Al} is the diffusion coefficient of Al atom along the dislocation conduit, but not the volume diffusion coefficient. X_{Al} stands for the mole consistency in the austenite at certain temperature, and can be solved indirectly by the solubility formula 4.17. a stands for the crystal lattice constant.

(B)Chemical Driving Force

The chemical driving force of AlN precipitation depends on the supersaturation of the aluminium and nitrogen element in the steel liquid. The equilibrium constant $K_{[Al][N]}$ of AlN is closely correlative with the temperature and structure of the matrix. According to the thermodynamics, the solubility product of AlN is shown as follows:

$$\log K_{[Al][N]} = \log k_s = \log [\%Al][\%N] = -\frac{14356}{T} + 6.40 \qquad (4.17)$$

where [%Al],[%N]are the quality percent of the aluminium and nitrogen element in the steel liquid.

Based on the hypothesis that the second phase precipitation is spherical, the critical driving force ΔG of nucleation mainly comprises of the change of ΔG_v and σ, ΔG_v is the chemistry free energy produced by the nucleation, and σ is the interface energy forming new phase surface.

$$\Delta G = \frac{16\pi\sigma^3}{3\Delta G_v^2} \lambda \qquad (4.18)$$

where λ is modify coefficient, when nucleus homogeneously, λ is 1, when nucleus uniform, λ is less than 1. As the value of λ uniform is difficult to confirm, λ is set 1. Under the half coherence condition, the value of interface energy is 0.75 J/m^2.

$$\Delta G_v = -(RT/V_P)\ln(k/k_s) \qquad (4.19)$$

where R is gas constant, T is absolute temperature when continuous cooling, V_P is mol volume of the precipitation, k is the actual solubility product of AlN, k_s is the balance solubility product of AlN.

(C)Model of Nucleation and Growth for the Second Phase Particle (Park S H et al., 1992)

For simplification, first hypothesize that the nucleation and growth of the second phase particles precipitate on the dislocation line simultaneously. Generally speaking, it is considered that the growth of AlN is controlled by the diffuse speed of Al in austenite. The radius of the precipitation particle is correlative with the quality equilibrium of atom which is needed by spherical particles growth and atom diffusing to grain surface, and the relation with time is shown as follows:

$$r = \alpha(D_{Al}t)^{1/2} \qquad (4.20)$$

where r is radius of the precipitation, α is growth speed of the grain, the relation between precipitation and body and solute consistency of the two is shown as follows:

$$\alpha = \left(2\frac{C_M - C_I}{C_P - C_I} \right)^{1/2} \tag{4.21}$$

where C_P, C_I is the equilibrium bulk concentration of the precipitation/ austenite interface and micro-alloy in austenite respectively, C_M is the bulk concentration of micro-alloy at the end of the diffusion section.

To this model, the radius at time t of the grain precipitating at time t_1 can be solved by 3.20. v is the volume of the single precipitation grain, then at time t the growth speed of the volume can be expressed as follows:

$$\frac{dv}{d(t - t_1)} = 4\pi r^2 \frac{dr}{d(t - t_1)} \tag{4.22}$$

The nucleus speed of unit volume J of the second phase is constant during the isothermal precipitating in austenite. The nucleation number of the second phase is Jdt_1 between t_1 and $t_1 + dt_1$, and the bulk rate of growth of the of the grain at time dt_1 is $Jdt_1 dv/dt$. From $t=0$ to $t = t_1$, the bulk rate of growth of the total volume V of the second phase is :

$$\frac{dV}{dt} = \frac{8\sqrt{2}}{3} \pi D_{A1}^{3/2} \left(\frac{C_M - C_I}{C_P - C_I} \right)^{3/2} J(t - t_1)^{3/2} \tag{4.23}$$

In order to translate the volume of the second phase grain into the precipitation volume fraction Y, multiply $(C_P - C_I)/(C_M - C_I)$ and competition parameter $(1 - Y)$ by formula 3.23, and then integral:

$$Y = 1 - \exp\left\{ -\frac{16\sqrt{2}}{15} \pi D_{A1}^{3/2} \left(\frac{C_M - C_I}{C_P - C_I} \right)^{1/2} Jt^{5/2} \right\} \tag{4.24}$$

After the precipitation finish, if the volume fraction and quality of the second phase is known, then the average radius of the second phase grain can be estimated by the follow formula:

$$r = \left(\frac{3 f V_P}{4\pi N_P} \right)^{1/3} \tag{4.25}$$

where N_P is the precipitation quality of the second phase, f is volume fraction of the precipitation.

(D)Calculation Methodology and Process of the Model

The formula above is deduced using isothermal conditions, and it is only applicable for the isothermal process. But the industrial produce is a continuous cooling process. At present, the principle of superposition is used to solve this problem. The principle of superposition and way is quoted from the literature (Bai D Q et al, 1993).

$$\sum_{i=1}^{n}\frac{\Delta t_i}{\tau_x(T_i)}=\sum_{i=1}^{n}\frac{1}{\tau_x(T_i)}\frac{\Delta t_i}{\Delta T_i}\Delta T_i=1 \qquad (4.26)$$

where $\tau_x(T_i)$ is time of the reaction reach to $x\%$ needed a T_i, $\Delta t_i/\Delta T_i$ is reciprocal of the cooling speed. If separate cooling process into adequacy tiny segment, and look every segment as isothermal process, then all the formula in this section can be used to CSP process.

Suppose that the nucleate ratio of the second phase during the isothermal is constant, it is different from the industrial process. During this process, the volume of austenite V_u where the second phase particles precipitate will decrease. If set the volume of austenite at the beginning as 1, then the volume will change from 1 to 0. So the actual nucleate ratio J^* is the function on time t, and the math expression is shown as follows (Liu W J and Jonas J J, 1989):

$$J^*=V_u J \qquad (4.27)$$

Since the nucleate ratio is considered as constant, which is bigger than actual one, this will conduce that the forecast value of the second phase becomes lower. But the actual cooling process can be divided into many tiny segments by principle of superposition. If the amount of segments is adequacy, this effect can be ignored.

4.3.2.2   Dynamics condition of AlN and simulation result

During rolling process, whether recrystallization and precipitation interact to each other and how the interaction proposes is the focus of the problem. This influences the model of dynamics of the second phase and its appliance. According to the literatures (Kwon O and Deardo A J, 1991), recrystallization and precipitation are interactional under certain condition(such as rolling, continuous cooling, and so on). So, it is very important to conforme the temperature of non-recrystallization temperature Based on the computer note about the actual production technics parameters, the non-recrystallization temperature of the low carbon steel by CSP is 928°C.

When the deformation temperature is higher than the non-recrystallization temperature, the second phase precipitation doesn't happen. This is because the austenite recrystallization decreased the driving force of deformation inducing precipitation, which restrains the precipitation. In reverse, precipitation is earlier than recrystallization. The reason is recrystallization doesn't happen because of the restrain by the precipitation process. In the austenite deformation zone, deformation strip and sub-grain and dislocation increase due to the deformation. This is because that AlN nucleate is priority in the dislocation line, which accelerates the precipitation AlN.

According to the literature (Wilson F G and Gladman T, 1988), when deformation speed rate is higher than $0.1s^{-1}$, AlN will not precipitate before recrystallization. The reason is the dynamics of recrystallization is more sensitive to deformation speed rate than precipitation. Plentiful observation and analysis on the strip by electron microscope show that the second phase in the thin crystalloid transmission sample is Al_2O_3 and MnS. And there is no AlN in sample of the first 5 passes.

Above the non-recrystallization temperature(T_{nr}),AlN will not separate out because of recrystallization and high deformation speed rate. In reverse, under the T_{nr}, AlN will not separate out too at a very high deformation speed rate. But after rolling, the defects, such as high dislocation density produced by the deformation accelerate the precipitation of AlN,which is called "deformation induces precipitation".

During rolling process, dislocation density increase distinctly as increase of the deformation. This kind of increase is much distinct in the non-recrystallization section. The appearance and amount of dislocations in different passes are shown in Figure 4.25 and Figure 4.26 respectively. In the first pass, the dislocation density is

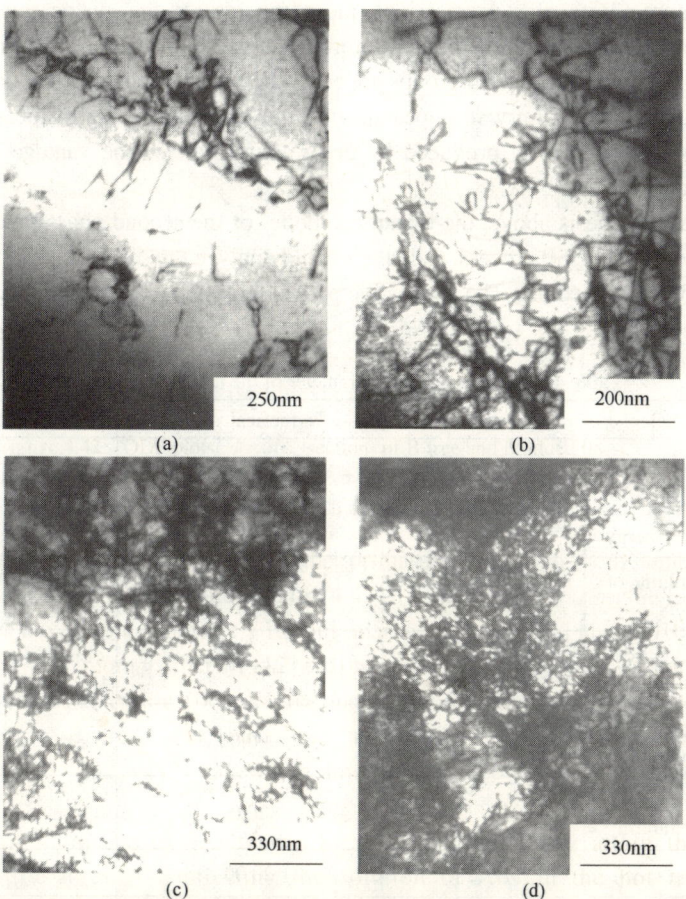

Figure 4.25 Appearance and amount dislocation in different paths during rolling
(a) 10%; (b) 30%; (c) 55%; (d) 96%

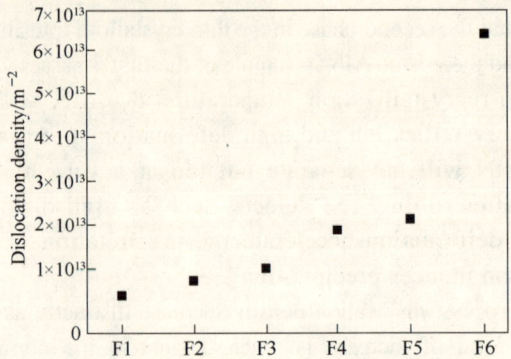

Figure 4.26   Change of the dislocation density in 6 passes

low due to the small deformation, low deformation speed ratio and high temperature. With the decrease of the temperature, the dislocation density accretion obviously with the bigger deformation and deformation speed ratio, and some dislocation tangles and groups appear. When cumulated deformation reaches to 96%, the dislocation wall appeared with the manifold of the dislocation. The high dislocation density produced by deformation will be the vantage point for AlN nucleation.

In the hypothesis above, the dynamics model of the second phase precipitation wass used in the CSP process. Calculation and analyze the dynamics characteristic of AlN were carried out. The correlative parameters needed in operation are shown in Table 4.7.

Table 4.7   The correlative parameter of the model in calculation

Parameter	Symbol	Numerical value	Literature
Diffusion speed of Al in austenite	$D_{Al}/m^2 \cdot s^{-1}$	$1.6 \times 10^{-2} \exp(-9000/RT)$	(chen,1984)
Interface energy	$\sigma /J \cdot m^{-2}$	0.75	(Leno et al, 1999)
Mole volume of AlN	$V_p/m^3 \cdot mol^{-1}$	1.33×10^{-5}	(Sun W P et al, 1992)
Crystal lattice constant of body	a / m	3.65×10^{-10}	(Liu W J and Jonas J J, 1989)
Finishing temperature	$T_F / ℃$	900.00	
Phase change temperature	$T / ℃$	820.00	
Cooling speed	$\dot{T} /℃ \cdot s^{-1}$	20.00	
Dislocation density	$\rho /m \cdot m^{-3}$	2.80×10^{13}	

According to Table 4.7, the results show that AlN of the first 5 passes doesn't precipitate (including dynamic precipitation) as the recrystallization and high strain speed. During the 6th pass, AlN doesn't precipitate dynamicly as the higher rate of deformation, and deformation inducement induces the precipitation of AlN at the end of the 6th pass. AlN particle is very small, and the diameter of AlN is about 2nm at the end of finishing precipitation. Comparing with the chemical phase analysis result, the calculation result is comparative reasonable. Comparing literature (Glandman and Pickering F-B,1967) with the experiment result, the growing speed of AlN is very slow during CSP process, so the size of AlN is less and uniform.

During CSP process, the dislocation density of the structure is higher than traditional technology as higher deformation quantity and speed. The nuclear of   AlN appears in the dislocation line and its size is small, which promotes the nucleation of $\gamma \rightarrow \alpha$ abundantly and makes the ferrite thinner.

During the traditional technology, AlN appears in the dislocation line preferentially. At first, the transition phase with fcc structure form, and then, AlN grain with hcp structure form as the reset of atoms (Wilson F G and Gladman T, 1988). During CSP process, whether the crystallography change of AlN exists or not and its effect on the later $\gamma \rightarrow \alpha$ phase transformation, is a task worth lucubrating deeply.

4.3.3   *Effect of fine AlN particles on structure and performance*

4.3.3.1   Effect of AlN particles on the precipitation of austenite section

When the second phase AlN precipitates from austenite, the nucleation occurs mainly in three modes, uniform precipitation in matrix, along grain boundaries and dislocation. Majority nucleation theories believe that uniform nucleation on the boundary defects, especially on boundaries and dislocation lines, has a significant meaning. When the second phase is induced to precipitate in deformed austenite, the nucleus in grain boundary and dislocation occupy the absolute advantage, and the uniform nucleus in body precipitate can hardly occur. AlN precipitation along the grain boundary and sub-boundary can availably pin the grain boundary and the sub-boundary, prevent their movement, and so more availably restrain the austenite grain growth than the uniform precipitation of AlN. However, these precipitations tend to grow assembly, so their size is obviously bigger than the one of uniform precipitation on dislocation and matrix. This weakens the restraining effect on austenite growth. On the other hand, it increases the damage to the toughness of the steel. Comparatively, the second phase AlN precipitating on the dislocation line distributes more uniform. The anchoring of the precipitation to the dislocation line and configuration can prevent the recrystallization of deformed austenite, and restrain the movement of austenite boundary and the growth of austenite grain. The coarsening of second phase AlN precipitate on the dislocation line is smaller than the one of grain boundary, so its size is small. In addition, it distributes equably and the damage to the toughness of the steel is little. Further more, it can influence the intensification of precipitation at a certain extent. To decrease the precipitation temperature and increase the deformation properly can enhance the available dislocation density. It is difficult for the dislocation to move, and so the dislocation entwisting or net forms, while the quantity of dislocation nucleus increases.

4.3.3.2   Effect of AlN precipitation during the phase transformation

During the CSP hot rolling, the solubility of element descends with the decrease of temperature. Supersaturated element Al and N will induce the precipitation at certain deformation and accelerated cooling condition. Some or all of the AlN particles precipitate in dislocation net and along austenite boundary. This will delay the reversion and recrystallization of the austenite and refine the grain, and establish the basement for $\gamma \rightarrow \alpha$ phase transformation. On the other hand, if AlN particles precipitate along the austenite boundary, the orientation relationship of precipitations will be controlled by austenite and its boundary energy. Because the crystal structure of AlN is different from austenite, and there is some miss match, the second phase particles precipitating from austenite is not spherical. The miss match between the precipitation and matrix reflects the precipitation effects. On the other hand, during the phase transformation, fine dispersed AlN particles enhance the nucleus core of $\gamma \rightarrow \alpha$, and refine the ferrite grain. Though the size of original austenite grain by CSP influences the refinement of ferrite grain, after many paths rolling, this effects decrease greatly because of the recrystallization and second phase particles.

The beginning temperature of $\gamma \rightarrow \alpha$ phase transformation for low carbon steel is about 820 ℃ . So, AlN will precipitate before the $\gamma \rightarrow \alpha$ phase transformation. The fine dispersed AlN particles restrain the recrystallization of deformed austenite, which greatly accelerates the deformation strip and the interphase area. At the same time, the nucleus sites increase the effective nucleus area of α , and makes α more finer. During rolling, the hard AlN particles are difficult to deform and disperse uniformly, which enhances the intensity at some extent.

4.4   Control on Soft Mechanism of Cold Rolling Thin Slab by Continuous Casting and Rolling

4.4.1   *Requirements of cold-rolled sheet for deep drawing to the property of cold rolling billet and the control methods on soften steel*

Based on the demand of shaping capability and cold rolled technology, hot rolled strips, as the cold-rolled billet, have to be accord with certain requirements in component, microstructure and performance before they can be supplied to the cold rolling. Table 4.8 shows the reference values of mechanical properties of SPHC,08Al and 03Al obtained by conventional tandem hot rolling. Data in Table 4.8 were got from production data and experimental data in laboratory.

Table 4.8   Reference values of mechanical properties of SPHC,08Al and 03Al after hot rolling

Steel grade	R_e/MPa	R_e/R_m	A/%
SPHC（CQ grade）	260~300	0.72~0.82	35~41
08Al（~DQ grade）	250~290	0.70~0.80	36~43
03Al（~DDQ grade）	240~280	0.68~0.78	37~45

In addition, to fulfill the formability of cold rolled sheet after anneal, the control of initial billet, finishing to gauge, cooling and coiling technology, mainly the control of grain microstructure and precipitates of steel especially the AlN, are quite important. It should be noticed that, in conventional production line, we usually accord with the principle-high temperature heating, high temperature roughing, high temperature finishing and low temperature coiling, in order to dissolve the most AlN in the austenitic matrix of steel, restrain the precipitates of AlN in the succedent rolling and cooling process, then precipitates the AlN in the anneal after cold rolling. It is important to the development of favorable texture of cold rolled sheet and increase the value of *r*.

Yield strength has a high phenomenon, which is between 330~390MPa, in the mechanical property of low-carbon hot rolled strip (Q195,08Al,SPHC and SS330) achieved by the recent product line of thin slab casting and rolling. This comes along with the difficulty in producing as the stuff for the steel of cold rolling and punching. We can attain the methods of control on soften low-carbon steel for cold rolled billet from the following aspects:

1. Designing and controlling of metallurgy components(C, Si, Mn, P, N, Al).
2. Controlling on heating, rolling, cooling and coiling technology.

3. Add microelement B, Ti into steel.

4. Rolling in the ferrite zone.

Recently, the primary soften-control methods are adding B micro-alloy or improving the hot rolling technology and component controlling in corporations.

4.4.2   *Mechanism of adding B micro-alloy into low-carbon steel on grain growth coursing and steel softening*

4.4.2.1   Action of adding B micro-alloy into steel on the coursing of grain growth

Based on controlling of metallurgy component, we can get the yield strength lower more if we add a small quantity of B into SPHC. Experiment results in CSP of LY steel show that yield strength of steel strip are most in the range of 270~290MPa, the average value of which is 288MPa, the average value of tensile strength is 357MPa, moreover elongate percentage behaves well, which achieves 44.7 %. The yield strength has been lowered down to 240~250MPa resulting from adding B in the amount of 50~60ppm, when producing low-carbon steel SS330 on the line of electrical furnace CSP in Zhujiang steel of Guangzhou. Figure 4.27 shows the longitudinal section of grain microstructure in 4.0mm 08Al steel strip which is added with a small quantity of B. We can see that the microstructure of steel strip, the grain size of which is about 15μm, is growth coarsened ulteriorly, and the grain brims become round and smooth, which are closed to the microstructure of 08Al steel strip produced by conventional technology.

There are results from some experiments show that the adding of a little quantity of B made the grain size grow increase about 3.2μm, and the effect of the changing content of B on the size of steel strip grains is shown in Figure 4.28.

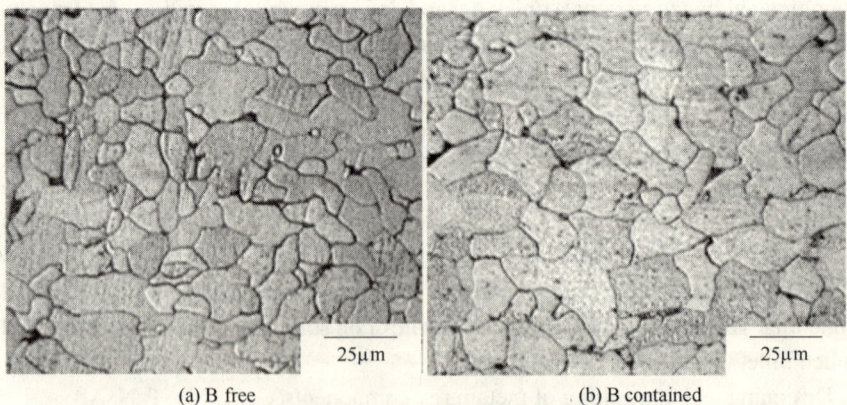

25μm   25μm

(a) B free   (b) B contained

Figure 4.27   The microscopic structure contrast of 50ppm 08Al hot rolled strip longitudinal section between B free and B add steel

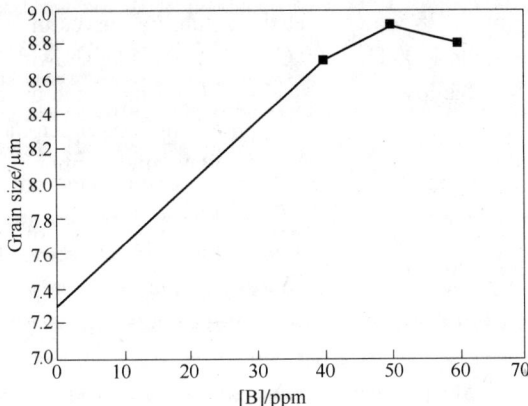

Figure 4.28 Effect of the changing content of B on the size of hot rolled strip grains

The phase diagram of Fe-B indicates that solubility of B in austenite is 40~80ppm. It's easy to calculate that in the hot rolled strip with 0.0031%B, the mass percent of B in the phase of BN procipitated out is 0.0016%. Therefore, there are 0.0015%(mass)B solid soluted in the austenite. The radius of B atom is so small that B solid soluted in the austenite can quite easily segregate to grain boundary, which reduces the grain boundary energy, impede the nucleation of proeutectoid ferrite at the austenite grain boundaries and reduce the nucleating rate N; B making no impact on the coarsening rate G gets the average grain amount in unit volume Z $(=K(N/G)^{3/4}$, K is proportional constant) become less and the average size of grain bigger.

The solubility of B in steel slows promptly with the dropping of temperature. The maximal solubility of B in substitutional solid solution and interstitial solid solution is 38.7 ppm(mass). In the cooling process, supersaturated B comes into being compound of FeB,Fe$_2$B.

4.4.2.2 Effects of adding B into steel on the precipitation in low carbon steel

(A) Effects of Adding B on the Quantity of Precipitates in Low Carbon Steel(AlN,BN)

As analysis mentioned above, nano-AlN precipitated in the process of producing low carbon steel by thin slab casting and rolling restrains the grain growth of austenite, which means grain refining of austenite, and accelerates the deformed α grain refining in the phase transformation $\gamma \rightarrow \alpha$. Well then, what change will take place in the precipitate of AlN after adding a small quantity of B into steel.

The solubility of AlN in austenite can be computed with the following equation:

$$\log[\text{Al}][\text{N}] = -\frac{6180}{T} + 0.725 \qquad (4.28)$$

From the equation 4. 28 we can get the solubility curves of AlN in austenite while the temperature is 1100℃, 1000℃ and 900℃ like showing in Figure 4.29. If the content of N in the low carbon steel is about 70ppm and the content of Al is 0.02~0.03 mass%, the thermodynamic temperature of precipitating of AlN is about 1000℃, which is to say that AlN precipitate after continuous cast, and AlN reserved from soaking will work on the grain refining.

When B is added, BN and AlN compete to precipitate. The solubility of BN can be computed by the following equation:

$$\log[B][N] = -\frac{13970}{T} + 5.24 \tag{4.29}$$

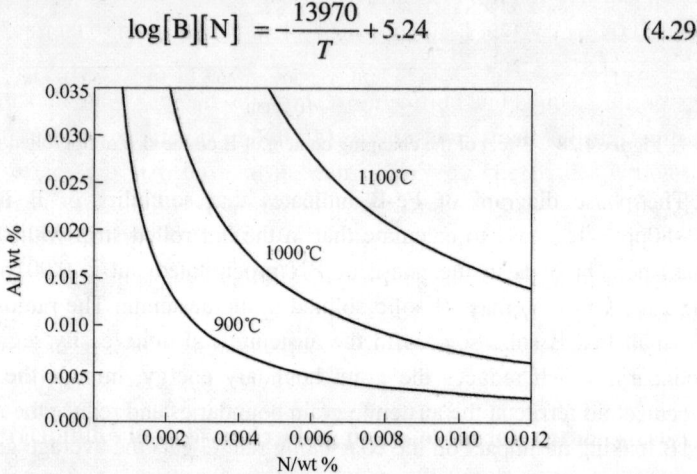

Figure 4.29　The solubility curves of AlN in austenite

The solubility curves of BN in austenite showing in Figure 4.30 can get from equation 4.29. It's obvious that the precipitating temperature of BN is above 1100℃. B atoms diffuse more easily than Al atoms considering the dynamics of precipitating, quantity of generation of AlN in the steel decreasing thereby weaken its influence to grain refining.

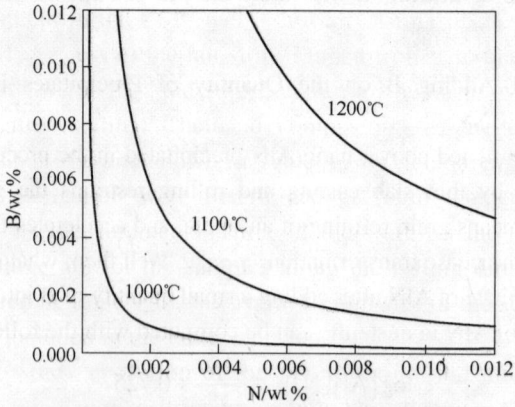

Figure 4.30　The solubility curves of BN in austenite

Y.L.Kang et al analyzed the precipitate of AlN and BN in steel with and without adding B into low carbon Al-killed steel sheets(main constituent: C0.04%, N0.004%, Al0.03%), which are produced on CSP line, adopting analysis of chemical phase analysis. Results from the experiment shows that the amount of precipitate AlN is 0.0021% without adding B into the steel, while the content of BN increase to 39ppm from null and AlN is almost null when adding B with a series content of 30ppm, 50ppm, 70ppm and the coiling temperature is 660℃ (Figure 4.31).

(B)The Effects of Adding B into Steel on the Shape and Size of Precipitated Fe-C Alloy and Sulfide

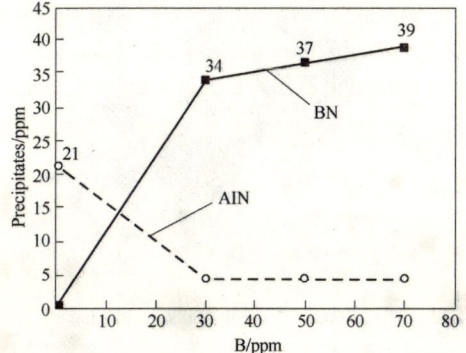

Figure 4.31   Effects of the content of B on the percentage composition of precipitation AlN and BN in low carbon steel (coiling temperature is 660℃)

The pattern and distributing of precipitates in hot rolled with and without adding B was observed by JEM-2000FX TEM in reference 48, in which the component was also analyzed. The observation shows that a small quantity of B has a certain influence to the size, shape and distributing of precipitated Fe-C alloy and sulfide. It's observed that there are a large quantity of spheric grains of Fe-C alloy with a size range of 20~50nm distributing diffused in the ferrite crystals without adding B in the steel; precipitated sulfide grains have a size range of 20~50nm with a globular shape (Figure 4.32). With adding B into the steel, precipitated Fe-C alloy grains with a globular shape or quadratic form, and a size range of 100~300nm distributes assembling relatively in a dot-line way; The size of precipitated sulfide grains is about 80nm with a round shape (Figure 4.33).

We need further studies on the mechanism of coarsening the precipitated Fe-C alloy and sulfide grains with adding B in the low carbon steel, yet this phenomenon shows that adding B has an influence on the low carbon steel softening.

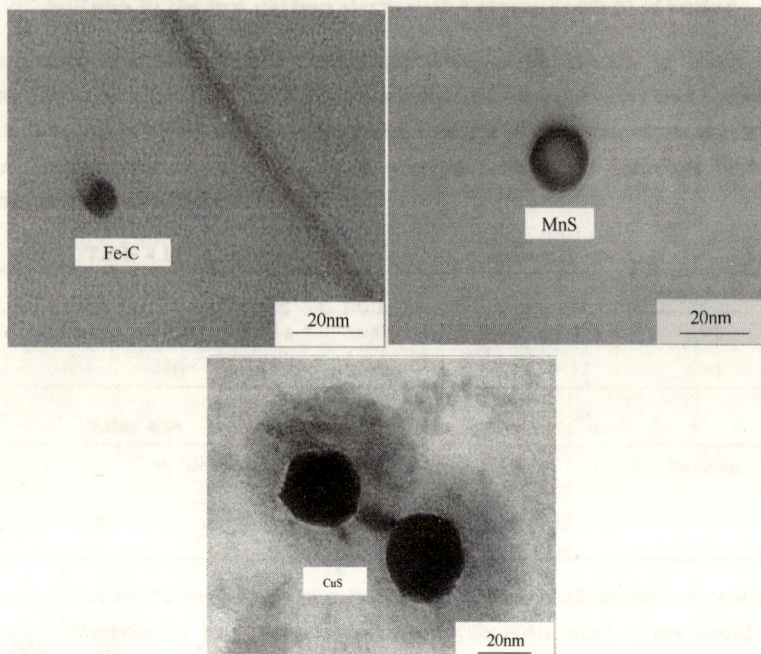

Figure 4.32   The grains of precipitated second-phase(B free steel)

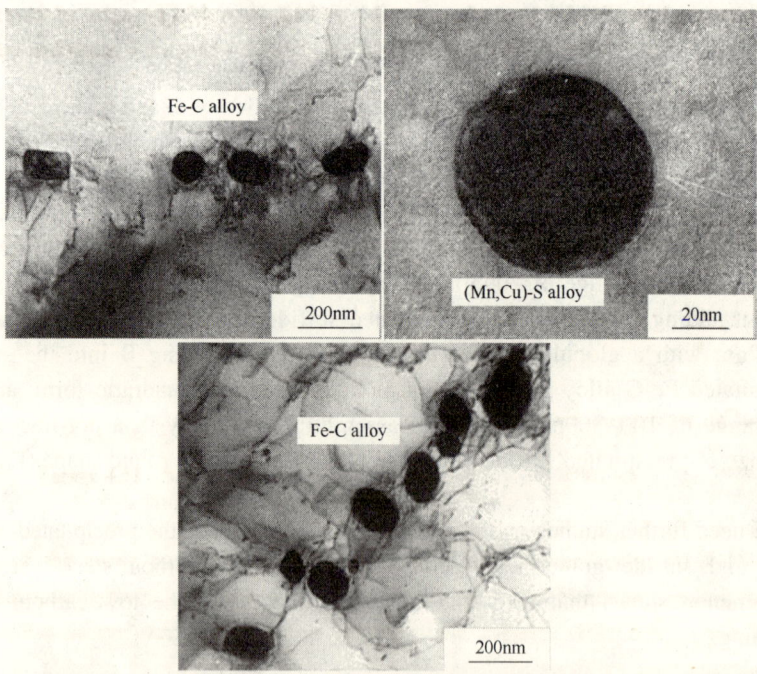

Figure 4.33   The grains of precipitated second-phase
(B contained,[B]=50ppm)

4.4.3   Effects of the hot rolling and cooling technology on the softening of low carbon steel

The methods mentioned above of control the reducing strength (softening) of low carbon produced by thin slab casting and rolling can also achieved by control the hot rolling technology besides adding B into the steel. Control the technologies of rolling and cooling is still the basic principle to coarsen the ferrite and precipitates. The author took relative researches with the CSP line in Handan Iron and Steel, and the followings are the main results.

4.4.3.1   The effects of finishing temperature on the performance of SPHC

Testing results of mechanics property of finishing strip from the experiments of finishing temperature are shown in Figure 4.34. It's obvious that tensile strength falls a little along with changing of finishing temperature, while the yield strength drops quickly, thereby the yield ratio lowers distinctly. The yield ratio drops from 0.78 to 0.84 when the finishing temperature rises from 855 ℃ to 909 ℃.

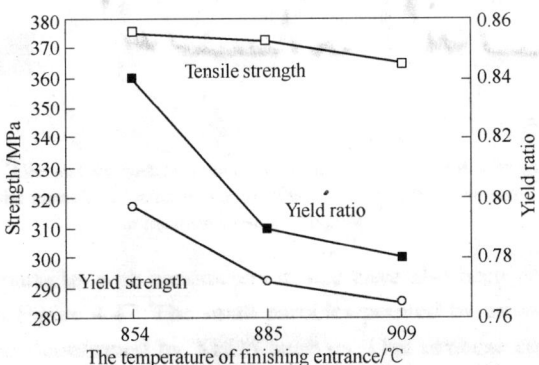

Figure 4.34   Effects of finishing reduction on the mechanical property of strips

4.4.3.2   The effects of finishing reduction on the property of SPHC

The effects of finishing reduction on the mechanical property of finished strip are shown in Figure 4.35. It's obvious that tensile strength of strips does not alter distinctly along with the increasing of finishing reduction, yet the yield strength is falling down in the beginning and then rising up. Thereby excessive finishing reduction, reaching 20%, leads to the increasing of yield ratio because of the increasing of yield strength. Therefore, the finishing reduction should not be excessive.

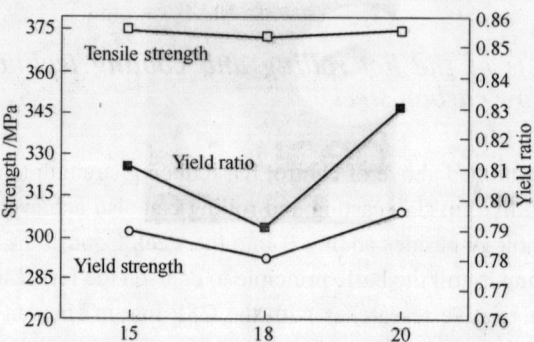

Figure 4.35   Effects of finishing reduction on the mechanical property of strips

4.4.3.3   The effects of coiling temperature on the property of SPHC

The effects of coiling temperature on the property of products are shown in Figure 4.36. The tensile strength of strips has a descending tendency along with the increasing of coiling temperature. The yield strength reduces distinctly where the coiling temperature is 633℃ and then rises up. The yield ratio is inferior where the coiling temperature is 633℃.

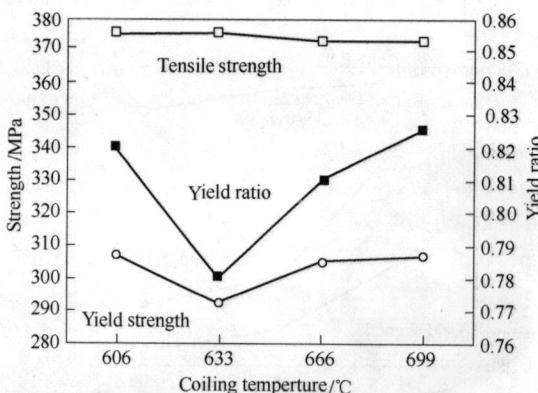

Figure 4.36   Effects of coiling temperature on the property of product

4.4.3.4   The effects of hot rolled lubrication on the property of SPHC

The effects of hot rolled lubrication on the property of finished strips are shown in Figure 4.37. It's obvious that adopting hot rolled lubrication lowers the yield strength and the tensile strength, and the descending ratio of the former is higher than that of the latter, thereby the yield ratio falls in a certain extent.

4.4.3.5   The effects of cooling methods on the property of SPHC

The effects of cooling methods on the property of product are shown in Figure

4.38. It's obvious that yield strength and tensile strength of products adopting the posterior cooling are lower than those adopting the anterior cooling, so is the yield ratio. Changes of cooling methods primarily change the cooling down ratio in the different steps of the whole cooling process. Changes of cooling down ratio in different temperature ranges in which the austenite in high temperature transforms to ferrite have different effects on structural transformation.

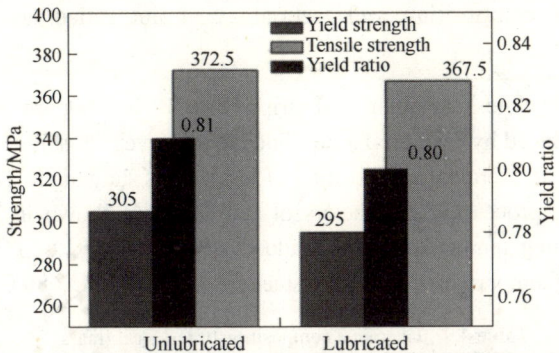

Figure 4.37   Effects of lubrication on the mechanical property of finished strips

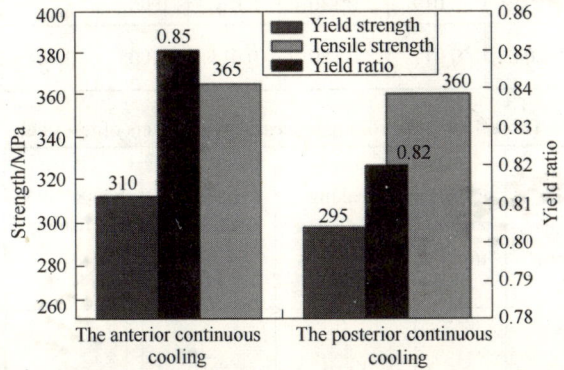

Figure 4.38   Effects of coiling-down on the mechanical property of finished strips

4.4.4   *The effects of the control method of different softening technology on the formability of cold-rolled sheet* 08Al

It's been proved that adding B micro-alloy can decrease the yield strength of billet of cold-rolled drawing sheet achieved by CSP technology. Yet there are few researches on the effects of B on formability, mechanical property and textures after the cold rolled and subsequent full annealing, while researches of the mechanical property and the formability after full annealing are very important projects. Y.L. Kang et al attained the basic formability index (r, n)

and mechanical property of the two different steel, with B 40~60ppm and without B, which were produced by the CSP technology at different coiling temperatures and then got full annealing by different overall reduction. They analyzed contrastively the effects of different coiling temperatures and overall reduction on formability, mechanical property and textures of cold rolled annealing sheets, and discussed the effects of B micro-alloy on punching property, mechanical property and textures of 08Al steel.

4.4.4.1   The composition and technology of hot rolled low carbon steel (08Al) of CSP

The finished thickness of hot rolled strips, with B 40~60ppm and without B, which are produced by CSP production line having seven finishing mill groups are both 2.7mm. The chemical composition of test steel is showing in Table 4.9, while the hot rolling processing parameters of test steel are shown in Table 4.10, in which the coiling temperatures of B added steel are 610℃,620℃,650℃,680℃ and the coiling temperatures of B free steel are 620℃,650℃,680℃,720℃.

Table 4.9   Chemical composition of test steel (mass) %

Steel grade	C	Si	Mn	P	S	B	Al$_s$
B free	0.029	0.019	0.130	0.010	0.003	—	0.025
B contained	0.043	0.017	0.180	0.014	0.005	0.004~0.006	0.025

Table 4.10   Hot rolling processing parameters of test steel

Slab thickness /mm	Slat thickness /mm	Pulling rate/m · min^{-1}	Soaking Temperature /℃	The temperature of fishing entrance /℃	The temperature of fishing exit /℃	Coiling temperature /℃
50	2.7	4.5	1150	1050	900	B added 610, 620, 650, 680 B free 620, 650, 680, 720

4.4.4.2   The technologies of cold rolling and annealing

Cold-roll the two different hot rolled strips 08Al (with and without B) produced by the CSP technology with different coiling temperatures in the four-high cold mill, with a series overall reduction of 65%, 70%, 75%, 80%, 85%. Full anneal the samples after the cold rolling adopting the same annealing system for the steel samples whatever with or without B. Raise the temperatures of the samples with B and without B to $T_1 = 550℃$ at a heating rate of 180℃/h and keep the insulation work for 1hour, then raise the temperatures to $T_2=710℃$ at a heating rate of 40℃/h and keep the insulation work for 2 hours, afterwards take the samples out of the coiling until cooling along with the coiling to room temperature.

4.4.4.3   The effects of coiling temperature and total cold-rolled reduction on r-value of steel 08Al with and without B

The effects of coiling temperature and total cold-rolled reduction on r-value of annealed steel 08Al with and without B are shown in Figure 4.39. On B added steel, the r-value is monotone increasing when the total cold-rolled reduction

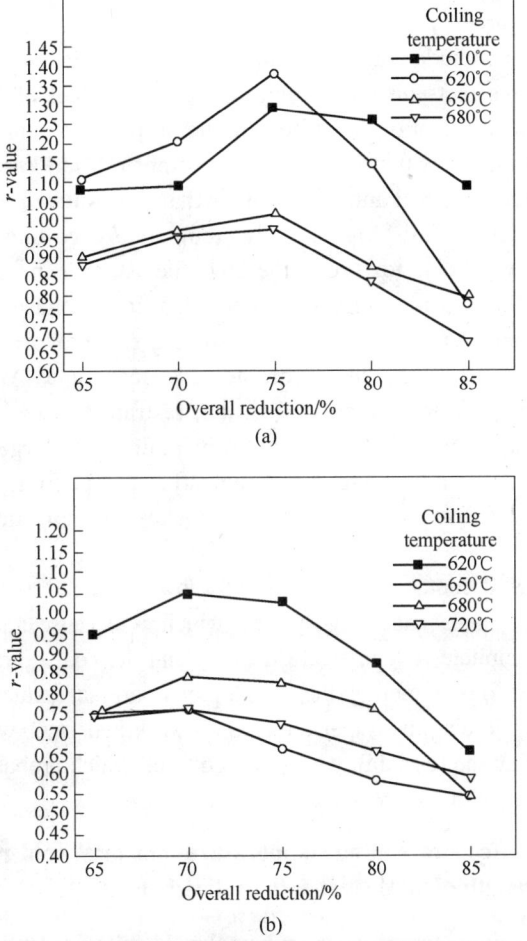

Figure 4.39   Effect of coiling temperature and total cold-rolled precipitation
on the r-value of B free and B contained 08Al steel

(a) B free steel; (b) B added steel

is between 65%~75%, while the r-value is monotone decreasing when the total cold-rolled reduction is between 75%~85%, otherwise, the r-value has a increasing tendency along with the coiling temperature falling and the r-value gets the maximum when the coiling temperature is 620℃. On B free steel, the r-value is monotone increasing when the overall reduction is between 65%~70%, while the r-value is monotone decreasing when the overall reduction is between 70%~85%, otherwise, the r-value also has a increasing tendency along with the coiling temperature falling and the r gets the maximum when the coiling temperature is 620℃. But when compared the Figure 4.39(a) and Figure 4.39 (b), we can find that the r-value of B contained steel is lower than the one without B in the condition of the same hot rolled technology and coiling temperature.

So, we could conclude that the coiling temperature and the overall reduction have significant effects on the r-value of punching steel 08Al, thereby they become the critical factor of the effects on the property of punching. Indirectly, this result also indicates that in the process of hot rolling, keeping the AlN in solid solution until the full annealing rather than precipitated in the hot rolling by high temperature finishing and low temperature coiling makes for the development of {111} textures, thereby the steel can attain favorable formability. In the condition of CSP technology, second-phase AlN precipitates with a small diameter restrain the development of unfavorable textures and promote the development of favorable textures. Fine AlN precipitates, impeding the nucleation of recrystallization, restrain the nucleation of grains with less driving force and the nucleation of grains with larger driving force, yet the latter takes an advantage in the nucleation competition. Therefore, AlN enhances the selectivity of nucleation, and makes for more intensive textures {111}.

The r-value of B contained steel is usually low compared with the steel 08Al without B at the same annealing system, which is because adding B leads to decrease the precipitate AlN in steel distinctly and the coarse precipitates of BN have little effect on promoting the development of the textures {111}. Some researches bring it out that superfluous B in Al-killed steel will decrease the r-value, worsening the formability of Al-killed steel, which probably as a result of the affluence of B with 40~60ppm.

4.4.4.4   The effects of coiling temperature and total cold-rolled reduction on the yield strength of 08Al steel with and without B

The effects of coiling temperature and total cold-rolled reduction on the yield strength of 08Al steel with and without B are shown in Figure 4.40. On the B added steel, the yield strength falls down distinctly along with the total cold-rolled reduction increasing at every coiling temperature when the total cold-rolled reduction is between 65%~75%, while the yield strength gets a increasing tendency when the overall reduction exceed 75%. The yield strength gets the minimum when the overall reduction is 75%.

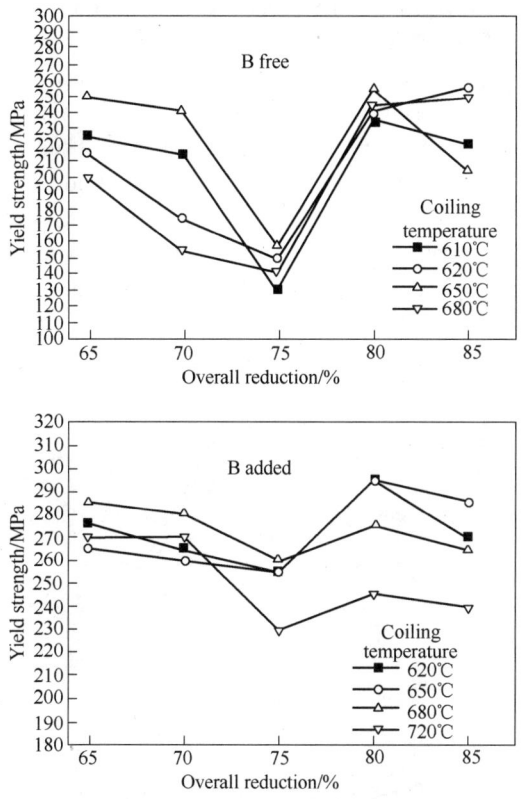

Figure 4.40 Effects of coiling temperature and total cold-rolled reduction on the yield strength of B free and B added 08Al steel

On the B added steel, the basic regularity of the yield strength is primarily the same with the B free steel. Through the comparing analysis, we can find that, in the condition of the same full annealing system, after annealing, the yield strength of the B contained steel is obviously higher than those without B, thereby after annealing the yield ratio of B contained steel is also higher than those without B. The B micro-alloy has a small solubility in steel existed as interstitial solid solution for solution strengthening. On the B in steel 08Al, some precipitate as BN, the others, after the full annealing, oppositely segregate around the grain boundary preventing the growth of grains of recrystallization, which leads to result that, after annealing, the yield strength of the B added steel is larger than those without B.

4.4.4.5   The effects of coiling temperature and the total cold-rolled reduction on elongation percentage

The effects of coiling temperature and the overall reduction on elongation percentage are shown in Figure 4.41. Through comparing analysis, the elongation of B free 08Al steel increases when the overall reduction is between 65% ~ 75%, while the elongation decreases when the overall reduction exceed 75%. The elongation of B added (40~60ppm) steel has a decreasing tendency along with the increasing of overall reduction. The reason is probably that the recrystallization temperature of B added 08Al steel drops down along with the increase of cold rolled reduction, and superfluous B micro-alloy can segregate more easily around the grain boundary, which cause the embrittlement of boundary, thereby the elongation decreases after annealing.

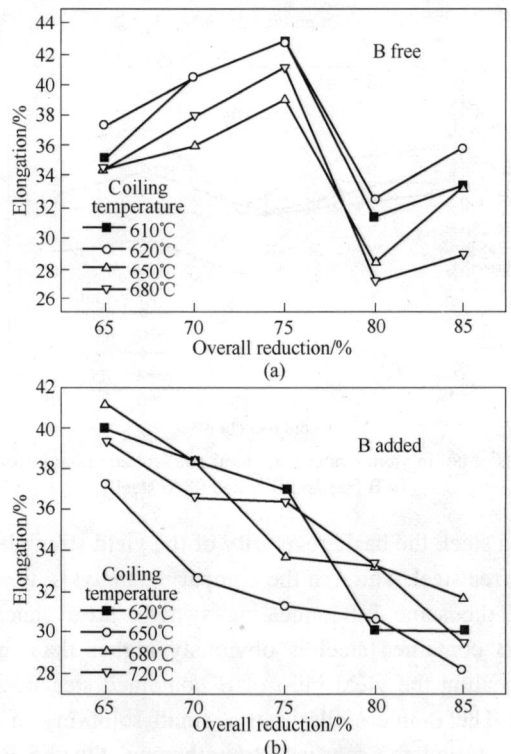

Figure 4.41   Effects of coiling temperature and total cold-rolled reduction on the elongation of B free (a) and B added (b)08Al steel

4.4.4.6   Texture analysis of B free and B added steel

Figure 4.42 is the ODF plots(ϕ_2=45° section) of B free and B added 08Al steel when the coiling temperature is 620℃ and the cold rolled reduction is 75%. We can find from the Figure: intensive fibrous texture, which departures a little from the perfect γ fiber (ϕ=54.7°), exists in both steel, otherwise, both steel have the α fiber texture, body-centered cubic texture {001}<110>and the Goss texture {011}<100>. Compared to B free steel, the Goss texture in B added steel is more intensive, of which the density increases from 1.0 to 2.0; body-centered cubic texture {001}<110> is also more intensive, of which the density increases from 2.0 to 4.0. In the condition of the same hot rolling technology, overall cold-rolled reduction and annealing system, adding B micro-alloy results with more intensive Goss texture and body-centered cubic texture in the annealing sheets. The component of γ fibrous texture decreases in a certain extent in B added steel, which is the reason why steel added B has a lower r-value than B free steel. The results from EBSD also approve that B added steel has less γ fibrous than B free steel.

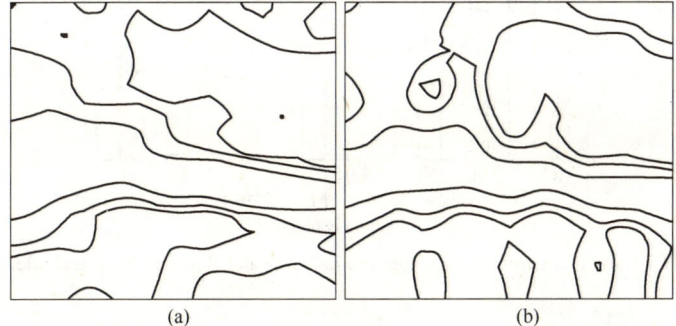

(a)　　　　　　　　　　　(b)

Figure 4.42　ODF plots(ϕ_2=45° section) of B free and B added 08Al
steel after annealing (levels: 1, 2, 4)

(a)B free;(b) B added

Quantitative analysis of texture to the primarily texture in both annealing samples through EBSD is shown in Figure 4.43. It's can be aware from the Figure: B free steel have more intensive γ fibrous marked by texture {111}<110> and {111}<112>, and more α fiber ({112}<110>) than B added steel. Otherwise, body-centered cubic texture {001}<110> and the Goss texture {011}<100> take less amount in B free steel, but more amount in B added steel. Texture {110}<110> and {332}<113> take more amount in B free steel than in B added steel.

As we all know, 08Al steel using for punching primarily attain the4 γ fibrous texture through controlling the solution of AlN in the hot rolling process and the precipitate in the later cold rolling full annealing. The small precipitated particles of AlN can improve the resistance, different from different orientation grains, of nucleation of recrystallization. The

{111}orientation grains with the most driving force predominate in the nucleation, as the AlN causes the largest resistance to the grains with the texture {100} and the least to those with the texture {111}. There are a lot of studies on all of those. In B added steel (40~60ppm), the quantity of precipitated AlN particles decreases promptly because B firstly joins with N forming into course particles of BN; then in the process of full annealing, coarse particles of BN have little accelerating effects on the development of γ fiber, thereby B added steel has less γ fiber than B free steel.

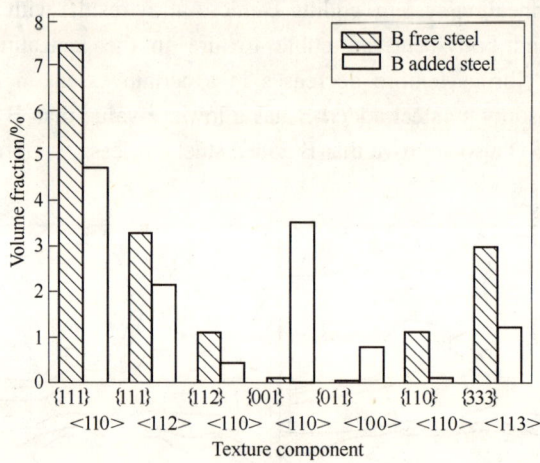

Figure 4.43   Volume fraction of micro-texture in B free and B added 08Al steel after annealing

4.5   Precipitations in the CSP Low Carbon Steels

4.5.1   *Introduction*

The most important characteristics of the CSP process (Compact Strip Production) that differ from the conventional process of cold charge with thick slabs are: quite short period for the solidification and much faster cooling rate subsequently for the slabs. For example, the typical cooling rate of thin slab with 50mm in thickness and a conventional slab (250mm thick) in the temperature region from 1560℃ to about 1400℃ is 120K/min and 9K/min respectively. The former is over ten times faster than that of the later one. The solidification of the thin slabs usually completed within one minute, which is only one tenth or less of the time for a conventional thick slab. A comparison of several important parameters between the CSP and conventional process is given in table 4.11 (Gadellaa,1994). These different aspects would have important effects on transformations especially precipitation of second phases in the steels.

On the other hand, the hot strips produced by CSP (Compact Strip Production) process were undergone different hot history. In other word, the CSP strips were produced through continuous casting-soaking-rolling-coiling without cooling down and reheating after casting. Thus the steel slabs with solidification structure are rolled straightway. Because the solidification rate is much higher than the conventional one, the supersaturation of elements such as O, S, N as well as certain microalloying elements would be also higher compared with the same composition steel produced by cold charge process. This may change the precipitation behavior of oxides and sulfides in the steels.

Therefore, accompanying manufacture of the hot strips produced by the CSP process, numerous metallurgical problems have to be reconsidered. Various physical and chemical processes in the steels during production may be very different from that in the traditional cold charge production owing to the varying of technical parameters. As precipitation of the second phase particles in steels is one of the most important factors to be considered in order to obtain the anticipant microstructure and properties of the steel. In this section, the progress about precipitation with nanometer scale in size in the EAF-CSP low carbon steels is going to be introduced and discussed.

Table 4.11 Comparison between the CSP and conventional process

Process	Conventional one (250 mm thick slab)	CSP process (50 mm thick slab)
Period of solidification/min	10~15	1
Cooling rate（1560~1400℃）/s^{-1}	0.15（9K/min）	2（120K/min）
γ-α transformation before rolling	Yes	Non
Total strain/%	99	96~98
Cumulative true strain	4.6~5.5	3.0~4.1
Maximum rolling rate/m·s^{-1}	20~25	10~13

4. 5.2 *Sulfide and oxide dispersive precipitates*

A great deal of research work about sulfides and oxides precipitations and their effects in steels have been reported in the literature(Li,1983; Mintz, 1989; Ito,1980a, 1980b) In the most cases these sulfide and oxide particles have been considered as inclusions, which are detrimental to properties of the steels. In order to avoid deleterious influences from these inclusions metallurgists have made great efforts for long time. It is indicated for the recent years that the size and distribution of the sulfide and oxide particles could be amended by adjusting the chemical composition and processing parameters. So the steel properties can be improved significantly (Huo et al, 2004b; Liu D et al, 2001; Liu D et al,2002a).

Low carbon steel strips produced by an EAF-CSP steel plant, Guangzhou Zhujiang Steel and Iron Co., Ltd., have been investigated by the present authors. The experimental results of the study showed that oxides and sulfides may precipitate as dispersive particles in low carbon steel strips produced by EAF-CSP process. Large numbers of fine oxide and sulfide precipitates with nanometers in dimension in the steels have been observed by using transmission electron microscopy (TEM) equipped with X-ray energy dispersive spectroscope (XEDS) on extract replica and thin foil specimens (Liu D et al,2002a;2002b 2002c).

The sulfides include manganese sulfide, iron sulfide and copper sulfides. Size of the larger sulfide particles is about 100~300nm, but small sulfides with tens nanometers or less in size have also been observed. The oxide particles are mainly Fe oxide, containing small amount of Si or Cr. Structure of the oxide precipitates consists with cubic system spinel structure with lattice parameter about 0.83nm determined by electron diffraction analysis. The results implied that these small particles should be complex oxides of Fe, Al et al. Remarkable strengthening and grain refinement effects can be obtained by the precipitates (Liu D et al,2002d).

4.5.2.1 Precipitates in slabs and rolling pieces of the low carbon steels

In the present work low carbon steels produced by an EAF-CSP process has been studied systematically. The samples examined in the present work were obtained from low carbon steel strips produced by an EAF-CSP line with six-stand continuous rolling mills. Chemical composition of the experimental steels (ZJ330) was analyzed. It consists of C 0.050%(mass)，Si 0.040%(mass)，Mn 0.38%(mass)，S 0.012%(mass)，P 0.027%(mass)，Cu 0.20%(mass)，Al 0.030%(mass)，Their composition is similar with that of the standard Q195, but the carbon content in the CSP steel is lower. Casting of the thin slabs is about 50mm thick. Thickness of the hot strips ranged from 1 to 6mm and with 135cm in width. Samples for the study were cut from the strips with thickness 4mm immediately after coiling. Chemical composition of the experimental steels (ZJ330) was analyzed and shown in Table 4.12. Yield strength, ultimate tensile strength and elongation were determined at room temperature by standard samples with six measurements. Three of them are for the transversal samples and another three are for the samples along the rolling direction. The average results are listed in Table 4.13, the average grain size of the strips is 5.7~5.8 μm, which is also included in the table.

In order to study evolution of the precipitation and microstructure in the steel accompanied with rolling procedure. A rolling piece of the steel was stopped rolling, while it was being rolled, and cooled rapidly to the room temperature. Thus different position of this rolling piece represents different compression of the steel slab. Samples for the present study were cut from this rolling piece after each pass as well as the slab. Numbering of the specimens is illustrated in Figure 4.44 and listed in Table 4.14 with the rolling parameters.

Table 4.12   Chemical composition of the experimental steel ZJ 330 (mass%)

No.	C	Si	S	P	Mn	Cu	Al	O	N
331	0.054	0.10	0.002	0.014	0.34	0.16	0.029	0.0030	0.0044
332	0.056	0.06	0.003	0.011	0.30	0.14	0.040	0.0036	0.0076

Table 4.13   Mechanical properties and grain size of the experimental steels

No.	$R_{eL}/$ MPa	$R_m/$MPa	$\delta/\%$	R_{eL}/R_m	Grain size /μm
331	351	394	35	0.89	5.7
332	326	394	40	0.83	5.8

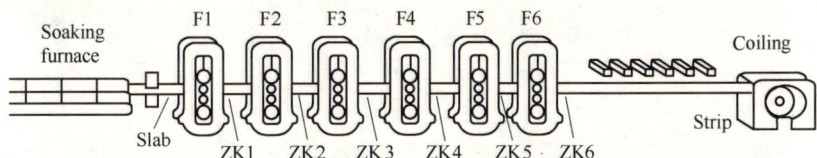

Figure 4.44   Schematic drawing of the CSP process and the specimen numbering in the present work

Table 4.14   Deformation temperature and compression of the specimens

Specimen No.	Slab	ZK1	ZK2	ZK3	ZK4	ZK5	ZK6
Temperature/℃	1100	~1020	~975	~942	~912	~887	~860
Compression/%	0	55	54	46	34	32	20

Longitudinal sections (along the rolling direction) of the samples from each rolling piece were polished and etched by 4% nital solution for optical and scanning electron microscopy (SEM) study. Thin foils and extract replicas of the samples were prepared for transmission electron microscopy (TEM) observations. In order to prevent oxidation or contamination on the specimen surfaces, the thin foil specimens were bombarded by ion beams for 30~60 min. just before the observations. Special care was also taken for the replicas. Both of SEM and TEM are equipped with X-ray energy dispersive spectrometers (XEDS). Electron microscopic investigation on the slab and strips has been carried out.

It is pointed out by the TEM observation that large number of small precipitates exist in all of the specimens, which were cut from the slab and the same rolling piece after each pass. These precipitates are clearly revealed in TEM micrographs. Their size is ranged from several tens to hundred nanometers. TEM micrographs of the replica specimens showing oxide and sulfide particles in the steel are given in Figure 4.45. The pictures in Figure 4.45 (a), (b) and (c) were taken from the slab, rolling piece ZK2 (after the second rolling pass) and ZK4 (after the 4th rolling pass) respectively. XEDS analyses were performed on

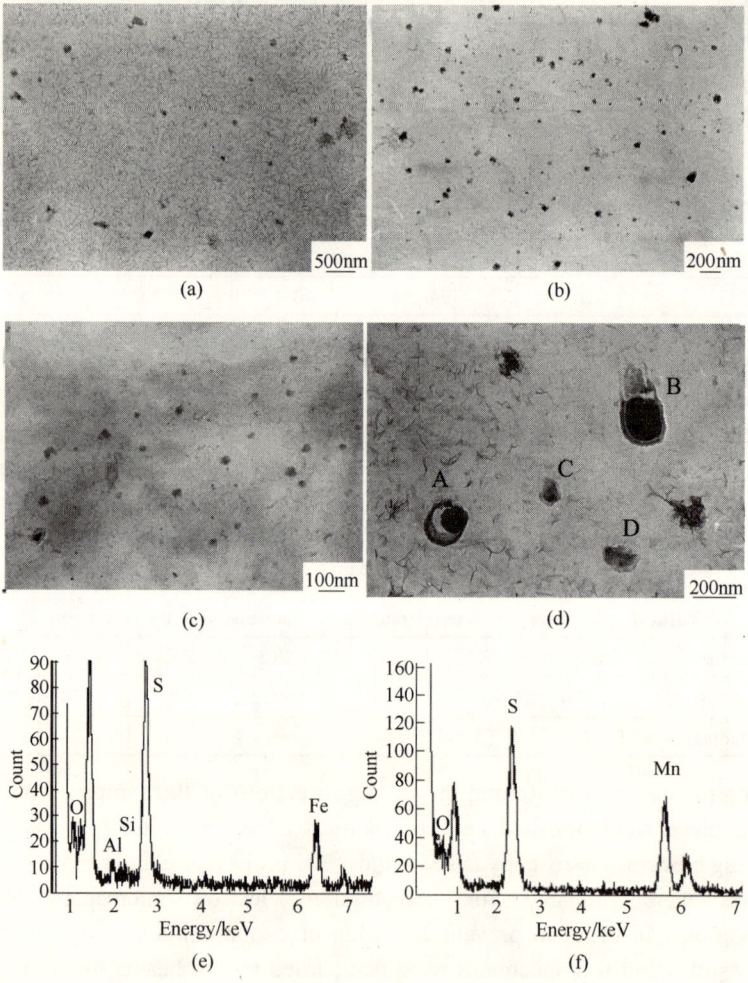

Figure 4.45　TEM micrographs of the replica specimens showing oxides and sulfides in the steel
(a) Slab; (b) Oxides and sulfides in ZK2(after 2nd rolling pass); (c) Oxides and sulfides in ZK4;
(d) Particles in the slab with larger magnification; (e) XEDS of particle A in picture (d);
(f) XEDS of the particle B in picture (d)

these particles one by one. Typical X-ray energy dispersive spectrums from the two particles A and B shown in Figure 4.45 (d) are given in Figure 4.45(e) and (f). They are FeS and MnS respectively. It can be seen that manganese and iron sulfides as well as iron oxides exit in the slab and all of the specimens in spite of they had been rolled through how many passes. There are no obvious differences in the size and distribution of these sulfide and oxide particles between the specimens, which were undergone different rolling pass as well as in the slab. But rolling deformation may have influence on the precipitation. It seems that the iron sulfides usually appear at the periphery of manganese sulfides, and the MnS was growing from oxide "core". Figure 4.46 shows an example of the complex sulfides. The iron sulfide may form by epitaxial growth from MnS particles.

Therefore, the sulfides and oxides with size from several tens to hundreds nanometers would start precipitation before hot rolling.

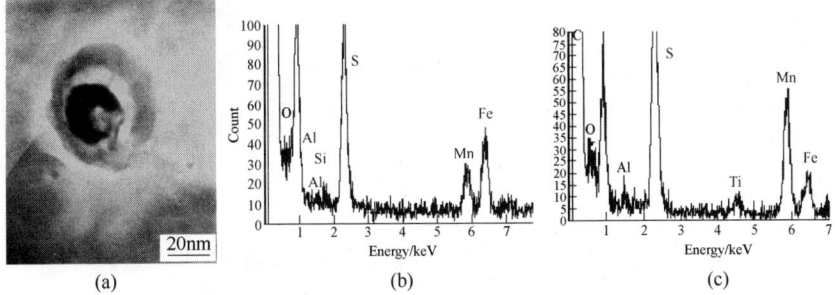

Figure 4.46   (a) One sulfide particle containing iron and manganese with a oxide core; (b) XEDS of the particle at location near periphery; (c) XEDS of the same particle at location close to the core

Copper sulfide particles with nanometers in size have also been observed in the steels as shown in Figure 4.47. The small particles pointed by arrows are copper sulfides, which were confirmed by XEDS analysis. One of these copper sulfides with its electron diffraction pattern is given in Figure 4.47 (b). Figure 4.48 shows the oxide particles in the steel, it is obviously that these precipitates should be iron oxide as pointed by XEDS analysis results.

Figure 4.48 shows the oxide particles in the steel, it is obviously that these precipitates should be iron oxide by their XEDS analysis results.

At the same time, it was revealed by the TEM observation that large number of dispersive precipitates formed in the ferrite matrix of the steel strips. A TEM bright field image of the thin foil specimen is shown in Figure 4.49. It is clearly pointed out by the TEM observations that these precipitates are smaller than 10~20nm in dimension. Most of them are located on dislocations or grain boundaries.

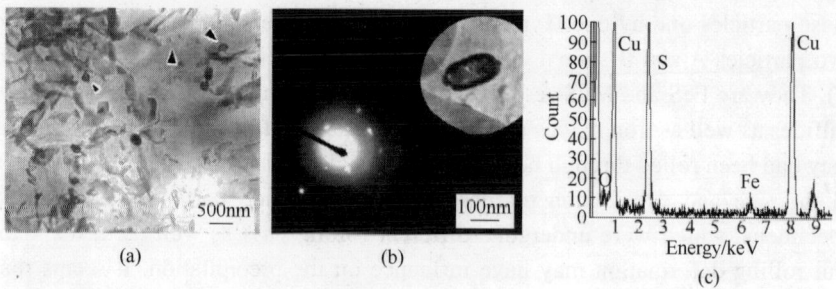

Figure 4.47   (a) Small sulfide particles formed in the low carbon steel strip, TEM micrograph of a replica specimen; (b)One particle with its diffraction pattern;   (c) XEDS spectrum of the particle in figure ;(b) Showing the copper sulfide

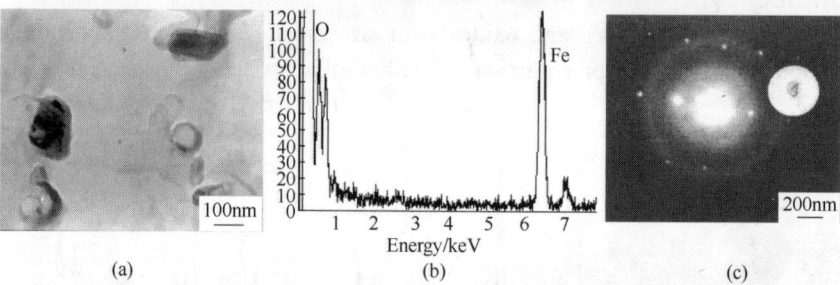

Figure 4.48   (a) Two oxide particles in the steel（TEM micrograph of a replica）; (b) XEDS spectrum from one of the particles; (c) An iron oxide particle with its diffraction pattern

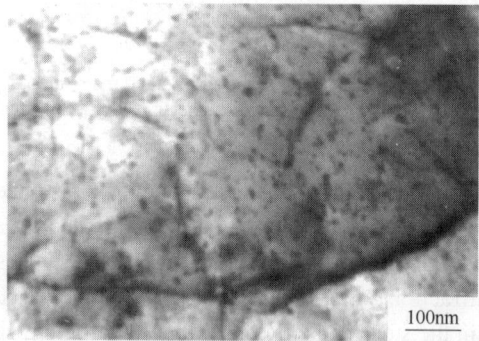

Figure 4.49   TEM bright field image of the thin foil specimen showing dispersive precipitates

In order to distinguish the nature of these precipitates, careful electron diffraction study was carried out. Three diffraction patterns of the precipitates are given in Figure 4.50. The diffraction constant L_λ was deduced from the ferrite matrix reflections. In these patterns, the weak diffraction spots with index *hkl* are from the dispersive precipitates, which were confirmed by the dark field imaging technique on TEM. The strong reflection spots were from the ferrite matrix and indexed *hkl*. The zone axes index for the three diffraction patterns of the precipitates in Figure 4.50 are $[001]_p$, $[114]_p$ and $[136]_p$ respectively, and $[001]_\alpha$, $[013]_\alpha$ and $[111]_\alpha$ are the zone axes for the corresponding ferrite matrix.

It is indicated by the diffraction analysis that the crystalline structure of these precipitates is consistent with cubic system structure of spinel ($MgAl_2O_4$), i.e. "the spinel structure" with space group (F d $\overline{3}$ m) in the crystallography. The lattice parameter a is about 0.83nm as determined by electron diffraction analysis. It can be seen from the diffraction patterns especially the $[001]_p$ pattern that those reflections with even index hkl and $h+k+l \neq 4n$ are forbidden reflections. This is the characteristics of spinel structure(Henry,Lonsdale,1969). It is pointed out by the above experimental results that the dispersive precipitates should be complex oxides with multiple elements such as Fe, Al. Because of their very small size, it is hardly to analyze the particle composition individually by XEDS technique one by one. The predominant contribution to a XEDS spectrum is always from the ferrite matrix.

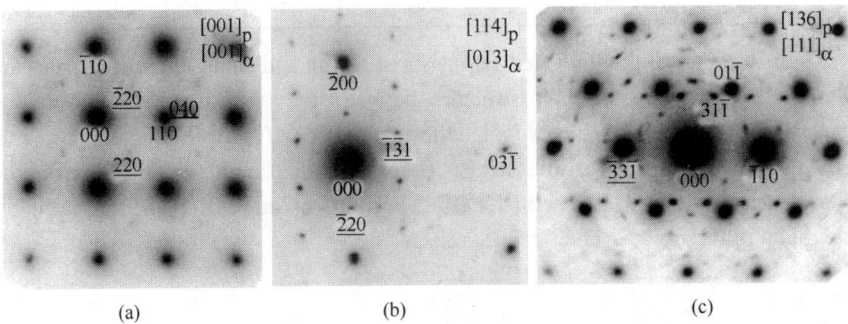

(a)   (b)   (c)

Figure 4.50 Electron diffraction patterns of the precipitates superposed on ferrite matrix
(a) [001]; (b) [114] ;(c) [136] zone axes of the precipitates

Crystallography orientation relationship between ferrite and the oxide precipitates can be deduced as:

$$[001]_p//[001]_\alpha, (\overline{1}10)_p//(010)_\alpha, (110)_p//(100)_\alpha$$

This is actually known as the Baker-Nutting orientation relationship between precipitates and α-Fe(Edington, 1975). It was reported that the cubic system carbides such as VC, V_4C_3, NbC precipitated from ferrite matrix hold this relationship. Thus the precipitates possess the same habit plane or the equivalent planes (i.e. variants) of the ferrite matrix. The orientation relationship implies that the precipitation could take place in ferrite matrix or in the α phase side during the $\gamma \Rightarrow \alpha$ transformation. These very small precipitates nucleated on the dislocations or grain boundaries. The dislocations formed by deformation are the preferential nucleation sites for the precipitation.

4.5.2.2　Sulfides in the low carbon steels with varying content of sulfur

Sulfide precipitation in the low carbon steels with varying content of sulfur has been studied experimentally. The sulfur content in the steels H-330 and L-330 is 0.01%(mass) and 0.001% (mass) respectively. Content of the other elements in the steels is seminar to each other as can be seen in Table 4.15. Their mechanical properties are given in Table 4.16.

Table 4.15　Composition (mass%) of the experimental steels

No.	C	Si	P	S	Mn	Cu	Thickness/mm
L-330	0.054	0.08	0.014	0.001	0.27	0.13	3.95
H-330	0.054	0.06	0.015	0.01	0.26	0.17	5.80

Table 4.16　Mechanical properties of the experimental steels

Steel	R_e/MPa	R_m/MPa	A/%	Bending
L-330	350	410	28	ok
H-330	325	430	35	ok

Microstructure of the both steels consists of ferrite and small amount of pearlite. Not much difference in microstructure between the two steel strips could be observed. In order to investigate the influence of sulfur content on the precipitation of sulfides in the steels, the particle size, number and distribution were tested by using TEM with XEDS. Micrographs and XEDS of the particles are given in Figure 4.51 and 4.52.

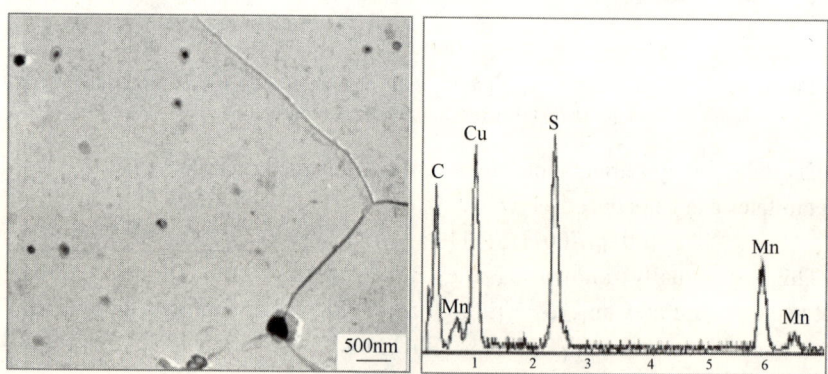

Figure 4.51　Sulfide particles in the steel strip of L-330 (0.001%S), TEM image of the replica specimen

Size of the most particles in the steel L-330 with lower sulfur (0.001%S) ranged around 100nm, only a few of them are larger than 150nm or smaller than 50nm. But in the steel H-330 with higher sulfur content (0.01%S) while the precipitate number increases, the average dimension of the particles also increases.

The size distribution covered a larger range; it is from 50nm even smaller to 300nm or bigger. The statistics for the particle size distribution of sulfide in the steel H-330 and L-330 are illustrated in Figure 4.53(Bai,2005 b).

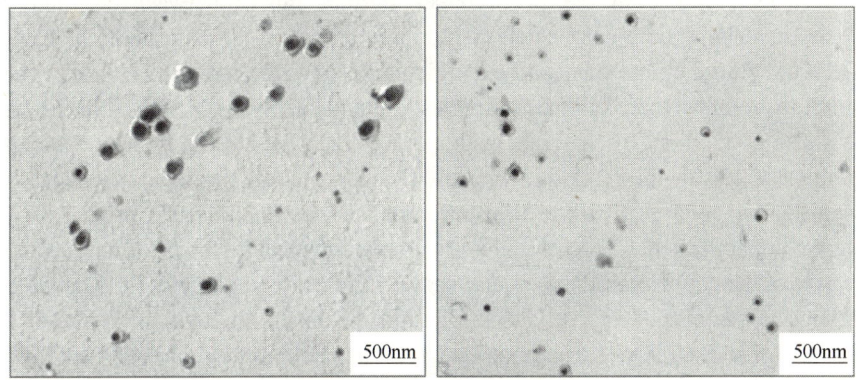

Figure 4.52 Sulfide particles in the steel strip of H-330 （0.01%S），
TEM image of the replica specimen

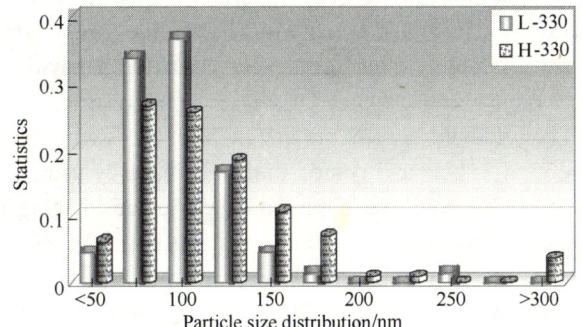

Figure 4.53 Statistics for particle size distribution of sulfide in strips of L-330 and H-330

The experimental results implied that for the steel with higher sulfur content the temperature at which sulfide start precipitation elevates. Therefore the sulfides would grow into larger size. At the same time nucleation rate of sulfides increases owing to the supersaturation of sulfur in the steel solid solution increases. This would result in increasing of both sulfide number and their average size in high sulfur content steel.

Besides the thin foil specimens, the precipitate powder samples were also prepared by electrolytic extracting of the strips in order to determine chemical constitute of the particles. To avoid interference of artificial X-ray signals from the specimen hold or supporting grids the fine powders were spread on specimen grids, which are made from Mo. The TEM observation and XEDS analysis were carried out on these extracting powder specimens by using a low background specimen stage, i.e. a beryllium stage. Large number of the precipitate particles was analyzed individually.

The experimental results showed that most sulfide particles contain either Mn and Cu or only copper. The number of pure Mn sulfide is quite small. The atomic ratio of Cu and S in the pure copper sulfides ranges between 1.2 and 2 approximately. Thus it can be considered that the copper sulfides should be Cu_2S and CuS. And the pure manganese sulfide particles were confirmed as MnS. The atomic ratio of Mn and S in these particles is about 1 as showed by XEDS analysis. It is also pointed out by the experiments that element Fe has rarely been detected in the sulfides for the replica specimens. However, this is discrepant from many investigation reports. In those literatures the sulfides in the steels produced by conventional thick slab process are considered mainly as MnS and iron sulfide.

Size of the copper sulfide is usually below 50nm, but the particles of (Mn, Cu)S is larger. Examples of the particles in thin foil specimens are given in Figure 4.54 and 4.55 with their X-ray spectrum. The spherical particles in Figure 4.54 are MnS and particle in Figure 4.55 is Cu_2S. The Fe peaks in the spectrum are from the ferrite matrix.

It seems the copper sulfides are quite important for the steels produced by the EAF-CSP process as a part of raw material is from the scraps containing small amount of copper (and some other metals). Precipitation behavior of the copper sulfides in the steels may cause significant change in microstructure and properties of the steels. To correlate the content varying in the sulfides with their dimension a statistics for the particle size and composition was made by using a SEM so that much larger view fields could be observed. Because the imaging resolution on SEM is limited, only particles with 100nm in dimension or larger were analyzed. This is also true for the XEDS microanalysis on the bulk specimens. All particles smaller than 100nm were treated as 100nm in this statistics. The experimental results are given in Figure 4.56.

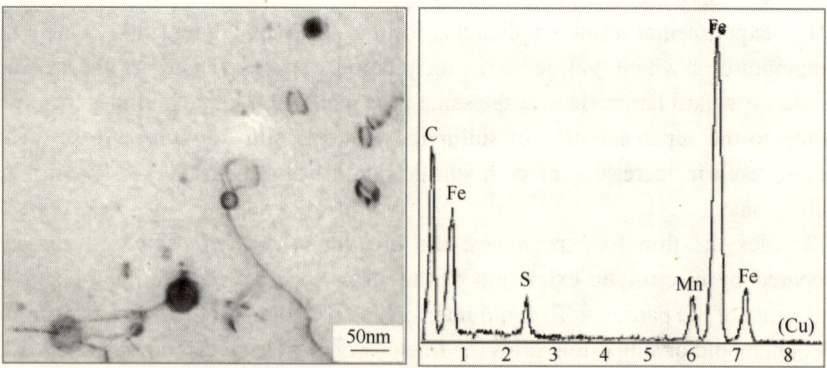

Figure 4.54　MnS particles in steel ZJ330，TEM image and XEDS of thin foil specimen. The Fe peaks are from the ferrite matrix

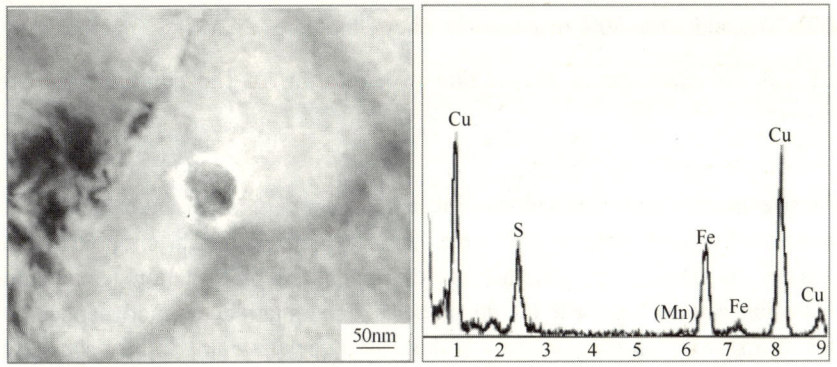

Figure 4.55　Copper sulfide (Cu_2S) particle in steel ZJ330，TEM image and XEDS of thin foil specimen. The Fe peaks are from the ferrite matrix

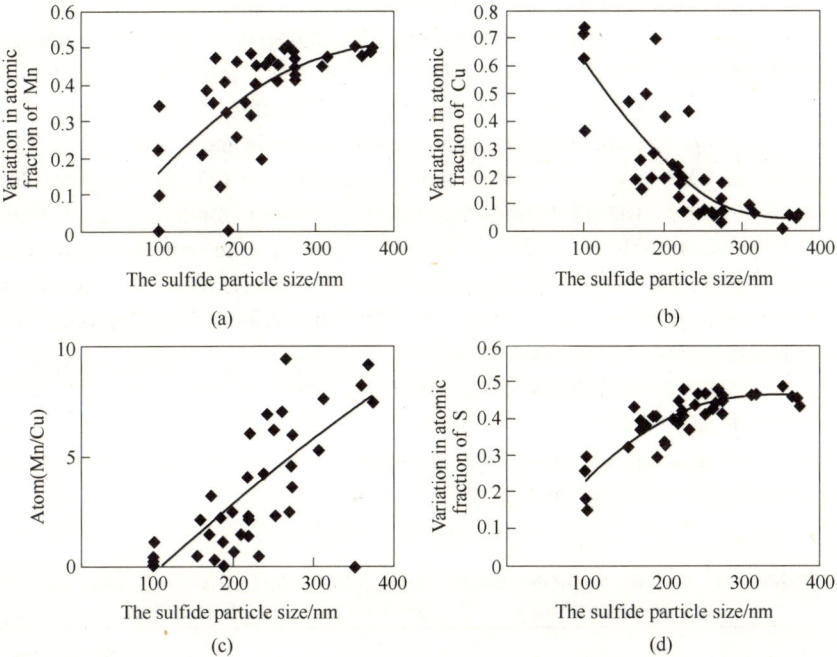

Figure 4.56　Variation in atomic fraction of Mn, Cu, S with the sulfide particle size

The variation in atomic fraction of Mn, Cu, S with the sulfide particle size is shown in Figure 4.56 (a), (b) and (c) respectively, and Figure (d) is the correlation between the particle size and the ratio of Mn /Cu in the particles. It can be seen that while the particle size increases, the fraction of Mn in the sulfides also increases along with decreasing of the Cu fraction. The ratio of Mn/Cu therefore increases. It can be concluded that the bigger sulfide particles such as 200~300nm in dimension are mainly MnS or with small amount of Cu, i.e. (Mn, Cu)S. In the particles with about 100nm in size the atomic fraction of Cu and S is about

60%~70% and 20%~30% respectively. They should be (Cu,Mn)$_x$S,   here $x>1$.

4.5.2.3   Mechanism of the sulfide precipitation in the condition of CSP process

(A) Thermodynamics Consideration

The size, number and distribution of the sulfides are very important parameters for control of the steel properties. Whereas these parameters depend on precipitation behavior of the compounds, that is depend on the precipitation temperature, nucleation rate and growth of the particles. Precipitation thermodynamics and kinetics of sulfide in the thin slabs of the CSP process is going to be discussed in the following text. Difference of the precipitation in low carbon steels between thin slab and the conventional thick slabs is also compared.

The equilibrium solubility product of Mn and S in delta and gamma phase is given in equation 4.30 and 4.31 respectively (Turkdogan et al, 1955; Ueshima et al, 1989; Wakoh et al, 1996). The temperature T_{MnS}, at which precipitation reaction of MnS starts, can be calculated by these equations. Therefore, the temperature T_{MnS} (δ) and T_{MnS} (γ) was calculated for the experimental steels and given in Table 4.17. Two of the CSP low carbon steels are considered, one (ZJ330-1) is with low content of sulfur (0.002%) and the other (ZJ330-K) contains higher sulfur (0.012%). In the table T_{MnS} (δ) and T_{MnS} (γ) represents the temperature of MnS formation in delta phase and gamma phase respectively. This MnS formation temperature in common low carbon steel Q195 produced by conventional thick slabs is also included in the Table 4.17.

$$\lg[\%Mn][\%S](\delta)=-10590/T_\delta+4.2489-0.07[\%Si] \tag{4.30}$$
$$\lg[\%Mn][\%S](\gamma)=-9090/T_\gamma+2.929-(-215/T_\gamma+0.097)[\%Mn]-0.07[\%Si] \tag{4.31}$$

Some other similar equations for MnS precipitation have also been reported (Yaguchi,1986) such as equation 4.32:

$$\lg[\%Mn][\%S]=-11625/T+5.02 \tag{4.32}$$

Table 4.17   Composition of the conventional steel Q195 and CSP steel ZJ330 (mass %) along with the thermodynamic temperature T_{MnS} for MnS precipitation

Steel	C	Si	Mn	P	S	Cu	Al	T_{MnS} (γ)/K	T_{MnS} (δ)/K
ZJ330-K	0.050	0.040	0.38	0.027	0.012	0.20	0.030	1722	1607
ZJ330-L	0.054	0.10	0.34	0.014	0.002	0.16	0.029	1487	1427
Q195 (GB700—88)	0.06~0.12	≤0.30	0.25~0.50	<0.045	<0.050	≤0.30	—	—	1817~1727

Though the thermodynamic temperature T_{MnS} for MnS precipitation can be calculated according to their equilibrium solubility product of Mn and S in the steels, but this is never the case in practice of the steel production. It should emphasize the difference between theoretical calculation and the practical situation in the steel at least in the following aspects.

Firstly, the solute elements distribution is far from the homogeneous condition. Partitioning of the solute elements takes place during solidification and cooling of the slabs. This leads segregation of the elements at certain locations such as phase interface and grain boundaries. Thus concentration of Mn and S at such locations would be much higher than the average value. As a result precipitation of sulfide would start at much higher temperature than the temperature T_{MnS} in these sites, where Mn and S enriched by segregation.

Secondly, transformation of delta to gamma phase may happen along with the precipitation reactions. Solute elements also redistribute between delta and gamma phase.

Thirdly, the actual temperature of the precipitation strongly depends on cooling rate of the steel. The system could never be thought as an "equilibrium condition".

But the calculation results according to equation 4.30 and 4.31 can still be used for understanding the phenomena in the steels.

It can be seen that temperature T_{MnS} in austenite region of the two experimental steels with low and high S content is 1487K and 1722K respectively, but in delta ferrite is 1427K and 1607K(see Table 4.17). Temperature for delta - gamma phase transformation in the steel (contain ~0.050%C,0.040% Si,~0.38%Mn) is about 1723~ 1698K（1450~1425℃）. The T_{MnS} in gamma region for a steel with 0.050%C,0.1% Si,0.4%Mn and 0.005%S is 1612K according to equation 4.31. It means that apart from the segregation MnS formation should occur mainly in gamma phase of the steels with low sulfur content (for example lower than 0.005%S, 0.4%Mn). But in the steel with higher S content MnS may form during delta-gamma transformation or in delta ferrite. It can be concluded that MnS precipitate in a temperature region before soaking of the slabs for the CSP process.

The CuS and Cu_2S start precipitation at much lower temperature comparing with MnS. An experimental study on steel containing 0.11~0.14C, 0.6Mn, 0.25Si, 0.22Cu and 0.025~0.037S (mass%) showed (Garbarg et al,2003) the complete dissolution temperature was 950℃ for CuS and Cu_2S, 1100~1150℃ for (Mn,Cu)S and 1300℃ for MnS during annealing. It is reasonable to consider CuS would start precipitation at temperature T_{CuS}, which is as 200~300K lower as T_{MnS}, and the temperature of (Mn,Cu)S formation ranges from T_{MnS} to T_{CuS} depending on the sulfur content. Because the soaking of low carbon steels is at about 1050~1100℃, hot rolling starts and finishes at about 1000℃ and 800℃respectively in the CSP production processing. The copper sulfides could form during the hot rolling even after rolling due to a small solid solubility of Cu in ferrite.

(B)Effects of microsegregation and cooling rate

Investigations about the redistribution or partitioning of solute elements during solidification and δ / γ transformation have been reported (Ueshima et al,1986;cornelissen,1986;Han,Cai,2000). The equilibrium partition coefficient $k^{\delta/L}$, $k^{\gamma/L}$, $k^{\gamma/\delta}$ and diffusion coefficient D^{γ} D^{δ} for element S, P, Mn, Si and C are listed in Table 4.18. Here $k^{\delta/L}$, $k^{\gamma/L}$, $k^{\gamma/\delta}$ is partition coefficient of the solute element between delta-phase and liquid, gamma phase and liquid as well as gamma phase and delta phase. And D^{γ}, D^{δ} is diffusion coefficient of the element in gamma and delta phase respectively(Lyman et al,1973; Tekko-Binran, 1981; Nakamura, Esaka,1981).

Table 4.18　Equilibrium partition coefficient and diffusion coefficient of elements in steel (Ueshima et al, 1986)

Element	$k^{\delta/L}$	$k^{\gamma/L}$	$k^{\gamma/\delta}$	$D^{\delta}/cm^2 \cdot s^{-1}$	$D^{\gamma}/cm^2 \cdot s^{-1}$
C	0.19	0.34	1.79	0.0127exp(−19450/RT)	0.0761 exp(−32160/RT)
Si	0.77	0.52	0.68	8.0 exp(−59500/RT)	0.30 exp(−60100/RT)
Mn	0.76	0.78	1.03	0.76 exp(−53640/RT)	0.055 exp(−59600/RT)
P	0.23	0.13	0.57	2.9 exp(−55000/RT)	0.010 exp(−43700/RT)
S	0.05	0.035	0.70	4.56 exp(−51300/RT)	2.4 exp(−53400/RT)
Al[①]	0.6			5.9exp(−241186/RT)	
O[①]	0.03			0.0371 exp(−96349/RT)	

① Data for Al and O are from Liu's work(Liu Z et al, 2002b).

Microsegregation behavior of C，Mn，Si，P and S has been investigated by theoretical analysis and experiments in C-Mn steels containing 0.05，0.13 and 0.24% C respectively. It is clear from the results (Ueshima et al, 1986) that all of these elements (C，Mn，Si，P and S) diffused from dendrite towards the liquid phase during solidification of the steel. They were getting enriched in the residual liquid at interdendritic areas. But partitioning of these elements during solid transformation is different from each other. Partition coefficient of Si, P, S between delta and gamma phase is smaller than one, i.e. $k^{\gamma/\delta} < 1$. During $\delta \rightarrow \gamma$ transformation Si, P, S would be enriched in delta phase. Contrarily, C and Mn diffuse from delta ferrite towards austenite as the $k^{\gamma/\delta} > 1$. Actually partitioning of Mn between delta and gamma phase can be ignored as its $k^{\gamma/\delta}$ is close to one. Carbon concentration is almost keeping in the equilibrium level owing to its high diffusion rate in the temperature region related to solidification and $\delta \rightarrow \gamma$ transformation.

In addition, carbon content and cooling rate affects redistribution of the solute elements. An example is given in Figure 4.57 (Ueshima et al, 1986), which shows the effect of carbon content and cooling rate on interdendritic segregation of Mn in C-Mn steel with 1.52%Mn. As cooling rate of a slab increases concentration variance between the interdendritic and dendrite arms enhances owing to the diffusion time for solute elements reduces.

The local content at interdendritic area also depends on diffusion coefficient of the solute elements and the distance over which the elements transit. In casting microstructure of slabs diffusion distance is usually considered as the second dendrite arm spacing (SDAS). Compare with the conventional thick slabs the SDAS is much smaller in the thin slabs as seen in Figure 4.58.

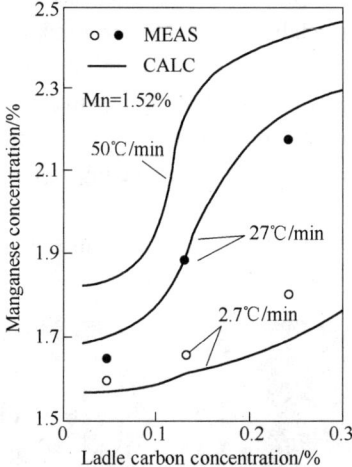

Figure 4.57   Effect of carbon content （with 1.52%Mn, 0.016%P）and cooling rate on interdendritic segregation of Mn (Ueshima et al, 1986)

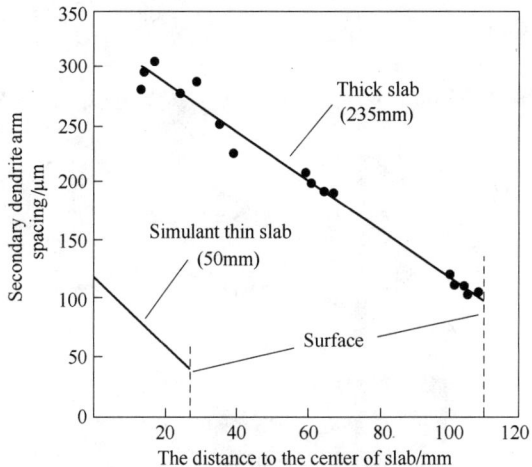

Figure 4.58   Secondary dendrite arm spacing in thin slab (50mm thick) and thick slab (235 mm thick) of a steel containing 0.1%C, 1.45%Mn, 0.07Nb, 0.08V%(Cobo,Sellars,2001)

The spacing of the primary and secondary dendrite arms can be given respectively by the following equations:

$$l_1 = 29.0 \times 10^3 R^{-0.26} G^{-0.72} \tag{4.33}$$

$$l_2 = 11.2 \times 10^3 R^{-0.41} G^{-0.51} \tag{4.34}$$

where l_1 and l_2 is the primary and secondary dendrite arm spacing respectively, μ m; R is velocity of the solidifying frontier, mm/h; G is the temperature gradient, K/mm.

It is clear from the above equations that the more solidification rate increases, the smaller dendrite spacing occurs. The solidification rate of a thin slab (50mm thick) is as about ten times rapider than that of thick slabs (250mm thick). Therefore, the average SDAS in thin slabs with 50mm in thickness is much smaller than that in the thick conventional slabs (250mm thick). Figure 4.58 shows the SDAS of thin slab (50mm thick) compared with that of thick slab (235mm thick) in a steel containing 0.1%C, 1.45%Mn, 0.07Nb, 0.08V% (Cobo, Sellars, 2001). As a result from the SDAS reducing, interdendritic segregation is weakening in the thin slabs.

In the present work, casting structure of the thin slabs was observed in various steels. Three optical picture of the casting structure are shown in Figure 4.59, and

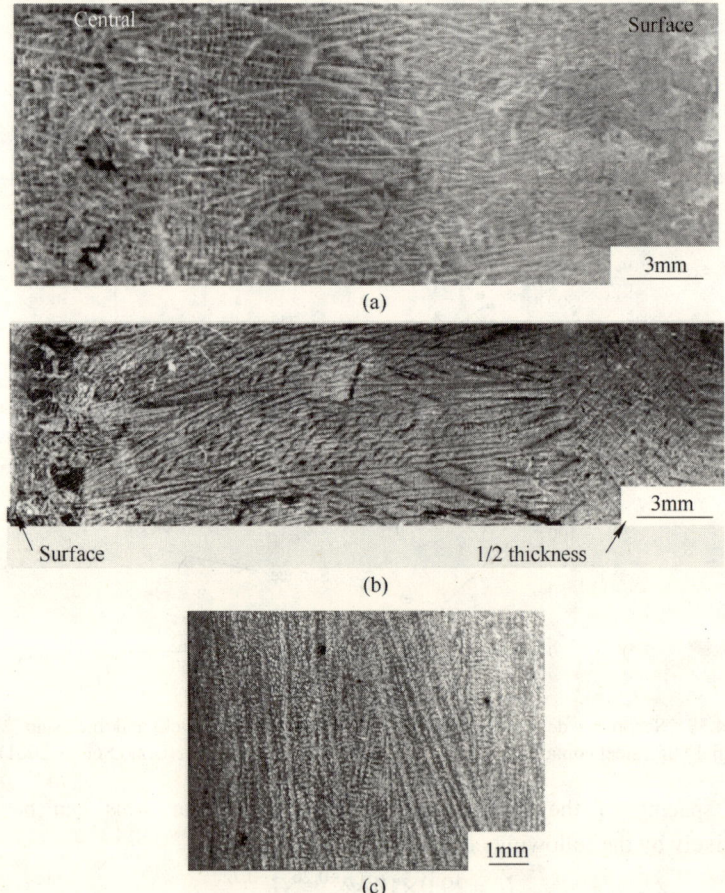

Figure 4.59   Cast structure of thin slabs
(a) Steel ZJ330; (b) Steel ZJ550; (c) ZJ460

composition of them is in Table 4.19. Measurements showed in casting structure of ZJ330 the primary dendrite spacing is 0.25~1.83mm, and the secondary dendrite spacing ranges from 52μm to 180μm with average value 99μm. It is much smaller compared with that in conventional thick slabs, SDAS of which is usually between 200μm and 500 μm.

Table 4.19   Composition of the experimental steels

Steel	C	Si	Mn	P	S	Cu	Ti	Al
ZJ330	≤0.06	≤0.10	0.3~0.50	≤ 0.025	≤ 0.02	≤ 0.20	—	0.02~ 0.040
ZJ460	0.05~0.07	0.3~0.5	0.3~0.50	0.09	≤ 0.02	≤ 0.25	minim	0.02~ 0.040
ZJ550L	0.17~0.19	~0.3	1.0~1.2	≤ 0.023	≤ 0.02			0.02~ 0.04

The smaller SDAS in the thin slabs is obviously resulted from increasing cooling rate. It leads very fine cast structure and relatively more homogeneous distribution of the solute elements such as S, P, Mn, Ti. In other words, microsegregation of the solute elements is not as strong as in thick slabs. This important aspect may have remarkable influence on precipitation behavior of various compounds especially sulfide, oxides, nitride as well as the carbonitrides. Microstructure and hence the properties of the steels would change notablely.

(C) Kinetics aspect of sulfide precipitation in the CSP steels

The size, number and distribution of sulfide particles actually depend on the precipitation kinetics in solid of the steel rather than thermodynamics except that in the liquid phase. Though kinetics of the second phase precipitation in alloys has been developed systematacially in the classical theories, a number of models were proposed in the recent years (Robson, Bhadeshia, 1997; Yin,Faulkner, 2003). Application of the models also reported in the literature. There is no attempt to evaluate the success of the models in this section, but only introduce some observations in the present work. The classical theory only briefly reviewed below.

(a) Nucleation

For homogeneous nucleation in steel the nucleation rate at time t could be described approximatively as the following equation:

$$J(t) \approx 10^{30} \exp(-\Delta F^*/k_B T) \cdot \exp(-\tau/t) \qquad (4.35)$$

where ΔF^* is the activation energy for the critical nucleus formation; τ is the incubation time for nucleation; T is absolute temperature the precipitation takes place; k_B is the Boltzmann constant. It is obviously the nucleation rate increases rapidly along with increase of the overcooling ΔT, namely with lowering the precipitation temperature T. Besides, the relation between overcooling and radius $r*$ of the critical nucleus as well as the activation energy $\Delta F*$ is given by the equation (4.36) and (4.37) respectively(Feng et al, 1990).

$$r* \propto 1/\Delta T \qquad (4.36)$$
$$\Delta F* \propto 1/\Delta T^2 \qquad (4.37)$$

Previous investigation on great number of metallic systems pointed out that almost all nuclei exist at catalyst sites from very early stage of the precipitation process. This is because the nucleation occurs very rapidly at heterogeneous sites. Besides, a very small amount of precipitates will lead reduce of the mean concentration of the solute in matrix. This concentration change can make the nucleation rate to decrease by one or two orders of magnitude. Large number of defects, boundaries and previous formed particles (such as oxides) exist in the steels. They all provide heterogeneous nucleation sites for the subsequent precipitations.

For example, at beginning of the continuous casting process, there existed 4~10ppm soluble oxygen, 20~30ppm sulfur, 44~76ppm nitrogen, 0.029%~0.040% aluminum and 0.30%~0.40% manganese in the liquid of the low carbon steels in EAF-CSP process. These elements would form various oxides during solidification and cooling process of the slabs. Analysis based on diffusion controlled growth model showed that during solidification MnO-FeO form but MnO-FeO-Al$_2$O$_3$ is the results when MnO growing from the primary oxide Al$_2$O$_3$. MnS formed on the MnO-SiO$_2$ particles. In aluminum killed steels ZJ330 by EAF-CSP process Al$_2$O$_3$ can precipitate within an extensive temperature region, from liquid steel to very low temperature, as reported by a thermodynamics calculation (Fu et al, 2002). Al$_2$FeO$_4$ is also present. All these prior particles will be able to work as heterogeneous nucleation sites for the subsequent precipitations especially sulfide particles.

Some observations on the sulfide formation have been obtained by the present authors. One of the experimental evidence is shown in Figure 4.60, where TiN particles acted as cores for copper sulfide precipitation in a EAF-CSP low carbon steel. Morphology of the particles is given in Figure 4.60(a) and (b), which are TEM images taken from a replica specimen set on molybdenum grid. X-ray energy spectrum in Figure 4.60(c) is from near periphery area of one particle. It can be seen from the XEDS that the particle is a copper sulfide probably is Cu$_2$S. Spectrum of the same particle but from the core area is with much stronger Ti speaks as indicated in Figure 4.60(d). Therefore, copper sulfide grew from the surface of Ti nitride particles. This is reasonable because the copper sulfide precipitate at lower temperature than that of the nitride. Another example is given in Figure 4.61 , where Al$_2$O$_3$ particles acted as "core" for precipitate of (Cu,Mn)S.

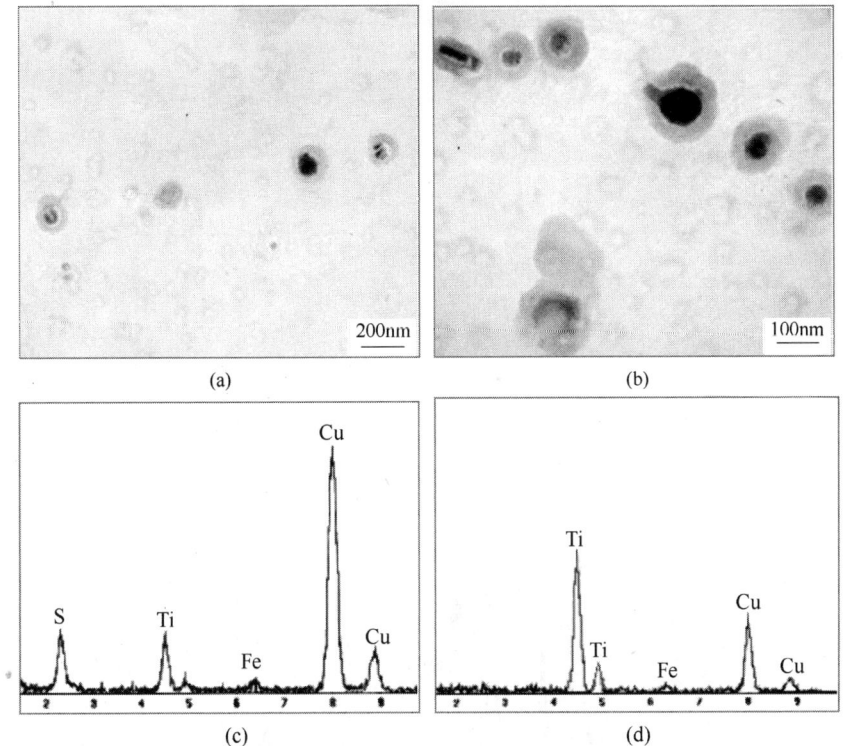

Figure 4.60   Copper sulfide precipitate on TiN particles
(a), (b) Morphology of the copper sulfide/TiN particles; (c) XEDS spectrum from one of the particle;
(d) XEDS from the core of the multiplex article

As a consequence of the heterogeneous nucleation on the oxide and/or nitride, the particle number and distribution of sulfides mostly depend upon the number and distribution of the available sites for nucleation.

Cooling rate of the slabs during solidification has notable effects on the precipitation process. According to the coupled model of microsegregation and precipitation during solidification (Liu Z et al, 2002a, 2002b) developed by Liu Z Z et al, oxide number and radius is greatly affected by the cooling rate. The oxide number increases with the increasing of cooling rate. The radius of oxide particles reduces when the cooling rate increases. Results of the calculation indicated that during solidification with a low cooling rate of 10K/min radius of the oxides would increase from 1μm, 3μm and 5μm into 6.6μm, 6.7μm and 7.4μm respectively, But at a higher cooling rate of 100K/min, the change of the oxide radius is from 1μm, 3μm and 5μm to 3μm, 3.8μm and 5.4μm respectively. The number of oxides in clean steels could be considered as 10^7cm^{-3}, 10^8cm^{-3} and 10^9cm^{-3} approximately corresponding to the cooling rate 10K/min, 100K/min and 500K/min respectively.

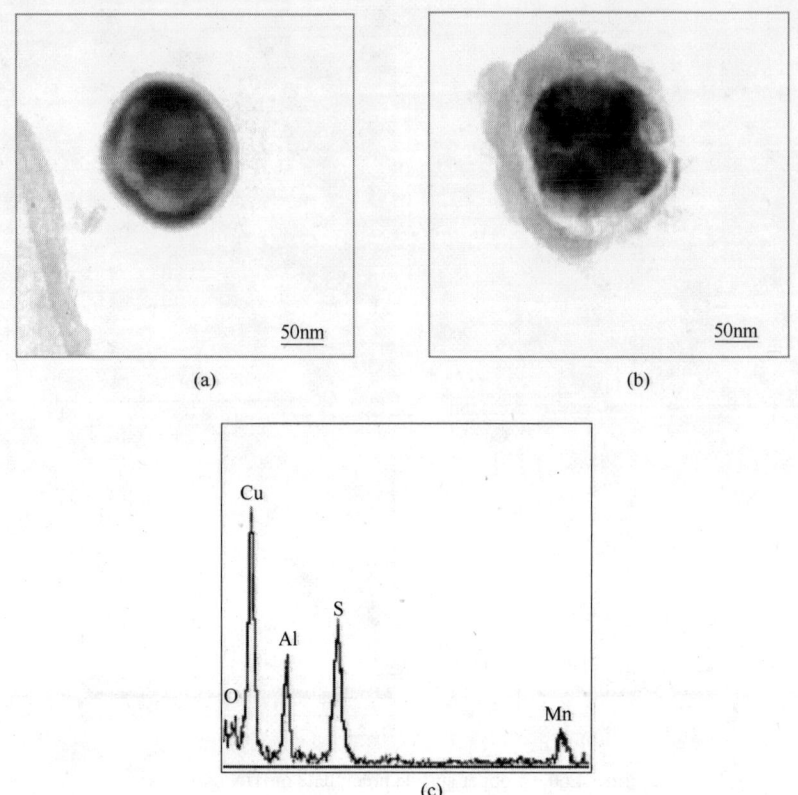

Figure 4.61   TEM micrograph showing precipitate of (Cu,Mn)S growing on Al$_2$O$_3$ particles

Results of the experimental investigation on effect of the cooling rate by Goto H et al showed (Goto et al,1994) a similar tendency, namely increase in the cooling rate results in increasing of the oxide number and decrease of average size of the oxides in a Ti deoxidized steel. But the oxide size observed is smaller than the value, which is calculated by the above coupled model.

Because cooling rate of 120K/min is typical for the 50 mm thin slab in the CSP process, while 9K/min is the cooling rate for conventional thick slab with 250mm in thickness. It is clear that the number of oxides, succedent the sulfides, should be one order of magnitude larger in the thin slabs than that in thick (250mm) slabs. On the other hand, size of the oxides is much smaller in the CSP slabs owing to its accelerated cooling rate. It implies that the difference in the precipitation behaviors of sulfides and oxides would bring remarkable change of the effects on steel properties.

(b) Growth of the precipitates

As soon as the critical nucleus form the growth of them starts. Kinetics of the growth is a complex problem involving number of variables. In steel production practices simplified approach or empirical equations are usually employed. Growth of sulfides and oxides in steels is considered as a diffusion controlled process.

According to the model of diffusion controlled growth developed by Zener-Wert -Ham, for three dimensional growth isothermally of the spherical precipitate after time t, the growth velocity v can be describe approximately as the following equation:

$$v = \alpha_\lambda \left(D/t \right)^{1/2} \tag{4.38}$$

Corresponding radius of the precipitate at time t is:

$$r\alpha \left(D/t \right)^{1/2} \tag{4.39}$$

where D is diffusion coefficient of the element, which controls the growth process.

α_λ is a parameter that takes into account the shape and growth dimensions of the precipitate as well as supersaturation in matrix and etc.

It is obvious from the above relations that at the growth stage, radius of the precipitate is proportional to the square root of the time and diffusion coefficient of the controlling element.

On the other hand, it was also reported that the average diameter $D(\mu m)$ of a spherical sulfide particle is related with the cooling rate V (K/min) of steel after solidification.

$$D = 13.9 V^{-0.30} \tag{4.40}$$

Therefore, when cooling rate of the solidified steel increases, size of the sulfides decreases in inverse proportion to $V^{0.30}$. As cooling rate of the thin slab (50mm thick) is about 120 K/min, but that for a 250mm thick slab is about 9 K/min (see Table 4.11), the size of sulfide particles in the thin slabs would be much smaller than that in thick slabs.

The diffusion coefficient of Mn in the delta phase is about 100 times larger than that in the gamma phase at the same temperature (see Table 4.18). It means that the growth rate of MnS particles in austenite region is much slower than in the delta-ferrite. Thus, compare with the conventional process with thick slabs, number of the oxides is much larger and the size is obvious smaller in the low carbon steels produced by EAF-CSP process.

The size of oxides and sulfides decreases with increasing the cooling rate. Under CSP process conditions, Al_2O_3 and MnS produced in the liquid-solid two phases region are inclusions with a size of several micrometers (e.g $<5\mu m$), but they would be precipitates with nanometer scale when form below the solidus.

(c) Coarsening (Ostwald ripening)

Coarsening of the precipitates will happen when a concentration gradient exists between small and large precipitates. In such condition, the larger particles continue to grow at consuming of dissolution of small particles. This final stage of precipitation is also referred to as Ostwald ripening. During coarsening process number of the precipitates decreases resulted from dissolution of the small particles and average size of the particles rises. The mechanism of coarsening is provided by the Gibbs-Thomson equation.

For diffusion controlled coarsening process the mean precipitate radius and number density of the precipitates N_V can be described by the classic LSW theory, reported by Lifshitz and Slyozov and Wagner. The mean radius $\bar{r}_t$ of the precipitates at time t as function of t is given by equations (4.41).

$$\bar{r}_t^3 = \bar{r}_0^3 + \frac{8}{9}\frac{\sigma D C_\alpha V_p^2 t}{RT} \tag{4.41}$$

where $\bar{r}_0$ is the initial average radius of the precipitates; σ is interfacial energy between precipitate and the parent phase; T is absolute temperature, at which coarsening of the precipitates takes place; V_p is molar volume of the precipitate; C_α is equilibrium concentration of the solute element in the matrix; R is the gas constant; D diffusion coefficient of the solute element in matrix, which controls the coarsening process. It can be described as equation (4.42).

$$D = D_0 \exp(-Q/kT) \tag{4.42}$$

Number density of the precipitates N_V as function of the time t can be written in equation (4.43).

$$N_V(t) = k_3(t-t_1)^{-1} - k_6(t-t_1)^{-4/3} \tag{4.43}$$

where $t > t_1$, $(t - t_1)$ is the time interval for the coarsening process, k_3 and k_6 are the rate constants (Doherty, 1996);

The first term in equation (4.43) is that from the original LSW model, the second term is the correction, involving the effect of decrease in solubility of the precipitates with time.

Though the equations (4.41) and (4.43) were derived for a particular set of assumptions, this model has got agreements with extensive experiment results very well. The changes of particle size with coarsening have also been investigated by computer simulations. In general, average size of the precipitates increases with cube root of the elapsed time t during coarsening process. But number of precipitates in unit volume, i.e. number density, N_V decreases with the elapsed time t as an inverse proportion relation.

The element, which controls the coarsening process, may be determined by the procedure proposed by Yong Qilong et al. They pointed out that the controlling element for coarsening should satisfy the condition with minimum value of the product $D C_\alpha$ Where D is diffusion coefficient of the element in matrix, C_α is equilibrium concentration of the element in matrix (Yong et al, 1993 and 2004).

The mean diameter of precipitates after elapsed time t during coarsening is given by equation (4.44).

$$d_t^3 = d_0^3 + \frac{64 D \sigma V_p^2 C_\alpha}{9 R T V_m C_p} t = d_0^3 + m^3 t \tag{4.44}$$

where, d_0 is the initial mean diameter of the precipitates; V_p is molar volume of the precipitates; V_m is molar volume of the matrix; C_p is equilibrium concentration of the element in the precipitates.

From equation (4.44) the coarsening rate m can be written as in equation (4.45).

$$m = \left(\frac{64 D \sigma V_p^2 C_\alpha}{9 R T V_m C_P} \right)^{\frac{1}{3}}$$

(4.45)

According to the above model coarsening of MnS particles in the CSP low carbon steel ZJ330 during soaking was calculated. The controlling element for this process is determined as sulfur by using the criterion mentioned above, namely this element is with minimum value of the product DC_α. Composition of the studied steel ZJ330 is in the Table 4.19, and diffusion coefficient of the elements in low carbon steels is listed in Table 4.20. Symbol D^δ denotes the diffusion coefficient in the delta ferrite, and D^γ is that in the gamma phase, i.e. austenite.

Table 4.20 Diffusion coefficient in low carbon steels D (cm^2/s)

element	D^δ (in δ-ferrite)	D^γ (in γ phase)
C	0.0127 exp(−19450/RT)	0.0761 exp(−32160/RT)
Mn	0.76 exp(−53640/RT)	0.055 exp(−59600/RT)
Si	8.0 exp(−59500/RT)	0.30 exp(−60100/RT)
S	4.56 exp(−51300/RT)	2.4 exp(−53400/RT)
P	2.9 exp(−55000/RT)	0.010 exp(−43700/RT)

Note: gas constant R= 8.3145 J/(mol • K) =1.987cal/(mol • K).

The soaking procedure for steel ZJ330 is at temperature 1373K for 30 minutes. The interfacial energy between MnS and matrix at 1373K was taken as the value σ =0.65J/m^2 from the result in a silicon steel calculated by W.P.SUN et al.(Sun et al, 1992).Results of the calculation showed that coarsening rate of spherical MnS particles in the steel ZJ330 at 1373K is about 4.5nm³/s. Therefore, during the soaking MnS particles with initial diameter 20nm and 40nm would grow into about 25 nm and 51nm respectively.

In contrast to the above results, for those sulfides precipitated in delta ferrite phase the coarsening rate is much larger. The faster coarsening of sulfides happened in delta ferrite is a consequence from the much rapidly diffusion and higher temperature. In the steels produced by conventional process with thick slabs sulfides usually form at higher temperature mostly in delta ferrite owing to higher sulfur content and slower cooling rate. Reheating of the thick slabs before rolling may cause further coarsening of the sulfides depending on the reheating temperature and time. Such a condition would lead sulfides appear as inclusions with large size.

The reason for sulfides with nanometers in scale distribute in the CSP steels can be summarized as following:

1. Clean steels with lower content of sulfur (<0.05%(mass)) leads the precipitation

takes place at lower temperature especially in the gamma phase region.

2. The CSP process provides accelerated cooling rate in temperature region from 1560 to 1400℃. It resulted in the increase of oxides number and decrease of their size obviously.

3. Decrease in growth rate of oxides, and sequent the sulfides, presents in the CSP steels. This is due to slower diffusion rate of the elements in austenite and at lower temperature. Reduce of the growth rate prevents that the inclusion particles with large size appear in the steels.

4. Smaller coarsening rate resulted from the lower soaking temperature with relative shorter elapse time.

4.5.2.4   Effects of the sulfide and oxide on formation of other phases

(A) Effect on ferrite formation during $\gamma \rightarrow \alpha$ transformation

It is known that second phase particles may act as nucleation catalysts for the succedent transformations. The precipitates in austenite can be effective preferential nucleation sites for the α phase (ferrite) formation as long as the misfit between α phase and the precipitates is small enough. In the present case the misfit between sulfides (including manganese sulfide, iron sulfide and copper sulfide) and ferrite was calculated and given in Table 4.21. Misfit of the iron oxide (wustite) with ferrite is also given in the table.

Table 4.21   Misfit (%) between ferrite and sulfide/oxide

$hkl_{\alpha\text{-Fe}} / hkl_{\text{MnS}}$	100 / 111	110 / 220	111 / 220	111 / 311
Misfit (α-Fe / MnS)	5.25	8.6	10.7	4.53
$hkl_{\alpha\text{-Fe}} / hkl_{\text{Cu}_2\text{S}}$	100 / 200	110 / 220	111 / 311	111 / 222
Misfit (α-Fe / Cu$_2$S)	1.6	1.6	2.48	1.82
$hkl_{\alpha\text{-Fe}} / hkl_{\text{FeS}_2}$	100 / 200	110 / 211	110 / 220	111 / 311
Misfit (α-Fe / FeS$_2$)	5.8	9.1	5.8	1.3
$hkl_{\alpha\text{-Fe}} / hkl_{\text{FeO}}$	100 / 110	110 / 200	111 / 211	111 / 220
Misfit (α-Fe / FeO)	5.9	5.9	5.9	9.3

Except FeS$_2$ (pyrite) and CuS, all of these precipitates have the same cubic structure, i.e. $Fm\overline{3}m$ space group. Their lattice parameters are as following:

MnS: a=0.524nm;

Cu$_2$S: a=0.56286nm;

FeO (wustite): a=0.4293nm;

Fe$_3$O$_4$: a= 0.83nm

α −MnS: a=0.5224nm, sodium chloride structure of cubic crystal at room temperature (Hansen,1956).

FeS$_2$ (pyrite): a= 0.5417nm, cubic crystal;

CuS   hexagonal lattice: a=0.379nm, c=1.633nm, c/a =4.332, corresponds to B18 type structure

γ– iron : lattice constant a=0.3656nm; α –iron a=0.2866nm

It can be seen that all of these precipitates are good catalysts for the α- iron formation owing to their very small misfit with the ferrite. But the overall effect of the nucleation by the precipitates on grain refinement also depends on their volume fraction in the steel. Thus it may not be very significant if the fraction of these sulfides and oxides is not large enough.

Some investigations on role of inclusions in ferrite formation have been reported. These inclusions include various oxide and sulfides (for example, TiO, Al_2O_3, SiO_2, MnO-SiO_2, MnS, (Mn,Cu)S etc.). It has been reported (Madariaga et al,1998) that acicular ferrite nucleate on MnS inclusions covered by a shell consisting of a CuS phase of the B18 type with a hexagonal structure in a medium carbon steel (with 0.37C, 1.45Mn, 0.56Si, 0.043S and 0.14Cu). The non-metallic inclusions have been considered as the most favourable nucleation sites for acicular ferrite. The mechanism of this effect is also discussed in the literature (Zhang, Farrar, 1996; Madariaga,Gutierreg,1997). In addition, in the zone near MnS particles manganese was being depleted. It raises the Ar_3 temperature so that the ferrite formation may be enhanced.

(B) Effects on nucleation of the succedent precipitates

Besides that sulfides could be the preferential nucleation sites of acicular ferrite, fine sulfide particles such as MnS and Cu_2S etc can also provide preferential nucleation sites for other precipitates especially the carbides. For example cementite was found grew from MnS cores (Faruhara et al, 1994). In the present study more evidence has been obtained (Liu D et al, 2002b and 2002d;Huo et al,2005). This can be seen clearly in Figure 4.62(a), where the rod-like particles are carbides and spherical particles are sulfides. The carbides seem to nucleate at the surface of sulfide particles. The XEDS spectrum (Figure 4.62(c)) from a rod-like carbide showed that except iron the carbides also contain small amount of Si. The dark core of the big particle in Figure 4.62 (b) is a copper sulfide containing Fe and Mn as pointed out by the X-ray spectrum shown in Figure 4.62(d). The white area surrounding the sulfide core is "carbide", a X-ray spectrum from the white area is given in Figure 4.62(e). It should be notable that an oxygen peak appears in this spectrum. Thus the actual composition and structure of these "carbide" particles needs further study to clarify.

It is more favorable condition energetically for CuS precipitation from austenite, that CuS precipitate onto the MnS particles rather than directly from austenite because of the large misfit between austenite (fcc lattice) and the hexagonal copper sulfide.

(C) Effect of sulfide and oxide on grain refinement

It is expected that effective grain refinement resulted from these small sulfide and oxide particles and grain boundary segregation of impurity elements can be obtained. These effects played very important role for greatly improving mechanical properties of the low carbon steel (Liu D et al, 2002c and 2003).

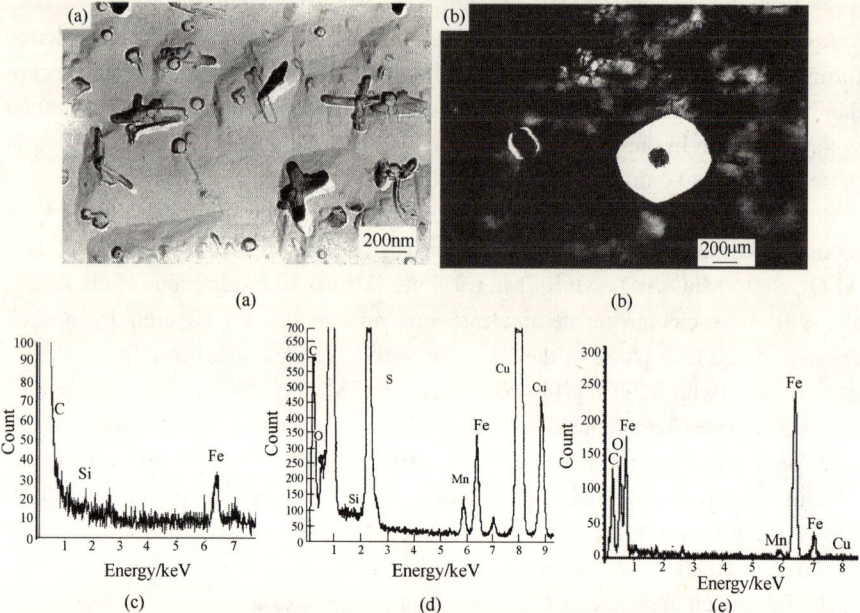

Figure 4.62 (a) Rod-like carbides (its XEDS spectrum is shown in Figure (c))grew from spherical sulfide particles, replica specimen; (b) TEM image of a thin foil specimen the dark core is copper sulfide with its XEDS spectrum in Figure (d); (c)XEDS spectrum of a rod-like carbide in Figure (a); (e) XEDS spectrum from the white area of the big particle in Figure (b)

Under existing of iron oxides and heavy deformation conditions, the nanometer scale sulfide precipitation can also be induced during rolling process, even if the soluble oxygen and sulfur contents are very low. Therefore, it is expected that the fine oxides and sulfides would contribute to the microstructure refinement and precipitation strengthening for low carbon steels. The grain refinement can be achieved by the effect that oxide and sulfide precipitates retard migration of the grain boundaries. Hence growth and coarsening of the austenite or ferrite grains may be suppressed.

It is already known that migrating grain boundaries would be held back by second phase particles. Suppose the grain size limited by this particle pinning is D_z and all of the particles have the same radius r. The grain size D_z can be expressed by equation (4.46), first suggested by Zener and modified later by Gladman (Martin et al, 1997).

$$D_z = \frac{r}{3f_v}\left(\frac{3}{2}-\frac{2}{Z}\right) \tag{4.46}$$

where Z is ratio of the maximum grain size to the average grain size, it may take a value between 2 and $\sqrt{2}$ in general; f_v is the volume fraction of randomly dispersed precipitates with the radius r.

It is evident that dispersive particles retard the migration of austenite or ferrite grain growth during recrystallization or the $\gamma \Rightarrow \alpha$ transformation. Thus fine precipitates can refine grain size obviously. The critical radius of the precipitates, which is effective for retardarce of a growing grain boundary or phase boundary, can be estimated as equation (4.47) (Paimiere et al, 1994). Only those particles with radius smaller than r_{crit} can be pinning the grain boundaries.

$$r_{crit} = \frac{6R_0 f_v}{\pi}\left(\frac{3}{2} - \frac{2}{Z}\right)^{-1} \quad\quad (4.47)$$

where r_{crit} is the maximum size of the particles that will be effectively counteract the driving force of grain growth; f_v is volume fraction of the particles in the microstructure; R_0 is the initial grain radius of the matrix.

In the low carbon steels ZJ330 produced by CSP process, there are two groups of the particles according to their size. One of them with dimension between ~30nm and 200nm may form at higher temperature probably before rolling. The other group is the dispersive precipitates with size smaller than 20nm. These particles seem to settle out at lower temperature such as during cooling or even coiling of the strips. It is very likely that deformation during rolling would have important effect on their precipitation. They may have significant influence on the grain refinement of ferrite and mechanical properties of the steel as their small size and large number.

Particles in the first group are mainly sulfides and oxides. According to the Zener model migrating grain boundaries would be pinned by the sulfide and oxide particles. Thus these particles can clog grain growth of original and recrystallized austenite. They may also drag grain boundaries of ferrite to prevent the grain coarsening after transformation.

In the present case the size of the intragranular sulfides ranged between 30~60nm, and that of the intergranular sulfides is about 200nm. As long as the volume fraction of the particles is determined, either by experiments or by calculation, grain size of the recrystallized austenite will be able to be estimated according to formula 4.46.

Interesting evidence about the dragging effect is shown in Figure 4.63. It can be seen in the SEM micrographs that the grain boundaries are with zigzag shape owing to pinning by the particles. Most of the boundaries are far from their stable positions. A particular example of the particle dragging effect on boundaries is shown in Figure 4.63(b), A moving grain boundary (from right upper towards the left lower direction in the picture) was bended into a hump by the particle hindering so that a ring of the grain boundary was left behind the moving boundary as pointed by an arrow in the picture.

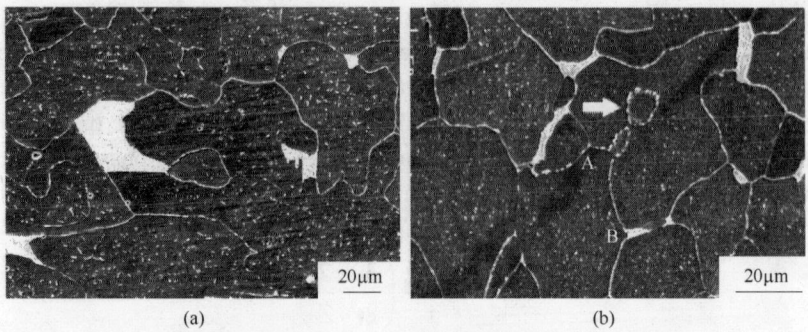

Figure 4.63   SEM micrographs

(a) Showing the grain boundaries are dragged by small particles in the steel; (b) A moving grain boundary AB
left a ring of boundary (pointed by arrow) behind, which was caused by the particles clogging

It is obvious that remarkable grain refinement effects and strengthening can be obtained by the oxide precipitates. Small sulfide particles may also contribute to the strengthening and grain refinement. Therefore, the oxygen and sulfur in steels could play beneficial role under favorable conditions.

4.5.2.5   Other nanometer precipitates in the steels

Very tiny dispersive precipitates have been observed in the thin foil specimens by TEM. Their dimension is ranged from several nanometers to about 20nm. It is indicated by the diffraction analysis that in certain area of the specimen, majority of the precipitates consists with cubic system spinel structure. The lattice parameter a is about 0.83nm as determined from the diffraction patterns. They seem to be the oxide Fe_3O_4 particles as reported previously (Liu D et al, 2002b).

Investigation on the CSP low carbon steels by electron microscopy with XEDS analysis was carried out by the present authors. The main components of the two steels are ZJ330 (with 0.05%C,0.1%Si,0.4%Mn) and ZJ590 (with 0.17%C, 0.3Si%,1.22% Mn). The observations showed that many small precipitates exist in the steels, typical morphology of these precipitates in strips of ZJ590 is cuboid in shape as shown in Figure 4.64 with their X-ray energy spectrum. Size of the quadrate particles is about 30~50nm. Chemical composition of the particles was analyzed individually by XEDS one by one. It is indicated by the analysis that these particles mainly contain carbon, oxygen and iron, in addition small amount of S and Cu or Si and Al also appears in the spectrum. A typical spectrum from the particle is given in Figure 4.64 (c). Certain kind of imaging contrast in central area of the particle can be observed when the image was enlarged.

Considering the nature of these precipitates, their formation in the CSP strips may be interpreted as the following. As already discussed above large number of sulfides and oxides formed at higher temperature. Under the condition of CSP process, particularly the rapid cooling rate, short period of soaking at lower temperature, large deformation during rolling etc., growth and coarsening of the sulfides and oxides had been suppressed or delayed. In addition, some sulfides such as copper sulfide may be induced by hot rolling. These particles with very small size remain in the steels, they provide large number of heterogeneous nucleation sites for the consequent precipitations.

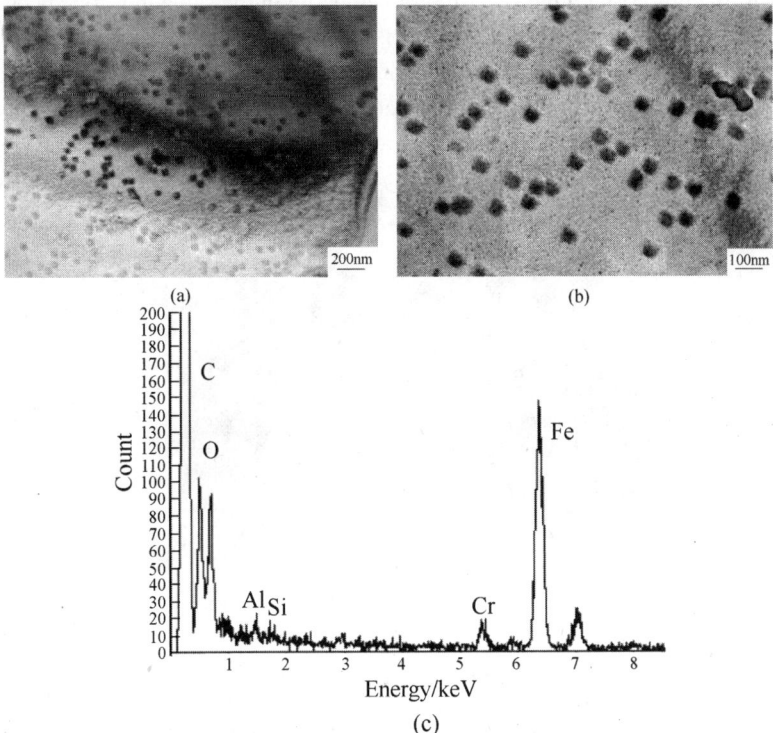

Figure 4.64   Precipitates in the ZJ590 steel strips containing 0.17%C(a,b), XEDS spectrum from one of the particles is given in (c)

Along with the temperature decreasing the condition becomes favorable for carbide formation. Carbides started nucleation on these small sulfide and oxide particles or developed directly by epitaxial growth from the particles. At earlier stage of the precipitation carbides may possess a transition structure, so that the minimum interfacial energy between carbide and the sulfide or oxide can be reached. As already mentioned in section 4.5.2.3, most of the sulfides and oxides possess the same cubic structure with lattice parameter varying around a value. The quadrate shape of the carbides probably implied an epitaxial growth mechanism for their formation. Therefore, these particles may be considered as iron carbides with Cr or other metallic elements. Each carbide particle contains a core, which is an oxide (such as oxide of Al,Si,Fe) or sulfide (sulfide of Mn, Cu etc.).

Analogous precipitates were also observed in steel ZJ330 containing lower carbon (0.05%C). Compare with that in steel ZJ590, size of the precipitates is smaller and number of them decreases. A TEM image from thin foil specimen of the strip ZJ330 is given in Figure 4.65 with X-ray spectrum. X-ray spectrum from one of the particles in the Figure 4.65 (b) shows an oxygen peak clearly, in addition peaks of Cu and S also appear. For some other particles Al and Si also present. In contrast with the spectrum of cementite in the same thin foil specimen, given in Figure 4.65(c), the intensity ratio of carbon peak to iron peak is obviously different from each other. Intensity of carbon peak is much larger in the precipitates(see Figure 4.65(b)). Furthermore the spectrum of cementite is "clean", only the peaks that from carbon and iron appear.

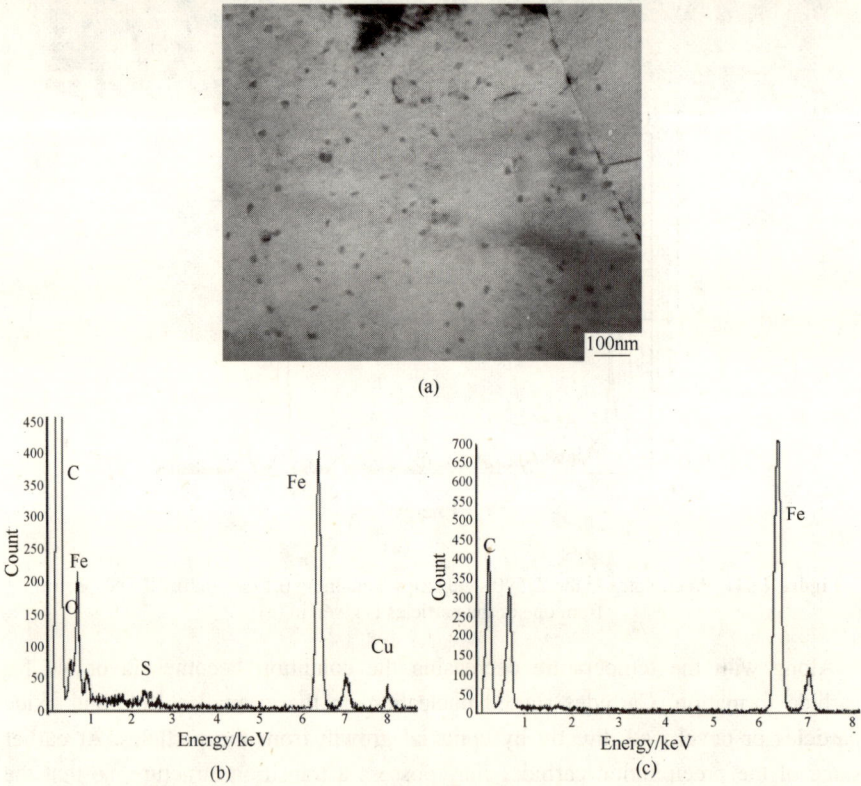

(a)

(b)   (c)

Figure 4.65   Precipitates in the ZJ330 strips containing 0.05%C
(a) TEM image; (b) X-ray spectrum from one of the particles;(c) X-ray spectrum from cementite in the pearlite of the same specimen

Thereby, it may be reasonable to consider the suggestions as following:

1. The dispersive particles are some kind of transition carbides, which nucleae or grow on the tiny sulfides and/or oxides.
2. Precipitation kinetics of these "carbides" and their distribution very likely

depends on that of the sulfides and oxides exist previously in the steel.

3. The nature of these metastable carbides is not yet really understood so far.

4. These fine precipitates may affect the microstructure and mechanical properties of the steels.

4.5.3 *Carbides and carbonitrides in* Ti *containing steels*

4.5.3.1 In general feature

The precipitation behavior of various carbonitrides in low carbon steels have been studied extensively (for years). But most of them were treated with the conditions of conventional cold charge process or special for laboratory studies. Whereas, there are distinct differences in the precipitation behavior between the steels produced by thin slab casting and rolling (TSCR) process and the conventional one. Typical course of the precipitation in steels for conventional cold charge productions is that precipitation (during cooling of the slabs) $\rightarrow$ dissolve (during reheating) $\rightarrow$ re-precipitation accompanying or after hot rolling. Compare with the conventional process, carbonitrides do not undergo the process, that the precipitates dissolve then re-precipitate. For a CSP process, — one of TSCR technology, soon after solidification the slabs are transited to the soaking furnace directly and followed by hot rolling.

It is evident that precipitation behavior of carbonitrides in the steels produced by CSP process is differ from that in the conventional cold charging processing. This discrepancy arises from the important differences between the two production processes. In the cold charging process cold slabs are reheated to a temperature over 1250 ℃ before hot rolling. Carbonitrides, which formed during cooling from casting of the slabs, have to dissolve during reheating, and then precipitate again induced by hot rolling or after rolling. In contrast to the conventional cold charging process, for direct charging of CSP process there is no dissolution of carbonitrides before hot rolling. Much more content of the solute elements remains in the solid solution. As reported by Kunishige et al (Kunishige,Nagao,1989), after soaking at 1150℃ for 20 min. 80 percent of Titanium remains within the solid solution for CSP process. In contrast to this condition, in the steels produced by the conventional cold charging process only about 20 percent of Ti remains in the solid solution, about 80 percent of Ti would be combined in nitrides. This situation leads change in the thermodynamics and kinetics of the precipitation obviously. Much higher supersaturation of the solute element Ti in the CSP process is very favorable for the precipitations.

Previous studies showed (Bai,2005; Bai et al,2005 and 2006) that some precipitation procedure at higher temperature region could be inhibited owing to the much faster solidifying rate and cooling rate of the thin slabs. This resulted in that the content of the solute elements in the solid solution before hot rolling is much higher than expected by the experiences from traditional steel productions. For example, in low carbon CSP steels with small amount of Ti additive, about 80 percent of titanium content remains in the solid solution at 1150℃. Thereby precipitation behavior of the familiar carbonitrides may obviously differ from that in the steels produced by conventional cold charge process.

As a consequent, large number of fine precipitates form during hot rolling or afterwards. On the other hand, remarkable strengthening can be obtained in these low carbon steels. One of the important evidences is that over 700MPa (Liu D et al,2006; Mao et al, 2005a; Mao et al, 2006) yield strength with good elongation has been obtained in the CSP low carbon strips (with chemical composition (mass%) 0.04%~0.07%C,Si: ≤0.6%, Mn: ≤0.6%, P: <0.12%, S: ≤0.01% and 0.12%Ti) produced by Zhujiang Iron and Steel Co., Ltd.. It is clear that precipitates play a great role in strengthening and refining microstructure of the steels.

The microstructure and precipitation behavior of the carbonitrides in the Ti-microalloyed steels produced by CSP process has been studied by various techniques. Different kinds of Ti carbonitride car bide and nitride precipitates have been observed. There are mainly three kinds of precipitates in the steels with Ti additive, i.e. dispersive, precipitates, precipitate arrays as well as those particles with larger size. The character of these precipitates can be summarized briefly as the following:

1. Precipitation in the slabs: The precipitates are comparatively larger, mostly with diameter over 20nm. They should form in the slabs at austenite temperature region before hot rolling. It is pointed out by electron microscopic study and XEDS analyses that these particles are mainly nitrides.

2. Strain induced precipitation: The reaction takes place in the gamma-phase during hot rolling. Products of this reaction could be fine nitrides or carbonitrides depending on the temperature and composition of the steels. Pure carbides usually form at a lower temperature in the low carbon steels considering that rolling is performed mostly from about 1000℃ to 850℃.

3. Precipitation during γ→α transformation: Precipitate arrays resulted from interphase precipitation reaction in the low carbon steels with Ti additive have been observed either in the slabs or the strips.

4. Precipitation in ferrite: Dispersive precipitates usually formed after rolling in the ferrite phase either before or after the coiling of the strips.

In this section only the results newly obtained by the present authors will be introduced.

4.5.3.2   Experimental investigation

Experimental samples were taken from the slabs and hot strips produced by EAF-CSP line. Composition of the steels studied in the present work is (wt%): 0.04%~0.07% C, ≤0.6% Si, 0.4%~0.6% Mn, <0.12% P, ≤0.01% S, about 60 ppm of N and small amount of Ti, which varies from 0.06% to 0.14 %.

The essential difference between the sampling steels is their titanium content, which is varied from 0.06% to 0.14% (wt%)Ti. The hot strips of these steels are with 2mm, 4mm and 6mm in thickness respectively. Slab samples (50mm thick) of the steel with 0.06%Ti were also studied. One of the samples was cut from a slab before soaking and cooled by the air, another sample was cut from a slab of the same steel but after soaking at 1050~1100℃ for 20min followed by spreading water. Samples were cut, ground manually then prepared by electrolytic polishing for TEM study. Extract replica specimens were also made.

(A)Precipitation at higher temperature

Different groups of the carbonitrides containing Ti were observed in the experimental steels. They have precipitated at different temperature region respectively during the CSP processing. At higher temperature region TiN precipitated during solidification of the steel slabs. These cuboid shaped nitrides are smaller than 2μm in size. A SEM micrograph showing the nitrides in a slab of the steel with 0.06%Ti is given in Figure 4.66(a). This slab was cooled in the air before soaking. Some of the nitrides could form by epitaxial growth from other precipitates such as sulfides or oxides. The dark core in a cuboid nitride particle in Figure 4.66(a) (pointed by arrow) was confirmed as sulfide (MnS) by XEDS analysis. Titanium sulfides also exist in the slab as shown in Figure 4.66 (b).

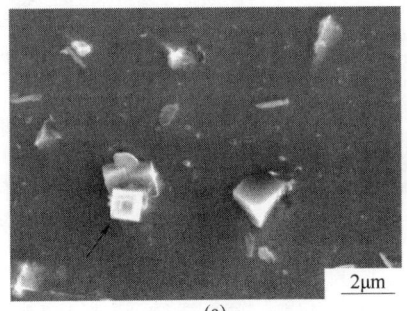 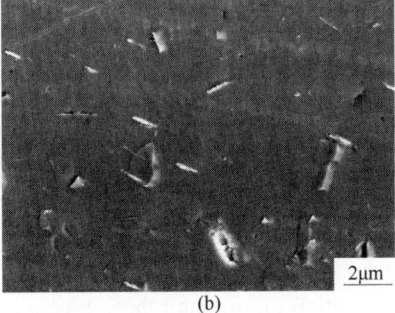

(a)	(b)

Figure 4.66   SEM secondary electron images of the slab cooled before soaking by air showing large precipitates formed at high temperature

(a) TiN particles with cuboid shape; (b) Rod-like particles of Titanium sulfide containing Mn, Fe

Compared with the slab cooled by air, number of the precipitates decreases obviously in the slab, which was cooled by spreading water after soaking at 1050~1150℃ for 20min. This observation implies that few carbonitrides precipitated during the soaking, Most of them precipitated during cooling of the slabs. The soaking at 1050~1150℃ for 20min followed by spreading water is insufficient for the precipitation. But cooling by the air for a slab with 50mm in thickness will be the condition of carbonitride formation in the steels.

(B)Precipitates in gamma-phase

Strain induced precipitation takes place in the gamma-phase during hot rolling. Products of this reaction could be nitrides or carbonitrides depending on the temperature and composition of the steels. Size of the most particles is about ten nanometers or lower. Austenite grain boundaries, sub-grain boundaries and crystalline defects are their preferential nucleation sites. Examples of the precipitates are shown in Figure 4.67 (a) and (b) for the steel containing 0.06% and 0.081%Ti respectively. It can be seen in Figure 4.67(a) that many particles are along some lines. This configuration implies the carbonitrides mainly precipitated along the grain boundaries and/or dislocations. In Figure 4.67 (b) compared with Figure 4.67 (a), there are two groups of the particles. One of them is the particles with tens nanometers in size. They showed some interaction effects with dislocations. Besides them many tiny particles distributed within the grains dispersively. These fine precipitates should form in the ferrite region.

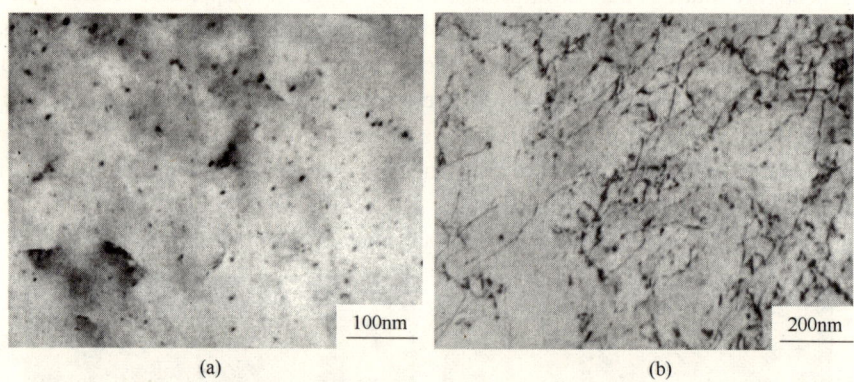

(a)   (b)

Figure 4.67　Carbonitrides precipitated in austenite region of the steel
(a) In a hot strip with 0.06%Ti (6mm thickness); (b) Precipitates and interaction with
dislocations in the strip with 0.081%Ti (6mm thickness)

(C)Interphase precipitation

(a) Experimental observation

Observation on the interphase precipitation of carbides in various steels has been reported (Honeycombe, 1976; Smith, Dunne, 1988; Ohmori, 1976) mainly for isothermal treated samples. In the present work the characterized distribution as arrays of the carbonitrides and/or carbides has been observed by transmission electron microscopy in the slab specimens as well as some hot strips. Figure 4.68(a) gives a TEM micrograph showing the particle arrays resulted from interphase precipitation in the slab with 0.06%Ti, which was cooled by water spreading after soaking at 1100~1150℃ for 20min. It can be seen that the precipitate arrays are quite regular with 55~65nm in spacing between the arrays. The interval between particles within a row is about 20~30nm. The particle size varies from 8nm to 15nm. Their average diameter is about 10nm.

The interphase precipitates of carbonitride also exist in the slab of the same steel but cooled in the air before soaking as given in Figure 4.68(b). As estimated on the figures, the particle row spacing is about 45~55nm and interval between the particles in it is 25~40nm. These particles sized between 10nm and 22nm with average diameter 16nm. It is obvious that the particle size in the slab cooled by air is larger than that in the water cooled slab sample. This deference could be understood as that the precipitates had grown for longer time owing to the slower cooling rate in the air cooled sample.

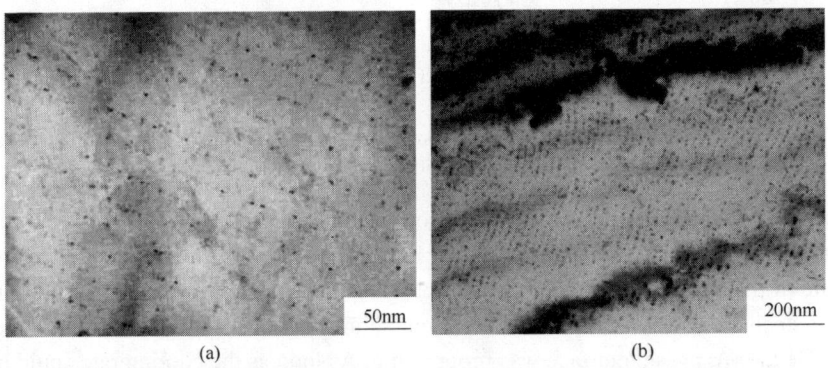

(a)　　　　　　　　　　　　　　　　(b)

Figure 4.68　(a) TEM micrograph showing interphase precipitation of carbonitrides in the slab (0.06%Ti), which was cooled by water spreading after soaking; (b) Interphase precipitation of carbonitrides in the slab (0.06%Ti) cooled by the air before soaking

The hot strip specimens with different Ti content and various thicknesses were all examined by transmission electron microscopy. No interphase precipitate arrays have been observed in the strips (4mm and 6mm in thickness) of the steels containing 0.06%Ti or 0.08%Ti, but only dispersive particles distributed randomly and those on the dislocations or boundaries exist.

However, in the hot strips with 0.12%Ti, carbonitride rows formed through interphase precipitation appear everywhere in the specimens. A typical morphology of the precipitate rows is shown in Figure 4.69. The interval between particle arrays varied from 40nm to 60nm with the particle average diameter 10nm. Dispersive precipitates distributed randomly also present in the specimens as can be seen in the figure.

(b) Controlling factors of interphase precipitation

It is pointed out by the experimental results that the precipitation behavior of the carbonitrides differs in different steels depending on the Ti content in solid solution of the steel. In the strips with lower Ti content（0.06%,0.08% or 0.10%Ti）only particles distributed randomly or along dislocations and boundaries have been observed. But in the strips with higher Ti content especially the steel with 0.121%Ti large amount of carbonitrides appeared by interphase precipitation. While titanium content was further increased to 0.135%Ti, the quantity of interphase precipitated carbonitrides decreases obviously. The reason, which causes interphase precipitation may be understood as in the following text.

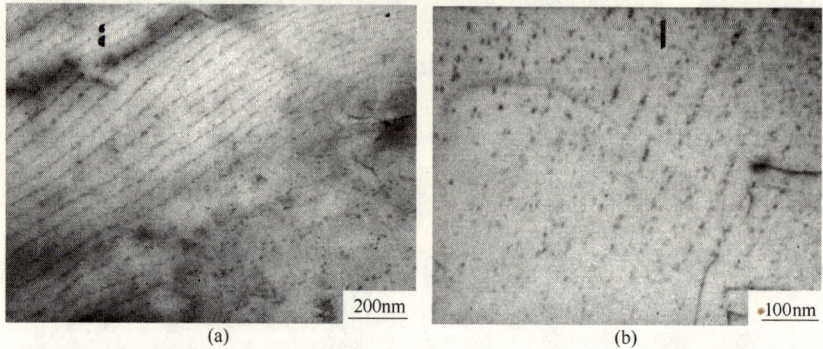

(a)　　　　　　　　　　　　　　　　　　(b)

Figure 4.69　(a) TEM micrograph of the strip (6mm in thickness) with 0.121%Ti showing the typical feature of interphase precipitation. (b) An enlargement from the same specimen area as in (a)

It has been pointed out by the previous work (Yong et al, 1989; He,Xu,1992) when interphase precipitation is taking place the carbonitride nucleated at ferrite side of the γ/α interface, which was in progress. For a continues cooling situation, the steels cool down and across the temperature region for γ→α transformation, while the γ/α phase interface was progressing. As long as the cooling rate could be meet the condition for the precipitation, carbonitrides nucleated at the moving interface preferentially. This periodical nucleation and growth resulted in the particles distributed as arrays. The locations where carbonitride arrays are sitting had been the position of moving γ/α phase interface.

The typical orientation relationship between the precipitates and ferrite matrix is the Baker-Nutting relationship. Location of the precipitate arrays actually had been a series of the γ/α interface position, at which the carbonitride nucleated repeatedly.

One of the conditions necessary for interphase precipitation is the supersaturation of the solute element, such as Ti, which can provide enough driving force. Compatibility between the phase transformation and precipitation is another requirement for this reaction. When migration rate of the phase interface meet the situation that kinetics of the precipitation requires, the precipitation could only take place. Therefore, the key factors for interphase precipitation to occur include: content of the solute element (Ti) in the solid solution; and cooling rate across the γ→α transformation temperature region. For the present case temperature region of the γ→α transformation is from about 850℃ to 600℃.

Both of the precipitation and γ→α transformation are controlled by diffusion.

Therefore, the spacing between the particle arrays depends on the diffusion rate of the solute atoms, here are titanium atoms. While the temperature decreases diffusion rate is going down. Thus the spacing of particle arrays also changes.

Particle arrays formed by interphase precipitation are observed in the slabs (50mm thickness) with 0.06%Ti, but not in the hot strips with 4mm and 6mm in thickness of the same steel. This fact can be interpreted as that the cooling rate for hot strips is too fast to create precipitates at the γ/α interface, carbonitride could only nucleate in the ferrite matrix after $\gamma \rightarrow \alpha$ transformation. It implies that all the experimental steels containing Ti more than 0.06% possess the potency for interphase precipitation. Cooling rate of the steel (slab or strip) determines whether this reaction can actually appear in the sample (Liu W, Jonas, 1998).

In both of the slabs cooled by the air and by water spreading, the actual cooling rate is slower obviously than that in the strips after rolling. Thus the interphase precipitation could appear even in the slabs with 0.06%Ti. But in the strips only those steels containing Ti more than 0.1% can meet the condition for the interphase precipitation. Most abundant of the carbonitrides appear as interphase precipitation in the strips with 0.12%Ti (6mm thickness). When the titanium content further increases such as 0.135%Ti, quantity of the interphase precipitates decreases apparently. This is due to that the precipitation temperature for the carbonitride is elevated along with the Ti content increases. They started formation at higher temperature before the $\gamma \rightarrow \alpha$ transformation. Only partial of the solute Ti retained in the solution, thus effective supersaturation for the interphase reaction reduced. This change leads that the precipitation behavior varies in the steel.

Apparent strengthening effect from the precipitates either by interphase reaction or by precipitation dispersively in ferrite can be obtained. Within the range from 0.045% to 0.095%Ti yield strength of the steel increases linearly while the titanium content increases. The yield strength of 700MPa is attainable for the hot strips. On the other hand, these precipitate arrays may be harmful for toughness and ductility at low temperature. It has been reported that in alloyed steel with vanadium flaw extending showed brittleness characteristics in the area with particle arrays (He, Xu, 1992). Therefore, opposite influence from the precipitates has to be considered when strength of the steels is increased by fine particles (Freeman,1971; Lagneborg, 2000).

Summary

1. In the microalloyed steels with Ti produced by the CSP process supersaturation of Ti either in the austenite or in the ferrite is much higher, the thermodynamics and kinetics for the carbonitride precipitation differs form that in the

conventional cold charging process obviously. The conditions in CSP process is more favorable for Ti-carbonitride or carbide precipitation either through interphase reaction or in the ferrite matrix. It is more effective for the small amount of Ti additive.

2. The interphase precipitation could take place in the steels with Ti content more than 0.06%. But in the strips with thickness less than 6mm only those steels containing Ti more than 0.1% can meet the condition for this precipitation process. Thus the particle arrays formed by interphase precipitation could only observed in slabs, not found in the strips (with 4mm or 6mm in thickness) of the low Ti steels. In the strips with 0.12%Ti interphase precipitation was the dominating mechanism for carbonitride formation. The titanium content in the solid solution and cooling rate across the $\gamma \rightarrow \alpha$ transformation temperature region are the controlling factors for interphase precipitation.

3. Apparent strengthening effect can be obtained by dispersive precipitates and the precipitate arrays of interphase reaction. But the opposite influence on toughness and ductility at low temperature may be caused.

References

Bai D Q, Yue S, Sun W P, et al (1993) Effect of deformation parameters on the No-recrystallization temperature in Nb-bearing steels. Metallurgical Transactions, 24A(10): 2151-2159

Bai Mingzhuo (2005b) Study on fine precipitates in low carbon steels produced by CSP process,Thesis for Master degree,University of Science and Technology Beijing

Bai Mingzhuo,Liu Delu,Lou Yanzhi (2005a) Study on precipitation behavior of Ti(C,N)in CSP low carbon steel with Ti addition ,J.of Univ.of Sci.and Tech. Beijing, 27(6),p 679-683

Bai Mingzhuo,Liu Delu,Lou Yanzhi,Mao Xinping,Li Liejun,Hou Xiangdong (2006) Effects of Ti additive on low carbon hot strips produced by CSP process,J. Univ. Sci.& Tech. Beijing,13(3),p 230-234

Bevis Hutchinson, Lena Ryde, Eva Lindh, et al (1998) Texture in hot rolled austenite and resulting transformation products. Materials Science and Engineering. A257, 9-17

Chen Jiaxiang (1984) Data directory for usual charts in steel-melting. Beijing: metallurgical industry press, (In Chinese)

Cobo S J,Sellars C M(2001)Microstructural evolution of austenite under conditions simulating thin slab casting and hot direct rolling,Ironmaking and Steelmaking, 28(3), pp 230-236

Cornelissen MCM (1986)Mathermatical model for solidification of multicomponent alloys,Ironmaking and Steelmaking,13(4),p 204

Doherty R D (1996)Diffusive phase transformations in the solid state,in Physical

Metallurgy,fourth edition ,ed. By Cahn R W and Haasen P,Elsevier Science B V, pp 1437-1448

Dutta B, Palmiere E J, Sellars. C M. Modeling the kinetics of strain induced precipitation in Nb microalloyed steels. Acta mater, 49: 785-794

Dutta B, Sellars C M (1987) Effect of composition and process variables on Nb(C,N) precipitaton in niobium microalloyed austenite. Materials Science and Technology, No.3, 197-206

Dutta B, Valdes E, Sellars C M (1992) Mechanism and kinetics of strain induced precipitation of Nb(C,N) in austenite. Acta metall. mater, 40(4): 653-662

Edington J W (1975)Practical Electron Microscopy in Materials Science,2,Electron diffraction in the electron microscope,Macmillam,London,p115

Feng Duan, et al (1990)Metal Physics Vol.2,Phase Transformation ,Science Press, Beijing ,p224

Flemming G, Hensger K E (1998) CSP for HSLA Hot Strip. 40th MWSP Conf. PROC., ISS, 775-786.

Freeman S (1971)The effect of second phase particles on the mechanical properties of steel,ISI London,p152

Fu Jie, Zhou Deguang, Li Jing, et al (2002) Control of oxygen, sulfur, nitrogen and its effects on microstructure and properties of low carbon supersteel. Journal of Yunnan University(Natural Sciences Edition), 24(1A): 158-162(In Chinese)

Fu Jie,Zhou Deguang,Li Jing,et al (2002),Control of Oxygen,Sulfur,Nitrogen and Its Effects on Microstructure and Properties of Low Carbon Supersteel,Journal of Yunnan University (Natural Sciences),24(1A),pp158-162

Fu Jie,Zhu Jian,Di Lin, et al (2000),Study on the precipitation behavior of TiN in the microalloyed steels,Acta Metall.Sinica,36(8),p 801

Furuhara T,Shimohata S,Wada K,Maki T (1994)Effect of ferrite substructure on precipitation of Fe_3C at MnS in an ultra-low carbon steel,Tetsu to Hagane,80 (4), pp64-69

Gadellaa Ing.Rob F,Kreijger Dr.Ir.Piet J,Cornelissen Dr.Ir.Marc C.M., et al (1994) Metallurgical aspects of thin slab casting and rolling of low carbon steels,2nd Europ.Conf.Continuous Casting (METEC 94),Vol. 1,Dusseldorf,June 20-22, 382-389

Garbarz B,Marcisz J,Wojtas J (2003)TEM analysis of fine sulphides dissolution and precipitation in steel,Materials Chemistry and Physics,81,pp486-489

Gladman, F B Pickering(1967) Grain-coarsening of austenite. Journal of The Iron and Steel Institute, No.6: 653-664

Goto H,Miyazawa K,Yamaguchi K,Ogibayashi S,Tanaka K (1994) Effect of cooling rate on oxide precipitation during solidification of low carbon steels,ISIJ International, 34(5), p414-419

Guo Liang (1999) Technology characters and product development of CSP. Metallurgy Translation, No.3, 32-35, 10 (In Chinese)

Han Zhiqiang,Cai Kaike (2000)Study on a mathematical model of microsegregation in continuously cast slab,Acta Metallurgica Sinica,36(8),p869-873

Hansen M (1956)Constitution of binary alloys,Metallurgy and Metallurgical Engineering Series,2nd ed., [McGraw Hill-Book Co.Inc.] ,p126 & p 950

He Zefu, Xu Jianping (1992), Study on flaw extension in the area with interphase precipitates of 15MnV steel,in Application basis of micro-alloying elements V,Nb,Ti in the low alloy steels,ed.by Liu Jiahe,Beijing Publishing Company of Science and Technology,p63

Henry N F M,Lonsdale K (1969)International tables for X-ray crystallography,1,The Kynoch Press,Birmingham,p686

Honeycombe R W K (1976)Transformation from austenite in alloy steels,Metall Trans,7A(7),p 915

Huo Xiangdong,Liu Delu,Sun Xianwen,Zhang Ruosheng,Mao Xinping (2004c)Grain refinement mechanism of low carbon steels produced by thin slab casting and rolling,Proc.of Second International Conference on Advanced Structural Steels, (ICASS-2004), Shanghai, April, p140-143

Huo Xiangdong,Liu Delu,Wang Yuanli, et al (2004b)Grain Refinement of low carbon steel produced by CSP process,J.Univ.of Sci.and Tech. Beijing ,11(2),p133-137

Huo Xiangdong,Liu Delu,Wang Yuanli,Bai Mingzhuo,Kang Yonglin (2005) Nanometer sulfides in low carbon steel produced by CSP process,Iron and Steel, 40(8): 60-64

Huo Xiangdong,Wang Yuanli,Liu Delu, et al(2004a) Microstructure and mechanical properties of low carbon steel strip produced by CSP Process,Journal of Iron and Steel Research,16(3),p55-59

Ito Y,Yonezawa N and Matsubara K (1980a)The composition of eutectic conjugation in Fe-Mn-S system,Trans.ISIJ,20,p19

Ito Y,Yonezawa N,Matsubara K (1980b)Effect of carbon on the composition of eutectic conjugation in the Fe-Mn-S system and equilibrium composition of sulfide in solid steel,Trans.ISIJ,20,p301

Kang Yonglin (1999) Quality control and formability of current automobile plates, Beijing, metallurgical industry press .(In Chinese)

Kang Yonglin (2004) New development of TSCR technology and microstructure, properties of the steel, Symposium of Materials, China, 2004, Beijing, 11，266-268 (In Chinese)

Kang Yonglin, Fu Jie, Liu Delu, Yu Hao (2006) Control of microstructure and properties of steels produced on TSCR line. Beijing: metallurgical industry press, (In Chinese)

Kang Yonglin, Fu Jie, Mao Xinping (2005) Synthetic controlling theory on microstructure property for thin slab casting and rolling steel and its application，Iron and Steel，Vol.40,No.7,41-45

Kang Yonglin,Liu Delu,Fu Jie,Li Jing,Yu Hao,Wang Yuanli (2001)Microstructural characteristics of low carbon steel strip produced by CSP technology,Iron and Steel, 36(6), p 40

Kang Yonglin，Yu Hao，Fu Jie，et al (2003) Morphology and precipitation kinetics of AlN in hot strip of low carbon steel produced by compact strip production. Materials Science and Engineering A351（2003-6）265-271

Khalid F A,Edmonds D V(1993)Interphase precipitation in microalloyed engineering steels and model alloy,Materials Science and Technology,9(5),p 384

Kunishige K,Nagao N (1989)Strengthening and toughening of hot-direct-rolled steels by addition of a small amount of titanium.ISIJ International,29(11),p940-946

Kwon O, Deardo A J. Internations between recrystallization and precipitation in hot-deformed microalloyed ateels. Acta metall mater, 39(4): 529-538

Lagneborg R (2000)The significance of precipitation reactions in microalloyed steels, HSLA Steels,2000,edited by Liu Guoquan,Wang Fuming,Wang Zubin, Zhang Hongtao, Metallurgical Industry Press, Beijing, pp 61-70

Leno M Cheng, E Bruce Hawbolt, Ray Meadowcroft T (1999) Modeling of AlN precipitation in low carbon steels. Scripta Materialia, 41(6): 673-678

Li Daizhong (1983) Non-metallic inclusions in steels,Science Press,Beijing,p65

Liu Delu,Chen Nanjing,Huo Xiangdong,Wang Yuanli,Fu Jie,Kang Yongling (2002d) Nano-scaled precipitates in low carbon steels produced by EAF-CSP process. Proceedings of International Symposium on Thin Slab Casting and Rolling (TSCR'2002), Guangzhou, p 323-328

Liu Delu,Fu Jie,Kang Yonglin,Huo Xiangdong,Wang Yuanli,Chen Nanjing (2002a), "Oxide and sulfide dispersive precipitation and effects on microstructure and properties of low carbon steels",J.Mat.Sci.Tech.,18(1),p7-9

Liu Delu,Huo Xiangdong,Wang Yuanli,Fu Jie,Kang Yonglin,Chen Nanjing (2001) Oxide and Sulfide Dispersive Precipitation In Ultra-low Carbon Steels,J.of Univ.of Sci. & Tech. Beijing. 8(4):314

Liu Delu, Huo Xiangdong, Wang Yuanli,Sun Xianwen (2003) Aspects of microstructure in low carbon steels produced by the CSP Process,J.of Univ.of Sci. and Tech. Beijing, 10(4),p1-6

Liu D L,Mao X P,Ni X Q, et al (2006)Carbonitride precipitations in low carbon Ti-microalloyed steels produced by CSP process, Proceeding, 2006 International Symposium on Thin Slab Casting and Rolling, Guangzhou, p10-16

Liu Delu,Wang Yuanli,Huo Xiangdong,et al (2002b)Electron microscopic study on nano-scaled precipitation in low carbon steels,J.Chinese Electron Microscopy Society, 21(3), p 283-286

Liu Delu,Wang Yuanli,Huo Xiangdong,et al (2002c) Grain Refinement and Strengthening of Low Carbon Steel by the CSP Process,Acta Metall.Sinica,38(6),p 647-651

Liu W J and Jonas J J (1998)Metal.Trans. 19A, p1403

Liu W J, Jonas J J (1989) Nucleation kinetics of Ti carbonitride in microalloyed austenite. Metallurgical Transactions, 20A(4): 689-697

Liu Zhongzhu,Gu Kejing and Cai Kaike (2002a)Mathematical model of sulfide precipitation on oxides during solidification of Fe-Si alloy, ISIJ International, 42(9), 950-957

Liu Zhongzhu,Wei Jun and Cai Kaike (2002b)A couple mathematical model of microsegregation and inclusion precipitation during solidification of silicon steel,ISIJ International,42(9),p 958

Luis A. LeDuc-Lezama，Miguelv.del Mercado，Rafael G.dela Pena (1997) Hot rolling of thin gage strip steel at Hylsa. Iron and Steel Engineer, 74(4): 27-31

Lyman T,Boyer H E,Carnes W J and Chevalier M W(eds) (1973)Metals Handbook, 8th ed, Metals Park, OH, Vol.8

Madariaga I and Gutierrez I (1997)Nucleation of acicular ferrite enhanced by the precipitation of CuS on MnS particles, Scripta Materialia,37(8),pp1185-1192

Madariaga I,Romero J L,Gutierrez I (1998)Upper acicular ferrite formation in a medium carbon microalloyed steel by isothermal transformation: nucleation enhancement by CuS, Metall. and Mater. Trans.A, 29A, p1003-1015

Majta J, Lenard J G, Pietrzyk M (1996) Modeling the evolution of the microstructure of a Nb Steel. ISIJ International, 36(8): 1094-1102

Mao X P,Sun X J,Kang Y L (2006)Physical metallurgy for the titanium microalloyed strip produced by thin slab casting and rolling process,Acta metal. sinica, 42(10), p1091

Mao Xinping (2005b)Theoretical and practical investigation on titanium microalloyed high strength erosion resistant steels produced by EAF-CSP,Thesis for Doctor Degree, University of Science and Technology Beijing

Mao Xinping,Sun Xinjun,Kang Yonglin, et al (2005a) Microstructure and properties of titanium microalloyed high strength strip produced by EAF-CSP,Iron and Steel, 40(9), p 65

Martin J W,Doherty R D,Cantor B (1997) Stability of microstructure in metallic systems (Second edition), Cambridge University press, Cambridge, p326

Medina S F, Mancila E. Static recrystallization modeling of hot deformed steels containing several alloying elements. ISIJ International, 36(8): 1070-1076

Michael Korchynsky, Stanislaw Zajac (1998) Technical economical efficiency of product produced by TSCR line. Vanadium and Nitrogen micro-alloyed steel symposium, Central Iron and Steel Research Institute, (In Chinese)

Mintz B,Mohamed Z (1989)Influence of Manganese and Sulphur on Hot Ductility of Steels Heated Directly to Temperature,Materials Science and Technology,5,p1212

Nakamura Y,Esaka H (1981)Tetsu to Hagane,67,p 8140

Ohmori Y (1976)Interphase precipitation of carbonitride in steels,Bulletin of JIM, 15(2), p 93

Palmiere E J, Carcia C I, Deardo A J (1994) Compositional and microstructural changes which attend reheating and grain coarseing in steels contenting niobium. Metallurgical and Materials Transactions. 25A: 277-286

Paimiere E J,Garcia C I,DeArdo A J (1994) Compositional and microstructural changes which attend reheating and grain coarsening in steels containing Nb, Metall. and Mater. Trans. A, 25A, p 277

Park S H, Yue S, Jonas J J (1992) Continuous-cooling-precipitation kinetics of Nb(C,N) in high-Strength low-alloy Steels. Metallurgical Transactions, 23A: 1641-1651

Rainforth W M, Black M P, Higginson R L, et al(2002) Precipitation of NbC in a model austenite steel. Acta Materialia, 50: 735-747

Robson J D, Bhadeshia HKDH (1997)Mater. Sci.Technol., 13, p 640

Smith R M, Dunne D P (1988) Structure aspects of alloy carbonitride precipitation in microalloyed steels. Materials Forum, (11), p166

Sun W P, Militzer M, Bai D Q, et al (1993) Measurement and modelling of the effects of precipitation on recrystallization under multipass deformation conditions. Acta metall. mater, 41(12): 3595-3604

Sun W P, Militzer M,Jonas J J(1992) Strain-induced nucleation of MnS in electrical steels. Metallurgical Transaction A, 23A(3): 821-830

Sun Z Q, Yang W Y, Qi J J, Hu A M (2002) Deformation enhanced transformation and dynamic recrystallization of ferrite in a low carbon steel during multipass hot deformation[J]. Mater. Sci. Eng. A334(1-2): 201-206.

Tekko-Binran (1981)(Handbook for Steel),by ISIJ,3RD ed., Maruzen, Tokyo, Vol. 1, pp. 193-194

Turkdogan E T, Ignatowicz S and Pearson J (1955) J.Iron Steel Inst., 180, p 349-354

Ueshima Y,Mizoguchi S,Matsumiya T,Kajioka H (1986)Analysis of solute distribution in dendrites of carbon steel with δ/γ transformation during solidification, Metal. Trans. B, 17B,p845

Ueshima Y,Sawada Y,Mizoguchi S,Kajioka H (1989)Precipitation behavior of MnS during δ/γ transformation in Fe-Si alloys,Metal.Trans.A,20A,p1375

Wakoh M,Sawai T,Mizoguchi S (1996)Effect of S content on the MnS precipitation in steel with oxide nuclei,ISIJ International,36(8),p1014-1021

Wang S R, Tseng A A (1995) Macro- and micro-modelling of hot rolling of steel coupled by a micro-constitutive relationship. Materials and Design, 16(6): 315-336

Wang Yuanli,Liu Delu,Shao Weiran,et al (2004)Influence of copper on quality of hot strip by EAF-CSP process,J of Univ.of Sci.and Tech.Beijing,11(1),p 57

Wilson F G, Gladman T. Aluminium nitride in steel. International Materials Reviews, 33(5): 221-286

Wriedt H A ,Hu Hsun (1976),Metall.Trans.A,7A,p 711-718

Xu Kuangdi, Liu Qingyou (2005) Study on grain refinement during thin slab casting and rolling，The third symposium proceeding on technology communication and development of TSCR. Tangshan，1-9. (In Chinese)

Yaguchi H (1986) Manganese sulfide precipitation in low-carbon resulfurized free-machining steel.Metall.Trans.A,17A,p 2080-2083

Yin Y F and Faulkner (2003)Simulations of precipitation in ferritic steels,Materials Science and Technology,19,p 91-98

Yong Qilong,Li Yongfu,Sun Zhenbao, et al (1993) Second-phase on grain coarsening time and temperature,Gangtie,28(9),p 45-50

Yong Qilong,Liu Qingyou,Liu Su,et al (2004) Theoretical Analysis on Controlled Element of Ostwald Ripening Process of Manganese Sulfide in Steels,Special Steel, 25(6), p7-9

Yong Qilong,Ma Mingtu, Wu Baorong (1989) Microalloyed steels-physical and mechanical metallurgy,Machinery Engineering Press,Beijing

Yu Yongning (2000) Principle of Metallography. Beijing, metallurgical industry press, 471-493. (In Chinese)

Yue Mantang, Yang Dejiang, Wu Longhua. Microstructure and properties of directly rolled thin slab. Iron and steel, 31(4): 74-79. (In Chinese)

Zhang Z and Farrar R A (1996) Role of non-metallic inclusions in formation of acicular ferrite in low alloy weld metal, Mater.Sci.Technol., 12, p 237-260

Zurob H S, Brechet Y, Purdy G (2001) A Model for competition of precipitation and recrystallization in deformed austenite. Acta mater., 49: 4183-4190

5
Microstructure Fining Theory of Low- carbon Bainitic Steel

The modern Low (Ultra-low) Carbon Bainitic Steel (ULCB) is a high-strength, high-toughness and multi-application steel. Its appearance is the consequent result of the social need and the development of the modern metallurgy technology in recent 30 years. Due to the sharp reduction of the carbon content in the steel, the disadvantageous effects of the carbon on the toughness of the bainite microstructure is eliminated completely, and the fine bainitic matrix microstructures with a high dislocation density can be obtained with the controlled rolling and controlled cooling. The strength of the steel does not depend on the carbon content in the steel any more, and it is primarily guaranteed by the following methods: fine grain strengthening (microstructures), dislocation and substructure strengthening, the precipitation strengthening due to the micro-alloying elements such as Nb, Ti, and V, as well as the sediment strengthening of the ε-Cu. The strength and the toughness of ULCB steel match perfectly, and especially the steel has excellent field welding performances and the capability of resisting HIC (hydrogen induced cracking). In the end of chapter, a theoretical concept is proposed for the further fining on the basis of the overview of fundamental microstructures and performance characteristics of the new steel. A theoretical concept is proposed for the further fining.

5.1 Social Needs for Low-carbon Bainitic Steel with a Grade of More than 600MPa

In the world, the characteristics for the low-alloy high-strength medium and heavy steel plates with excellent welding performances, are large usage as well as its multi-applications. At present, the steel is largely used in the equipments such as various engineering machinery, large electric shovels, bulldozers, dump trucks, oil &gas pipelines, drilling platforms, drilling machines and coal synthesized excavating machinery (hydraulic stands, drag conveyors), which are commonly used in many fields such as energy source, traffic, raw material industries and various engineering constructions. The common characteristics of the equipments are that the steel should be required to have a high strength (generally tensile strength of more than 600MPa), a high toughness or a low-temperature toughness (especially for the equipments used in a cold region), good welding performances and a cold formability (generally with a simple welding process required, without treatment before or after welding), a good cold bending (including wide cold bending) property. In addition, the steel should also have a good fatigue resistance and a certain corrosion resistance. To reduce the cost of manufacturing various equipments and improving technological properties, the steel is generally expected to have low carbon and alloying element contents, be adapted for different needs, and have a wide selecting range in the properties and specifications so as to meet the requirements of different customers. For example, in the construction of the oil & gas pipelines, if X80 or X100 steel is selected instead of X52 steel, large amounts of material can be saved because the pipe wall can be thinned sharply, and the pipe pressure is also raised and more energy sources are conveyed. For large members such as bridges, buildings, the weight-reduction requirement of these members can be met. Therefore, the social needs for the steel with a grade of more than 600MPa are increasingly wider and larger.

The primary drives to develop the low-carbon bainitic, high-strength, high-toughness and multi-application steel, are the complete meeting for social needs, reduction in the production and use costs of the high strength and toughness steel, and meeting for technological requirements such as welding. Of course, there are also two key technology factors for the appearance of large batches of commercial low (ultra-low) carbon bainitic steels in the practical industrial mass production in recent years. One is the development of the metallurgical production technology. The first is the large-scale application of the ladle metallurgy technology, which makes it possible to mass-produce the low (ultra-low) carbon steel; thus, in steel making, after the carbon content is decreased sharply, the contents of the gases such as oxygen, nitrogen in the steel are decreased, and the reclamation of various trace elements is controlled. In the hot processing technology, the complete development of TMCP technology, realizes the full-process control of the steel production. The other key technology factor is the complete development of the study and applications on micro-alloying elements such as Nb, Ti, V, B, especially the study and applications on the combined effect of trace Nb and Nb-B, Nb-Cu-B, playing a prominent role in the development process. At present, in the world, there have been a series of low (ultra-low) carbon bainitic steels formed, with the yield strength of more than 600MPa, widely used in oil pipelines, engineering machinery, oil production platforms, maritime facilities, bridges and military boats and ships.

In China, the development for the low (ultra-low) carbon bainitic steel starts very late. At the end of 1980s, the study for Nb-bearing ultra-low carbon bainitic pipeline steel, was carried on by University of Science and Technology Beijing and Baoshan Iron and Steel Corporation, and the trial run was done using a 300t converter. At the beginning of the 1990s, the study and development for Nb micro-alloyed low (ultra-low) carbon bainitic steel with grades of DB590 and DB685 for engineering machinery, was carried out by University of Science and Technology Beijing and Wuhan Iron and Steel Corporation, and the steel was produced on a scale of several thousand tons annually and used in many fields such as engineering machinery, mining equipments, etc. In 1998, National Basic Research Program of China（973 Program）was launched; In order to develop a new generation of super-fine, low-cost and energy-saving steel, a creative thought for intermediate-temperature transformation microstructure ultra-fining and TMCP+RPC process control technology were developed, and ultra-fine microstructure low-carbon bainitic steel series with grades of 500~800 MPa were built. At present, produced by the leading metallurgy enterprises such as Anshan Iron and Steel Corporation and Wuhan Iron and Steel Corporation, over 300000 tons of steel plates with different grades, have been put into market and used widely in many fields.

5.2 Strengthening Mechanism of Low (Ultra-low) Bainitic Steel

Carbon is an important element for strengthening matrix, especially for the strengthening of the ferrite; but in the low (ultra-low) carbon bainitic steel, because the carbon content has dropped very low, then though the full bainite microstructures are easy to be obtained, the strength drop caused by the carbon reduction, must be compensated by other methods. The study shows, the strengthening mechanisms of the bainitic steel can be primarily concluded into the following aspects:

1. Fine bainite bundles. For the low (ultra-low) carbon bainitic steel, by taking advantage of the modern steel-making production technology, using the ladle refining and the continuous casting, taking advantage of controlled rolling in the high-temperature non-recrystallization zone, to obtain slender deformed austenite grains; the elements (generally Mn, Cu, Nb, Mo, B, etc.) that can raise the hardenability are added a little in the steel. Under air-cooled after rolling, the deformed austenite can be transformed into the fine bainite microstructures with various shapes, then the size of the bainite lath bundles or the granular bainite lumps, is equivalent to the significant grain size. The microstructure fining contributes much to the strengthening of the bainitic steel. The primary purpose of describing

the bainite microstructure fining technology in the paper, is to fully fine the significant grain size and reach the maximum raisement of the all-round properties.

2. High dislocation density. In the cooling process, the bainite is formed in shearing mode, and considerable number of transformation dislocations are produced in the process; on the other hand, the transformation product can inherit large amounts of deformed dislocations produced during deformation in nonrecrystallization zone in the austenite, which accordingly makes the dislocation density in the bainite high, and the yield strength of the steel is raised significantly.

3. Carbide precipitation and ε-Cu aging strengthening (approximately 10nm). The elements such as Nb, Ti, V, Cu, Mo, B added in small amount in the steel, are precipitated on the high-density dislocations and substructures, generating the obvious strengthening effect.

4. Solid Solution Strengthening of the Carbon in the Ferrite. The carbon content in the steel has been reduced to 0.04% or so, the cementite can not generally be produced under the cooling condition, so the problems such as the harm of the carbon, the influence of the cementite on the bainite toughness, are completely eliminated, and the steel has excellent welding performances(Garcia et al,1992); under each cooling condition, in the coarse grain heat affected zone, the bainite microstructures with a high toughness can be obtained, and the impact transition temperature of the steel can be decreased to about$-60℃$; by the precipitation strengthening of Nb, Ti, V and ε- Cu, the yield strength of the material can reach over 500MPa, and the toughness is obviously higher than that of the common low-alloy high-strength steel. It is a typical low-cost, high-performance, energy-saving and multi-application steel.

5.3 Primary Characteristics of Several Kinds of Low-carbon Bainitic Steels Developed in China

5.3.1 CCT curve characteristics of the steels

For the steel (C 0.036%, Mn 1.33%, Nb 0.049%, B 0.0029%) trially produced in Baoshan Iron and Steel Corporation, the B_s point measured is within $605℃(20℃/s)$ ~645 ℃ (5 ℃ /s). The pre-deformation before cooling influences the phase transformation temperature, and the B_s point ascends by approximately 10~15℃; when the steel is cooled at more than 4℃/s, there is no proeutectoid ferrite. Typical CCT curves for DB590 Steel are shown in Figure 5.1. When the steel is cooled at more than 2℃/s, there is basically no ferrite appearing in the steel; after cooled at 6℃/s, there is no martensite in the steel.

When a certain amount of Cu is added in the steel, the ferrite transformation range further moves to the right; when the cooling rate is more than 0.2℃/s, there is basically no ferrite in the sample. In the meantime, due to the Cu addition, the starting point of the bainite transformation lowers, and the B_s point of the steel does not vary basically with the cooling rate in a rather large cooling rate range, kept at 600℃ or so; Thus, it can be guaranteed that the microstructure uniformity can be maintained in a large range of the plate thickness, and the medium and heavy plates will have basically similar bainite microstructures in the sequent cooling process（as shown in Figure 5.2(He et al,1997).

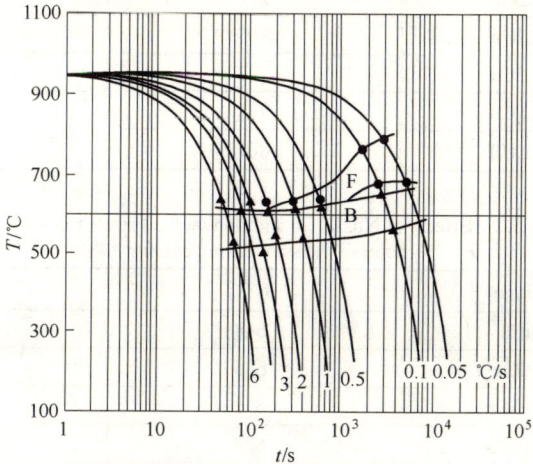

Figure 5.1   Typical CCT curves of DB590

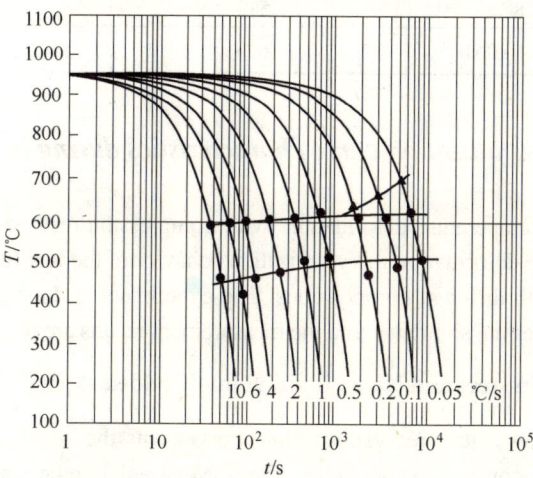

Figure 5.2   CCT curves of steel with Cu addition

Table 5.1 and 5.2 show typical examples for the effects of three elements, Cu, Nb, B, on the phase transformation point. In the steel with 0.05%C, 1.05%Mn, 0.7%Cu, when B (10~15ppm) or Nb(0.04%) individually, or Nb and B compoundly are added and Cu addition changes, the phase transformation point change of the steel during being heated or cooled, reflects obviously the combined effect.

Table 5.1   Effects of Nb, B, Cu addition on phase transformation points Ac_1 Ac_3

Steel Grade	$Ac_1/{}^\circ C$	$Ac_3/{}^\circ C$
Without B	807	915
Nb+B+0Cu	828	918
Nb+B+0.5Cu	811	901
Nb+B+0.7Cu	805	895
Nb+B+1.5Cu	787	889
Nb+B+1.8Cu	747	840
Nb +0.7Cu+0B	807	915

Table 5.2   Effects of Nb, B, Cu addition on the bainite transformation point of the steel during cooling

Steel Grade	$B_s/{}^\circ C$	$B_f/{}^\circ C$
Without B	648	526
Nb+B+0Cu	666	523
Nb+B+0.5Cu	651	508
Nb+B+0.7Cu	627	489
Nb+B+1.5Cu	598	475
Nb+B+1.8Cu	549	435
Nb +0.7Cu+B+0Nb	632	503

5.3.2   *Recrystallization curve characteristics during hot-processing*

Using the high-temperature deformation twice compression method, to measure the high-temperature deformation recrystallization behavior of the low (ultra-low) carbon bainitic steel with different compositions. The experiment is done on a MTS tester and a Gleeble thermal simulator, and the measurement results are the followings:

5.3.2.1   C-Mn steel and Nb or B individually added steel

Figure 5.3 shows the recrystallization curves of the steel after 25% hot deformation. According to the figure, the C-Mn steel is recrystallized fast after deformation at 1000℃, and the recrystallization will be completed in 10s; even the deformation temperature is dropped to 900℃, the recrystallization after deformation will be completed in 20~30s. If B is added individually in the C-Mn steel, the recrystallization is delayed slightly. But when a little Nb is added into the

C-Mn steel, the recrystallization behavior changes obviously after deformation, in 20s after deformation at 1000℃, the softening percentage is only 50%, and the recrystallization will only start after several thousand of seconds after deformation at 900℃. This shows, after trace Nb is added in the C-Mn steel, it is likely that the steel starts to enter the non-recrystallization zone at 900℃ during rolling(Djahazi et al,1992a;Djahazi et al,1992b;He et al,1991).

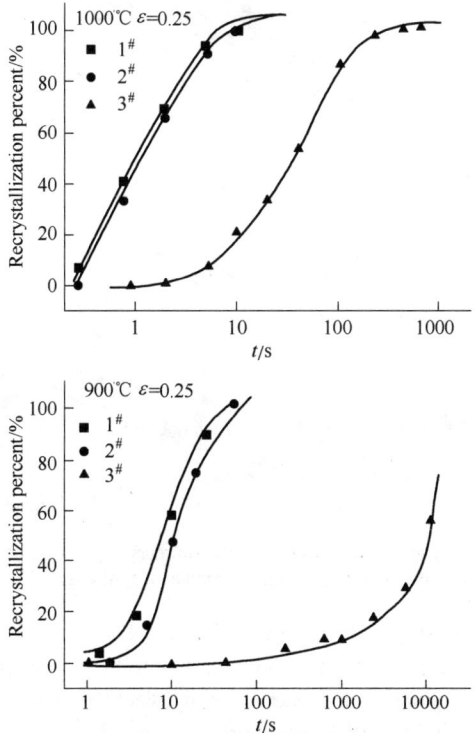

Figure5.3　High-temperature deformation recrystallization behavior of C-Mn-Nb-B steel

5.3.2.2　When alloying elements such as Nb, B, Cu are combinedly added

When alloying elements such as Nb, B, Cu are combinedly added in the steel, the high-temperature deformation recrystallization behavior is shown in Figure5.4. The result shows, the recrystallization will be completed in 10s after heated and deformed at 1050℃, in 150s after deformed at 1000℃, and the recrystallization only starts after about several hundred of seconds after deformed at 950℃. With Nb, B, Cu added together, the temperature range of the non-recrystallization zone of the steel is extended to higher than 950℃, accordingly the deformation accumulation in non-recrystallization zone can be raised obviously in the industrial production.

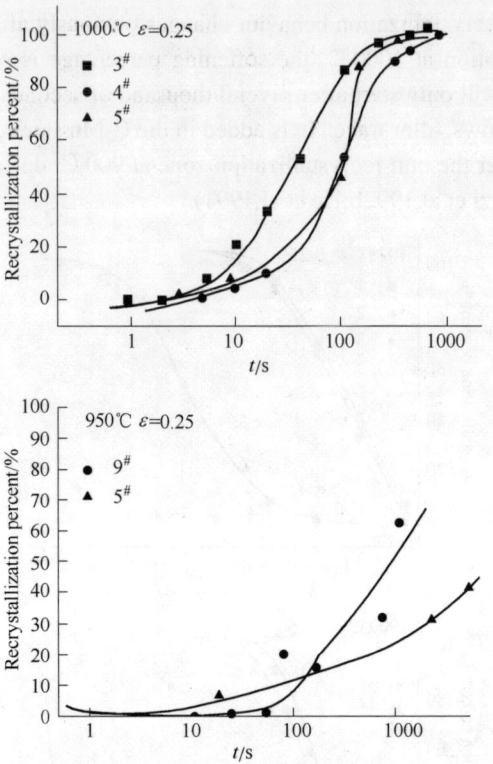

Figure5.4   High-temperature deformation recrystallization of the Nb-B
steel after alloying elements such as Cu, Mo are added

The combined analysis for the effects of Nb and B on the recrystallization of the
steel, shows that the effect is seemed to be relative to the co- segregation occurred at
the austenite grain boundaries; the interaction between Nb and B is very strong, and
many kinds of compounds will form. From the atomic radius of the two elements,
the sum of Nb and B atomic radii is equivalent to the double of Fe atomic radius, so
there is a tendency for Nb and B atoms to form a Nb-B pair in the austenite, and the
formation of the Nb-B pair will accelerate the diffusion of Nb in the matrix to a
certain extent, makes the solute drag force on the grain boundary movement
enlarged. On the other hand, the experiment has also proved that B addition will
accelerate the precipitation of Nb(C, N) in the steel, and the B atom will enter
directly the carbonitride of Nb (See Figure5.10); these can all influence the
high-temperature deformation recrystallization behavior of the Nb-B steel.

5.3.3   PTT curve characteristics of the steel

After the steel is rolled in the high-temperature non-recrystallization zone, the
strain induced precipitation of fine Nb(C, N) will occur. The precipitate is

primarily precipitated on the deformed austenite grain boundaries and the internal dislocation network, which will handicap the recovery and disappearance of the dislocations after rolling, and stabilize the dislocation structure, and provide more chances for the phase transformation nucleation during the subsequent cooling, in the meantime, stop the growth of the transformation products (new phases) and fine the final microstructures. The experimental study shows, when Nb and B, Cu are combinedly added, their combined effect will further accelerate the precipitation, and further decrease the transformation temperature when cooling, accordingly further fine the final microstructures.

Based on stress relaxation after hot deformation, the starting and finishing time (P_s and P_f) of the strain induced precipitation are measured in the steel; A MTS tester and a Gleeble thermal simulator are used to control the process parameters such as the deformation amount, temperature, time, etc.; record the stress change curves in the stage of relaxation, and obtain the results needed.

Figure 5.5 shows the stress relaxation curves of the test steel after heated at 1100℃, cooled to 850℃with 5% deformation. According to the figure, when no

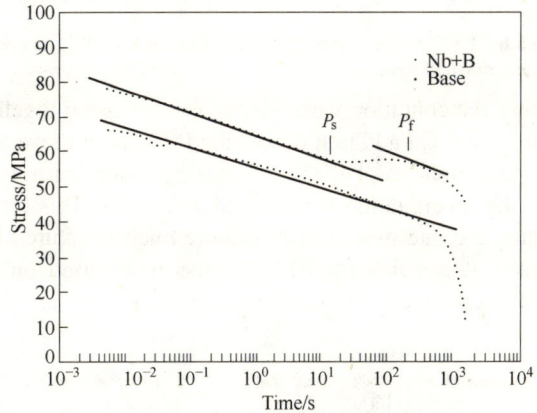

Figure. 5.5   Strain relaxation curves of No. 1 and 4 steel after 5% deformation at 850℃

Nb is added in the steel, there is no strain induced precipitation in the steel after deformation, and then the stress relaxation curve basically descends linearly. But after Nb, B are added, there will be a stage symbolizing the precipitation starting and growing up of the Nb(C, N) within the 18~180s range of the stress relaxation curve, thereby, the starting and finishing time (P_s and P_f points) of the precipitation can be determined. The precipitation of the micro-alloying elements in the steel, is relative to the combined effect of the pre-deformation temperature, pre-deformation amount and elements added in the steel. Figure 5.6 shows, when the steel is only held at the hot deformation temperature without hot deformation, though there is Nb(C, N) precipitation in the steel with composition of 0.05%C-0.035%Nb, even if at the fastest precipitation temperature, the precipitation will start in 100s, and P_f point appears after 2×10^4 s; it is hard to use such precipitation process in the whole TMCP production process. Figure 5.7 shows the dynamic curves (PTT curves) of the strain induced precipitation of Nb (C, N) in the steel after Nb individually or Nb, B compoundly are added. According to the figure, when Nb is individually added, the fastest precipitation of Nb (C, N) occurs at 800℃ and lasts 16s or so; In the meantime, after Nb and B are added together, the nose point temperature of the precipitation curve is increased to 850℃, the P_s point is at 6s.

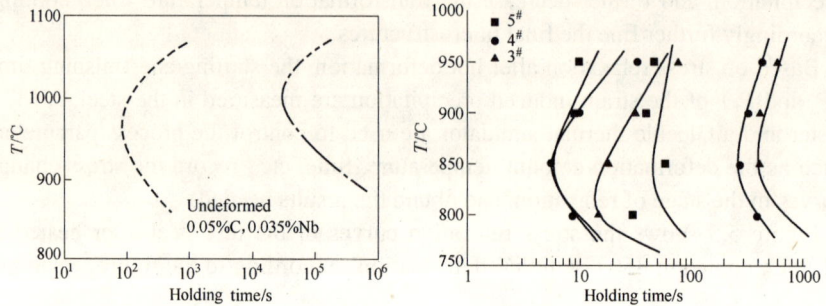

Figure 5.6   PTT curves of the undeformed steel

Figure 5.7   PTT curves of the Nb-B steel

Figure 5.8 shows the condition when Nb, B, Cu are added together in the steel. According to the figure, Cu addition makes the PPT curve move to the left(Zhou et al,2000); after deformation at 850℃, the precipitation starts in 3~4s, and the finishing time of the precipitation is advanced to 20~30s. This creates conditions for further adopting the intermediate-temperature microstructure ultra-fining PRC process, and makes it possible for RPC process to be used on the continuous rolling mill as well as the medium plate mill.

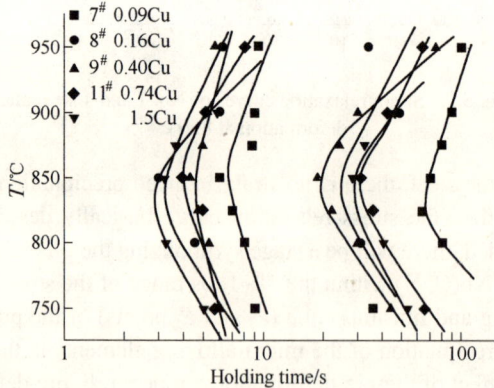

Figure 5.8   PTT curves of the Nb, B, Cu steel

The previous studies show, the Nb particles are precipitated gradually and grown up during holding after deformation, and their nuclei can be on the boundaries such as grain boundaries or phase boundaries, or on the existing precipitated particles in the steel. Figure 5.9 gives the Electron Microscope (EM)-energy spectrum analysis of the precipitate. The result shows, Nb-bearing compounds are gradually precipitated on the nuclei, TiN, and grown up. In addition, the EM energy loss spectrum study also shows (Figure 5.10), after trace B is added compoundly it can enter the Nb (C, N) precipitates and Nb (C, N, B) compound forms. Therefore, the effect of B on the Nb precipitation is not merely shown on the co-segregation of Nb, B on the grain boundary, the formation of Nb-B pair, and the effect on the diffusion velocity of Nb; besides, when trace B is added in, it enters the precipitate Nb (C, N), equivalent to increasing the concentration of C and N atoms (especially it will segregate on the boundary of the precipitate or nearby), and accordingly will accelerate the strain induced precipitation.

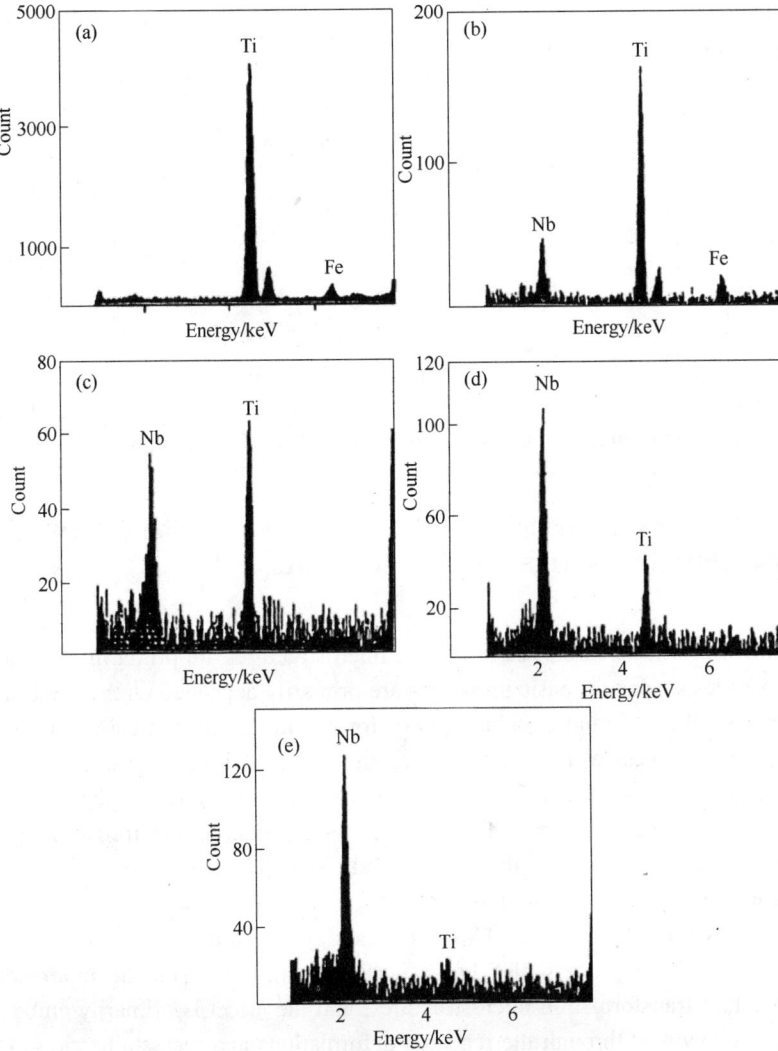

Figure 5.9   EM energy spectrum analysis of precipitation

Cu addition can accelerate the precipitation, and the acceleration become more and more obvious with the increase of the Cu content (from 0.09% to 1.5%). The cause analysis for the phenomenon shows, when Cu is added in the steel, under the same pre-deformation, the processing hardness degree is higher obviously than that of the steel without Cu; accordingly, after the same 20%~30% deformation, the steel strength is increased with the rising of Cu content, and correspondingly the dislocation density (ρ) and the distortion stored energy in the grain are raised obviously; the phenomenon may be relative to the solid solution strengthening effect of the Cu atom in the steel. In addition, some studies show, Cu in the austenite influences the activity of C, and Cu addition raises the activity of C in the steel and accordingly accelerates the precipitation of Nb (C, N).

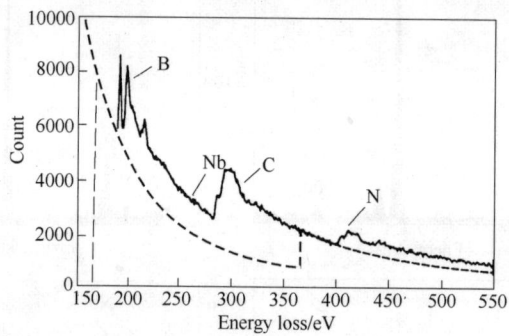

Figure 5.10 Energy loss spectrum analysis of Nb (C, N, B)

5.4 Theoretical Thought for Furthering Fining the Intermediate-temperature Transformation Microstructures

The low (ultra-low) carbon bainitic steel microstructures are primarily the bainite with various shapes; its basic properties are primarily depended on the sizes of the bainite bundles or granular bainite lumps formed in the intermediate-temperature transformation, besides relative to the design for composition and the precipitation of micro-alloying elements. The previous study shows, the effect of the size of the substructures produced during the intermediate-temperature transformation on the steel strength, is similar to that of the grain size (H-P formula), with a linear relation shown in Figure 5.11, too.

The previous study shows, TMCP technology can promote the fining of the ferrite grains; the process also has a certain fining effect on the intermediate temperature transformation microstructures, and the effect is primarily embodied on the followings: through the repeated deformations and recrystallization in the recrystallization zone, to fine the austenite grains, and the fining also shorten the subsequent intermediate temperature transformation bainite bath to shorten; Figure 5.12 shows the variation of the bainite lath size after cooling, when the high-temperature austenite grain size changes from 200μm to 20μm.

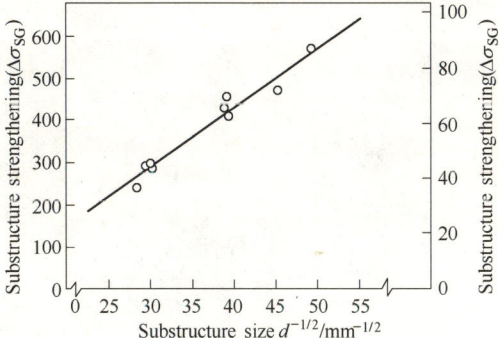

Figure 5.11 Relation between the substructure size in the steel and the steel strength

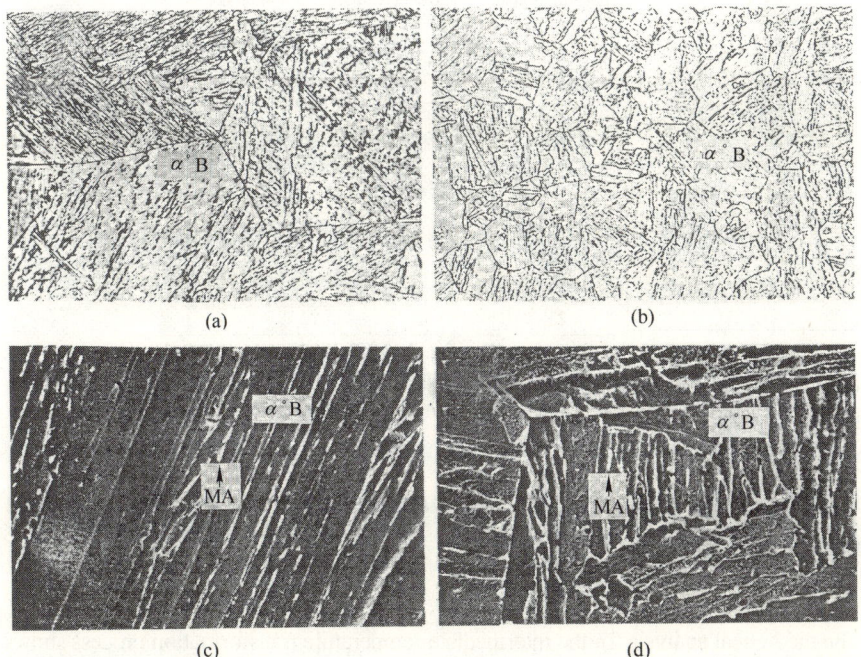

(a)   (b)

(c)   (d)

Figure 5.12   Microstructure of a low-carbon bainitic steel after
cooled at 5℃/s to room temperature
(a), (b) Optical micrographs; (c), (d) Scanning micrographs; (a), (c) For original
austenite equi-axle grains with a size of 200 μ m; (b), (d) For original
austenite equi-axle grains with a size of 20 μ m

In addition, the deformation in the non-recrystallization zone will also fine the bainite microstructures produced after cooling. Figure 5.13 and 5.14 show, the obvious deformation zones in the deformed austenite, promote the fining of the bainite microstructures, and the increasing of the deformation amount decreases gradually the volume fraction of M/A islands in the intermediate temperature transformation products.

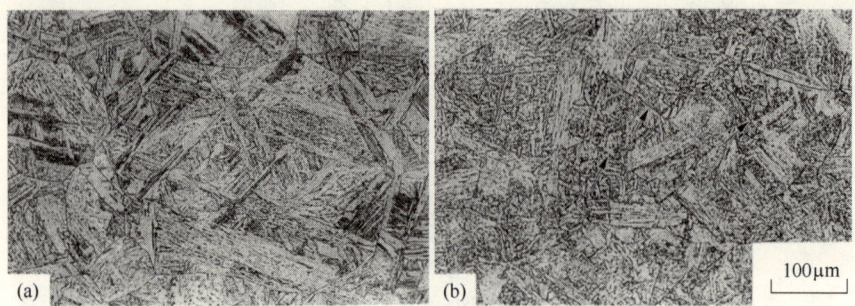

(a)   (b)   100μm

Figure 5.13 Bainite microstructures acceleratedly cooled (30°C/s) after
(a) No deformation and (b) 50% deformation at 780~800°C

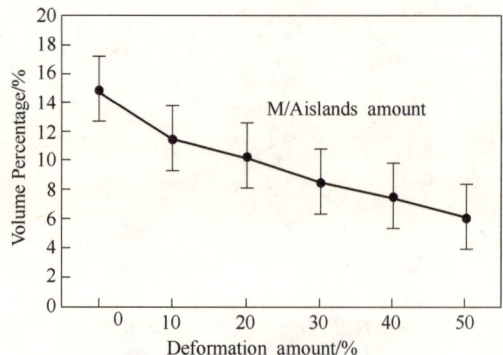

Figure 5.14 Relation between Deformation and M/A islands

5.4.1 *Basic key points for intermediate temperature transformation microstructure fining*

The theoretical analysis for the intermediate-temperature transformation process shows, to obtain the fully fined intermediate-temperature transformation microstructures (primarily referring to the bainite), besides providing nucleation sites as many as possible in the parent phase before transformation to increase the nucleating percentage, the more important is to restrict effectively the growth of the new phases. For the general diffusion transformation, such as the proeutectoid ferrite transformation, the growth velocity of the new phases is not fast, so the goal of fining the final microstructures can be achieved primarily by increasing the transformation nucleation sites. But for the intermediate-temperature transformation microstructures, especially the bainite in the low (ultra-low) carbon steel, because it belongs to the shearing transformation associated with diffusion, once nucleated, its growth is extremely fast; if the microstructure growth is not restricted, the bainite coming from a firstly nucleated center will rapidly overwhelm other potential nucleating centers nearby, thus even if there are many possible nucleation sites during cooling, the fully fined transformation microstructures can not be obtained at last. Therefore, an effective method for fining the intermediate-temperature transformation microstructure, is to promote the nucleation as well as restrict the growth.

5.4.2 *Theoretical background for proposing the relaxation-precipitation-controlling transformation (RPC) technology*

According to the general TMCP theory, in order to fully fine the transformation microstructures, the recovery should be inhibited as much as possible after deformation in non-recrystallization zone for controlled rolling, and large amounts of deformation dislocations produced during processing should be retained as much as possible until the transformation starts, therefore, the shorter the time interval between the completion of the final rolling and the beginning of accelerating cooling is, the better. According to the thought, it seems that, the higher the dislocation density in the parent phase of the deformed austenite is, the finer the new phase microstructures are, while the effect of the evolution and properties of the dislocation configuration on the phase transformation and its products, is not emphasized. The studies in recent years show, however, the evolution of the dislocation configuration in the deformed austenite is just important for the fining of the transformation product, sometime even decisive. In fact, if the micro-alloyed steel is cooled quickly immediately after deformation in the austenite non-recrystallization zone, most of deformation dislocations in the steel are tangled with each other at the beginning of the transformation, and the dislocation configuration will promote the nucleation of the intermediate-temperature transformation microstructure to a certain extent; but from the growth handicapping of the new phases, the dislocation configuration effect is not good. In addition, if the austenite is cooled quickly immediately after deformation, the micro-alloying elements do not have time to precipitate, and the pinning effect of the precipitation on the dislocation and the effect of the precipitates as the potential nucleation sites of the new phases, can not be performed. It is obviously disadvantageous for the fining of the intermediate-temperature transformation microstructure. If the austenite is relaxed for some time after deformation and then cooled, taking advantage of the special processes such as the continuous dropping of the dislocation density during relaxation, continuous changing of the dislocation structure, and the gradual increasing of the volume fraction of the precipitate, a new way for fining the intermediate-temperature transformation microstructure may be discovered, and an appropriate process will be established for the practical production.

In history, the effect of the relaxation on the ferrite transformation has been emphasized. In the study of the ferrite transformation, Ohtsuka et al(1988) found, if the Nb-bearing micro-alloyed steel is firstly isothermally held for sometime after deformation and then cooled, the polygonal ferrite grains obtained is finer than that under directly cooled after deformation. He concluded the phenomenon that the NbC precipitate grains strain-induced in the austenite had provided nucleation sites for the ferrite. During isothermal holding after the austenite deformation, large amounts of dislocations produced during formation will decrease the density because of the recovery, but the actual transformation product is finer instead. It seems that the promotion effect of the precipitation on the ferrite nucleation, exceeds the negative effect of the dislocation decreasing. The experimental result from Zhang et al.(1996) also shows, the ferrite is easily nucleated on the boundary between the austenite and the inorganic nonmetallic compounds such as NbC.

From the aspect of promoting the nucleation, it is natural to propose the effect mechanism of the precipitation process on the ferrite fining, but the possible effect of the precipitation in the austenite on the intermediate-temperature transformation, has not been emphasized so far. The causes may come from two aspects: Firstly, there has not been a clear intermediate-temperature transformation mechanism by far; secondly, the velocity of the intermediate-temperature transformation is far larger than that of the equilibrium microstructure, making it hard to observe its nucleation and growth.

Bhadeshia et al(1991). ever discovered the phenomenon of the acicular ferrite nucleating on the inclusions in the grain. They thought the acicular ferrite was just the bainite nucleated intragranularly. But due to the detrimental effect and uncontrollability of the inclusions, the discovery has no direct application value. However, if the acicular ferrite could also nucleate on the deformation induced precipitates as the polygonal ferrite did, a new microstructure fining technology might be developed. Because the deformation induced precipitation process is controllable, and the nanometer-sized precipitate particles not only are harmless, but also have many other beneficial effects in the steel. Because the precipitation process is also the recovery process of the dislocation structure at the same time, to make the technology practical, it is needed to look for the optimum time to maximize the combined effect of the dislocation structure and the precipitation. For this reason, it is necessary to deeply study the interaction details between the dislocation and the precipitation, as well as their effects on the intermediate-temperature transformation.

5.4.3   *Basic ideas of TMCP+RPC technology*

Theoretical concepts are based on:

1. The bainite transformation is a shearing transformation associated with diffusion. Once nucleated, the phase grows fast. The actual bainite size is primarily determined by the growth conditions. Therefore, to fine the bainite microstructure, besides increasing its nucleation, the more important task is to slow down its growth.

2. When the micro-alloyed steel is deformed at a high temperature, there are large amounts of tangled dislocations in the austenite grain. The study shows, the high-density dislocation tangling can increase the nucleation number of the bainite, but the growth can not be stopped (EM observation shows, the shearing transformation products directly run through the high-density range). However, if the deformed metal undergoes a recovery process before the phase transformation, the disordered dislocations will be recovered and polygonized, with a series of nanometer-sized dislocation cell structures formed; the misorientation between the dislocation cells increases continuously with the polygonization process, and they divide the actual deformed grains into many independent small spaces, restricting the sequent phase transformation to occur primarily in the cell, stopping the growth of the bainite.

3. The study shows, the ability for the pure dislocation cell structure to handicap the shearing transformation product, is not enough; but if there are large amounts of nanometer-sized micro-alloying elements particles precipitated on the cell walls before transformation, they will pin the dislocations, accordingly can obviously raise the strength of the cell wall, make it act as the grain boundary.

4. It is found that, under the specific design and process conditions, before the bainite transformation during cooling, a certain amount of acicular ferrites with different orientations will be formed in the deformed austenite grains and their spatial 3-D configuration is tablet. These tablet ferrites will form a spatial network, which further partitions the deformed grains, restricting the growth spaces of the bainite during the sequent transformation.

Proceeding from the theoretical concepts, the newly-developed intermediate-temperature transformation microstructure ultra-fining process is shown in Figure 5.15:

1. Full deformation of the micro-alloyed steel in the non-recrystallization zone, makes the high-distortion accumulation produced in the deformed austenite,

sharply raising the dislocation density in the matrix. In the low-carbon bainitic steel, adding micro-alloying elements such as Cu, Nb, B together, will result in obvious combined effects; these elements will statically and dynamically segregate and precipitate on the boundaries in the deformed austenite matrix, making it hard to be recrystallized after hot deformation, and the steel can enter the non-recrystallization zone at 950℃ or so. Through multi-pass rollings and interval stayings, after final rolling, there are large amounts of tangled deformation dislocations, deformation zones and various sizes of the micro-alloying element precipitates (after several passes of rollings ahead, precipitated in the interval staying processes) in the deformed austenite, as shown in Figure 5.15 (a).

2. After final rolling and deformation, the steel plate is air-cooled at about 2℃/s; During the stage, the recovery occurs in the deformed austenite (the deformation temperature for the final rolling is taken within the non-recrystallization zone, then it is generally hard to be recrystallized); through the processes such as climbing, sliding out, mutual annihilation, etc., the number of the deformation dislocations decreases; in the meantime, large amounts of low-energy dislocation walls are formed through the rearrangement of the deformation dislocations in the grains. The linkage of short sections of dislocation wall, forms the dislocation cell structures and subgrains; with the merging of the subgrains and further joining in of the dislocations, the misorientation between subgrains is increased gradually, and the deformed austenite grain is partitioned into small parts with a certain orientation, as shown in Figure 5.15 (b).

3. During the dislocation relaxation process, the micro-alloying elements will precipitate, and Nb, Ti will precipitate in the form of (Nb，Ti)(C,N, B) on the dislocations and the dislocation cell structures. Due to the use of the micro-alloying design, and the addition of Cu, Nb, Ti, B, etc., the strain induced precipitation starts soon; they firstly pin the dislocations, but considering from the energy, more precipitation occurs on the dislocation network and subgrain boundaries. The fine precipitates on the dislocation walls (or subgrain boundaries), pin and stabilize the substructures. With the growing up and thickening of the precipitates, their coherency with the matrix disappears, and the heterophase boundaries will appear. The process is shown in Figure 5.15 (c).

4. For the deformation austenite after the relaxation process above, during sequent accelerated cooling, at the beginning of transformation, the deformed austenite grain with such dislocations and precipitation configurations, is different from one with a disorderly distribution of large amounts of the tangled dislocations without relaxation after deformation. Firstly, the subgrain boundaries with a certain misorientation, are the preferential sites for nucleating; if nearby there are the precipitates with a heterophase boundary with the matrix, it is more advantageous for the transformation to nucleate preferably. Therefore, large amounts of new

phases can be generated in the deformed austenite grains. Secondly, the subgrains have developed to a certain extent after relaxation, and there is a considerable misorientation between subgrains, so the growth of intermediate-temperature transformation products (primarily are various bainites) nucleated on the subgrain boundary, are handicapped by the front subgrain boundary, and can not run through it. Therefore, the bainite is nucleated much but not grown up, and the final intermediate-temperature transformation microstructures will be obviously fined (as shown in Figure 5.15 (d)).

According to the thought described above, if taking advantage of the combined micro-alloying effect, increasing sharply the deformation in non-recrystallization zone and accelerating the precipitation of the micro-alloying elements, through the relaxation after rolling, subgrain structures with a considerable misorientation and the micro-alloying element precipitates will be formed in the grains, and the ultra-fined intermediate-temperature transformation products may be obtained during accelerated cooling. Of course, the fining effect is closely related to the dislocation relaxation rate (subgrain formation rate) and the precipitation rate of the micro-alloying elements (the starting time and finishing time of the precipitation). When the two rates match well, that is, the precipitation has started, the subgrains with a certain misorientation have been formed but not grown up, and it is anticipated that the fining effect should be optimal.

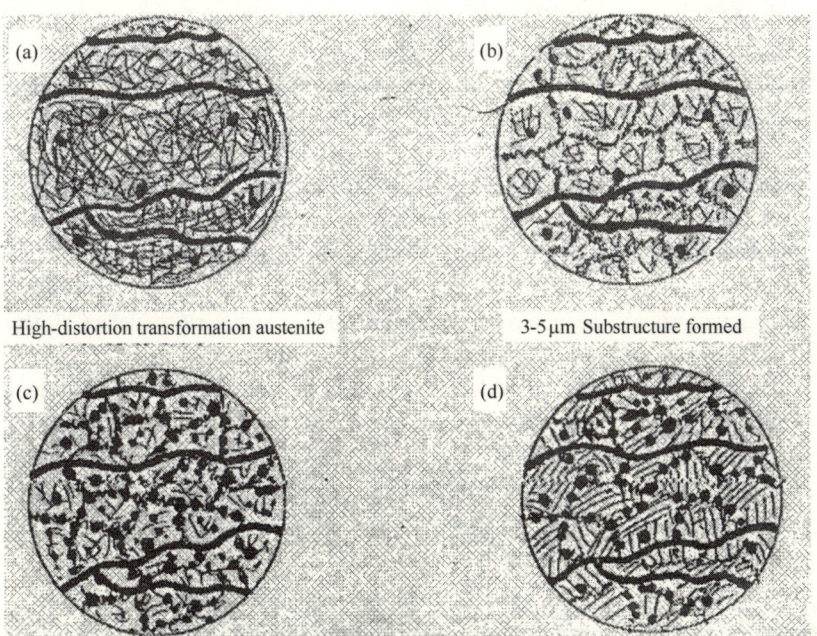

Figure 5.15   Schematic diagram for the fundamental principle of the intermediate-temperature transformation microstructure

5.5　Ultra-fining Process, Actual Fining Effect and Typical Microstructures

A newly-developed intermediate-temperature transformed microstructure ultra-fining technology, includes composition design of the micro-alloy steel, optimized Relaxation-Precipitation-Controlling transformation (RPC) technology, analysis for the effect of process parameters on ultra-fining, forming mechanism of ultra-fining microstructures, properties, deformation and fracture patterns of ultra-fining microstructures, and the stability and weldablity of the fined microstructure, etc.. It involves the strengthening, fining and microstructure-controlling of the whole kind of bainitic steel.

5.5.1　Selecting composition range of micro-alloying elements fully performing ultra-fining process effect

5.5.1.1　Principle of composition design

In order to fully perform RPC technology to achieve the purposes of controlling the fining of intermediate-temperature phase transformation microstructures, and strengthening and toughening greatly the micro-alloy steel, the followings should be considered in the steel compositions design:

1. Economical purity (S<0.005%; P<0.01%) should be guaranteed, the carbon content in steel dropping to 0.05% or so, smooth processing and welding of the steel can be done after the high strength is guaranteed.
2. Proceeding from the high strength requirement of the steel, the microstructure should be bainite or bainite+martensite polyphase microstructure. Transformation temperature should be controlled at about 600℃, and various defect structures should be fully used to fine phase transforming microstructure.
3. Alloy elements should be added in the steel as little as possible. Compound adding technology of the micro-alloy elements should be fully used to strengthen the steel.

In fact, typically selected basic composition ranges of the steel are shown as Table 5.3. Carbon equivalent of the steel is approximately 0.4, located within Range I on Graville diagram, where HAZ cold cracks are not sensitive during welding.

Table 5.3　Ranges of compositions (mass%)

C	Mn	Si	S	P	Cu	Mo	Ni	Nb	B	Ti
0.03~ 0.07	1.4~ 1.8	0.25~ 0.55	≤0.005	≤0.01	0.2~ 0.6	0.1~ 0.3	0.2~ 0.4	0.03~ 0.09	0.0005~ 0.0020	0.01~ 0.08

5.5.1.2 Starting points of composition selection

In the design for basic compositions of the steel, the following factors should be considered:

1. To use low-carbon method to guarantee the steel has high toughness as well as weldability under high strength.
2. To add a certain amount of Mn, Si and a little Ni to strengthen the solid solution and change the phase transformation point of the steel.
3. To adopt Nb-B combined addition to guarantee that the upper limit of non-recrystallization range is raised to $T_{stop} > 950\,^{\circ}\mathrm{C}$ during the controlled rolling, so as to guarantee the deformation accumulation in crystal within non-recrystallization range and that full bainitic and martensitic microstructures can be obtained under a cooling rate of above $3\,^{\circ}\mathrm{C/s}$.
4. To take advantage of strain induced precipitation and aging strengthening effect of micro-alloying elements such as Nb, Ti (and a little Mo, Cu), to control the precipitated particle size to 10nm or so.

5.5.1.3 Strength evaluation

Based on the considerations above, yield strength of the steel during cooling at 3 $^{\circ}\mathrm{C/s}$ after hot-rolled, can be evaluated by the following formula:

$$\sigma_s = \sigma_o + \sigma_A + \sigma_D + \sigma_P + \sigma_{IN} + kd^{-\frac{1}{2}}$$

where,

1. σ_o is Lattice frictional resistance, approximately 50MPa according to references.
2. σ_A is Solid solution strengthening capability, calculation formula:

$$\sigma_A = \sum_i k_i(x_i)$$

k_i is the solid solution strengthening coefficient (MPa/mass%) of No. i element, x_i is the concentration of No. i compound in the solid solution. If calculated by the middle limit of the alloy design composition (Mn 1.6%, Si 0.4%,Cu 0.4%, Ni 0.3%, Mo 0.2%, P 0.01%). The scales of element contents in solid solution to total addition are: Mn and Mo contents in solid solution respectively take 90% and 50% of the adding amount; while Cu, Si, P, Ni contents all take 100%. In addition, the selecting coefficient k_i for each alloy element takes Si (86), Mn (50), Cu (39), Mo (22), P (470) or Ni (20). Evaluated strengthening item, σ_A, resulted from the solid solution strengthening, is approximately 133MPa.
3. σ_D is Dislocation strengthening, evaluated by the general formula of the dislocation density to the yield stress:

$$\sigma_D = \mu b \rho^{\frac{1}{2}}$$

After large deformation in high-temperature non-recrystallization range and the phase transformation of bainite and martensite, the dislocation density is very high in the matrix, and evaluated dislocation surface density ρ is $1 \times 10^8 \sim 2 \times 10^8/mm^2$, $\mu = 8 \times 10^4$ MPa, $b = 2.5 \times 10^{-7}$mm, taking $\rho = 1.5 \times 10^8/mm^2$ when calculating. Caused strengthening:

$$\sigma_D \approx 244MPa$$

4. σ_P is Precipitation strengthening:

$$\sigma_P = 0.298 \left(\frac{\mu b}{l} \right) \ln \left(\sqrt{\frac{2}{3}} \cdot \frac{d}{b} \right)$$

According to actual precipitation of Nb (C, N) and ε is Cu, taking the precipitated particle diameter $d=10$nm, the precipitate space $l=200$nm, evaluated $\sigma_P \approx 103$MPa.

5. σ_{IN} is Strengthening caused by interstitial atoms, primarily strengthening of carbon and nitrogen atoms, the approximate formula can be used: $\sigma_{IN} = 9 \times 4 \times 10^4 \times f$.

The value of f is about 10^{-3} (most of C and N atoms entering the precipitate phase), strengthening caused: $\sigma_{IN} \approx 94$MPa.

6. σ_I is Grain fining. The item is evaluated by the generally controlled rolling grain size, and other defect effects have been considered in the item "dislocation strengthening" above.

To take $d_z \approx 10\mu$m, the strengthening caused: $\sigma_I = 20 \times (d_z)^{-\frac{1}{2}}$

Evaluated $\sigma_I = 20 \times (10 \times 10^{-3})^{-\frac{1}{2}} = 200$ （MPa）

In the controlled rolling and controlled cooling steel, strengthening effects of grain boundary and dislocation are actually the same type, so σ_D and σ_I can not be calculated repeatedly. The larger is taken.

The strength (σ_s) after generally hot rolled, is finally evaluated to be $\sigma_s = 50 + 130 + 244 + 103 + 94 = 624$MPa.

In RPC process, a low final-rolling temperature will be adopted, as well as water cooling and tempering after deformation and relaxation, which increases sharply the dislocation density ρ in the steel and the substructure is further fined. According to the existing references, compared to the general quenching and tempering, the treatment enhances approximately 80~100MPa, so the yield strength of the steel at controlled rolling and controlled cooling and accelerated cooling states, should be approximately 680~700MPa. Existing studies on the RPC process show, after the control of the newly-developed RPC process, the bainite structure in the steel will further fine, the actual significant bundle size is approximately 3 μm, the precipitate space of the bainite is within 100mm range, the yield strength of the steel will be enhanced 10%~15% approximately compared with that of the generally controlled rolled and controlled cooling steel. Therefore, the actual yield strength is anticipated to reach Grade 800MPa.

7. Carbon equivalent in the steel is calculated with the following formula:

$$C_{eq}=C+Mn/6+(Ni+Cu)/15+(Cr+Mo+V)/5$$
$$=0.04+1.6/6+(0.4+0.3)/15+(0.2)/5$$
$$=0.04+0.27+0.047+0.04$$
$$=0.397$$

The steel is located in the middle and lower sections of Range I in Graville diagram, and sensitivity of carbon equivalent to the cold crack is fundamentally eliminated, so it is easy to be welded.

5.5.2 *Typical process of relaxation-precipitation-controlling transformation (RPC) technology*

Newly-developed TMCP (Thermomechnical Control Process) technology, the basic process of relaxation-precipitation-controlling transformation (RPC) technology(He et al,2003), is: After proper micro-alloying designing, the steel billet should undergo two stages of controlled rollings. To enter the steel billet into the non-recrystallization range to roll below 950℃. During rolling within the temperature range, because clustering and precipitating of alloy elements such as Nb, Ti, B in the deformed matrix, make it hard to recrystallize, large amounts of distortion accumulation is produced in the deformed austenite, and the dislocation density rises rapidly. Because of deformations time after time in the range and stays between deformations, after final rolling, there are large amounts of deformed dislocation, deformation zones, and various sizes of the micro-alloying element precipitates in the deformed crystal.

After final rolling, the steel plate is cooled in the air at 2℃/s or so. During cooling, deformed crystal will revert and polygonize, and the deformed dislocations will re-arrange or disappear. Reverting results in the dislocation cell substructures (or subcrystals) formed in the deformed austenite with diameters of 3~5 μm. With the continual adding of the deformed dislocations, the included angle between subgrains will increase, and micro-alloying elements such as Nb, Ti, B will non-equilibrium segregate and precipitate (deformation induced precipitating) on the boundary of the cell structure consisting of dislocations.

After the relaxation control above, the steel plate is quenched directly or acceleratedly cooled. Because there are large amounts of substructures and precipitates (especially those precipitates which have large sizes and lose the coherency with the matrix) in deformed grains, interfaces between them and the matrix will become advantageous places for phase transformation. During cooling, new phases will be formed firstly on them; these preferentially formed acicular ferrite or bainite in the crystal, partition the original austenite grain into different zones. When bainite and martensite transform in each substructure during further cooling, their lath length is hampered by the subgrain boundaries and acicular ferrite or bainite formed in the early stage, which makes the lath structure thinner and shorter, achieving the ultra-fining of the microstructure. The technological process is shown in Figure 5.16(Shang et al,2001).

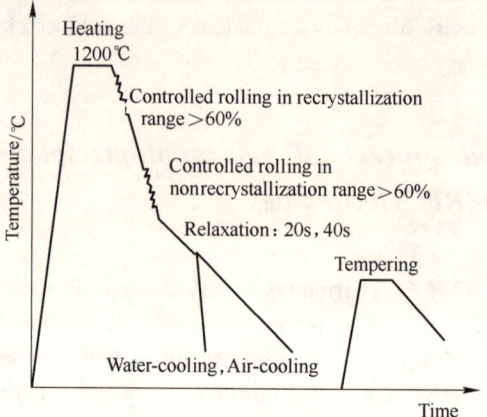

Figure 5.16   Process diagram for RPC

In the stage of controlled rolling, enough deformation should be guaranteed so that the original austenite grains will be fined and enough defect density will be accumulated in the deformed austenite. After final rolling, the steel plate will be air-cooled continuously for a predetermined time. The air-cooling time is the relaxation time, and the air-cooling end temperature should be above the temperature Ar_1. After relaxation, the steel plate is subsequently acceleratedly cooled or directly quenched. In order to make strength, toughness and elongation percentage uniform and improve comprehensive properties, the steel plate should be tempered after rolled.

5.5.3   *Typical fining microstructures under RPC process and its comparison with other processes*

Typical continuous cooling phase transformation curve of the steel is shown in Figure 5.17(Shang et al,2003a). When the steel is heated at 0.05°C/s, the measured Ac_1 and Ac_3 of the steel are respectively 817°C and 915°C. When the steel is cooled at 0.5~30°C/s, there is no generally proeutectoid ferrite produced during cooling; starting points of bainite phase transformation (B_s) are all approximately 600°C. Therefore, this kind of steel will not transform within a large cooling temperature range, which is advantageous for relaxation process. Meanwhile, this can make steel plates with different thicknesses or different parts of the same steel plate (cooling rates are different) obtain similar bainite microstructures.

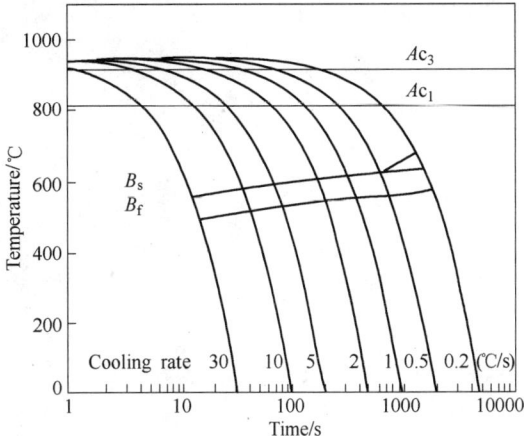

Figure 5.17 CCT diagram of the test steel with typical gradients cooled after austenitized at 950°C

Micrographs of the steels cooled at different cooling rates are shown in Figure 5.18. According to the pictures, when the cooling rate is large (30°C/s), the microstructure is obvious lath bainite and a part of granular bainite, and the grain boundary of the original austenite is clear; Lath bundles in different directions partition the original austenite grain into different zones. With the decrease of the cooling rate, the original austenite grain boundary is maintained, but the amount of the lath bainite in the grains decreases and is gradually replaced by the granular bainite with irregular shapes; lath bundles are more and more indistinct and become disordered lath lumps. When the cooling rate decreases to 0.2°C/s, according to the expansion curve, the proeutectoid ferrite begin to form; But from the microstructure, it is hard to observe the ferrite structure and to definitely identify what the local small white lumps are at the original grain boundaries.

For the steel rolled by RPC technology, its microstructure is primarily lath bainite. Figure 5.19 shows micrographs along the rolling section and on the plate surface of the steel that is relaxed for 20s and then directly quenched after final rolling(Shang et al,2003b). According to Figure 5.19, because of the controlled rolling in the non-recrystallization temperature range, the original austenite grain is rolled into the flat, and the intermediate-temperature transformation products are primarily lath bainite, as well as a little granular bainite with irregular shapes or acicular ferrite; Figure 5.19(b) shows the microstructure along the rolling section, and each group of lath bundles has different orientation, intercrossing and partitioning. Because the lath structures are very fine, lath details can not be distinguished under a common optical microscope.

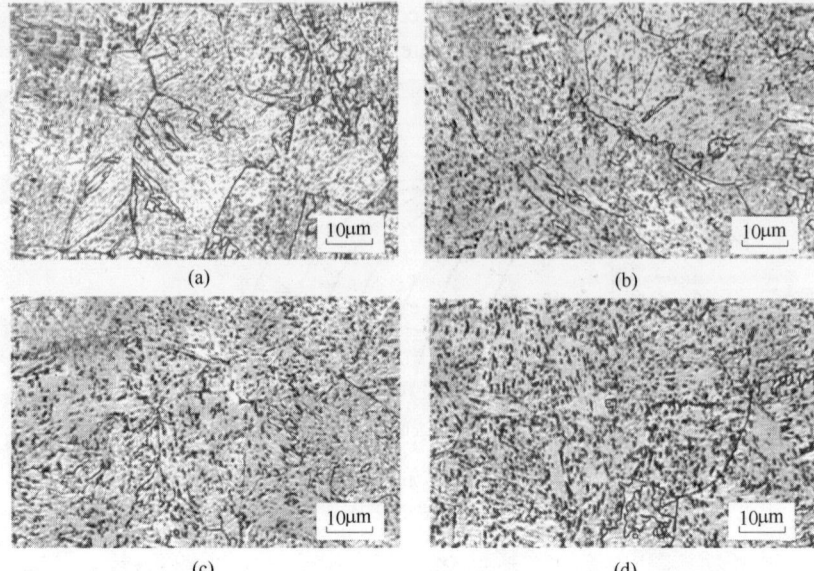

Figure 5.18   Typical microstructures of test steel cooled at
different cooling rates after heated at 950℃
(a) 30℃/s; (b) 5℃/s; (c) 1℃/s; (d) 0.2℃/s

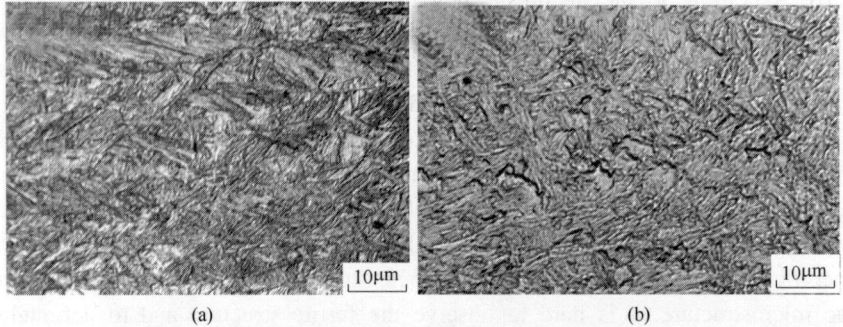

Figure 5.19   Micrographs of steel rolled by PRC process, along
rolling section (a) and on plate surface (b)

Figure 5.20 shows a SEM micrograph of the steel after RPC process. According to Figure 5.20, there are two kinds of typical microstructure: one is the lath structure, and the other is irregular strip granular bainite or acicular ferrite (as shown A, B, C and D in Figure 5.20). Bainite lath width is less than 0.5μm, and laths in the same direction forms a lath bundle with an average width of 4~6μm; the boundary between adjacent lath bundles is clear, and there is intermittent or thin residual austenite film between bainite laths.

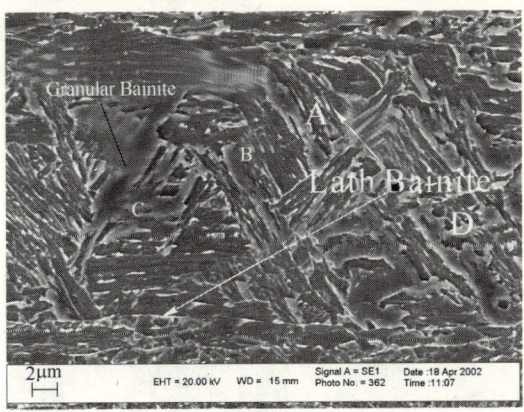

Figure 5.20 Two kinds of typical microstructures of RPC process

Figure 5.21 shows an image taken by Transmission Electron Microscope (TEM), and the microstructure is clearer. According to the figure, the appearances of the lath bainite are similar to ones in Figure 5.20, and lath width and length accord basically with those in the figure above, cross-distributing lath bundles blocking each other, with lath width and length restricted. There are large amounts of lath bundles with different orientations in one original austenite grain, with a lath length of 4~6 μm and width of about 0.3 μm; the dislocation density inside the lath is very high but nonuniform.

Figure 5.21 TEM micrograph of fined microstructure

By comparison, Figure 5.22 and Figure 5.23 show the SEM micrographs of the same steel air-cooled and reheated & quenched after final rolling. According to the figures, the air-cooled microstructure is primarily granular bainite with irregular shape; in flattened original austenite grains, the boundary between bainite granula is not clear, and there are obvious granular M/A islands. The microstructure of the re-quenched steel is different from ones under the two previous processes. Due to reheating, the flattened original austenite grain boundaries disappear. After quenching, the microstructure is granular bainite and lath bainite/martensite; the granular bainite accounts for more percentage, and the lath structure generally runs through the whole original austenite grain.

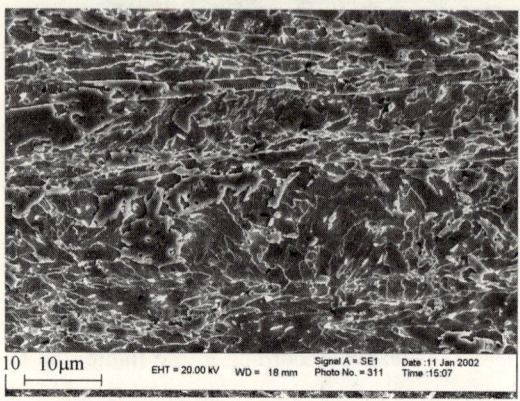

Figure 5.22   Microstructure of air-cooled granular bainite after controlled

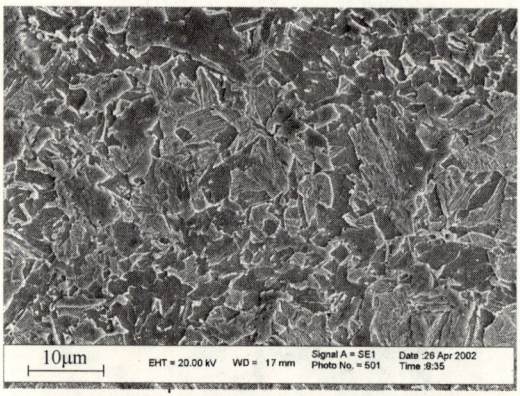

Figure 5.23   Reheated and quenched microstructure

According to the microstructure comparison of the three processes above, the microstructure of RPC process is the finest, consisting of primarily the fined bainite lath bundles, with a little granular bainite and acicular ferrite dispersing in the original austenite; the microstructure of air-cooling process is primarily granular bainite; the microstructure of the reheated and quenched sample is a mixture of the granular bainite and the lath bainite/marstensite.

Mechanical properties of the steel treated by three processes are obviously different, and Table 5.4 shows the comparison of their mechanical properties. The result shows, the yield strength of the steel treated by the general controlled rolling and air-cooling process, is less than 600MPa, but can reach 600MPa after quenching and tempering; but if RPC process is used, the yield strength can reach 690MPa without tempering and more than 800MPa after tempering. Therefore, compared to the common quenching and tempering process, RPC process can increase yield strength by 30%, without obvious decrease of the plasticity. Microstructure analysis of the three processes shows, one of major causes of strengthening is bainite structure fining and different microstructure types obtained by RPC process.

Table 5.4　Mechanical Properties of steels treated by different processes

Properties / Process	R_{eL} / MPa	R_m / MPa	δ_5 / %
Controlled rolling and air-cooling	565	800	20
Quenching and tempering, tempering at 630℃ for 1h	619	655	19
RPC rolling	690	869	17
RPC, tempering at 630℃ for 2h	816	851	18

5.5.4　Effects of RPC process and composition on microstructure and properties

In order to discover the effects of many factors such as RPC process, micro-alloying element composition design on the microstructure and properties of the low-carbon bainite high-strength steel, we make 5 kinds of test steel with different compositions, as shown in Table 5.5. Series 1 steel is for the standard compositions, Series 2 for with a high Cu content, Series 4 for without Mo, Series 5 for without Mo or B, Series 6 for with a high carbon content (0.08%). 5 kinds of steel all undergo TMCP+RPC process flow shown in Figure. 5.16.

Table 5.5　Composition table for grade 800MPa test steel making

Composition	C	Si	Mn	P	S	Als	Cu	Ni	Mo	Nb	Ti	B
Series 1	0.04	0.35	1.60	0.01	0.005	—	0.30	0.25	0.25	0.050	0.040	0.0010
Series 2	0.04	0.35	1.60	0.01	0.005	—	0.50	0.25	0.25	0.050	0.040	0.0010
Series 4	0.04	0.30	1.60	0.008	0.0039	0.010	0.29	0.26	<0.01	0.050	0.040	0.0008
Series 5	0.037	0.30	1.57	0.009	0.0059	0.007	0.28	0.25	<0.01	0.049	0.033	<0.0005
Series 6	0.08	0.30	1.48	—	—	—	0.42	0.23	0.26	0.056	0.020	0.0013

5.5.4.1   Effect of relaxing time

After controlled rolling, Series 2 steel test is water-cooled with relaxation of 10s, 20s, 40s; starting temperatures of the water cooling are respectively 820 ℃, 780℃ and 730℃. After water-cooling, and tempering at 680℃ for 1h, the resultant properties are shown in Table 5.6. According to the table, after RPC process, the yield strength of the steel reaches up to 840MPa, with an elongation of more than 18% and a transverse impact energy at -20℃ over 60J. If relaxing time is short, the strength will be low; the strength for a relaxing time of 40s will drop slightly.

Table 5.6   Mechanical properties of steel after different relaxing processes and then tempering at 680℃ for one hour

Relaxing time / s	R_{eL} / MPa	R_m / MPa	δ / %	A_{KV}/J[①]	
				20℃	-20℃
10	805	823	18	91	67
20	843	883	19	92	63
40	825	835	19	144	61

① Transverse impact energy.

Figure 5.24 shows hot-rolling microstructures of test samples water-cooled after relaxed for different time. According to Figure 5.24(a), if there is no relaxation after rolling, the microstructure after quenching is thick and long lath bainite; bainite lath bundles tend to run through the original austenite, and there is strip or lump austenite or M/A islands in lath bundle or between lath bundles, as shown in Figure 5.24(c); when the relaxing time increases to 20s, as shown in Figure 5.24(b), the lath bainite becomes finer and shorter, the bundle size obviously small, and the boundary of the lath bundle is hard to be distinguished under an optical microscope because of disorderedly distribution of the lath bundle orientation. Under high magnification SEM, there is intermittent thin film between fine bainite lath bundles, and the boundary of the lath bundle is clear.

Results show that relaxing time influences the water-cooled microstructure. On the one hand, the relaxing time will influence the size of the bainite lath bundle and the width of the bainite lath, as well as disordering degree of the bainite bundle orientation; on the other hand, relaxation influences the fine structure of the bainite morphology, such as distribution, number and stability of the residual austenite or M/A islands. Of course, relaxation will also change the distribution and number of precipitates in the bainite.

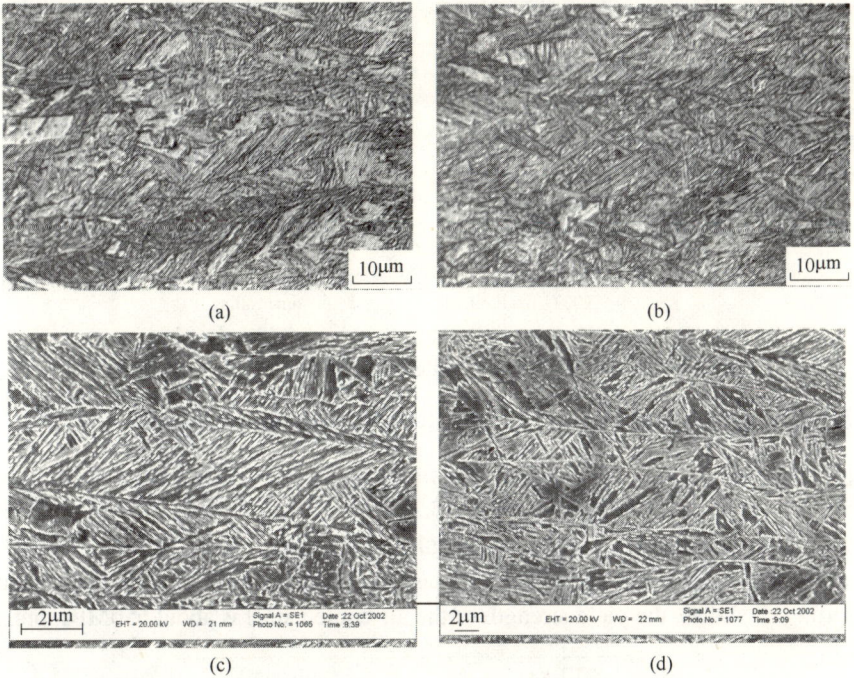

(a) (b)

(c) (d)

Figure 5.24 Microstructures of steel water-quenched with no relaxation (0s)
(a) , (c) and relaxation (20s) (b), (d) after final rolling

5.5.4.2 Effects of final-rolling temperature

Figure 5.25 shows the properties of Series 1 steel plates after final rolled at 900℃ and 850℃, then air-cooled and relaxed to 730℃ and water-cooled, and tempered at 600℃ and 680℃. It shows, when the final rolling temperature is high, the yield strength of the test samples will be low, but toughness after tempering is better.

Figure 5.26 shows the difference of impact toughness at −20℃.

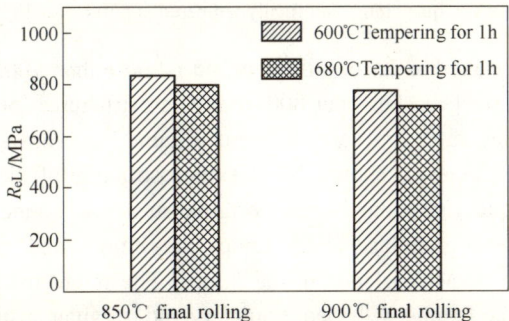

Figure 5.25 Effect of final-rolling temperature

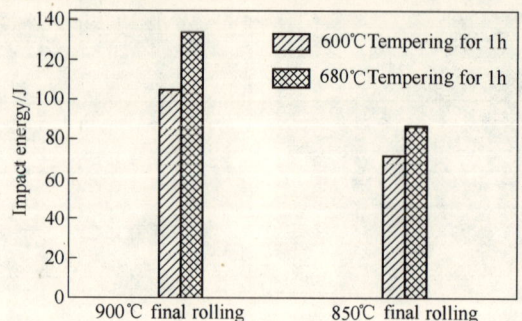

Figure 5.26　Effect of final-rolling and tempering temperatures
on impact toughness at －20℃

5.5.4.3　Effects of cooling rate on microstructure and properties

In RPC process, the cooling rate after final rolling and relaxation influences the microstructure and properties. Figure 5.27 shows the strength of Series 6 steel air-cooled after final rolling, and strengths of the steel relaxed for 40s, then oil- and water-quenched respectively, and last tempered at 650℃ for 1h after final rolling. It shows, the yield strength of the air-cooled steel is about 650MPa, but

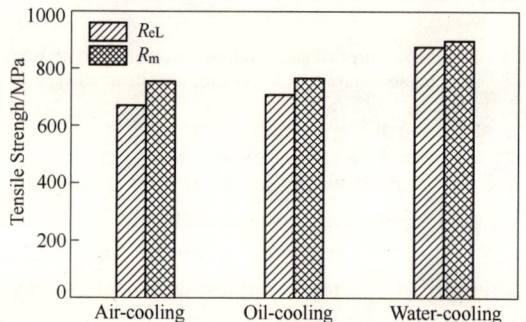

Figure 5.27　Strength of series 6 steel air-cooled after final rolling,
and relaxed after final rolling for 40s, followed by oil or
water quenching, and finally tempered at 650℃ for 1h

that of the steel relaxed and then oil-quenched is more than 700MPa, and that of the water-cooled steel reaches over 800MPa. Microstructures for the steel cooled at different cooling rates are very different. Figure 5.28 shows micrographs of three kinds of processes. It shows that the microstructure of the steel air-cooled after rolled is typical granular bainite; original austenite boundary is clear, but boundaries between granular bainite lumps are blurry, and there is irregular residual austenite or M/A islands in the lumps. The microstructure of the steel oil-quenched is lath bainite with clear boundary and irregular strip granular bainite. Width of the lath in lath bainite is very large (2~3μm), there is residual austenite in strip granular bainite or between laths, and laths in the same direction form lath bundles with different orientations. For the steel water-quenched after relaxation, laths are straight and there is a clear boundary between laths, while the acicular ferrite disorderly distributing in original austenite partitions the original austenite grains into different zones, and lath bundles with different orientations grow in these small zones with smaller sizes.

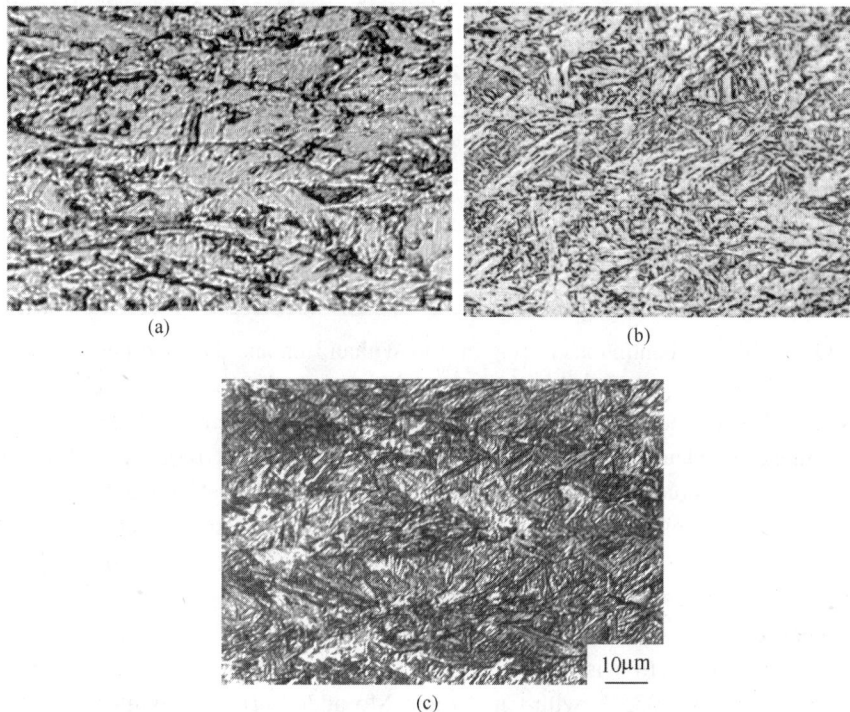

(a)

(b)

10μm

(c)

Figure 5.28   Microstructures of series 6 steel air-cooled after final rolling (a),
and relaxed after final rolling for 40s, followed by oil (b)
or water quenching (c), and finally tempered at 650℃ for 1h
(a) Air-cooled after rolled; (b) Relaxing for 40s, oil-quenched;
(c) Relaxing for 40s, water-quenched

5.5.5   *Strength, plasticity and toughness of the steel from industrial Trial Production of RPC process*

Industrial production was done on a commercial production line by using Relaxation –Precipitation -Controlling transformation (RPC) process.

In Medium Plate Factory of Wuhan Iron and Steel Corporation, the trial production of the steel plate with a thickness of 12mm was done, and the raw material was DB685 continuous casting billet with a carbon content of 0.07%.

After heated at 1250℃, the billet underwent two stages of controlled rolling, with the rolling reduction at each stage >60%, relaxed for 20s after rolled, cooled by the rolling mill's high-pressure scaling water until the final cooled temperature reaches about 500℃. The steel plate was tempered at 650~700℃ for 1 hour, and its properties are shown in Table 5.7. Due to a high carbon content, the steel plate has a high strength, with an impact toughness at -20℃ of about 60~70J.

Table 5.7   Properties of the plate with a thickness of 12mm after tempered

Tempering temperature	Yield strength / MPa	Tensile strength / MPa	δ_5 / %	ψ / %	A_{KV} (-20℃ Longitudinal)/J
650℃	895	910	16	60	57, 63, 62
680℃	843	875	17	59	65, 59, 64
700℃	820	863	18	60	73, 72, 75

On a 1700 hot continuous rolling mill in Wuhan Iron and Steel Corporation, the trial rolling for the plate with a thickness of 8mm was done, and the raw material is DB685 continuous casting billet with a carbon content of 0.04%. After blooming, the plate slab was delivered into the rolling mill at 1000℃, final rolled at 840℃, air-cooled for 12s after final rolling, and coiled at 500~550℃. After sampled at the coil head, and properties of the plate after tempered at 600℃ are measured as: R_{eL}=738~755 MPa, R_m=780~790 MPa, δ_5=18%, −20℃, longitudinal A_{KV} (7.5mm, non-standard sample) =112~164J.

The details of the trial production in Heavy Plate Factory of Anshan Iron and Steel Corporation is as follows: the carbon content of the steel for trial production was 0.035%, with Cu, Ni and Mo added (Total amount<1%); The billet underwent two stages of controlled rolling after heated at 1250℃, rolling reduction at each stage >60%, and the rolled steel plate is 20mm thick. After rolled, the steel plate is air-cooled and relaxed for 20~40s, laminar cooled to 300~550℃ range, and tempered at 650~700℃. The properties of the steel plate are: R_{eL}=785~815 MPa, R_m=810~840 MPa, δ_5=15.5%~16.5%, −40℃ Transverse A_{KV}=78~190J.

On a 1780 continuous rolling mill in Anshan Iron and Steel Corporation, the sheet coil with a thickness of 8mm is rolled in a trial production from the billet with the same compositions. Blooming temperature is 1180℃, final rolling temperature 850℃, controlled cooling for 8s after rolling, coiling temperature 560℃, hot-rolling sampling properties (longitudinal) at the coil head are as follows:R_{eL}=685~700MPa, R_m=765~775MPa, δ_5=15%~17%, −20℃ A_{KV}(Non-standard sample) = 0℃ 96~102J, −20℃ 95~101J, −40℃ 99~106J.

The results above show, by means of the newly-developed RPC technology, with the carbon content <0.06% and alloy contents <1.0%, steel of Grade 800MPa with ultra-fine intermediate-temperature transformed microstructure can be produced; Mechanical properties of the fined steel after tempered are stable, especially a good low-temperature toughness ($-40°C$, impact energy of about 100J). At present, the process has been used in mass production in the leading metallurgical corporations in China, and obvious achievements have been made.

5.6   Study on Fining Process Parameters of Intermediate-temperature Transformed Microstructure Through Thermo-mechanical Simulation

RPC process is a brand-new technical thought of fining intermediate-temperature product. In order to basically understand the actual effect of process factors on fining, thermo-mechanical simulation experiment must be done systemically. Under the premise of fixing the other factors, to study on the effects of one process parameter such as deformation amount, deformation temperature, relaxing time on microstructure fining, further reveal the change in the intrinsic microstructure and corresponding micro mechanism in the process, and find out the effects of these process parameters on microstructure fining(Wang et al,2006;Wang et al,2002a).

The compositions (mass%) of the test steels for the thermo-mechanism simulation are: 0.035C-1.74Mn-0.16Si-0.094Nb-0.080Ti-0.29Cu-0.33Ni-0.0020B and Fe-40%Ni (C, Nb, B) alloy. The former composition is the same to that of a newly-developed high-strength low-carbon bainitic steel, while Fe-Ni alloy is designed because the alloy can not transform during being cooled to the room temperature, and as a result, microstructure details at high temperature can be directly observed from the quenched microstructure, especially the change of defect configuration inside deformed austenite during high-temperature relaxation. The two kinds of material are hot forged into ϕ 14mm sticks after heated at 1200°C, and machined into ϕ 8mm×12mm test samples for thermo-mechanism simulation.

The thermo-mechanism simulation process is: To heat the samples to 1250°C quickly and keep for 20 min, then cool them at 2°C/s to the deformation temperature, and water cool them after deformation and holding at the same temperature for different time, as shown in Figure 5.29. Primary deformation in non-recrystallization range is adopted in the process, so the grain size of the original

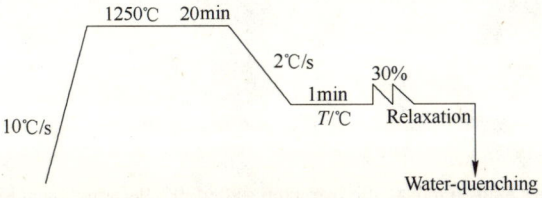

Figure 5.29   Hot-deformation process of test steel

austenite is very large; though the microstructure of final product is greatly finer than that of test samples without relaxation, its actual size is still large. It is convenient to do the observation by means of metallography and for quantificational statistics by adopting the process. Study is performed by means of optical microscopy, TEM and EBSD technology.

5.6.1 *Microstructure evolution after deformation and relaxation under different temperatures*

After the test samples are heated at 1250℃, austenite grain size is very large, approximately 300μm. After 30% deformation at 850℃ and relaxed for different time, and then water-cooled, their microstructures are shown in Figure 5.30 (a) ~ (d). According to the figures, after those treatments, its microstructure

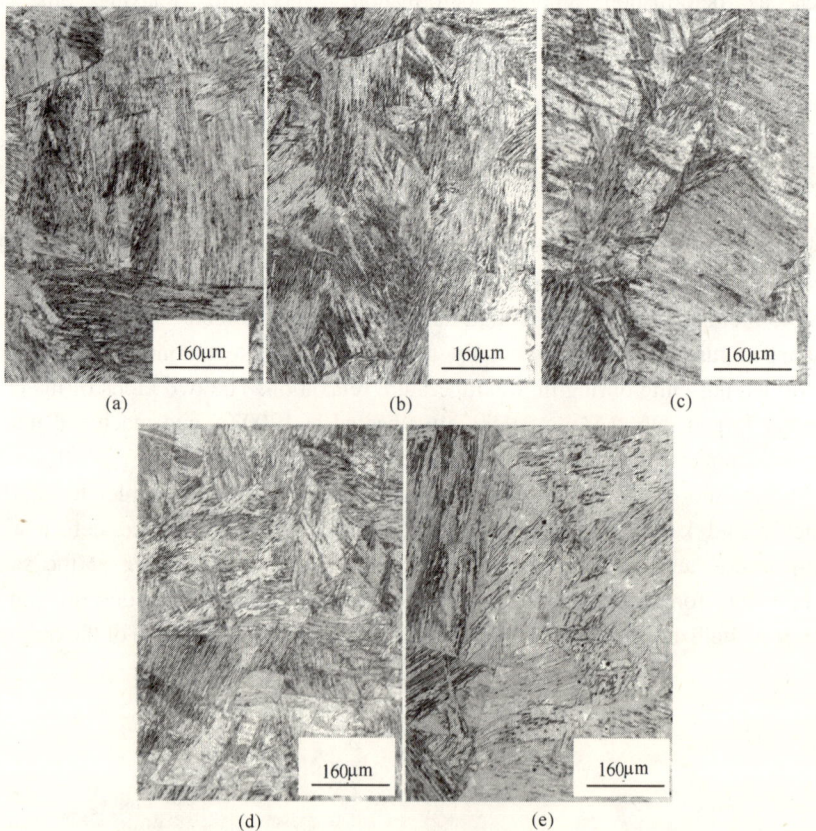

Figure 5.30   Optical microstructures after 30% deformation at 850℃
and relaxation for different time
(a) 0s ; (b) 30s; (c) 60s; (d) 200s; (e) 1000s

is typical lath bainite, as well as a little martensite and granular bainite; partitioning phenomenon can be seen in an original austenite grain, and each zone has a clear boundary; in a bainite zone, if laths are in the same direction, parallel to each other, they are called a bainite bundle. By contrasting Figure 5.30(a) ~ (e) , we will find: in the test samples without relaxation, the size of the bainite bundles is larger, laths are longer and in most of the zone laths almost run through the original austenite grains; with the increasing of the relaxing time, the lath structure is fined obviously, and the bundle size gradually becomes small. When the relaxing time is 30s, in part of zones, mutual partitioning of lath bundles can be seen obviously and the size becomes small, though the size of lath bundles in part is still large. When the relaxing time is 200s, the size of lath bundle is the smallest and uniform, and the fining effect is the best; when the relaxing time is 1000s, the size of lath bundle increases again. Therefore, the relaxation can result in obvious fining effect, and the relaxing time is one of the important factors influencing final microstructure. By contrasting Figure 5.30 (a) ~ (e) , you can see that the amount of granular bainite increases with the extending of relaxing time, especially in the sample with the relaxing time of 1000s.

When the deformation temperature is decreased to 800℃, typical optical microstructures of the samples after 30% deformation and relaxed for different time are shown in Figure 5.31 (a), (b). According to the figure, the samples'

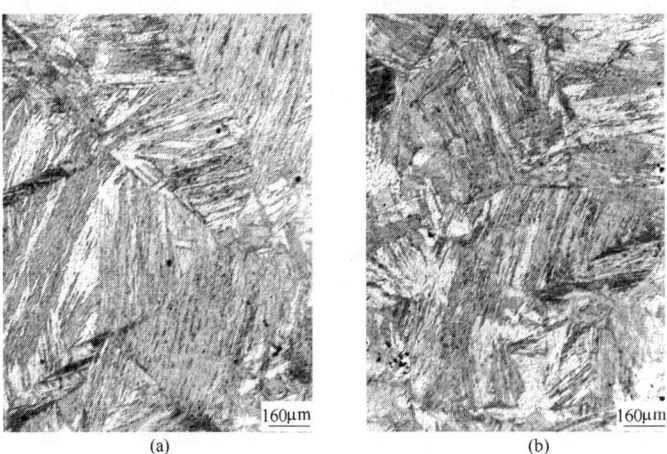

(a)   (b)

Figure 5.31   Optical microstructures after 30% deformation
at 800℃ and relaxation for different time
(a) 0s; (b) 60s

microstructures are primarily still lath structure after thermo-simulated by the process. Compared to Figure 5.30, the figure shows that the size of bainite bundles in the samples is small but the boundary of bainite bundle is not clear, with a certain amount of granular structure in the microstructure. The effect of the relaxing time on the microstructure accords with results in the samples deformed at 850℃, and only the time of the optimum fining effect is advanced to 60s.

Optical microstructures after 30% deformation at 900℃ and relaxation for different time, are shown in Figure 5.32 (a), (b). According to the figure, their microstructures consists primarily of lath structure. Compared to Figure 5.30, the figure shows that the size of bainite bundle in the samples is large but the boundary of the bainite bundle is regular. Effect tendency of relaxing time on the microstructure accords with results in the samples deformed at 850℃, and the bainite structure fining effect is the best only at a relaxing time of 60s.

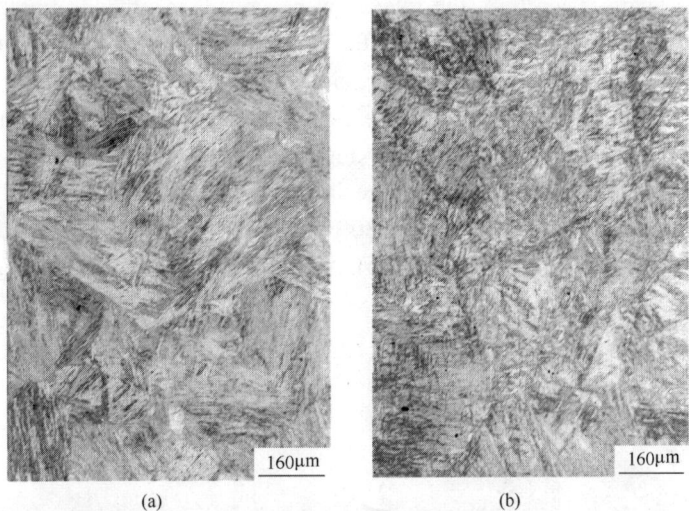

160μm

160μm

(a)   (b)

Figure 5.32   Optical microstructures after 30% deformation at
900℃ and relaxation for different time
(a) 0s; (b) 60s

Optical microstructures after deformed for 60% at 850℃ and relaxed for different time, are shown in Figure 5.33 (a), (b). According to the figures, the steel microstructures consists primarily of lath structure. Only the size of the bainite bundles in the sample becomes small obviously when the deformation amount increases, and the shape of bainite bundle is irregular. The change tendency of bainite size to relaxing time accords with the result in the sample deformed for 30%, although the size of the bainite bundles is the smallest in the sample with a relaxing time of 60s.

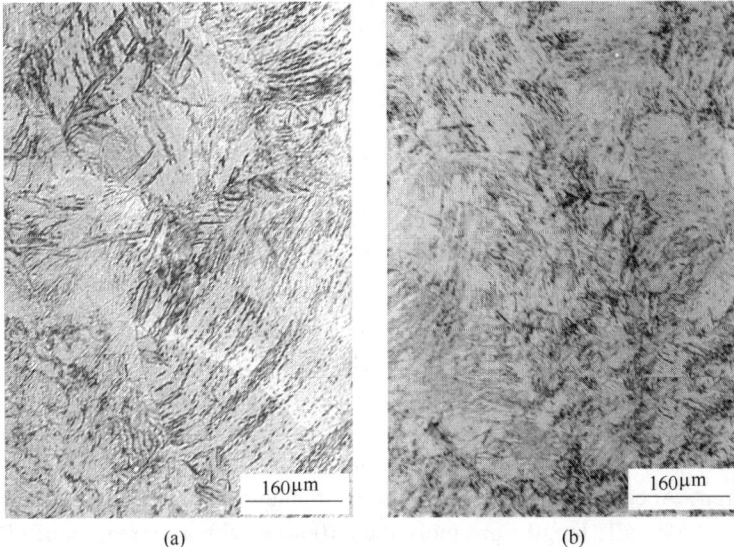

Figure 5.33   Optical microstructures after 30% deformation
at 850℃ and relaxation for different time
(a) 0s; (b) 60s

5.6.2   *Quantitative statistics of bainite bundle size*

In order to obtain quantitative results for the size fining of the bainite, quantitative statistics is made under an optical microscope for the size of the bainite bundles under different conditions, and statistics of 100 bainite bundles are made for each sample. Maximum length of the parallel laths acts as the length of the bainite bundle, the maximum in perpendicular direction as the width of the bainite bundle. The averages of lengths and widths are calculated, and a curve of the bainite bundle size varying with the relaxing time under different conditions is plotted.

Figure 5.34 shows the change curves of the bundle size with different relaxing time at 850℃. According to the figure, the bundle size in the sample without relaxation is very large, with a length of more than 300μm and a width of more than 230μm; with the increasing of the relaxing time, the bundle size fines obviously; when the relaxing time is 200s, the bundle length decreases to approximately 50μm, the width to approximately 30μm, respectively, decreased by 7~10 times compared to the sample without relaxation. However, with continuous increase of the relaxing time, bundle size becomes large again. Therefore, with the increasing of the relaxing time, the fining effect improves; but there is an optimum of the fining effect, and the curve firstly descends and then ascends.

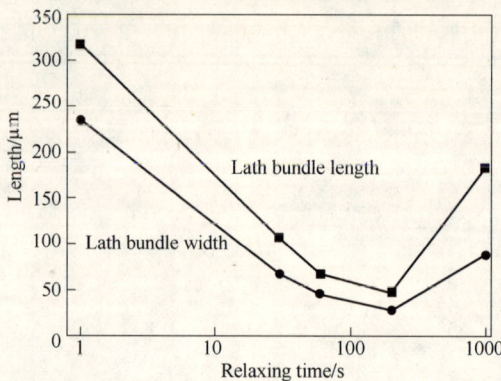

Figure 5.34　Variation of bundle size with relaxing time after 30% deformation at 850℃

Figure 5.35 shows the distribution histograms for 100 bundle sizes measured. According to the histograms, in the samples without relaxation, most of the bundle lengths are more than 100μm, with a maximum of 600μm; the bundle widths are more than 35μm, with some especially wide. When the relaxing time is 200s, most of the bundle lengths are less than 110μm, and widths are within 3~70μm.

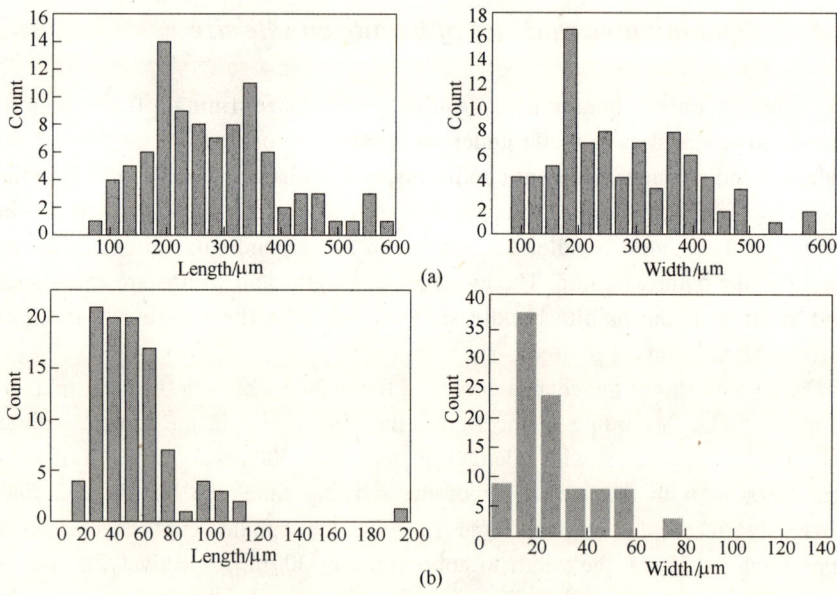

Figure 5.35　Distribution histograms of bundle size after 30% deformation at 850℃
(a) 0s; (b) 200s

When the deformation temperature changes, the variation of the bundle size with the holding time is shown in Figure 5.36. Under three deformation temperatures, the bundle sizes of the samples cooled immediately after deformation, are different from each other, but their fining laws with the relaxing time are similar, and their fining effects at ~60s are especially close to each other. However, things are different if the holding time is longer than 60s, and in this case fining after deformation at 850℃ is improved. To extend the time after deformation at 800℃ and 900℃, the bundle sizes begin to increase. Therefore, the 60s is the optimum under the condition.

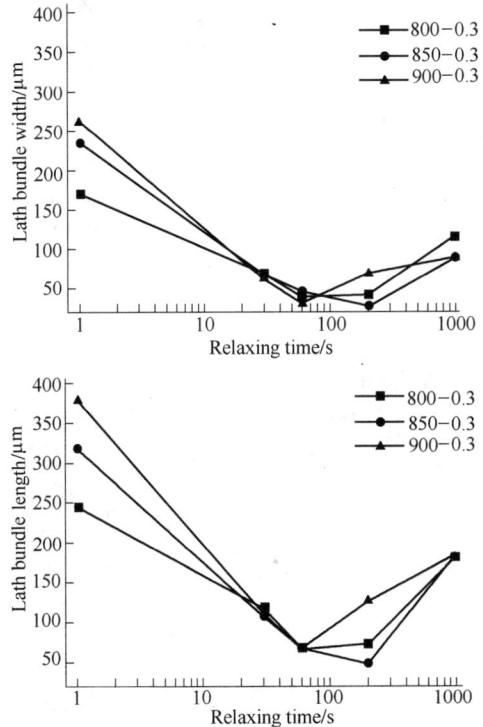

Figure 5.36 Variation of bundle size with relaxing time under different deformation temperatures

With the same deformation temperature but different deformation amount, Figure 5.37 shows the statistics of bundle sizes of the samples with different relaxing time after 30% or 60% deformation at 850℃. According to the figure, the bundle sizes with different deformation are different, but they became similar soon after relaxation. Furthermore, after a relaxation of longer than 60s, the bundle sizes of the samples with large deformation amount become larger instead, so the optimum relaxing time is 60s.

According to comparison of the fining curves under three different parameters, different RPC processes all obviously make the bainite bundle microstructure fined, and the influencing laws of the relaxing time are similar, fining effects all reaching the optimums within a certain zone. Under thermo-simulation conditions of the study, the optimum condition is the relaxation for 60~200s after 30% deformation at 850℃.

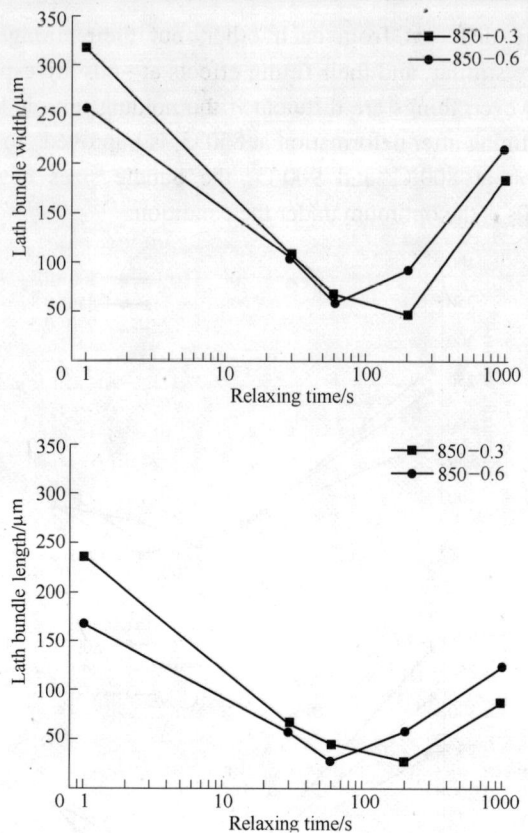

Figure 5.37　Curves of bundle size to relaxing time under different deformation

5.7　Forming Mechanism of Typical Fining Microstructures

5.7.1　*Two kinds of typical microstructure morphology in samples after RPC process*

According to the study on strain induced precipitation of the Nb-bearing micro-alloyed steel, in the samples after relaxed for different time and water-cooled after austenite deformation in non-recrystallization regions, the sizes and the distributions of the precipitated particles are different, as well as the microstructures of the matrix(Yang et al,2001). In the further thermo-simulation, it is found that the difference of the micro-structure is primarily embodied by the thickness of the structure; the difference of micro-structure types is little, and the lath bainite is predominant in the microstructures of all the samples water-cooled, but the lath length or the bundle size of bainite in different samples is different in orders of magnitude. The deformation and relaxing temperatures are very high, generally in the austenite range, so the bainite can not be directly produced during the isothermal relaxation, but some process occurred in the deformed austenite during relaxation, influences the bainite transformation during subsequent water cooling. The austenite in the steel can not be kept to the room temperature, so, for micro-alloyed steel, it is impossible to directly figure out what happened in the austenite by means of the rapid quenching from a high temperature. However, Fe-40%Ni alloy, due to its tremendous thermal lag effect, can keep the face-centered cubic structure to the room temperature. The micromechanism of intermediate-temperature transformation microstructure during the fining of RPC technology, can be known by means of the parallel tests of the alloy and steel samples.

On the basis of synthesizing the experiment results of the micro-alloyed steel and the Fe-Ni alloy, at present, there are two kinds of mechanisms proposed for the phenomenon of the relaxation promoting the intermediate-temperature transformed microstructure in the micro-alloyed steel after deformation:

1. During the recovery of the deformed austenite, discrete or tangled dislocations rearrange and form dislocation cell boundaries(sub-boundaries) with a large misorientation, and these cell boundaries is strengthened by the pinning of the strain induced precipitation, which will promote the bainite to nucleate intragranularly and handicap the growth of the bainite.

2. (Nb, Ti) (C, N) particles precipitated and thickened during the relaxation, promote the acicular ferrite to nucleate intragranularly, the acicular ferrite (its 3-dimension shape is slice, and "acicular" embodies the cross-section effect) firstly formed before the bainite transformation, partitions the original austenite into many small isolated zones, and the subsequent bainite growth is restricted in these small zones, so the bainite structure is fined. When the relaxing time is extended to the precipitate thickening stage, the number of precipitated particles decreases, the pinning effect weakens, the dislocation cell structure grows, and the acicular ferrite prefers to nucleate on the massive precipitated particles, so the effect of the second kind of fining mechanism is enhanced. But if the relaxing time is too long, severe thickening will cause the decrease of the number of precipitated particles, similarly disadvantageous for the second kind of mechanism, and the global fining effect weakens.

Figure 5.38 shows typical microstructure morphology of the samples with an isothermal relaxation of 60s and 200s after 30% deformation at 850℃. The actual effects of the two kinds of fining mechanisms can be obviously reflected by the micrographs of the two kinds of typical intermediate-temperature transformed microstructures. According to Figure 5.38 (a) , the fine bainite bath bundles intersect with each other, but there are no other structures such as the acicular ferrite between lath bundles, so it results from the first kind of fining mechanism, that is, the dislocation cell boundaries formed during the recovery of the deformed austenite, promote the nucleation and handicap the growth. In Figure 5.38 (b) , the phenomenon for the lath or acicular ferrite partitioning the original austenite grains and isolating the lath bundles, can be seen obviously, so it is the main symbol of the second kind of fining mechanism.

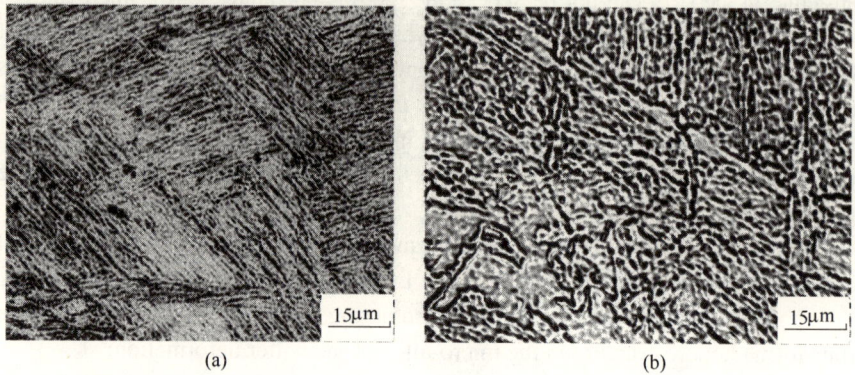

(a)　　　　　　　　　　　　　　　　　　(b)

Figure 5.38　Two kinds of typical fined microstructures

5.7.2　*Formation and influence of substructure during relaxation*

Study on the dislocation recovery and polygonizing processes after the austenite deformation, is done by means of Fe-40%Ni (C, Nb, Ti, B) alloy without phase transformation during cooling(Wang et al,2002b).

Figure 5.39 shows the evolution process for the dislocation configuration of Fe-40%Ni Alloy with different relaxing time. According to the figure, after deformation at 900℃, if Fe-Ni alloy is quenched directly without relaxation, its dislocation density will be very high, primarily lumps of tangled dislocations, as shown in Figure 5.29 (a). If Fe-Ni alloy is relaxed for a certain time after the austenite deformation, the dislocations in austenite will recover, that is, they can slip out of the grain and enter the grain boundaries, or positive and negative dislocations counteract, which decreases the dislocation density. Meanwhile, the recovery process is primarily the rearranging of dislocations, these tangled dislocation lumps will polygonize and form short low-energy dislocation arrays that connect with each other and form a dislocation wall; with the joining-in of other dislocations, the misorientation on both sides of the dislocation wall becomes gradually large, forming complete dislocation cell structure (or called subgrain) (as shown in Figure 5.39 (b), (c)). With the increasing of the relaxing time, the size of the cell structure (subgrain) increases gradually. With completing of the dislocation polygons, the misorientation on both sides of the dislocation wall (that is, both sides of the subgrain) will reach a certain extent so that the dislocation cell wall acts as the grain boundary.

Figure 5.40 shows the EBSD scanning diagram of the misorientation of each

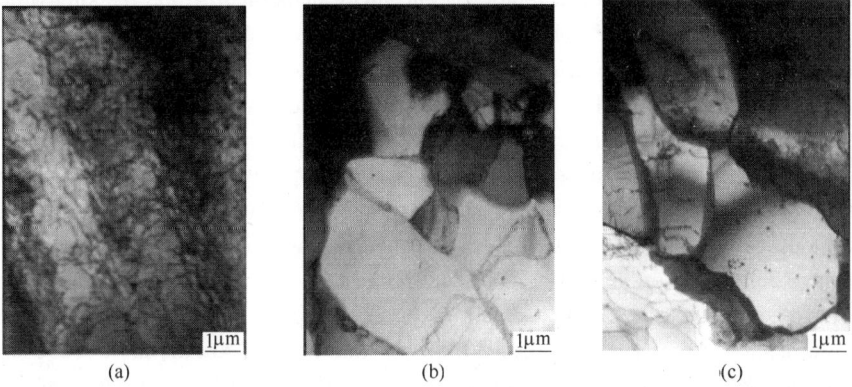

(a)　　　　　　　　　　(b)　　　　　　　　　　(c)

Figure 5.39　Evolution process for dislocation configuration of Fe-40%Ni alloy with relaxation for different time after deformation at 900℃

(a) 900℃ without Relaxation; (b) 900℃, Relaxation for 60s; (c) 900℃, Relaxation for 1000s

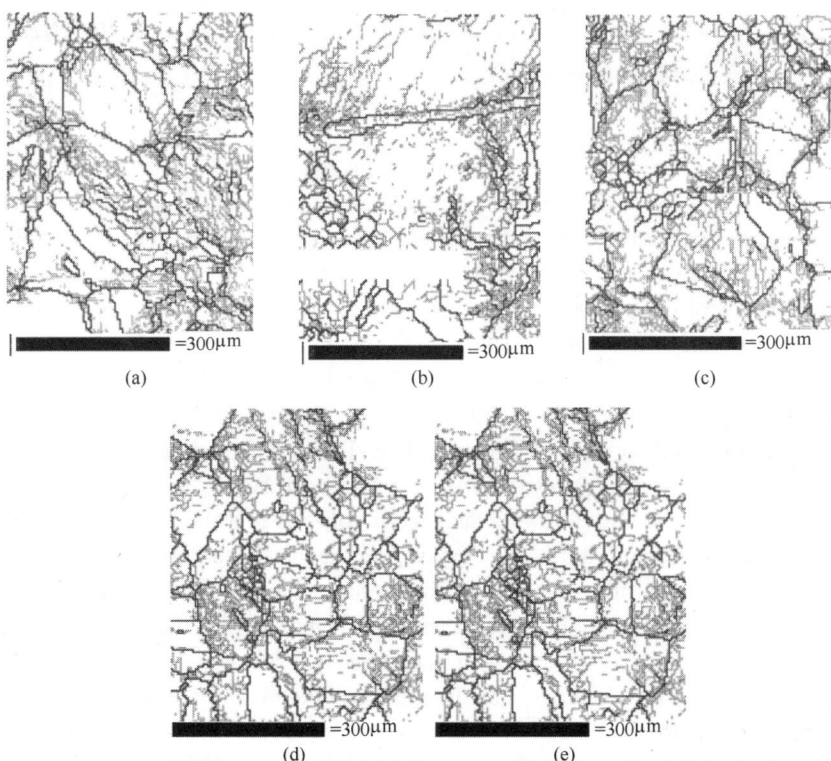

(a)　　　　　　　　　　(b)　　　　　　　　　　(c)

(d)　　　　　　　　　　(e)

Figure 5.40　EBSD diagram for misorientation of each zone in grains of Fe-Ni alloy after relaxed for different time after deformation at 850℃

zone in the deformed grain of the Fe-Ni alloy after 30% deformation at 850℃ and relaxation for different time. It reflects the forming and evolving processes of the substructure with a certain crystallographic misorientation with the relaxing time in the deformed original austenite grain. In the figure, the thick lines stand for interfaces with a misorientation of more than 15°, the medium lines for 10°~15°, the thin lines for 3°~10°. High-angle interfaces are primarily the boundaries between the original austenite grains, and low-angle complete interfaces result from the deformation zones, the recovery and the polygonized dislocation cell walls. According to the figure, if the deformed austenite is directly quenched without relaxation, the density of medium- and low-angle boundaries in the original austenite grain is not large or complete; if the austenite is relaxed for a certain time after deformation, many complete substructures will appear in the matrix, and these substructures are completed gradually. If the relaxing time is 200s, the substructures in the deformed grains are the most complete; but if further relaxed to 1000s, the sizes of substructures will increase and the coarsening will occur.

5.7.3 *Induced precipitation in deformed austenite and Its effects* (*Yuan et al,2004; Yuan et al,2003*)

Precipitation process of micro-alloying elements in the austenite generally includes four stages: segregation of micro-alloying elements, and nucleating, growing and thickening of the precipitates. However, due to micro nonuniformity of the composition and microstructure of the actual grains, the occurrence and development of the precipitation in each zone of the austenite are non-uniform; therefore, on the whole, the four stages will sometimes overlap each other. In the undeformed austenite, precipitation is slow and a few particles usually begin to precipitate only by isothermal holding at a temperature below the one predicted by the equilibrium phase diagram for more than 1000s. This is because the barrier potential for the uniform nucleation is very high and the precipitation is hard to occur, and there are only a few advantageous zones such as the grain boundaries which become nonequilibrium nucleation sites in the undeformed austenite. In addition, though the diffusion of interstitial atoms such as carbon and nitrogen is very fast, but the volume diffusion coefficients of the substitutional solid solution atoms are smaller for several orders of magnitude in contrast.

Deformation can accelerate greatly the precipitation. For example, for the Nb-bearing micro-alloyed steel, the precipitation will occur immediately if isothermally held for about 5s after deformation at 850℃. The reason for deformation accelerated precipitation comes from two aspects: one is that large amounts of dislocations multiplied during deformation provide the precipitate phases with large amounts of nonequilibrium nucleation sites, in which the nucleation barrel potential is prominently decreased; the other is that these dislocations become the rapid diffusion channels for micro-alloying elements, accelerating micro-alloying elements to segregate at the precipitating positions. Due to this reason, the precipitation in the deformed austenite is usually called Strain Induced Precipitation.

Strain induced precipitation during relaxation is studied by means of the stress relaxation method. Figure 5.41 shows the flow chart of the experience. To heat the samples to 1250℃ and isothermally hold it for 20 minutes, completely redissolve the existing precipitate, and obtain large austenite grain sizes to decrease the effect of the grain boundaries on the precipitation. Then cool the samples slowly to the deformation temperature at 2℃/s and isothermally hold it for 1min to make temperature inside and outside the sample uniform, and then deform it. To hold the sample isothermally after deformation, measure the variation of the axial stress with the holding time, plot the stress relaxation curve of the samples, and determine the occurrence and development of the precipitation as well as the precipitating degree.

Figure 5.42 shows the stress relaxation curve of a kind of Nb-bearing steel after 30% compressive deformation at 850℃. According to the figure, the stress relaxation

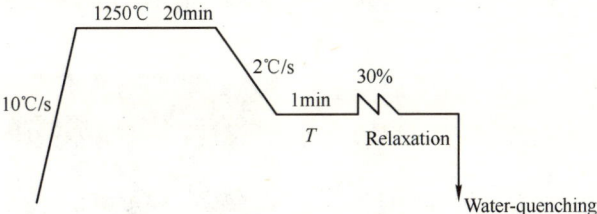

Figure 5.41 Flow chart of stress relaxation

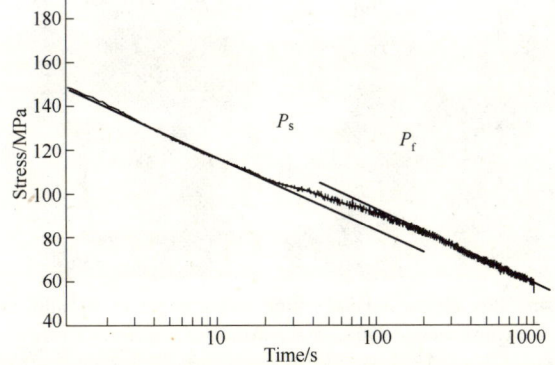

Figure 5.42 Stress relaxation curve of Nb-bearing steel after 30% compressive deformation at 850℃

curve can be divided into three stages. The first stage is approximately 20s from the end of deformation to the relaxation, and the stress descends linearly with the logarithm-time in the stage, according with the basic law of mechanical property index changes in a general recovery process. When the relaxing time is about 20s, the stress relaxation curve suddenly swerves upward, descending speed of the stress is slower than the one predicted by the logarithm-time law, symbolizing the start of the second stage. The second stage lasts approximately 200s, and then the stress relaxation curve swerves again and enters the third stage. The curve gradient in the third stage becomes the same to one in the first stage, and the stress descends again according to the logarithm-time law.

Observation by TEM (Figure 5.43) of Fe-Ni（Nb-Ti-B-C）alloy treated by the same process, shows that there are large amounts of (Nb, Ti)(C, N) particles with the size of less than 10nm distributing along dislocation lines in the samples with a relaxation of 60s and 200s. The distribution density of the precipitates on the nodes of the cell boundary dislocation network is very high as well as on the discrete dislocation lines, which shows this kind of precipitation handicaps obviously the recovery process. With the extending of the relaxing time, the ratio of particles with a size of more than 10nm increases and the distribution density of the precipitates decreases, the dislocation gradually breaks away from the pinning of the precipitates, and the coherency between the precipitates and the matrix gradually disappears.

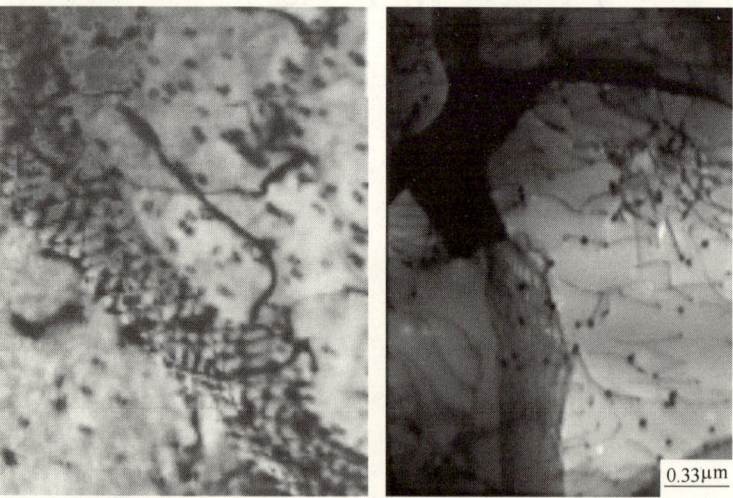

0.33μm

Figure 5.43   Precipitates and dislocations in Fe-Ni-Nb-Ti-B-C alloy after 30% deformation at 850℃ and relaxation for different time

Figure 5.44 shows the morphology of precipitates in the extracted carbon replica from the steel samples after held for 20 minutes at 1250℃ and cooled to 850℃ at 2℃/s, held for different time after 30% compressive deformation. Figure

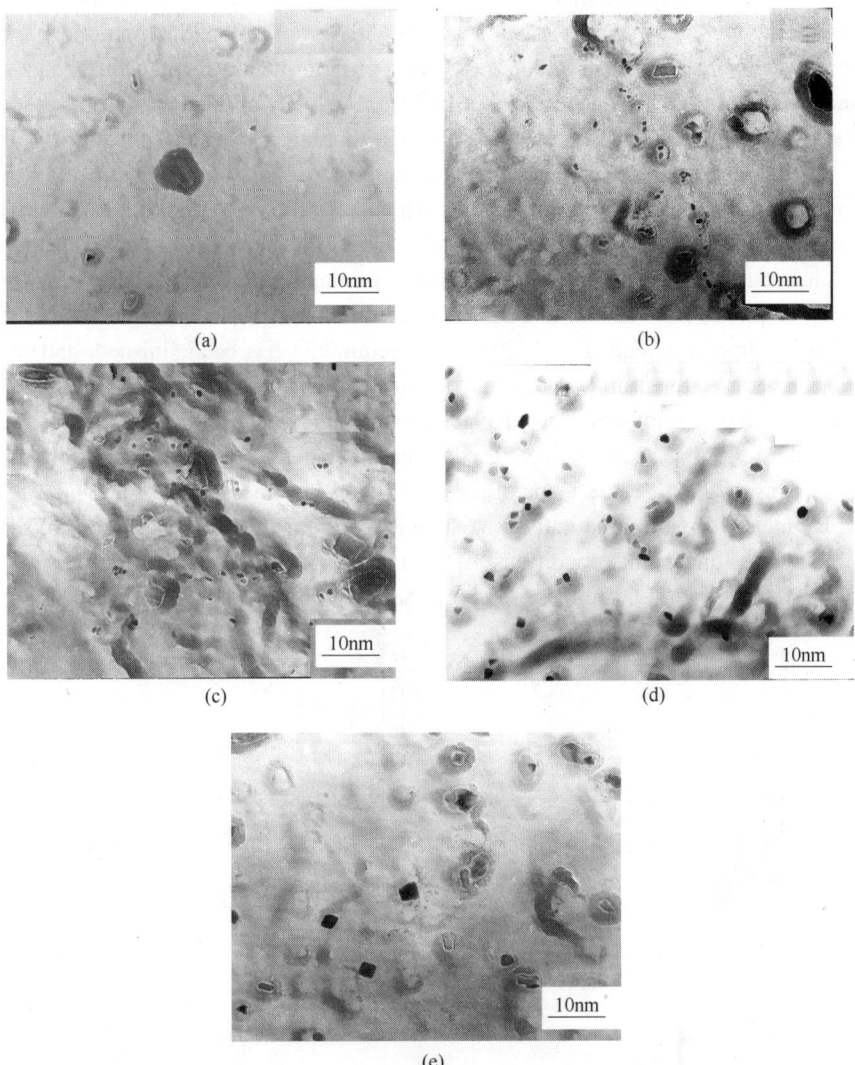

Figure 5.44   Morphology of precipitate after 30% deformation at 850℃ and relaxation for
(a) 0s; (b) 30s; (c) 60s; (d) 200s; (e) 1000s

5.44 (a) is the EM (Electron Microscope) picture of the sample without relaxation.
It is generally thought that the precipitate with a size of less than 2~3nm is hard to
be observed under EM due to the limited extraction replica technology. According
to Figure 5.44 (a) , the fine precipitate particles can hardly be seen; several large
inclusions sometime can be seen in the sample. As shown in Figure 5.44 (a) , the
arrow indicates the inclusion formed during solidification and dropped during
extraction. Figure 5.44 (b) shows the morphology of the sample with a relaxation
of 30s, and some fine precipitate phases can be seen; they are small in the size and

few in the number, displaying the strip or slightly-crooked line distribution, so the precipitates prefer to form on the dislocation or deformation strip under the strain induced condition. This is because the diffusion velocity of the solute atoms along the dislocation pipeline direction is higher than that in other directions; the distortion energy at the defects such as deformation zones or substructures is higher, and it is easy for atoms such as Nb and B in the test steel to segregate at these defects. Therefore the precipitates will prefer to nucleate on the dislocation or deformation zone and grow fast. When the relaxing time is extended to 200s, the precipitates have grown to 10nm or so, with a uniform distribution. When the relaxing time is extended to 1000s, the precipitating has been finished, and the particles have grown up and coarsened, and the density decreases obviously. The shape of the precipitates also changes during precipitation. They are fine and irregular dot- or ellipse-shaped at the initial stage of precipitation; with the increasing of the time, the shape of the precipitates becomes a regular polygon.

By means of EM, quantitative statistics is made for the size distribution of the precipitates under the conditions of relaxation for different time after 30% deformation at 850℃, and the results are shown in Figure 5.45.

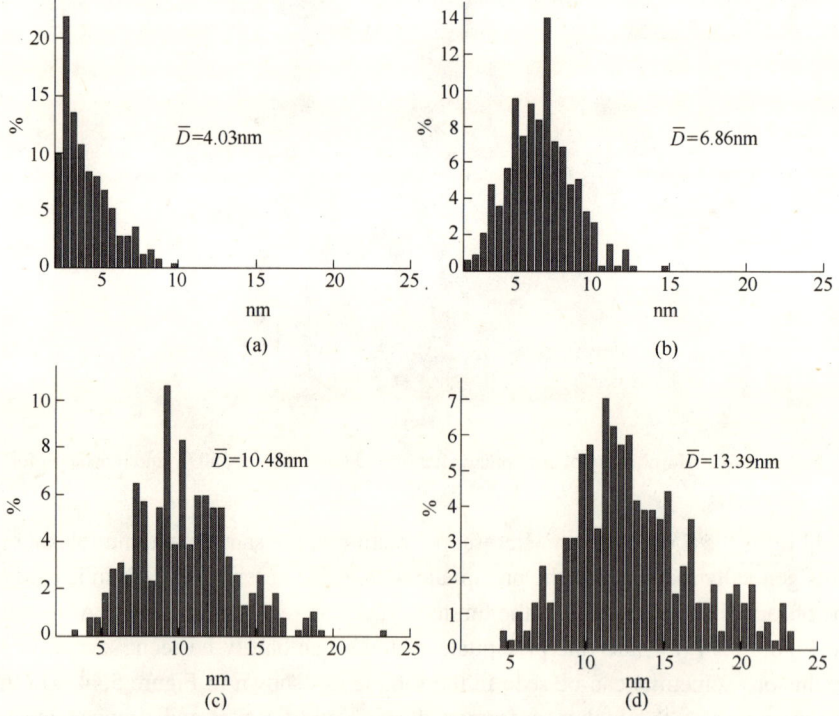

Figure 5.45   Size distribution of the precipitates under 30% deformation at 850℃ and relaxation for different time

(a) 30s; (b) 60s; (c) 200s; (d) 1000s

According to Figure 5.45, the size distributions of the precipitates with different relaxing time, all accord with the normal distribution, and the peak value is close to the average size. With the increasing of the relaxing time, the peak position moves gradually to the right, the average size changes from 4nm for 30s to 10nm for 200s, and it has reached 13nm at 1000s. But according to the distribution diagram, the nucleating, growing and coarsening of precipitate accord with the general law, but starting and finishing point of each stage are not clear. According to the changing law of the average size to the time, the precipitate growth is fast in the initial stage of the relaxation, but obviously slowed down later. This may be because the precipitates are nucleated in the zones with high density dislocations, and grow quickly due to the fast diffusion along the dislocation pipelines as well as the segregation of elements such as Nb, B on the high-energy defects. But with the growing up of the particles, gradually their pinning effect on the dislocations is lost, and the dislocation density decreases with the extending of the relaxing time. Therefore, the predominant pipeline diffusion of the solute atoms turns to the volume diffusion, so the growing velocity decreases.

For the simple alloy system, carbide or nitride precipitation of Nb, Ti, has been reported for many times. The precipitate phases in the austenitization temperature range are primarily carbides and nitrides of Nb and Ti. Djahazi found that undissolved particles of TiN in the Nb-bearing steel can become the nucleating center of NbC or Nb(C, N). In compoundly-added Nb, Ti micro-alloyed steel, the Ti-rich carbides are predominant when the temperature is high, and Nb-rich carbides when low. During the isothermal holding, the precipitates are Ti-rich in the initial stage of nucleation, and the Ti/Nb ration decreases during the growth. There are many micro-alloying elements in the test steel, and the elements such as Cu, B, Ni, Mo all influence obviously the precipitation of the complex (Nb,Ti) (C,N). In order to further study the evolution of the composition of the precipitates, the composition change of the precipitates is analyzed by means of Analysis Electron Microscope JEM-2010F and Nanobeam EDS analyzing technology. Figure 5.46 shows the results.

According to Figure 5.46, when the relaxing time is 60s, there are two kinds of precipitates: one is fine and slightly spheroidic with a size of less than 5nm, which are analyzed to be the pure Nb(C,N) precipitates, as shown in Figure. 5.46 (a). Figure 5.46 (b) shows (Nb,Ti)(C,N). It has a larger size and its shape is close to an irregular polygon, and a mass of analyses for the particle composition show that there is few pure Nb(C,N) precipitates (the Si peak in the energy spectrum comes from the impurity in the carbon film). When the relaxing time is 200s, there is no pure Nb(C,N) found; therefore, during the growth of the precipitate in the Nb-Ti bearing steel with a high Ti content, Ti will randomly replace Nb and form complex precipitate phases. Energy spectrum analysis also shows there is some Mo in the precipitate when the relaxing time is 200s and 1000s. The analysis of Ti,

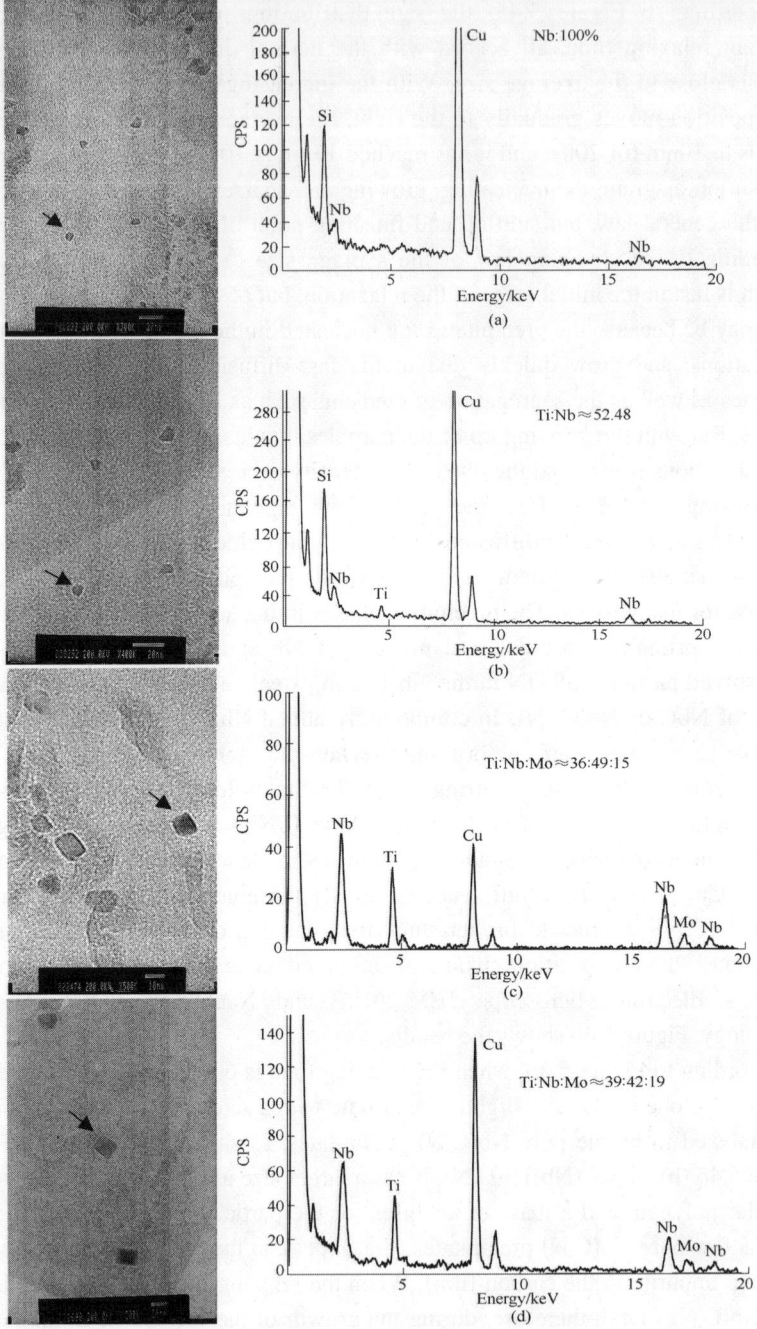

Figure 5.46　Composition change of precipitates after 30%
deformation at 850℃ and relaxation for different time
(a) 60s; (b) 60s; (c) 200s; (d) 1000s

Nb and Mo in the precipitate with different relaxing time shows that the relative contents of Ti and Nb change obviously with the extending of the relaxing time. From the predominant Ti content to the decrease of the Ti/Nb ratio, finally the content of Nb exceeds that of Ti in the precipitate. When the relaxing time is 200s, Mo has appeared in the precipitate and the content of which increases with the relaxing time. When the relaxing time is 1000s, the change of the relative ratio of Ti and Nb is not significant, while the Mo content continues to increase.

Mo appears in the precipitate under the isothermal relaxation at 850℃, but according to the diffraction experiment, the precipitate is still face-centered cubic structure(as shown in Figure 5.47). It is obvious that Mo partly substitutes the lattice position of Nb or Ti. According to the change of the Ti/Nb ratio with relaxation varying from 200s to 1000s, the probability of Mo replacing Nb is larger than that of Mo replacing Ti. Under the experimental condition in the paper, the solubility of Mo in (Nb,Ti)(C,N) is very large, which causes Mo to diffuse into the precipitate from the austenite matrix during the precipitation.

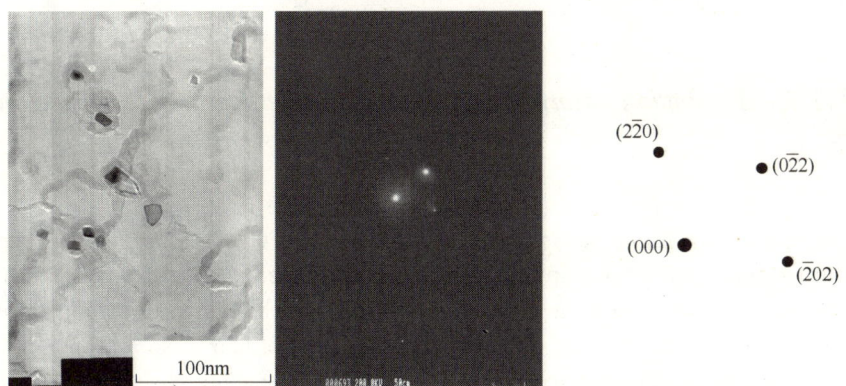

Figure 5.47　Diffraction pattern of precipitates in a sample with 30% deformation at 850℃ and relaxation of 1000s

The results above show, with 30% deformation at 850℃ and a relaxation of 200s, the polygonal dislocation network structure forms completely, and there is large amounts of strain induced precipitates on the dislocation network, so the dislocation network is stabilized effectively and the microstructure fining is promoted. If the relaxing time extends again, due to the coarsening of the strain induced precipitates, the number of the particles decreases, the polygonal dislocation network grows up and the fining effect reduces. When the deformation temperature increases, because the dislocation recovery is fast, polygonization is speeded up, but the strain induced precipitation is correspondingly delayed, so the stability of the dislocation polygon structure is deteriorated with the optimum fining time shortened, and the fining effect weakened. The increase of the deformation amount will promote the dislocation relaxation and the polygonization, and the corresponding strain induced precipitation is accelerated, so the corresponding optimum fining time is shortened. When the deformation temperature decreases, though relaxation and strain induced precipitation on the dislocations are both decelerated, because the high-density dislocations exist and the dislocation relaxation is hard to proceed, the high-density dislocation network becomes the preferential nucleation sites and promotes greatly nucleating of the bainite, and the optimum fining time is advanced. Only under the condition of 30% deformation at 850℃ and held for 60~200s, the relaxation evolution of the dislocation structure matches the strain induced precipitating pace, which makes the dislocation polygon structure pinned and more stable, and effectively fines the microstructure. However, under other deformation conditions, due to the development dismatch of the two factors, though the effects of the low-temperature relaxation and large amounts of deformation are better than those under 30% deformation at 850℃ in the short-time relaxation, the fining effect is weakened rapidly with the increasing of the relaxing time, and comprehensive effect is not good.

5.7.4　Formation, Morphology of acicular ferrite and its effect on fining

The other reason for microstructure fining caused by RPC process is, there is quite a bit acicular ferrite (or strip granular bainite) produced in the deformed grains. The acicular structure is a production during the phase transformation. The formation mechanism of the microstructure has not yet known so far, but some conditions influencing the formation of the acicular structure have been widely studied, concluded into the followings:

1. Inclusions such as MnS or other precipitate phases promote the formation of the microstructure.
2. The acicular ferrite is easily produced in the transformation products given a large deformation accumulating and high-velocity cooling.
3. Relaxation of the deformed austenite will influence the formation of the acicular ferrite.

5.7.4.1　Morphology characteristics of acicular ferrite

In the low-carbon bainitic steel, the acicular structure differs with common bainite in the morphology as well as properties. Table 5.8 shows hardness and elastic modulus of three kinds of microstructure measured by the nanometer indenter (each datum is the average of three measurements). By comparison, the hardness of the acicular ferrite is the lowest, then that of the granular bainite is higher, and that of the lath bainite is the highest. The comparison shows the acicular ferrite is the structure firstly formed during cooling. It partitions the original austenite grain, and restricts the subsequent growth of the granular or lath bainite. The morphology of the acicular structure under optical microscope is acicular, but its 3-dimension reconstruction study shows that the spatial morphology of the acicular ferrite is plate-like (as show in Figure 5.48). Therefore, during the continuous cooling, the acicular ferrite produced in the preliminary stage partitions the original austenite, and handicaps the growth of subsequent bainite transformation products in space, achieving the purpose of restricting and fining the bainite structure(Wu et al,2002).

Table 5.8   Nanometer indentation properties of three kinds of typical microstructure

Lath bainite		Granular bainite		Intragranular ferrite	
Loading 10mN		Loading 10mN		Loading 10mN	
E/GPa	H/GPa	E/GPa	H/GPa	E/GPa	H/GPa
262	4.64	247	4.03	232	3.39
$\sigma = 30.5$	$\sigma = 0.47$	$\sigma = 16.6$	$\sigma = 0.34$	$\sigma = 10.5$	$\sigma = 0.34$

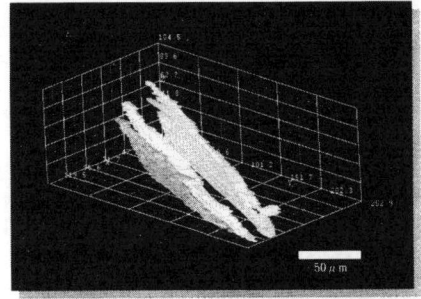 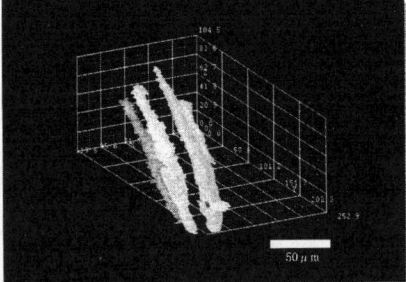

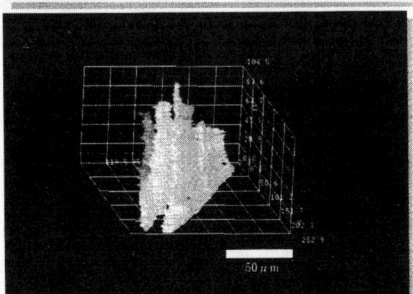

Figure 5.48   3-D morphology of the acicular ferrite

5.7.4.2   Effect of relaxation on formation of acicular ferrite

During the relaxation of the RPC process, the dislocations recover and polygonization are done; Meanwhile, the precipitated particles under the strain induction of the micro-alloying elements, are primarily pinned to the dislocation cell wall. On the one hand, this precipitation strengthens the substructure boundaries; on the other hand, these particles precipitated on the sub-grain boundaries may become the nucleating sites of the acicular ferrite during cooling, which will be advantageous for the acicular ferrite to nucleate preferentially inside the grains. Therefore, during relaxation, formation of the dislocation cell structure, precipitation, growth and distribution of the strain induced precipitates, will all influence the nucleation and growth of the acicular ferrite, and finally influence the fining effect of the intermediate-temperature phase transformation products. When the test steel is relaxed for different time after final rolling and before quenching, Figure 5.49 shows the microstructure pictures of the acicular structure under a scanning electron microscope. Figure 5.49 (a), (b) show the microstructure of the test steel directly quenched after rolling without relaxation. According to the figures, the primary microstructure is the lath bainite; the parallel lath bainite bundles with large sizes almost run through the original austenite grains, and there will be occasionally interceptive acicular ferrite appearing between bundles. For the steel relaxed for a certain time after final rolling and deformation, Figure 5.49 (c), (d) show that there is large amounts of acicular structure in the microstructure,

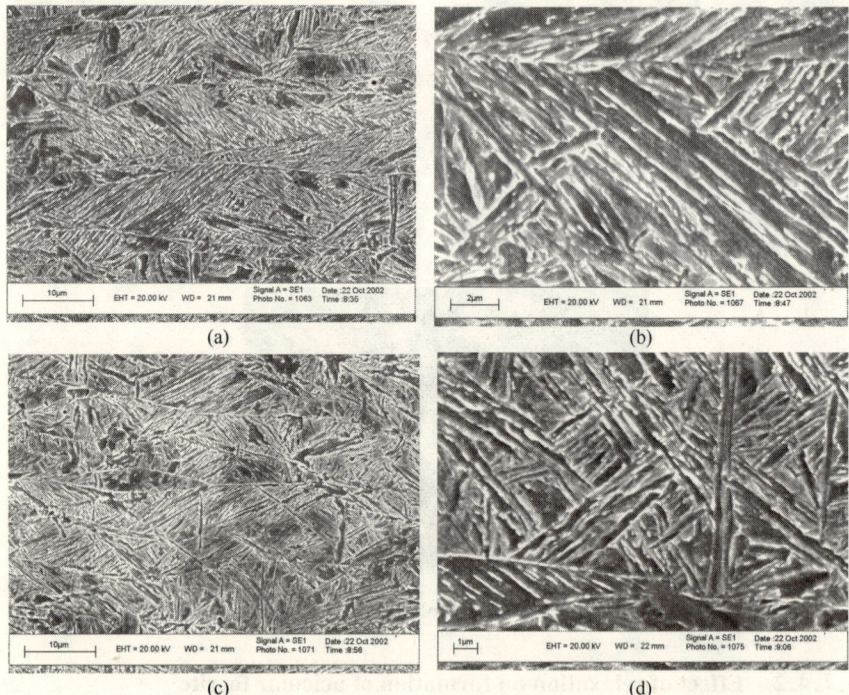

(a)

(b)

(c)

(d)

Figure 5.49   SEM micrographs of samples after different relaxation; (a) and (b) without relaxation, (c) and (d) direct quenching after relaxation for 20s

including long aciculae running through the whole original austenite grain as well as short aciculae intercrossing each other. These acicular structures have clear outlines, and there is no or very little of other phases (such as the residual austenite or M/A islands) inside the microstructure. (Shang et al,2005) Therefore, the relaxation has obvious effect on the formation of the acicular ferrite. However, the sizes of the precipitate are very small during relaxation, so the direct coincidence relation between them and the acicular ferrite, as well as the nucleating details of the precipitate, needs further experimental studies to be clarified.

5.8   Study on the Variation of Microstructure and Properties of Fined Steels during Tempering and Its Cause Analysis

The intermediate-temperature transformation microstructures treated by RPC process, are micrometer- or submicrometer-sized. The specific interfacial area of the fine microstructures is very large; according to the thermodynamic law, it has the tendency to lower the interfacial energy by coarsening. The intermediate-temperature transformation microstructures themselves are a kind of metastable microstructures, with a high free energy and a spontaneous tendency to evolve to an equilibrium microstructure. Therefore, it is an important task to keep the stability of the fine intermediate-temperature transformation microstructures (Wu et al,2005;Wu et al,2004).

5.8.1   *Hardness changes and their difference between the microstructure-fined steel and the quenched and tempered steel with the same compositions*

The compositions (mass%) of the test steels are 0.06C, 1.68Mn, 0.058Nb, 0.020Ti, 0.30Mo, 0.33Cu, 0.22Ni, 0.0032B. After rolled by RPC process, one part of steel plate (thereafter called "RPC rolled Sample") is directly heated to 650℃, isothermally held for different time, and then air-cooled; the other part of steel plate is reheated to 900℃, isothermally held for half an hour, and then water-quenched (thereafter called "Reheated and Quenched Sample"), and tempered at 650℃ for different time. The microstructure evolutions of the two kinds of samples in the tempering process, are investigated by means of hardness measurement and optical microscopy.

Optical micrograph (Figure 5.50) shows, the original microstructures of the two kinds of samples are both predominately lath bainite and a little granular bainite and lath martensite. The primary difference between the microstructures is that RPC rolled Sample grains are flattened, displaying the directivity.

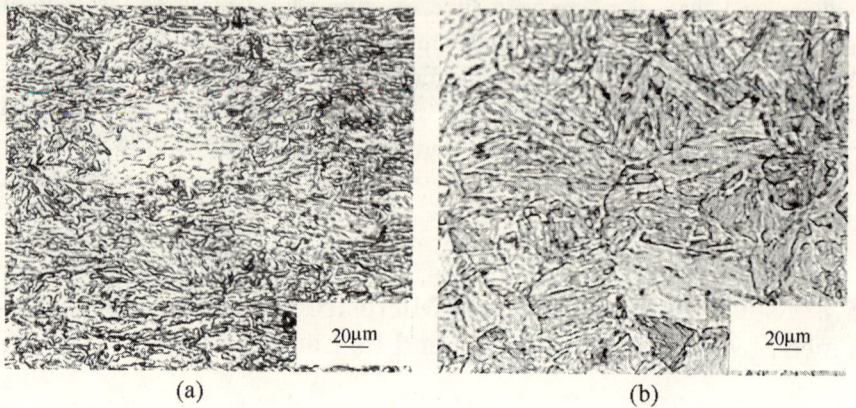

(a)   (b)

Figure 5.50   Original microstructures of two kinds of samples before tempering
(a) RPC rolled sample; (b) Reheated and quenched sample

Vickers hardness measurements show, the hardness of RPC rolled Sample of the same steel is obviously higher than that of Reheated and Quenched Sample, and this is because the high-density dislocations introduced in the austenite during RPC process rolling, are inherited by the bainite formed after transformation; the austenite formed during reheating is equivalent to the undeformed austenite, and the dislocation density in the bainite produced in the sequent quenching process, is lower than the former, therefore, the distortion energy of RPC rolled Sample is obviously higher than the latter. Figure 5.51 shows the hardness changes of the two kinds of samples with the tempering time. According to the figure, hardness variation curves for the two kinds of samples both display the three-stage characteristics. At the beginning of tempering, the hardness descends fast, and this

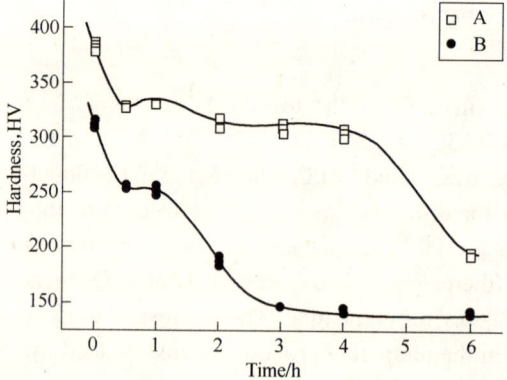

Figure 5.51   Variation of vickers hardness with tempering time for two kinds of samples
A: RPC rolled sample;B: Reheated and quenched sample

is the first stage; then, the decrease of hardness tends to slow down with the time, and this is the second stage; in the third stage, the hardness descends sharply again. The change tendency of the hardness, is similar to the recovery-recrystallization of the deformed metal in the annealing process; in fact, it has been shown that it is a recovery -recrystallization process itself, though the bainite generated after transformation has not undergone the re-deformation.

The driving force of the recovery -recrystallization comes from the distortion energy of the high-density non-equilibrium defects. In this work, though the bainite is not re-deformed, the defect density is still very high, so it has the tendency to reduce the defect density and change towards the equilibrium microstructure. These defects come from two main sources: Firstly, the high-density dislocations generated during the austenite deformation and inherited by the bainite during the sequent transformation; secondly, the transformation dislocations generated during the bainite transformation.

However, tempered hardness changes of the two kinds of samples are different; the second stage of Reheated and Quenched Sample is shorter than that of RPC rolled Sample, that is, the softening of the Reheated and Quenched Sample is faster than that of RPC rolled Sample. This seems, though the dislocations in RPC rolled Sample include those produced during deformation and those generated during the bainite transformation in the deformed austenite, the distortion energy should be higher obviously than that of Reheated and Quenched Sample, therefore, the driving force of the recovery-recrystallization should be larger. The fact is just contrary, however. Here we must notice that the actual speed of the process is dependent on the combined effect of the two factors: the driving force and the resistance. The driving force of the recovery-recrystallization is large but the measured softening process is very slow, which shows it is given a rather large resistance and the resistance becomes the determinant influencing the process speed.

5.8.2 *Microstructure stability in tempering process*

Figure 5.52 and Figure 5.53 show the microstructure changes of the two kinds of samples in the tempering process. For RPC rolled Sample, after tempered for 0.5 hour, there is no obvious change in the microstructure, but the hardness has descended a lot; this shows the change in the stage primarily occurs in a more micro scale that can not be discerned by an optical microscope, that is, occurring inside the bainite lath. Corresponding EM observance (Figure 5.54) shows, in the RPC process rolled and untempered sample, the dislocation density is obviously higher than that of the sample tempered for 0.5h, primarily tangled dislocations. According to the configuration, the dislocations can be easily classified into the

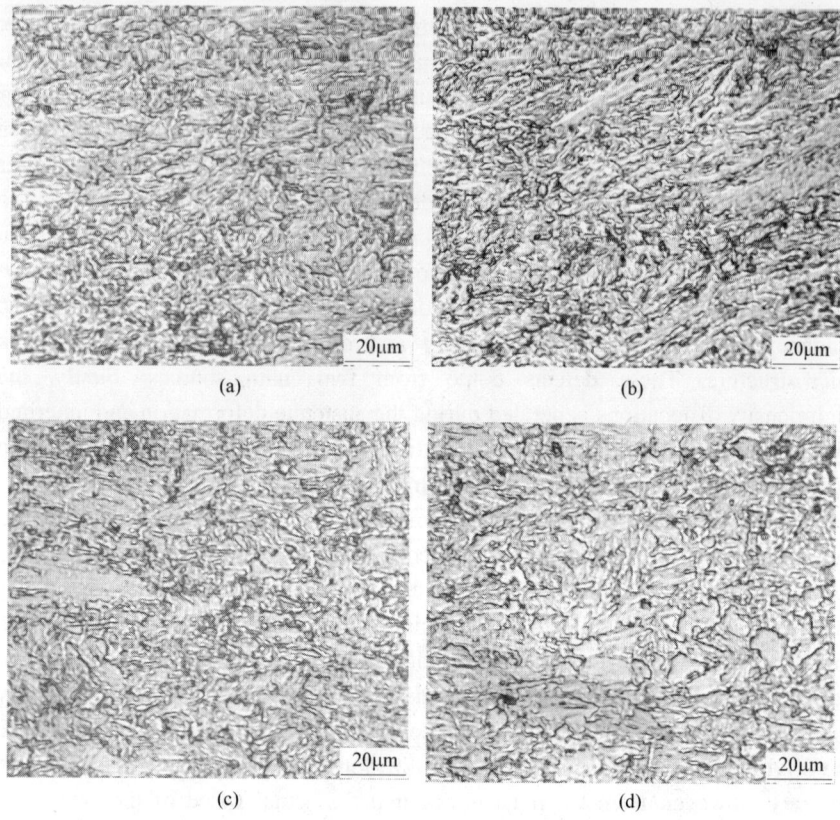

Figure 5.52   Microstructures of RPC rolled sample after tempered for different time
(a) 0.5h; (b) 2h; (c) 4h; (d) 6h

two kinds: For the first kind, the dislocations are tangled with each other and pinned by the fine precipitates; for the second kind, the distribution is uniform, with straight dislocation lines, and there are no precipitates on the dislocations. After tempering for 0.5h, it is observed that the dislocation density is reduced, especially the second kind of dislocations with a uniform distribution is decreased sharply, the tangled dislocation distribution in the sample tending to form a cell structure. After tempered for 2h, the laths are locally widened, seeming to be the result of combining of the adjacent laths. In the sample after tempered for 6h, polygonal ferrite appears, which corresponds to the second sharp descending of the sample hardness.

In Reheated and Quenched Sample, no large amounts of tangled dislocations are pinned; the phase transformation dislocations introduced during the bainite transformation disappear soon in tempering. After tempered for 2h, large amounts of polygonal ferrite appear. After tempered for 4h, the microstructure consists completely of polygonal ferrite; in the meantime, the residual strip austenite and its decomposition products distributed on the bainite lath boundaries before tempering, become spheroidal, irregularly distributing on the ferrite grain boundaries or inside the grains.

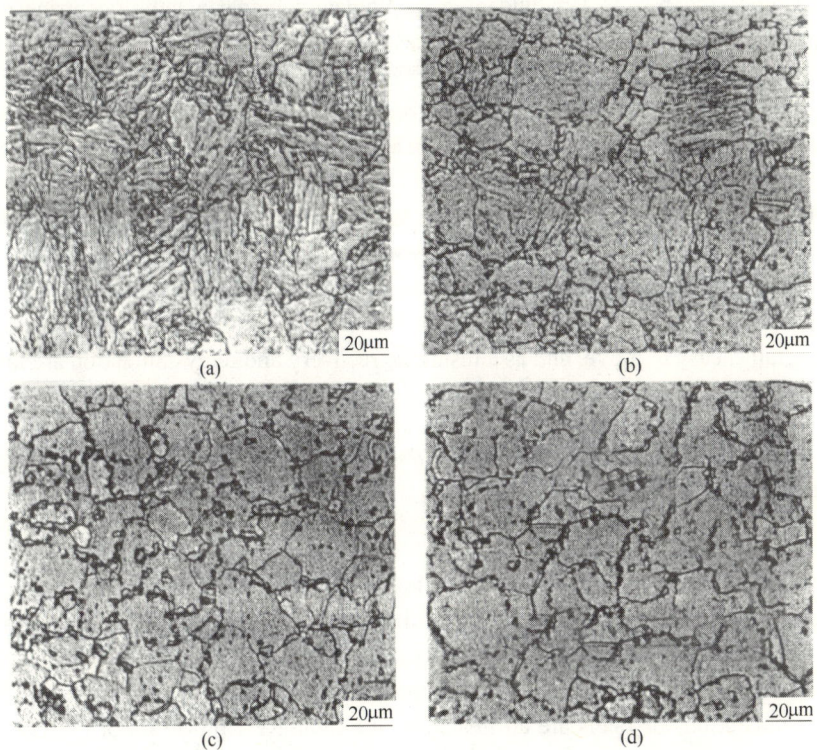

Figure 5.53   Microstructures of reheated and quenched sample after tempered for different time
(a) 0.5h; (b) 2h; (c) 4h; (d) 6h

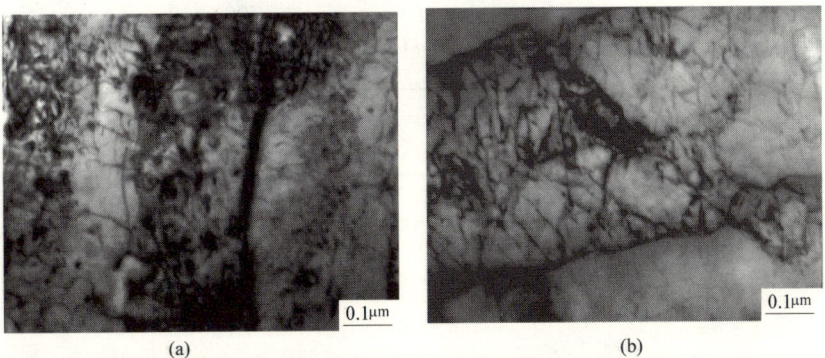

Figure 5.54   Dislocation configuration of RPC rolled sample before and after tempered
(a) Before tempered; (b) After tempered for 0.5h

The results above show: The softening process of the fine lath bainite microstructures occurring in the tempering process, includes the followings in turn: part of dislocations disappearing in the laths, most of dislocations forming the cell structures, the bainite lath widening, combination between laths occurring and polygonal ferrite forming. In RPC process samples, before phase transformation, the deformation dislocations in the austenite are pinned by the strain induced precipitates produced in the relaxation process; after phase transformation, these dislocations pinned are kept wholly, hard to freely move, and this becomes a decisive factor to handicap the recovery and recrystallization of the bainite. In reheated samples, after re-austenization, a part of the precipitates redissolve, and originally pinned dislocations break away from the pinning and disappear; therefore, before tempering, the transformation dislocations generated during the phase transformation and not pinned by the precipitates, are predominant inside the grains, easy to move, and as a result the recovery and recrystallization are fast.

5.8.3 *Effect of tempering temperature on mechanical properties of the steel*

Due to the use of the specific micro-alloying composition design and the special Relaxation-Precipitation-Control transformation (RPC) process, the steel has a good age hardening effect. Figure 5.55 shows the yield strengths of No.1, 2 ,4 micro-alloyed steel in Table 5.5 after tempered at different temperatures for 1h. The three kinds of steels are all treated by the same RPC process. For No.1 steel, after rolling yield strength is approximately 700MPa. after tempering at 400~500 ℃, the strength ascends slowly; after tempering at 600℃, the strength is enhanced obviously and reaches the peak value; further raising the tempering temperature, the strength descends somewhat; but if tempering at 700℃, the strength is still higher than the rolling one. For No.2 steel with a higher content of Cu (0.5%), the

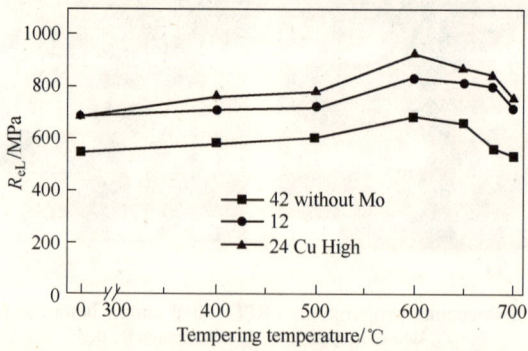

Figure 5.55   Strength of RPC processed steel after tempered

strength after tempering is obviously higher than that of No.1 steel; with the increase of the tempering temperature, the ascending tendency of the strength is larger than that of No.1 steel; when tempering at 600℃, the strength reaches the peak value, with the yield strength over 900MPa. For No.4 steel without Mo, with the increase of the tempering temperature, the strength change tendency is the same to that of No. 1 steel, but the strength is lower about 100MPa than that of No.1 steel; after tempering at 600℃, the strength reaches 650MPa.

Figure 5.56 shows the low-temperature transverse impact toughness of three kinds of steel with different composition. According to the figure, for No.1, 2 steel with a higher strength grade, after tempering, the strength ascends, but the impact toughness descends; after tempering at 700℃, the strength is higher than the rolling one, and the toughness is equivalent to the rolling one. For No.4 steel, even if the strength reaches the maximum after tempering, but the impact toughness is still rather good, with A_{KV} at−40℃ larger than 100J.

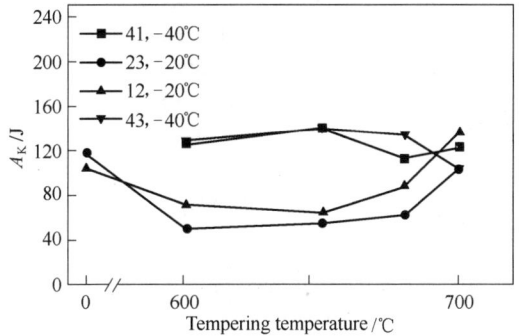

Figure 5.56   Toughness of RPC processed steel after tempered

5.9   Concluding Note

Since the issuing of "Ultra-fine Grain Steel" (Chinese edition), the iron and steel industry develops rapidly in China. The steel yield has reached 400~500 million tons, and the yield of the high-performance micro-alloyed steel is multiplied. In China, for large amounts of engineering machinery, coal mining machinery, excavating equipments, heavy trucks, railway locomotives, container frames, and largely used harbor machines, Grade 600~800MPa and 1000MPa steels are needed largely. Considered from the resource utilization, energy consumption and the cost, it has not been a development direction to meet the needs by means of the quenched and tempered steel with a high alloy content; therefore, a new generation of low-cost, high-performance, energy-saving ultra-fine bainitic steel, has a vast range of developing prospect.

At present, in China, the leading metallurgical enterprises all have mass-produced the ultra-fined low-carbon bainitic steel. By the end of 2006, approximately 300 thousand tons of steel products with the strength of 500~800MPa, thickness of 8~60mm, and ten steel standards, have been produced using the process described earlier and put into market by many steel works such as Anshan Iron and Steel Corporation, Wuhan Iron and Steel Corporation, Jinan Iron and Steel Corporation. The product performances have reached the advanced level of the steel with the same strength grade abroad, with a good application effect. The alloy addition range(except for the conventional elements) in the steel is 0.3%~1.2%, without quenching process, the prices are within 5000~7000 RMB/t, with a high economic benefit.

The intermediate-temperature transformation ultra-fining technology has been developed to produce bridge steel, ship building, marine platforms, military products, pipelines, etc. Of course, there is still much work to be done during further generalization and application. How to make the ultra-fine microstructure steel meet the different needs from various industries, realize the smooth use under various processing, welding and service conditions, will be the key for the new generation of steel to be completely developed and applied.

References

Babu S S, Bhadeshia H K D H (1991) Mechanism of the transition from bainite to acicular ferrite. Mater Trans. JIM 32(8): 679-988

Djahazi M, He X L, Jonas J J, et al (1992a) Nb(C,N) Precipitation and Austenite Recrystallization in Boron-Containing HSLA Steels. Metall. Trans. 23A:.2111-2120

Djahazi M, He X L, Jonas J J, et al (1992b) Influence of Boron on the Nature and Distributions of Strains Indueed Precipitation in (Ti,Nb) HSLA Steels. Mater. Sci.Tech. 8: 628-635

Garcia C I, Lis A K, Pytel S M, et al (1992) Ultra-low carbon bainitic steel plate steels: Processing, microstructure and properties. Trans. Iron & Steel Soc. AIME 13: 103-112

He X L, Djahazi M,, Joans J J, et al (1991) The Non-equilibrium Segregation of Boron During The Recrystallization of Nb-treated HSLA Steels. Acta Metall. Mater. 39(11): 2295-2308

He X L, Shang C J, Yang S W, et al (2003) A Relaxation-precipitation-Phase Transformation Controlling technique for producing high strength low alloy steels. Chinese Patent, ZL01115650.3, Oct. 2003

He X L, Yang S W, Zhou T (1997) In: Chandra T, Sakai T (ed) THERMEC'97 Int. Conf. on Thermomechanical Processing of Steel and other Materials, Warrendale, PA, 1997

Ohtsuka H, Umemoto, M, Tamura I (1988) Effects of Holding After Deformation on the Subsequent $\gamma \rightarrow \alpha$ Transformation Behavior in a HSLA Steel. In: THERMEC-88, Tokyo.

ISIJ, 1988: 352-359

Shang C J, Hu L J, Yang S W, et al (2005) Formation and controlling of acicular ferrite in low carbon microalloyed steels. Acta Met.Sin. 41(5): 471-476 (in Chinese)

Shang C J, Wang X M , He X L, et al (2001) A special TMCP used to develop an 800MPa grade HSLA steel. J. Univ. Sci. Tech. Beijing 8(3): 224-228

Shang C J, Wang X M, Yang S W, et al (2003a) Processing technique and microstructure fining of high strength low carbon bainitic steels. Acta Met.Sin. 39(10):1019-1024 (in Chinese)

Shang C J, Yang S W, Wang X M, et al (2003b) Influence of relaxation process on the microstructure and properties of low carbon bainitic steel. Mater. Sci. Foru. 426-432: 1439-1444

Wang X M, He X L, Yang S W, et al (2002a) Refining of intermediate transformation microstructure by relaxation processing. ISIJ Inter. 42(12): 1553-1559

Wang X M, Shang C J, Yang S W, et al (2002b) A study on mechanism of phase transformation controlling technique for microstructure fining. Acta Met.Sin. 38: 661-666 (in Chinese)

Wang X M, Shang C J, Yang S W, et al (2006). The refinement technology for bainite and its application. Mat.Sci. Eng. A. 438-440: 162-165

Wu H B, Shang C J, Yang S W, et al (2004) Microstructure and mechanical property of tempered ultra-fine low carbon bainitic steels. Acta Met.Sin. 40(11): 1143-1150 (in Chinese)

Wu H B, Yang S W, Yuan S Q, et al (2005) Evolution of Microstructures in a Low Carbon Bainitic Steel during Reheating. Mater. Sci. Foru. 475-479: 121-124

Wu K, Enomoto M, et al (2002) Three-dimensional morphology and growth kinetics of intragranular ferrite idiomorphs formed in association with inclusions in an Fe-C-Mn alloy. ISIJ Inter. 42(10): 1144-1149

Yang S W, Wang X M, Shang C J, et al (2001) Relaxation of deformed austenite and refinement of bainite in a Nb-containing microalloyed steel. J. Univ. Sci. & Tech. Beijing 8(3): 214-217

Yuan S Q, Yang S W, Nie W J, et al (2004) Interaction between the dislocation and precipitates during the isothermal relaxation after deformation in Fe-Ni-Nb-Ti-C alloys. Acta Met.Sin. 40(8): 887-890 (in Chinese)

Yuan S Q, Yang S W, Shang C J, et al (2003) Strain induced precipitation in a multi –microalloyed steel containing Nb and Ti during processing. Mater. Sci. Foru. 426-432: 1307-1312

Zhang S, Hattori N, Enomoto M, et al (1996) Ferrite nucleation at ceramic/austenite interfaces. ISIJ International 36(10): 1301-1309

Zhou G, Wen M, Li P, et al (2000) The Influnce of Cu, B content on strain induced Nb(C,N) precipitates during hot deformation in an ULCB steel. *Acta Metall. Sin.(English letter)* 13: 623-628

6
Microstructure Refining and Strengthening of Martensitic Steel

The improvement of delayed fracture (DF) and fatigue resistance for steels, especially the former of martensitic steel, through microstructure refining and strengthening are the main concern in this chapter. Firstly, the effects of microstructure refinement in toughening and improving DF property of martensitic steels are studied. Secondly, methods for strengthening grain boundaries such as reducing the amount of segregated embrittling elements at grain boundaries and controlling grain boundary carbides are discussed. Thirdly, the effect of controlling hydrogen trap through microalloying element carbides on improving DF resistance is investigated. Fourthly, the effect of cleanliness on the fatigue performance of martensitic steels is discussed. Finally, new high strength martensitic steels ADF series with excellent combination of toughness, DF and fatigue resistance as well as its characteristics and industrial applications were introduced.

Introduction

Higher-strength materials are objectives for which material scientists have strived for many decades. Among these efforts, martensitic steel was the earliest success, which is now still widely chosen for the structural component applications （Hsu,1999）. This is because tempered martensitic steels can offer a good balance between high strength and excellent toughness by deliberately adjusting compositions (carbon and other alloying elements) and designing specific thermal processes.

Fatigue and delayed fracture are the two important mechanisms for the failure of metallic materials in service. With increasing the strength of martensitic steel, its toughness generally decreases, and its fatigue failure susceptibility increases, particularly its delayed fracture susceptibility increases remarkably. Therefore, the application of higher strength martensitic steel requires the improvement of its toughness, fatigue and delayed fracture resistance simultaneously. In late 1990s, Japan, Korea and China have all implement national research programs with a huge financial support, named as "Ultra Steel", "High Performance Structural Steels for 21st Century" and "New Generation Steel", respectively. Research and development of 1500 MPa grade steel for practical applications was one of the important subjects among all of these programs (Sato, 2000; Lee, 2000; Weng, 2000).

6.1   Challenges of High Strength Martensitic Steel

Toughening of high strength martensitic steels has been an important subject of extensive studies over past several decades and remarkable achievement has been obtained. Therefore, the improvement of delayed fracture and fatigue resistance is mainly concerned thereafter.

6.1.1   *Delayed fracture*

Delayed fracture (DF) is a phenomenon in which components such as bolt or pre-stressed concrete steel bar suddenly fail after a certain period of duration after loading. It is a kind of environmentally enhanced embitterment, resulting from the interaction among materials, environment and stress (Matsuyame,1989;Chu,1988). As stress corrosion cracking (SCC) of high strength martensitic steel in aqueous environment is actually a hydrogen-induced cracking phenomenon, therefore, the DF discussed in this chapter is referred to either hydrogen-induced DF or SCC in aqueous environment of high strength martensitic steel.

DF, appearing in the structural components, can be classified into the following two categories according to the source of hydrogen(Nakayama,1999): 1. DF caused by hydrogen absorbed from the actual environment, for example, bolts served in bridges are easily subject to DF due to a long exposure to such actual environments as rainwater, dew, etc. 2. DF caused by hydrogen absorbed from manufacturing processes, such as pickling and electroplating. For example, electroplated bolts may fail after loading for several days or even a few hours.

In the first category, hydrogen is actually from the corrosion reaction due to the long exposure to aqueous environment; While in the second one, hydrogen is from acid aqueous solution used in the pickling and plating processes, and then it diffuses after loading and is enriched in the stress concentrated region (Nakayama,1999).

Figure 6.1 summaries the critical DF stress for some typical low alloyed and tempered martensitic steels with various tensile strength (Matsuyama,1989). It can be seen that DF susceptibility has a strong relationship with strength, particularly when tensile strength exceeds about 1200MPa, the fracture stress decreases significantly, which severely limits the applications of higher strength martensitic steels. Therefore, DF is a major challenge for applications and receives continuous attention and efforts for decades.

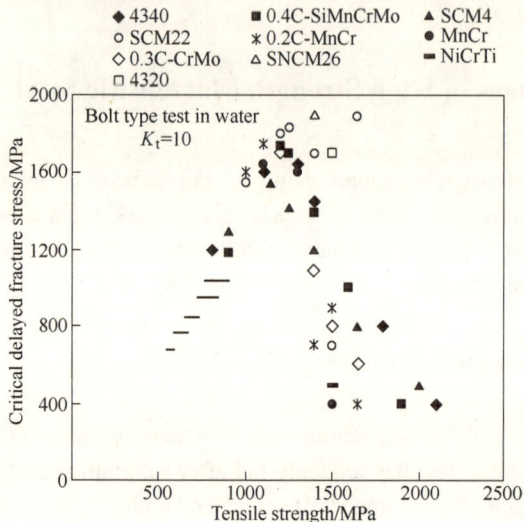

Figure 6.1   Variations of critical delayed fracture stress with tensile strength
for some typical low alloyed and tempered martensitic steels

Compared with other types of failures, DF of high strength steels exhibits the following characteristics (Hui et al,2001;Matsuyama,1989):

1. DF susceptibility is significantly enhanced when the tensile strength exceeds about 1200 MPa;
2. DF often occurs at ambient temperature and its probability increases with temperature up to 100℃, which is different from the low-temperature brittle fracture;
3. Occurrence of DF seldom companies with obvious plastic deformation, which is different from the creep failure;
4. DF occurs under static loading, i.e., strain rate is zero, which is different from fatigue failure;
5. DF takes place under the stress much lower than the steels' yield strength;
6. DF susceptibility is most enhanced when tempered around 350℃, a typical temperature for the so called tempered martensite embrittlement;
7. DF is dominated by the cracking along the prior austenite grain boundaries, and generally exhibits intergranular fracture.

Since DF is induced by hydrogen, how hydrogen facilitates crack initiation and propagation will be a key point. In general, the solute hydrogen in iron, an endothermic reaction, is not more than $0.001 \times 10^{-4}\%$ at ambient temperature; while the required quantity of solute hydrogen to induce DF is around $0.1 \times 10^{-4}\%$ or even higher, which is much more than the real solute amount (Omura,2005;Kushida,1998). Therefore, the experimentally measured quantity of hydrogen to induce DF is not the hydrogen in real solute condition, but the one stored in various traps in the steel.

In general, hydrogen in low-energy traps (also termed as reversible traps) can diffuse at ambient temperature, and is termed as diffusible hydrogen; while the one in high-energy traps (also termed as non-reversible traps) cannot diffuse at ambient temperature and then termed as non-diffusible hydrogen. It is often believed that hydrogen released at the temperature range of $200\sim400\,°C$ can diffuse while it cannot at the temperature higher than $400\sim600\,°C$ during thermal desorption analysis test (Suzuki et al,1993). Since DF often occurs at ambient temperature, it is considered that such fracture results from diffusible hydrogen rather than non-diffusible hydrogen, which has been supported by some experimental evidences (Matsumoto et al,1996;Suzuki et al,1993). For example, Matsumoto et al.(1996) quenched and tempered SCM440 steel with tensile strength of about 1200 MPa followed by hydrogen charging and nickel electroplating, then they did slow strain rate test and hydrogen thermal desorption test after baking at different temperatures. Their results show that the amount of released hydrogen decreases with increasing baking temperature when it is lower than $200\,°C$;while it increases with baking temperature when it is higher than $200\,°C$. Thus, it could be concluded that DF is relevant to the amount of released hydrogen at temperature lower than $200\,°C$. It should be noted that deformation-induced generation of vacancies and their clustering have been considered to be promoted by hydrogen and to play a primary role on the DF susceptibility of high strength steel as presented by others (Nagumo, 2001; Nagumo et al, 2001).

From the aforementioned recognition, in the development of DF resistant high strength steels, a rational approach can be taken in response to the DF process composed of the entry of hydrogen, the transportation and accumulation of hydrogen to stress concentrated region such as prior austenite grain boundaries, and the formation of cracks. The proposed approach comprises:

1. Preventing the entry of hydrogen;
2. Rendering the absorbed hydrogen harmless;
3. Improving microstructural homogeneity such as grain boundary properties.

6.1.2　Fatigue failure

Fatigue is another common failure mechanism of structural components in service, and has been extensively studied for more than one century. Unfortunately, accidents or even disasters, resulting from fatigue failure, still happen almost every day. Therefore, solutions to prevent such failure is a strong demand with the development of modern industries such as automobile, machines, construction and railway.

It is known that there is a good correlation between rotating bending fatigue strength, σ_w, of smooth specimens and tensile strength, R_m, for low or medium strength steels as follows (Murakami et al,1989):

$$\sigma_w = 0.5R_m \ (R_m \leqslant 1200 \ \text{MPa}) \tag{6.1}$$

In this case, fatigue cracks tend to initiate from the surface and therefore are termed as surface fracture. However, when the tensile strength exceeds about 1200 MPa, the linear correlation does not hold and there is more scatter or even declination in fatigue strength values and the origins of fatigue fracture of high strength steels are not always at the surface but often some distance away, particularly for high-cycle fatigues and therefore are termed as internal fracture. The fracture surface often exhibits a small smooth spot at the crack origin, which is usually called a "fish-eye" (Figure 6.2). In this case, the fatigue strength is generally much lower than the predicted value by equation 6.1, and could be calculated by the following equation (Murakami and Usuki, 1989):

$$\sigma_w = 1.56(HV + 120) \times \frac{1}{(\sqrt{area})^{1/6}} \tag{6.2}$$

where $\sqrt{area}$ is square root of the projected area of small defects or inclusions, μm and HV is Vickers hardness, kgf/mm^2. Obviously, reduction of the size of internal defect can remarkably increase the fatigue strength.

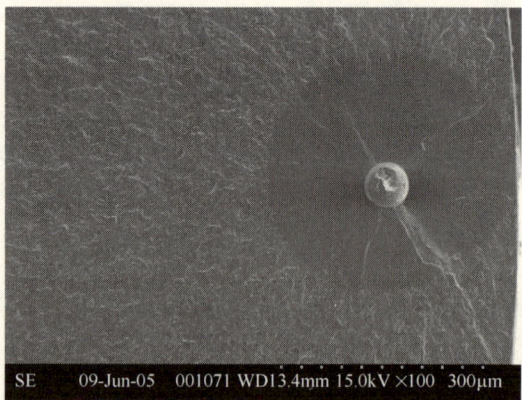

Figure 6.2　A typical fish-eye fracture originates from internal inclusion (60Si2CrVA steel, tensile strength R_m=1930MPa, applied stress amplitude σ_a=765 MPa, number of cycles to failure N_f=8.1×10^5 cyc)

It is often observed that the aforementioned fish-eye fracture in high strength steels originates from internal defects, which are mostly non-metallic inclusions, but in some cases are microstructural defects (Perkins et al,2005; Abe et al,1996). Prevention of fish-eye fracture would certainly improve the fatigue property of high strength steels.

It needs to be noted that conventional fatigue data have been limited to fatigue lives up to 10^7 cycles. While in many industries, the required lifetime of many components such as in engine, automobile, railway, airplane, offshore structures, bridge and specific medical facilities, often exceeds 10^8 cycles. In fact, it has been found that components or structures, made of high strength steels, still suffer fatigue failure at higher number of cycles, though these steels was considered to display a fatigue limit at a high number of cycles (typically$>10^6$) (Zhang et al,2006;Furuya et al,2005;Wang et al,1999). Time and cost constraints rule out the use of conventional fatigue tests to fatigue lives more than 10^7 cycles to check structural materials, for example, it takes almost three months to do a 10^9 cycles test with conventional fatigue tester at the frequency of 100Hz. With the development of ultra high frequency (20kHz) fatigue testing system in recent years, it is possible to conduct very high cycle fatigue testing.

6.2 Microstructure Refinement in Toughening and Improving DF Property of Martensitic Steels

The most common strengthening mechanisms of steel consist of solid solution strengthening, work (dislocation) hardening, precipitation strengthening and grain refinement strengthening. Among them, only grain refinement can improve not only strength but also toughness. It has been shown by many experiments that the strength of ferrite+pearlite steel could be doubled and its toughness be improved by grain refinement(Weng,2003). Similarly, refinement of microstructure in quenched and tempered martensitic steels is expected to improve both toughness and DF resistance, especially the latter (Hui et al,2004;Kawasaki et al,1987;Proctor et al,1969).

6.2.1 *Technologies for martensitic microstructure refining*

The conventional method to control the prior austenite grain size of martensitic steels is the addition of some alloying elements, such as Al, Ti, V and Nb, to prevent the growth of austenite grain during austenitizing. These elements could form strong carbide, nitride or carbonitride to inhibit austenite grain growth. Fine grained steels with austenite grains finer than ASTM No.8 grade could be obtained by this method. Particularly, we have successfully achieved grains finer than ASTM No.10 grade by the suitable addition of V and Nb elements into conventional 42CrMo steel (Hui et al,2004;2005).

Besides such microalloying technique, fast heating or thermal cycling, thermomechanical processing and magnetic/electric field processing are also popular techniques adopted in industries to refine the martensitic microstructure. The adoption of these techniques depends on the geometry and dimension of structural components and has to be studied case by case. For example, Neturen Co., Ltd. in Japan has successfully developed a new kind of high frequency induction heating technique to produce high strength spring steel wire for cold winding with grain size finer than ASTM No.8 (Kawasaki et al,1987). In addition, 42CrMoVNb steel with ultrafine prior austenite grain as fine as 2μm, was obtained through rapidly cycling heat treatment (Hui et al,2005).

6.2.2   *Effect of microstructure refinement on strength and toughness*

Grain refinement strengthening is actually via more grain boundaries available to resist slip of dislocations, which then leads to a higher yield stress R_{eLs}. Relation between grain size and yield stress is now commonly known as the Hall-Petch equation:

$$R_{eLs}=\sigma_0+k_y d^{-1/2} \qquad (6.3)$$

where σ_0 is the friction stress, k_y is the yield stress intensity factor and d is the grain diameter. If various strengthening mechanisms are considered to contribute to σ_0. Equation 6.3 could be changed to (Maropoulos et al,1993):

$$R_{eLs}=\sigma_i+\sigma_{ss}+\sigma_p+\sigma_d+\sigma_{sg}+\sigma_t+kd^{-1/2} \qquad (6.4)$$

where σ_i is the internal friction stress, mainly the Peierls stress, σ_{ss} is the solid solution strengthening, σ_p is the precipitation strengthening, σ_d is the dislocation strengthening, σ_{sg} is the strengthening due to sub-grains, and σ_t is a crystallographic texture strengthening parameter.

Refined lath martensitic microstructure leads to higher yield strength generally by introducing more boundaries. The key microstructure parameter is the packet size, or the lath size (Swarr et al,1976;Smith et al,1971). Interface boundaries between laths are generally low angle boundary while those between packets are large angle boundary. Both types of boundaries could obstruct the movement of dislocation.Low angle boundary shows smaller resistance to crack propagation than that of large one, which behaves like austenite grain boundary and plays the dominant role on preventing crack propagation. It can be seen from Table 6.1 that smaller prior austenite grain could lead to smaller packet width, but has no obvious influence on lath width. Therefore, the "grain size" d in equation 6.4 is actually referred to packet width, D_p, for the martensitic microstructure.

Table 6.1   Microstructure parameters of 42CrMoVNb steel as-quenched or tempered at 200℃

Grain size d / μm	Packet width D_p / μm	Lath width l / μm	Retained austenite content V_{Ar} / %
2	1.0	0.45	4
4	2.3	—	3
8	3. 5	0.48	<2
20	12.1	—	2

Figure 6.3 shows that both the tensile strength and the yield strength increase remarkably when prior austenite grain in 42CrMoVNb steel was refined from 8 μm to 4 μm, but no further increase can be observed when it was further refined from

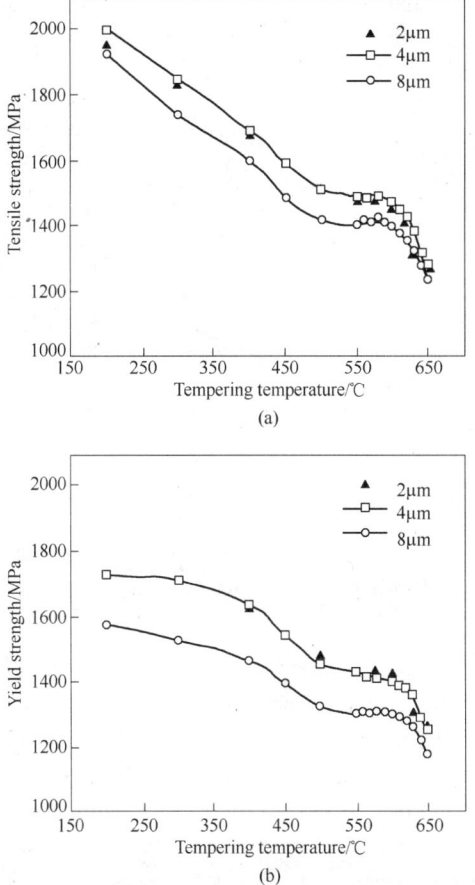

Figure 6.3   Variations of tensile strength
(a) yield strength; (b) with tempering temperature for 42CrMoVNb
steel with different prior austenite grain sizes

4 μm to 2 μm. Moreover, the increase of yield strength is more significant than that of the tensile strength when the microstructure is refined. Dependence of the yield strength of 42CrMoVNb steel on the packet width is given in Figure 6.4, where the experimental data on 42CrMo steel was also given. It can be seen that k_y, or the slope of the $\sigma_s \propto D_p^{-1/2}$ plot in Figure 6.4, decreases dramatically when prior austenite grain size d is less than 4 μm, implying that the strengthening mechanism does change; whilst k_y of 42CrMo steel keeps constant. When the prior austenite grain of 42CrMoVNb steel is refined to 2 μm by fast thermal cycling, a lot of blocky martensitic microstructure could be observed (Figure 6.5), which is very similar to the one in 5NiCrMoV steel after thermal cycling observed by Porter and Dabkowski. Such blocky structure could not be found in 42CrMo steel when prior austenite grain size is refined to 4.7μm by thermal cycling. The exact reason why the blocky martensite lowers the value of k_y is not clear up to now. It has been speculated that it might result from the fact that high dense dislocations distribute uniformly within entire grain rather than within laths (Hui et al,2005;Porter and Dabkowski,1970).

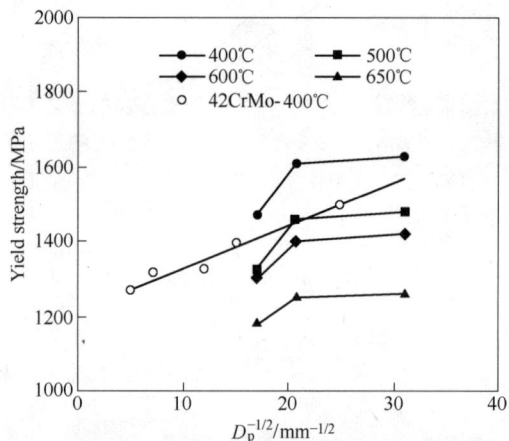

Figure 6.4   Variation of yield strength with martensitic packet width D_p of steels 42CrMoVNb and 42CrMo

With increasing tempering temperature, improvement on the strength of 42CrMoVNb steel by packet refinement decreases, that is, strengthening by packet refinement is getting weaker at higher tempering temperature, as shown in Figure 6.3, which is consistent with results on 0.2%C steel (Swarr et al,1976). This is because carbides situated at packet boundaries get coarser and spheroidized at higher tempering temperature, leading to a weaker strengthening by packet boundaries.

Obviously, the contributions to σ_0 by other various strengthening mechanisms are usually quite remarkable for the martensitic steels, which could cover the strengthening effect by packet refinement if such refinement is not large enough. Therefore, refinement of martensite packets is generally aiming at improving toughness and DF resistance besides strengthening.

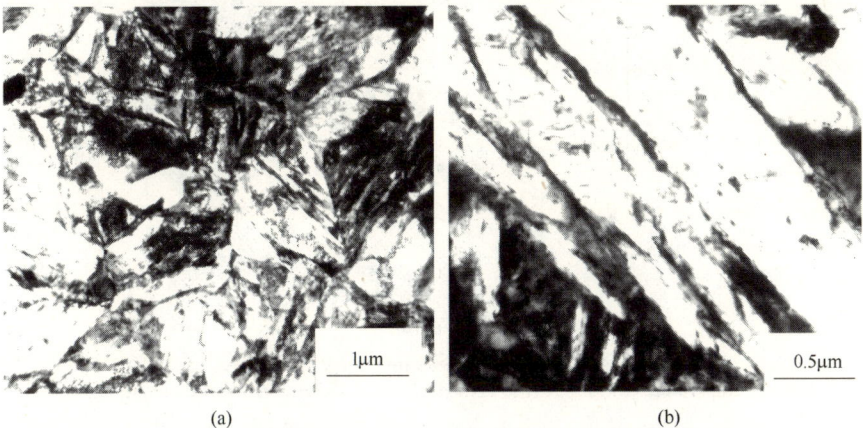

1μm   0.5μm

(a)   (b)

Figure 6.5 TEM morphologies of 42CrMoVNb steel quenched after fast thermal cycling with prior austenite grain size d=2 μm
(a) Blocky martensite structure; (b) Lath martensite structure

At the same level of strength or hardness, Charpy V-notched impact energy A_{KV} of the 42CrMoVNb steel increases with refining packet and the increase is more significant at lower strength or hardness levels (Figure 6.6). The ductile-brittle-transition-temperature T_K, defined by the temperature at which A_{KV} equals to 20J, exhibits the Hall-Petch relationship with packet width D_p,

$$T_K = 319.5 - 135.7\ln D_p^{-1/2} \qquad (6.5)$$

It can be summarized that the refinement of martensite packets could improve both strength and toughness, particularly the latter.

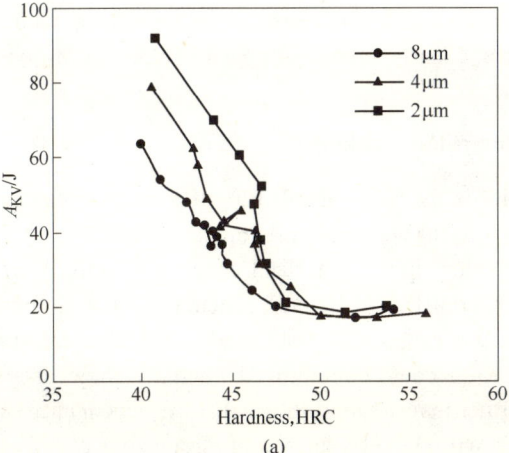

(a)

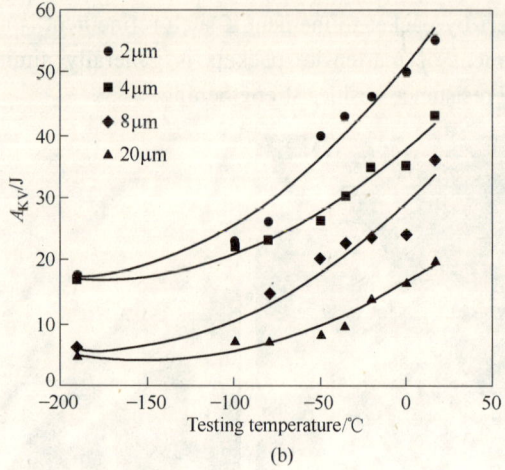

Figure 6.6   Variations of impact value A_{KV} with hardness (a) and testing temperature (b) for 42CrMoVNb steel with different prior austenite grain sizes

6.2.3   *Effect of microstructure refinement on DF resistance*

DF in high strength steels generally initiates from prior austenite grain boundaries and then propagates along them. Therefore, besides carbides and segregation of impurities at grain boundaries, prior austenite grain size is another major factor affecting DF. Extensive studies have been carried out to clarify the influence of prior austenite grain size on DF behavior in high strength steels since 1960s (Li et al,1990;Padmanbhan and Wood,1983;McDarmaid,1978). Unfortunately, these research results did not lead to a definite agreement, and could be classified into three categories as follows: 1. Change of prior austenite grain size has no or little influence on DF resistance; 2. DF resistance is enhanced with increasing prior austenite grain size; and 3. DF resistance is enhanced with decreasing prior austenite grain size. Clearly, more work need be done to resolve such conflicting opinions in the future.

6.2.3.1   Stress corrosion cracking

Austenite grain size in the range of 4.7~120μm could be obtained in a commercial 42CrMo steel by varying austenizing temperature and applying thermal cycling and the SCC behaviors in 3.5 pct NaCl aqueous solution were investigated by using bolt-loaded modified WOL type specimens. It was found that threshold stress intensity factor, K_{ISCC}, decreases gradually with increasing prior austenite grain size, d, but K_{ISCC} could be improved when d is larger than 65μm, as shown in Figure 6.7. Further investigation shows that the dependence of K_{ISCC} on d has a strong relationship with the relevant size of plastic zone ahead of the crack tip, R, and d (Hui,2003). That is to say, when d is 65~120 μm and larger than R, K_{ISCC} increases with increasing d and when d is 4.7~22 μm and smaller than R, K_{ISCC} decreases with increasing d.

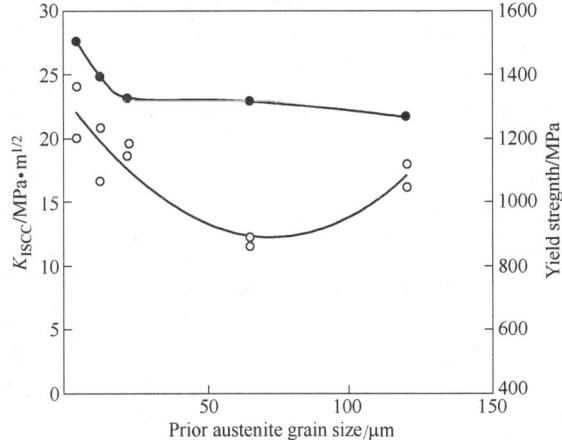

Figure 6.7   Variations of yield strength and K_{ISCC} with prior austenite grain size d of commercial 42CrMo steel tempered at 400 ℃

Stress intensity factor, K_I, has great influence on the fracture morphology of SCC. SEM observation on the fracture area, where its K_I is close to K_{ISCC}, shows that the failure mode is intergranular for all the specimens with different grain size (Figure 6.8). This implies that microstructure refinement cannot change the mechanism of SCC. Therefore, further effort should be made to achieve stronger grain boundaries especially under the condition of stress corrosion.

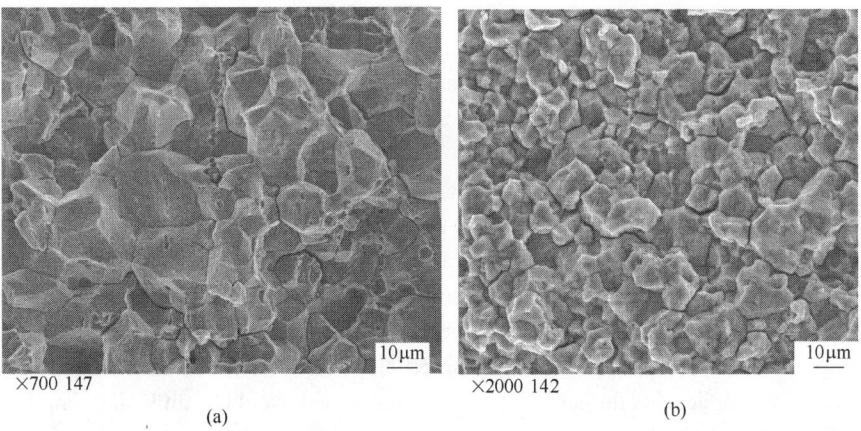

×700 147

(a)

×2000 142

(b)

Figure 6.8   Fracture surfaces near K_{ISCC} area of modified WOL specimens of commercial 42CrMo steel tempered at 400 ℃ for grain sizes of 22 μm(a) and 4.7 μm (b) , showing fracture characteristic to be all intergranular

6.2.3.2   Sustained load tensile delayed fracture

K_{ISCC} is the threshold stress intensity factor for crack non-propagation and measured under the plain strain condition. The real DF process in components such as bolts, however, consists of crack initiation and propagation, and crack initiation often plays particularly important role (Yamasaki and Takahashi,1997). Therefore, the sustained load tensile test was carried out by using round notched tensile specimens in Walpole solution to investigate the influence of microstructure refinement on DF behavior of martensitic steels (Hui et al,2004).

Stress concentration factor K_t is 2.7 at the notch of the specimen with the gauge diameter d_0=5mm and the notch size d_N=3mm. DF susceptibility is greatly affected by the environmental capacity to charge hydrogen. Higher hydrogen-charging capacity means severer DF susceptibility. Due to the effect of cell closure, the value of pH at the crack tip of low alloyed steel inserted into the aqueous solution is around 3.5, which is predefined as the most critical value simulating actual environments (Chu,1988). So Walpole solution with pH=3.5±0.5 was adopted in the tests at room temperature. In the sustained load tensile test, static stress was applied to the specimen and the time-to-fracture was measured. The DF critical stress, σ_c, was defined as an applied stress below which no DF occurred within a specified period t_c (here t_c was chosen as 200 hours) in the solution. σ_N is the maximum notch tensile strength measured by tensile test in air with the same notched specimen. The ratio of σ_c / σ_N is termed as delayed fracture strength ratio(DFSR), which is used to evaluate the DF resistance of the tested steels.

Strength has a significant influence on DF resistance for the martensitic steels. In the studied range of strength, DFSR of 42CrMoVNb steel decreases with increasing strength (Figure 6.9), which is consistent with the results in literature (Matsuyama, 1989). At the same level of tensile strength, DFSR could be improved remarkably when the prior austenite grain size d decreased from 20 μm to 8 μm; but improved a little slower when d decreased from 8 μm to 4 μm; and there was no noticeable increase when d decreased from 4 μm to 2 μm (Figure 6.9a). As mentioned above, due to the refinement of austenite grain, the increment of yield strength is higher than that of tensile strength, for example, the ratio of yield strength to tensile strength rose from 0.92 to 0.98 when d decreased from 20μm to 2 μm. Therefore, the variation of DFSR with yield strength is more significant (Figure 6.9b) and DFSR could be improved with decreasing d until it reached 4μm, beyond that DFSR changed very little. This implies that further austenite grain refinement would be difficult to improve DF resistance of high strength martensitic steels.

Fracture appearance of the notched tensile specimen after DF in solution could be divided into three zones: zone of crack initiation, zone of crack propagation and shear zone. Among them, crack initiation and sub-crack propagation dominate the DF process (Yamasaki and Takahashi,1997). Figures 6.10 and 6.11 show the fracture morphology in the crack initiation zone of 42CrMoVNb steel with different austenite grain sizes. Obviously, when the steel was tempered at higher temperature such as 600℃, the failure mode is mainly intergranular for the coarse grain(d=20 μm); while it is mainly transgranular when d was refined to 4~8 μm; and again mainly intergranular when d was further refined to 2 μm. When the steel was tempered at lower temperature such as 440℃, all the specimens with different grain size show mainly intergranular failure. This demonstrates that the failure mechanism changes with increasing tempering temperature for the fine grain(d=4~8 μm); but it does not change with tempering temperature for the ultrafine grain(d=2 μm).

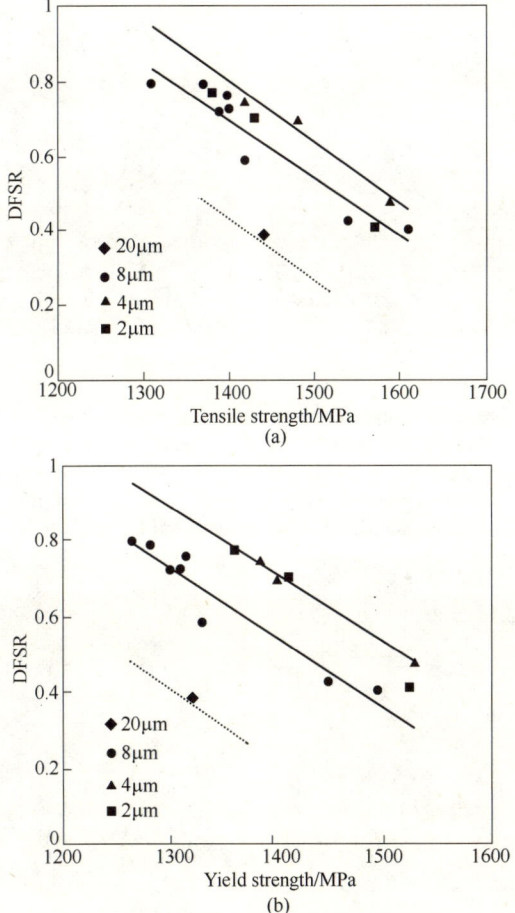

Figure 6.9 Variations of delayed fracture strength ratio(DFSR) with tensile strength (a) and yield strength (b) of 42CrMoVNb steel with different prior austenite grain sizes

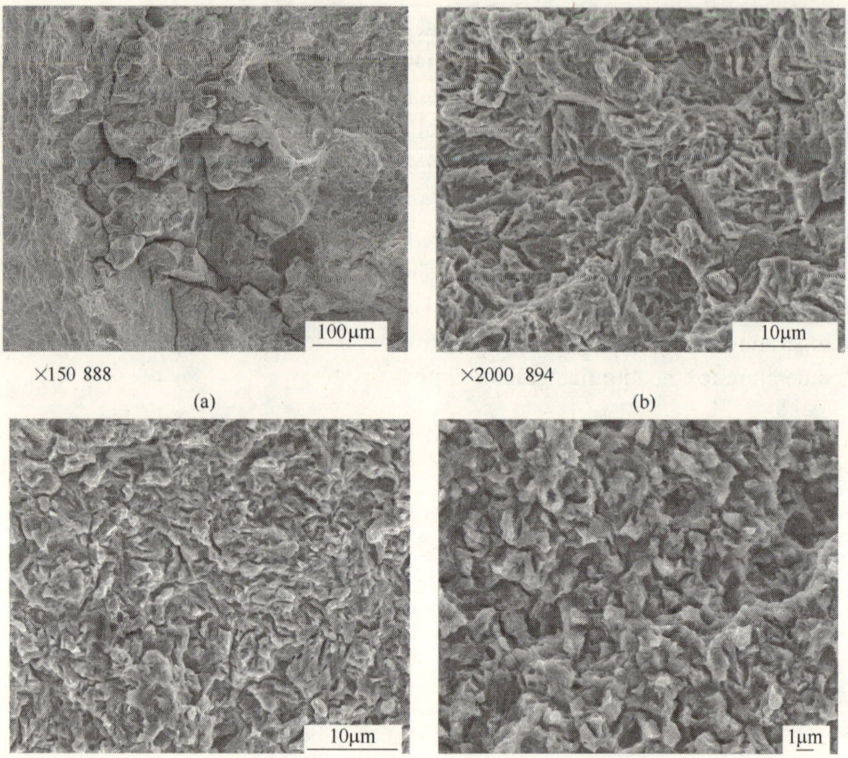

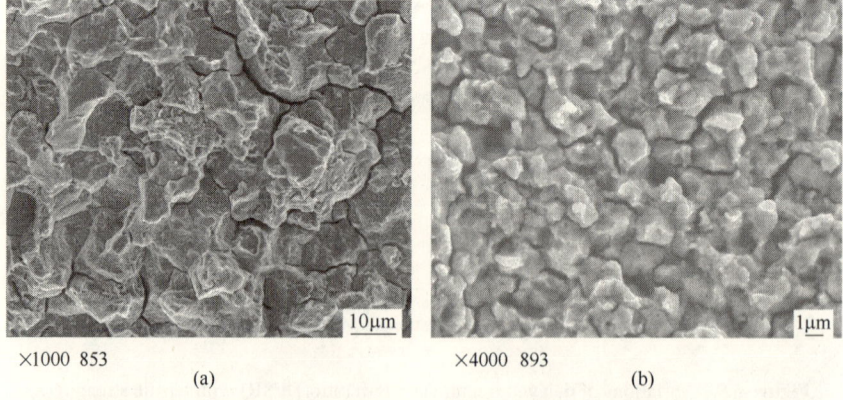

100µm

×150 888

(a)

10µm

×2000 894

(b)

10µm

×2000 477

(c)

1µm

×4000 889

(d)

Figure 6.10   Fracture surfaces in crack initiation area of sustained load tensile delayed fracture specimens of 42CrMoVNb steel tempered at 600℃ with grain sizes of 20 µm (a), 8 µm (b), 4 µm (c), 2 µm (d), showing fracture characteristic to change from intergranular to transgranular when grain size is refined from 20 µm to 8 ~ 4 µm, while still intergranular when grain size is refined to 2 µm

10µm

×1000 853

(a)

1µm

×4000 893

(b)

Figure 6.11   Fracture surfaces in crack initiation area of sustained load tensile delayed fracture specimens of 42CrMoVNb steel tempered at 440℃ with grain sizes of 8 µm(a) and 2 µm(b), showing fracture characteristic to be all intergranular

6.2.3.3   Discussion of the dependence of DF resistance on grain size

The refinement of prior austenite grain may influence DF of high strength steels by the following two ways:

1. DF process is relevant to the plastic deformation of steel (Chu,1988). Local plastic deformation could be easily developed when hydrogen exists because hydrogen promotes the emission and movement of dislocation, so that it may reach a critical condition even when the applied stress is lower than that when hydrogen does not exist. Therefore, when the stress concentrated(σ_{yy}) in local area such as the front of dislocation pile-up is equal to the atomic combination stress $\sigma_{th}(H)$ which is reduced due to the interaction of hydrogen, hydrogen induced cracking could nucleate at this stress concentrated area. Grain boundaries are obstacles to dislocation movement, which could lead to pile-up of dislocations just in the front of boundaries.

According to Stroh's dislocation pile-up theory, the maximum nominal stress in front of dislocation pile-up is (Chu et al,2000)

$$\sigma_{max} = \sqrt{\frac{4L}{3r}}(\tau_a - \tau_f) \qquad (6.6)$$

where L is length of dislocation pile-up and is $L=d/2$ (d is diameter of grain) for polycrystalline because dislocation is initiated from the center of grains; r is the distance to the front of dislocation pile-up, τ_a is the external stress applied to the dislocation, τ_f is the stress resistant to dislocation movement, i.e. friction stress. When hydrogen exists, there is additional stress τ_H applied on the hydrogen-contaminated dislocation. In this case, the external stress τ_a in equation 6.6 should be substituted by the total stress applied on the contaminated dislocation with $\tau=k\tau_a$

$$\sigma_{max}(H) = \sqrt{\frac{2d}{3r}}(k\tau_a - \tau_f) \qquad (6.7)$$

where k is constant. When τ_a reaches a critical value, τ_c (H), σ_{max} (H) is equal to σ_{th} (H). This will lead to the formation of microcrack with a length of c, as illustrated in Figure 6.12. Therefore, the condition for the nucleation of hydrogen-induced microcrack may be described by:

$$\sqrt{\frac{2d}{3c}}[k\tau_c(H)-\tau_f]=\sigma_{th}(H) \qquad (6.8)$$

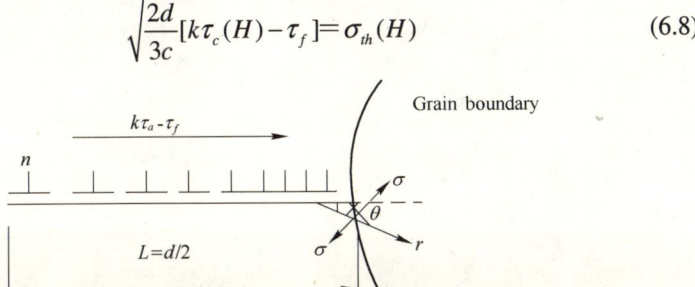

Figure 6.12   Schematic of dislocation pile-up before grain boundary

So the threshold stress for the nucleation of hydrogen induced crack, τ_c (H), is

$$\tau_c(H) = \left[\tau_f + \sigma_{th}(H) \left(\frac{2d}{3c} \right)^{-1/2} \right] \times \frac{1}{k} \tag{6.9}$$

In addition, the number of dislocations piled up in the front of boundaries, n, is

$$n = \frac{\pi(1-\nu)(\tau_a - \tau_f)}{\mu b} \times d \tag{6.10}$$

According to equations 6.9 and 6.10, τ_c (H) is proportional to $d^{-1/2}$ and n is proportional to d. Therefore, n decreases when grains are refined. This will lead to the applied nominal strain allocated in more grains and then a reduced stress concentration. As a result, τ_c (H) increases significantly when grains are refined.

2. Prior austenite grain boundary surface area per unit volume, S_V, increases dramatically when grains are refined. S_V could be deduced from the measured mean linear intercept of grains on the polished surface, L, by:

$$S_V = 2/L \tag{6.11}$$

Figure 6.13 gives the variation of S_V with L. S_V will increase by 10 times when the grains are refined from 20 μm to 2 μm. Such sharp rise of grain boundary surface will significantly reduce the segregation of impurities such as P and S to grain boundaries, leading to much cleaner boundaries with less segregation of impurities. This is the reason why the fracture mechanism changes from intergranular to transgranular failure in the impact test at room temperature when the grain was refined from 22 μm to 4.7 μm (Figures 6.14a and 6.14b) for the commercial 42CrMo steel (with 0.023%P and 0.018%S). Whilst for the high cleanliness 42CrMoVNb steel, the fracture mode is all transgranular even when impact test is carried out at -192℃ when the grain is refined to 2~8 μm, as shown in Figures 6.14(c) and 6.14(d). It can be concluded that grain refinement results in cleaner boundaries with less impurities segregated and then strengthened boundaries, which could inhibit the initiation and propagation of microcracks along boundaries and finally improve the DF resistance. This is quite

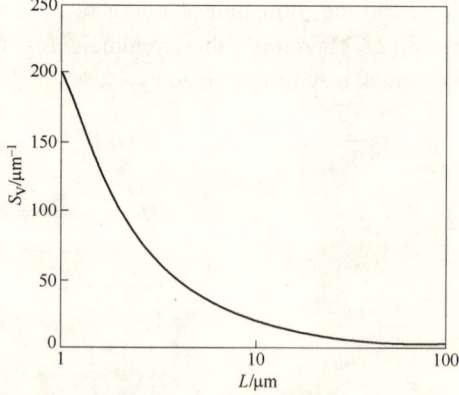

Figure 6.13   Relationship between grain boundary area per volume S_V with average grain intercept L

consistent with Benerji et al's observation on AISI 4340-type steels having prior austenite grain size in the range of 20~100 μm.

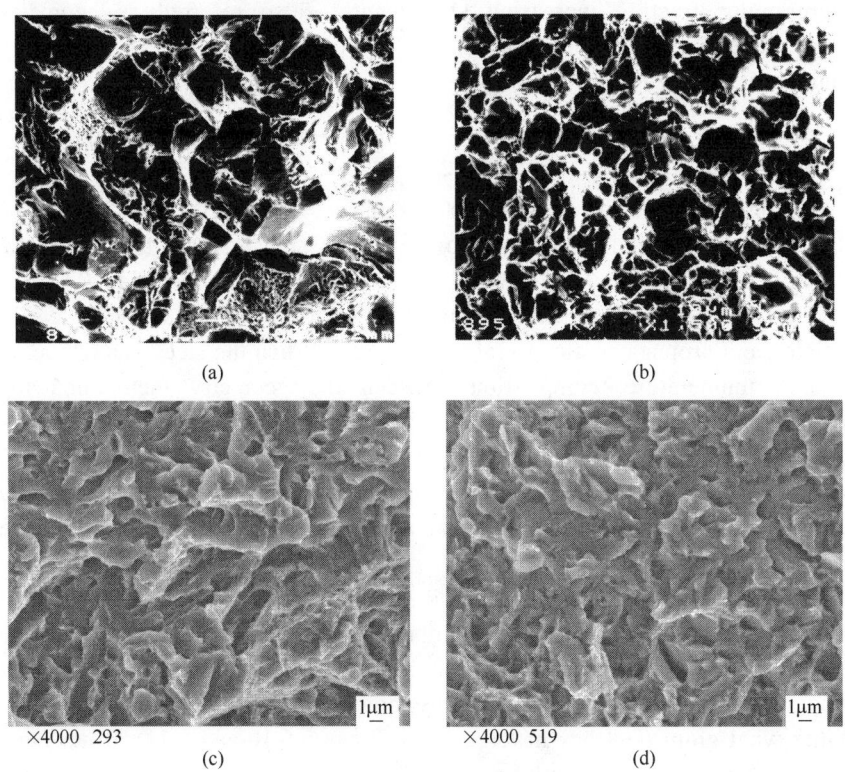

(a)　　　　　　　　　　(b)

×4000 293　　　　　　　×4000 519
(c)　　　　　　　　　　(d)

Figure 6.14 Fractographs of impact specimens tested at room temperature (20℃) for commercial steel 42CrMo tempered at 400℃ (a, b) and tested at −192℃ for 42CrMoVNb steel tempered at 600℃(c, d)

(a) grain size 22 μm, intergranular fracture; (b) 4.7 μm, transgranular;

(c) 8 μm, transgranular ; (d) 2 μm, transgranular

Moreover, a sharp rise of S_V could lead to a reduced amount of hydrogen trapped in boundaries. Tien (1976) has calculated that for a hydrogen content of 10×10^{-6} as the grain size decreased from 100μm to 10μm, the hydrogen coverage decreases from saturation condition to about 1 site in 10 coverage, which is obviously also beneficial to the improvement of DF resistance.

In summary, DF resistances of the high cleanliness 42CrMoVNb and the commercial 42CrMo steels are both improved by the grain refinement due to the boundary strengthened by the two aforementioned mechanisms.

Nevertheless, DF resistance of the 42CrMoVNb steel could not be further improved when grain is refined to 2 μm, although it is still higher than that when grain size is 8 μm(Figure 6.9). This phenomenon results from the fact than when the grain size is too small, the plastic zone ahead of the crack tip would cover more boundaries, which might then lead to the probability of intergranular fracture increasing significantly (also referred as geometry factor). The size of the plastic zone, R, may be calculated from the following relation (Chu,1988)

$$R = \frac{1}{2\sqrt{2}\pi}\left(\frac{K_{ISCC}}{\sigma_s}\right)^2 \tag{6.12}$$

For the 42CrMoVNb steel, when d=8μm, σ_s=1320 MPa and K_{ISCC}=37.1 MPa • m$^{1/2}$, the calculated R is 89 μm, which is much larger than d. In the presently investigated range of grain size(2~20 μm), d is less than R. When d=2 μm, R/d is even more than 45, therefore, hydrogen induced crack is easily initiated and propagated along grain boundaries. When the steel was tempered at high temperature, competition between the geometry factor and the boundary strengthening could result in DF mechanism changing from transgranular fracture when d=4~8 μm to intergranular fracture when d=2 μm(Figure 6.9). In addition, the appearance of blocky structure might be also a reason for intergranular fracture when d=2 μm, but it needs more data to have a deeper insight.

The contents of impurities such as P and S in the tested 42CrMoVNb steel are quite low; thus, segregation of impurities at grain boundaries should be weak for the ultrafine grained specimen. When the steel was tempered at low temperature, however, all DF specimens show mainly intergranular fracture no matter what grain size they have(compare Figures 6.10 and 6.11). It has been reported that the distribution of carbides in high strength steel has a significant effect on DF resistance (Hui,2003;Li et al,1992). In low-temperature tempered states, there is a serious segregation of carbon in the form of thin film carbides at prior austenite grain boundaries, so that the entered hydrogen will enrich at grain boundaries, leading to low-stress intergranular fracture. After tempering at high temperature, both the coalescence of the film carbides at the grain boundaries and the increase of carbide precipitation within grains cause the decrease of hydrogen trapped at grain boundaries and thus the decrease tendency of intergranular fracture. This implies that the improvement of DF resistance requires not only grain refinement but also controlling carbides at grain boundaries.

6.3   Grain Boundary Strengthening in Improving DF Property of Martensitic Steels

DF susceptibility of the tempered martensitic microstructure is closely related to the prior austenite grain boundary strength(Briant et al,1978;Davis et al,1964). Therefore, strengthening of grain boundary is an effective way to inhibit crack initiation and propagation along grain boundaries so that DF resistance could be improved. Methods for strengthening grain boundaries include: 1. To reduce the segregated amount of embrittling elements at grain boundaries; 2. To control grain boundary carbides; 3. To refine prior austenite grains. The last has been presented in section 6.2, so the former two methods will be discussed below.

6.3.1   *Reducing segregation of impurities at grain boundaries*

To lower the contents of P and S, impurities in steels could reduce their segregation at grain boundaries, which would lead to cleaner and stronger boundaries to inhibit crack initiation (Komazaki et al,2003;Wittig et al,1990; Weng et al,1987). Consequently, DF resistance of high strength steels could be improved (Namiki et al,1984;Isokawa et al,1983). An example is shown in Figure 6.15. Results of SCC test and sustained load tensile test indicate that both K_{ISCC} and DFSR of the high clean 42CrMo steel are significantly higher than those of the commercial 42CrMo steel (Hui,2003).

Nevertheless, the possible lowest contents of P and S are constrained by steelmaking technology and the production cost. Another alternative is to add some elements into steels which can reduce or even dimish the segregation of S and P at boundaries. It can be done by two ways: 1. Add elements to capture impurities and then reduce their segregation at grain boundaries, such as use Mo to scavenge P; 2. Reduce the concentration of alloying elements that promote P segregation in austenite, such as Mn, Si and Cr. The first method will be discussed later, and the below is to discuss the second one.

In Cr-Mo steels, it has been proved that Mn and Si could promote the segregation of P in austenite, so that removal of these two elements could lower the segregation of P (Yu et al,1980). Banerji et al (1978) investigated the fracture behaviour in hydrogen in 4340-type steels made by different melting processes, and found that variation of P and S(P $0.003\% \sim 0.015\%$, S $0.003\% \sim 0.024\%$) seems to have no significant influence on fracture mechanism (all are intergranular failure) and threshold stress intensity factor K_{th}, but variation of Mn and Si does. At the same level of strength, high clean Ni-Cr-Mo steel with very low content of Mn and Si exhibits much higher K_{th} than that with the addition of Mn and Si. The aforementioned high clean 42CrMo steel contains very low contents of Mn and Si besides low contents of P and S. Therefore, the excellent DF resistance of high clean 42CrMo steel is related to its very low contents of Mn and Si.

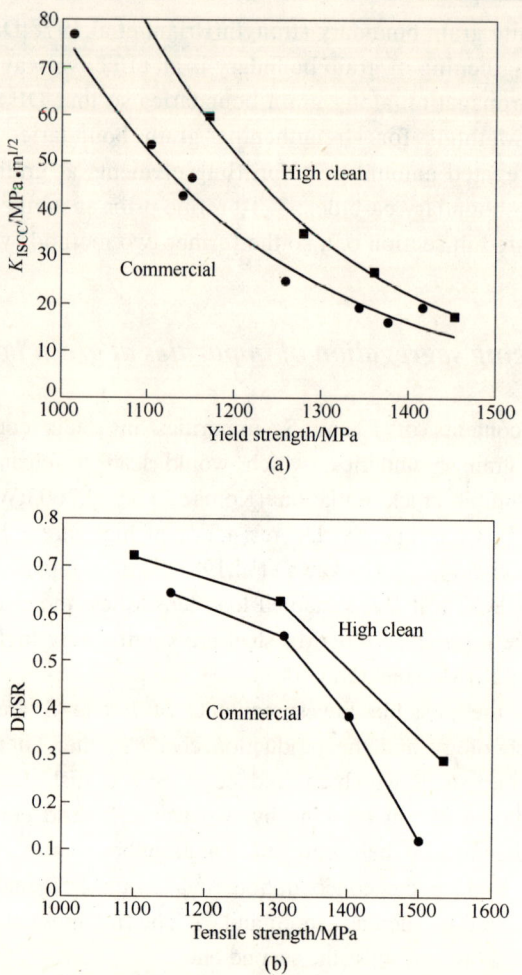

Figure 6.15 Variation of K_{ISCC} (a) and DFSR (b) with strength of 42CrMo steel
(Commercial: 0.023P-0.018S-0.006O-0.007N-0.65Mn-0.33Si;
High cleanliness: 0.001P-0.002S-0.002O-0.003N-0.06Mn-0.06Si)

It is worth to point out that carbon seems to have more significant influence on DF resistance than P and S. In the reported data on segregation of impurities at grain boundaries analyzed by Auger electron spectroscopy, it could be found that not only P and S but also C all segregate at grain boundaries (Namiki et al,1984;Isokawa et al,1983;Craig,1982), the latter mainly forms carbide at boundaries during tempering. Despite of this fact, most researchers emphasize the outstanding influence of P and S segregation but neglect the influence of carbon segregation. Li et al (1992) have found that when tempering temperature increases for high strength Cr-Mo steels with different carbon contents, P concentration at grain boundaries changes little;

whilst S and N concentrations rises. Correspondingly, K_{ISCC} increases significantly and the fracture mode changes from intergranular fracture to the mixture of intergranular and transgranular fracture. It has been stated above that DF resistance increases with increasing tempering temperature for both commercial 42CrMo steel and high clean 42CrMo and 42CrMoVNb steels, and their fracture mechanism also changes correspondingly. This indicates that the segregation of P and S at grain boundaries may just enhance DF susceptibility to a certain extent, but may not a dominant factor.

6.3.2   *Controlling grain boundary carbide*

Interface between carbides and the matrix are strong hydrogen traps in steels (Chu,1988). If carbides are mainly situated at grain boundaries, hydrogen will be enriched at boundaries as well, which would lead to boundary embrittlement and thus DF crack may nucleate at boundaries and propagate along them. Therefore, controlling grain boundary carbides such as changing the morphology of boundary carbides, reducing the quantity of carbides at boundaries or even obtaining carbide-free boundaries would improve the DF resistance of martensitic steels.

6.3.2.1   Increasing tempering temperature

As mentioned above, tempering temperature has a significant influence on DF behavior of martensitic steels. At low-temperature tempering, film-type carbides often form at grain boundaries, leading to more hydrogen trapped at boundaries and thus poor DF resistance. At high-temperature tempering, film-type grain boundary carbides are broken and spheroidized, leading to less hydrogen trapped at boundaries and retardation of intergranular crack propagation. On the other hand, lots of carbides precipitate within grains, thus leading to more hydrogen trapped within grains. Both could strengthen grain boundaries and then improve DF resistance. Figure 6.16 shows the change of SCC fracture mode from intergranular to transgranular for 42CrMoVNb steel with increasing tempering temperature (Hui et al,2006). Figure 6.17 summaries the results of K_{ISCC} of four high strength steels tempered at different temperatures (Hui et al,2006;Li et al,1992;Chu et al,1981). K_{ISCC} increases slowly with tempering temperature when it is relatively low; but increases rapidly when the tempering temperature is high.

Nevertheless, higher tempering temperature generally means lower strength for low-alloyed steels. One feasible solution to the purpose of obtaining a better balance between strength and DF resistance is the addition of secondary hardening elements Mo and V. Both elements could form carbides at high tempering

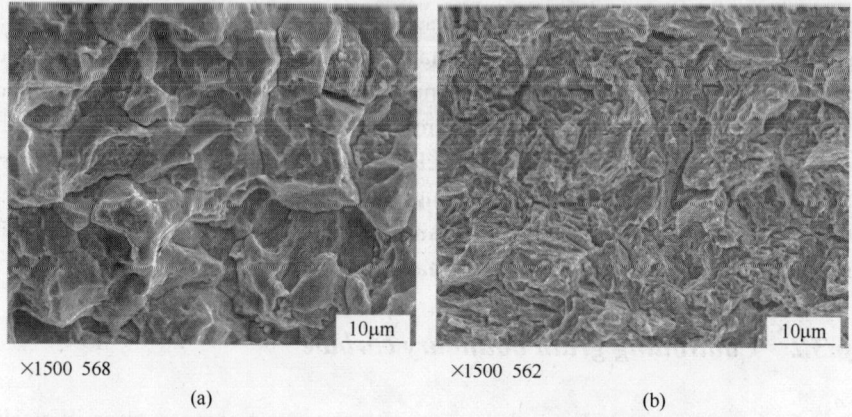

×1500 568   ×1500 562

(a)   (b)

Figure 6.16   Fracture surfaces of SCC specimens of 42CrMoVNb steel tempered at different temperature, showing the change of fracture from intergranular dominant mode (a) to transgranular dominant mode (b)

(a) 410℃, K_{ISCC}=10.5 MPa · m$^{1/2}$; (b) 600℃, K_{ISCC}=37.1 MPa · m$^{1/2}$

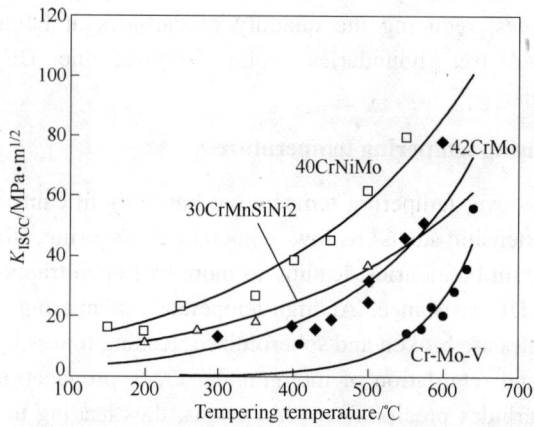

Figure 6.17   Variations of K_{ISCC} with tempering temperature of four high strength martensitic steels

temperature, which not only contribute to higher strength but also act as hydrogen traps. Figure 6.18 shows the variations of K_{ISCC} and yield strength with tempering temperature. DF resistance rises with increasing tempering temperature at the same level of strength for the 42CrMoVNb steel. This indicates that high tempering temperature is a very effective way to improve DF resistance for high strength steels.

6.3.2.2   Intercritical quenching

Another alternative to improve DF resistance is to introduce suitable amount of proeutectoid ferrite along prior austenite grain boundaries into tempered martensite matrix. It is considered that the soft phase along grain boundaries results in reduction of film-like grain boundary carbides and retardation of intergranular crack propagation (Choi et al, 2001; Wu et al,1984).

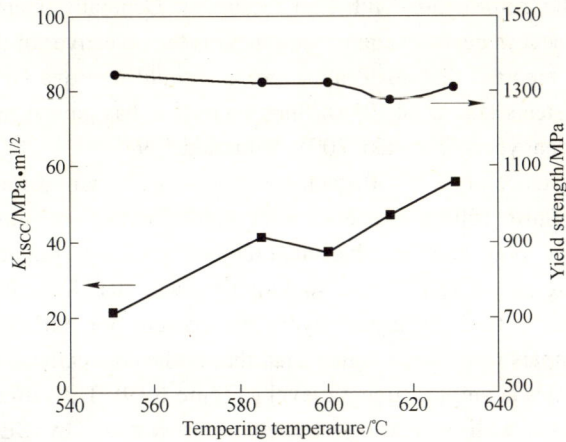

Figure 6.18   Variations of K_{ISCC} and yield strength with tempering temperature of 42CrMoVNb steel

Intercritical quenching of proeutectoid carbon steels is an efficient treatment to achieve the above goal. When the steel is heated to the intercritical region, i.e. two-phase region of ferrite plus austenite, and then quenched, dual phase microstructure of grain boundary ferrite and martensite can be obtained. Since ferrite occupied parts of austenite grain boundaries, the quantity of carbides precipitated along boundaries is reduced. When an additional intercritical quenching process below Ac_3 was inserted between quenching and tempering of 30CrMnSi steel, it was found that tendency to intergranular failure decreased and the threshold fracture stress σ_c increased remarkably (Wu et al,1984). Choi et al (2001) added 3%Si into 0.45C-0.3Mn-0.5Cr-0.05V steel to increase Ac_3 temperature so that the steel is in the two phase region of $\gamma+\alpha$ at the usual austenitizing temperature of 870℃. Result of sustained load tensile test shows that the tested steel has better DF resistance than that of conventional AISI 4135 steel.

After intercritical quenching and tempering, the amount of diffusible hydrogen absorbed is lower than that of full martensite, as measured by hydrogen thermal desorption test (Choi et al,2001). In addition, carbon concentration at grain boundaries is also reduced significantly and mostly precipitates as carbides, as analyzed by Auger electron spectroscopy (Wu et al,1984). This proves that the formation of ferrite along grain boundaries can reduce the amount of grain boundary carbides so that less hydrogen is trapped at grain boundaries. Consequently, DF resistance could be improved.

6.3.2.3   Ausforming process

Ausforming process (also called thermomechanical processing) is a technique to combine plastic deformation with heat treatment. Generally, increased strength with improvement in ductility and/or toughness is the objectives of this process. In 1960s, it was reported that ausforming process could improve DF resistance of high strength steels (Lei et al,1979). Such technique has gained more and more attention in recent years (Terasaki, 2001; Yamasaki,1998).

The DF resistance of SCM440 steel was investigated after ausforming process, consisting of finish rolling temperature at 810℃, reduction ratio of 50% and cooled by water spray, and the subsequent tempering by high frequency induction with the heating rate of 150℃/s and soaking time was 10s (Terasaki,2001). It was found that the critical diffusible hydrogen content for failure (H_C) in the ausformed samples were much higher than that in the conventional quenched and tempered samples at similar strength level (Figure 6.19). The difference between them is reduced with increasing strength. Observations by SEM and TEM revealed that in the non-ausformed samples, carbides appear as a continuous film at grain boundaries at low tempering temperature, but the film was broken at high tempering temperature; whilst in the ausformed samples grain were elongated along the rolling direction and boundaries are serrated and carbides did not appear continuously at boundaries and even there are some boundaries free of carbides no matter what temperature is employed for tempering. Further observation by AFM clarifies that fine carbides are uniformly distributed within grains (Yamasaki,1998). Microstructure refinement and change in carbide distribution are considered to be responsible for the improvement of DF resistance of martensitic steels.

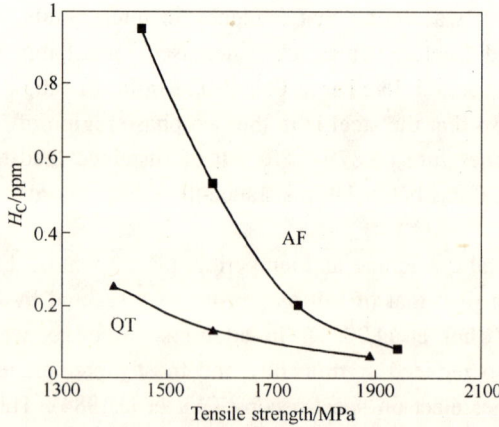

Figure 6.19   Relationship between the critical diffusible hydrogen content for failure H_C and tensile strength for the ausformed (AF) samples and the conventional QT samples of SCM435 steel
(Terasaki, 2001)

6.3.3 *Effect of* Mo *alloying*

Mo as a common alloying element is added into the structural steels generally for the two objectives: one is to improve hardenability; the other is to prevent temper embrittlement (Dumoulin et al,1980;Archer et al,1970). Besides the addition of Mo could increase the strength of martensitic steels due to the precipitation of Mo containing carbides, Mo could also strengthen grain boundaries, as proved by Weng in 1980s (1984). Our work again shows that Mo can segregate at prior austenite grain boundaries and thus strengthen them, leading to improved DF resistance (Hui et al,2004,2002).

When various contents of Mo were added into 40CrV steel, it was found that the strength-tempering temperature curve shifts up when the content of Mo increases, particularly at tempering temperature higher than 500℃ due to the precipitation hardening of Mo/V alloy carbides, as shown in Figure 6.20. Results from the sustained load tensile test and SCC test are given in Figure 6.21. DFSR and K_{ISCC} of the tested steels both decrease obviously with increasing strength. In general, increasing content of Mo leads to higher DFSR and K_{ISCC} until 1.15%Mo, beyond which DFSR and K_{ISCC} decrease a bit but are still higher than those with low Mo content (Figure 6.22) (Hui et al,2004). Therefore, DF resistance does not have a monotonous dependence on the content of Mo in the investigated range of strength variation.

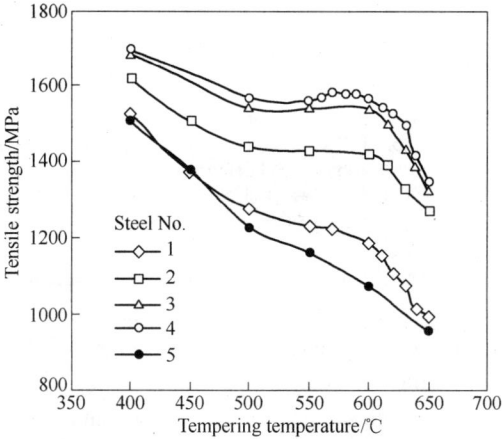

Figure 6.20 Variations of tensile strength with tempering temperature of 40CrV steels with various molybdenum contents

(No.1: 0.40C-1.1Cr-V, base steel; No.2: 0.50Mo; No.3: 1.15Mo; No.4: 1.54Mo; No.5: 42CrMo)

The beneficial effect of Mo on improving the DF resistance of martensitic steel

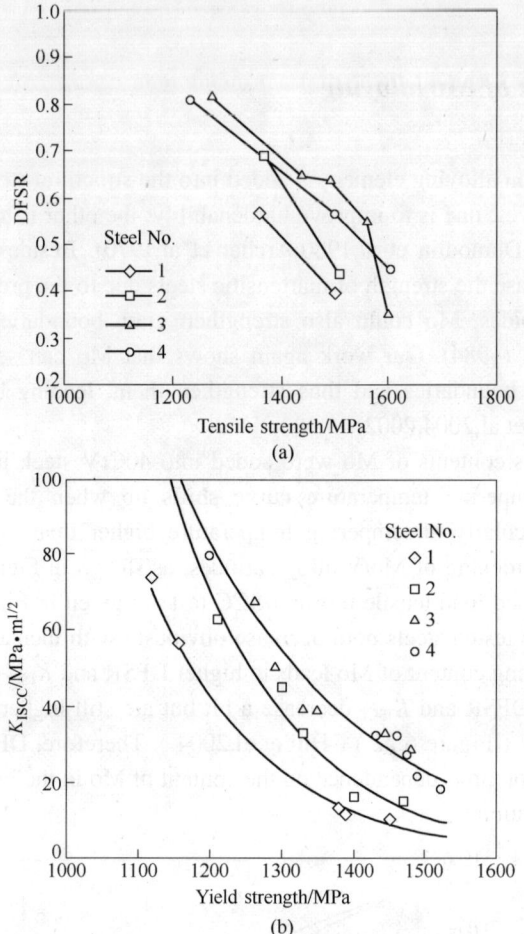

Figure 6.21   Variations of delayed fracture strength ratio (DFSR) (a) and threshold
stress intensity factor of SCC, K_{ISCC} (b) with strength of 40CrV steel with
various molybdenum contents
(No.1: 0.40C-1.1Cr-V, base steel; No.2: 0.50Mo; No.3: 1.15Mo;
No.4: 1.54Mo; No.5: 42CrMo)

is suggested to be the results of one or more of the following factors (Hui et al,2004): 1. The retardation of softening and secondary hardening of Mo raise the tempering temperature for a given strength; 2. Mo-carbides precipitated during high-temperature tempering act as hydrogen traps; 3. Segregation of Mo at grain boundaries to control impurities and strengthen grain boundaries.

6.3.3.1   Mo raising tempering temperature

As mentioned above, for low-alloyed steels, higher tempering temperature generally leads to reduce strength and improve DF resistance. DF resistance of the

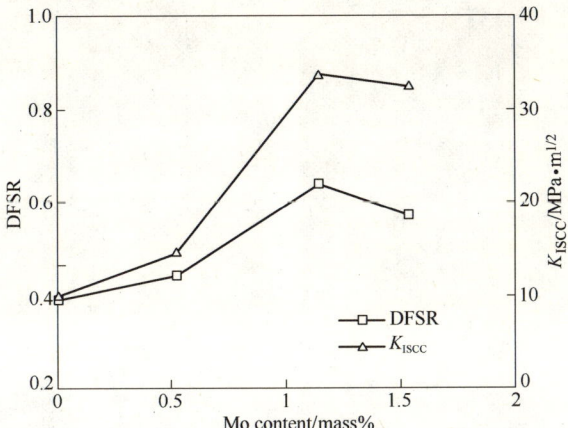

Figure 6.22 Variations of delayed fracture strength ratio (DFSR) and threshold stress intensity factor of SCC, K_{ISCC} with molybdenum content of 40CrV steel

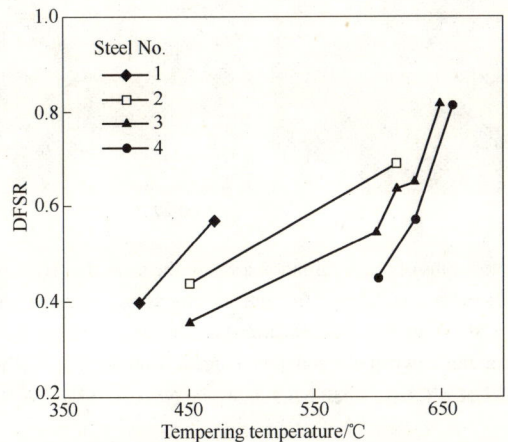

Figure 6.23 Variations of delayed fracture strength ratio (DFSR) with tempering temperature of 40CrV steel with various molybdenum content (open symbols corresponding to tensile strength is 1500 MPa)

(No.1: 0.40C-1.1Cr-V, base steel; No.2: 0.50Mo; No.3: 1.15Mo; No.4: 1.54Mo)

tested 40CrV steels with various Mo content increases with increasing tempering temperature, as shown in Figure 6.23, where open circles correspond to the tensile strength of 1500 MPa and the tempering temperatures for No.1, 2, 3 and 4 steels are 410, 450, 615, 630℃ respectively. The failure mode was mainly intergranular for No.1 and 2 steels and mainly transgranular for No.3 and 4 steels(Figure 6.24). For No.1 steel, DF resistance increases with increasing tempering temperature until 500℃, indicating that Mo raising tempering temperature is an important reason for the improvement of DF resistance.

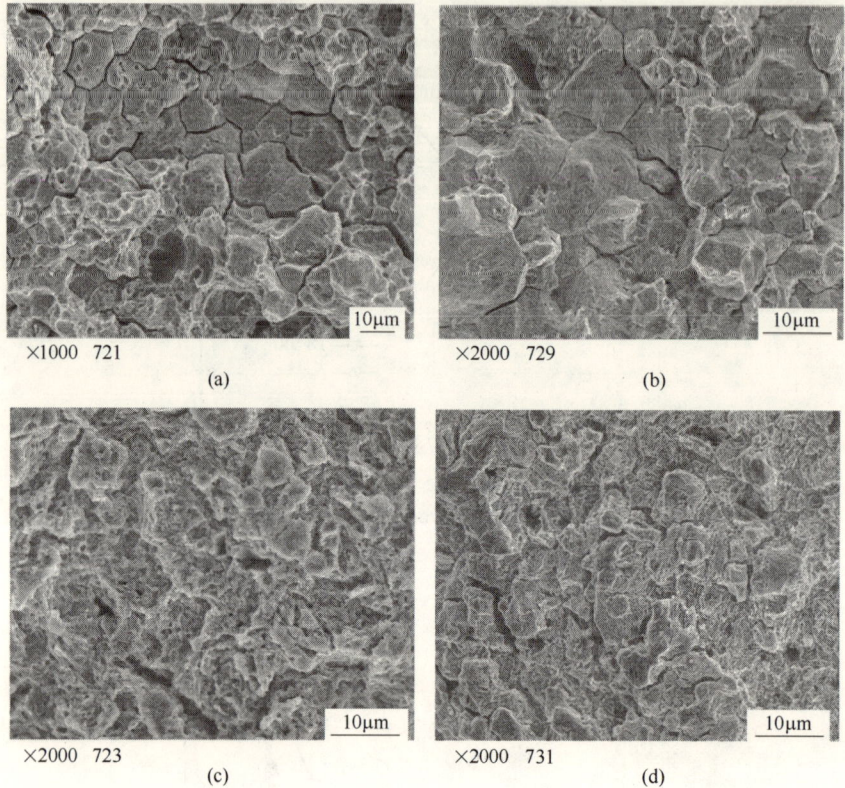

×1000 721

(a)

×2000 729

(b)

×2000 723

(c)

×2000 731

(d)

Figure 6.24   Fractographs of crack initiation area for the steels No.1(a),2(b),3(c) and 4(d)
of sustained load tensile delayed fracture specimens with a tensile strength of
1500 MPa, showing fracture characteristic changes from intergranular to
transgranular when molybdenum content is higher than 1.10%
(No.1: 0.40C-1.1Cr-V, base steel; No.2: 0.50Mo; No.3: 1.15Mo; No.4: 1.54Mo)

6.3.3.2   Mo carbide as hydrogen trap

By extensive studies on carbides under various heat treatment processes, it has
been proved that the precipitation of Mo_2C at high temperature tempering in No.3
steel could improve DF resistance (Hui et al,2004), which is consistent with the
observation on 0.41C-1.0Cr-0.7Mo steel (Gojic et al,1997). Such beneficial effect
may be related to the larger carbide/matrix interfacial area and longer times
required for accumulating sufficient hydrogen at the interface to assist the crack
initiation and propagation.

It should be noted that the Mo_2C carbide in the coherent condition may
deteriorate the beneficial effect of Mo on DF resistance, as reported by the
experimental results on the secondary hardening high alloyed AF1410 steel
(Zhong et al,1995). This is one of the reasons why a bit over-aging is employed

for strong secondary hardening steels.

6.3.3.3 Mo controlling impurities and strengthening grain boundaries

Segregation of Mo at grain boundaries could reduce segregation of P at grain boundaries, which may lead to higher boundary bonding strength and consequently higher DF resistance. The distribution of Mo in the former tested 40CrV steels with various Mo content was analyzed by TEM, EDS and EELS (Electronic Energy Loss Spectroscopy) to further examine the influence of Mo on grain boundary bonding strength (Hui et al,2004).

By the EDS microanalysis of No.2~4 steels at different positions, it was found that the solute Mo could easily segregate at grain boundaries besides the rest Mo forms carbides. Such Mo segregation does not change with tempering temperature. Figure 6.25 gives the EDS microanalysis results of Mo concentration across one boundary in No.2 steel tempered at 585℃. Mo concentration reaches the maximum of 1.7% ± 0.4% at grain boundary, while it decreases sharply with the increasing distance h from the boundary; for example, 0.7% ± 0.1% at $h=2$ nm and close to the bulk concentration at $d=10$ nm. Microanalysis in the No.2 steel tempered at 500℃ and 650℃ both gave very similar results too.

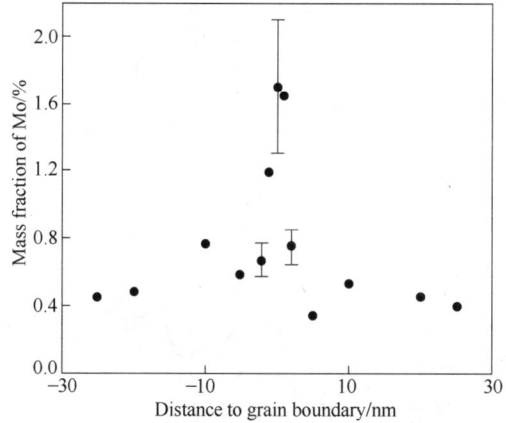

Figure 6.25 Result of energy dispersive X-ray spectroscopy (EDS) analysis showing the distribution of Mo around grain boundary of No.2 steel (0.50 %Mo) tempered at 585 ℃ for 2h

Zhang et al (2001) has successfully used EELS and EDS mapping techniques to study the grain boundary of 42CrMo1VNb and 42CrMo steels. Figure 6.26(a) shows the Fe edge of EELS recorded at bulk and grain boundary(GB) of 42CrMo steel. The grain boundary has a tall, narrow peak at the onset of Fe edge compared with the short and broad Fe edge of the bulk. This indicates the grain boundary is weaker than the bulk so that intergranular fracture occurred in this steel as the experiment observed. Figure 6.26(b) shows the result of EELS measurement on a typical boundary of 42CrMo1VNb steel (EDS elemental mapping has showed that there was some Mo and Cr segregation in that grain boundary). The result shows that the grain boundary has a short and broad peak at the onset of Fe edge compared with the peak of the bulk, indicating that the grain boundary is stronger than the bulk. This is in agreement with the experimental result that transgranular fracture occurred in the sample of 42CrMoVNb steel. Since 42CrMo1VNb steel contains more Mo than 42CrMo steel, it can be concluded that the segregation of Mo at grain boundary could increase grain boundary strength.

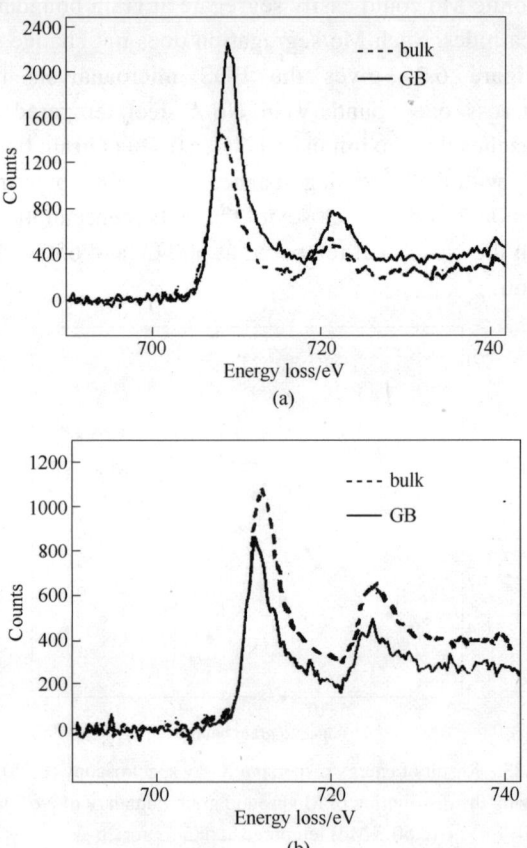

Figure 6.26   Electron energy loss spectra (EELS) of Fe edge in the grain boundary (GB) for 42CrMo tempered at 550 ℃ (a) and 42CrMo1VNb steel tempered at 600 ℃ (b)

6.3.3.4   Influence of Mo content

It has been mentioned that the best DF resistance is achieved at 1.15 %Mo, beyond which no further improvement is observed. Grobner et al. (1979) studied the effect of increasing Mo content of 4130 type steels on hydrogen sulfide stress cracking resistance and found that the optimum Mo content was 0.75% Mo or 0.90% Mo depending on the test method applied. They thought that this phenomenon might result from the effect of Mo on carbide formation. TEM examination revealed that the M_3C cementite starts to be replaced by Mo_2C as Mo content exceeds 0.75 %, leading to less Mo solute in the matrix by tying up much of the Mo, and preventing it from controlling tramp elements. Consequently, DF resistance is reduced.

Since V in the studied steel has a stronger affinity to carbon than Mo, precipitation of Mo_2C is possible only when Mo content increases to 1.15% and the quantity of Mo_2C increases significantly when Mo content increases to 1.54%, leading to remarked increase of strength when the steel tempered at 550~600℃. However, the quantity of the precipitated Mo_2C is not large enough to lower the DF resistance significantly. Therefore, the DF resistance in 1.54 %Mo steel is still much higher than that in 0.50%Mo steel and in base steel.

6.4 Controlling of Hydrogen Trap in Martensitic Steels to Improve Its DF Resistance

There are many kinds of defects or microstructural heterogeneities in steel can act as hydrogen trapping sites, such as dislocation, microvoid, grain boundary, inclusion and precipitate (Chu,1988). The function of a trap is related to the diffusivity of hydrogen that controls the kinetics of entry or accumulation at stress concentration, thus influencing DF resistance.

Microalloying elements, such as V, Ti and Nb, have an extensive application in high strength low alloyed steels because their additions have remarkable beneficial influence on grain refinement and precipitation strengthening. They all have strong affinity to carbon and nitrogen and can form stable carbides or carbonitrides, which could act as hydrogen traps. The application of microalloying elements in the purpose of improving DF resistance of high strength steel has gained much attention recently (Hui et al,2005;Omura et al,2005;Wei et al,2003).

Figure 6.27 shows the results of the sustained load tensile tests of the dependence of DF resistance on the tensile strength and the V content in 42CrMo steel (Hui et al,2003). An increasing content of V leads to more dispersed VC precipitates during high temperature tempering and also more undissolved VC particles during austenitizing(Figure 6.28). As a result, more hydrogen are captured by VC, leading to the curve of DFSR vs. tensile strength shift to up-right corner and DFSR increases with V content.

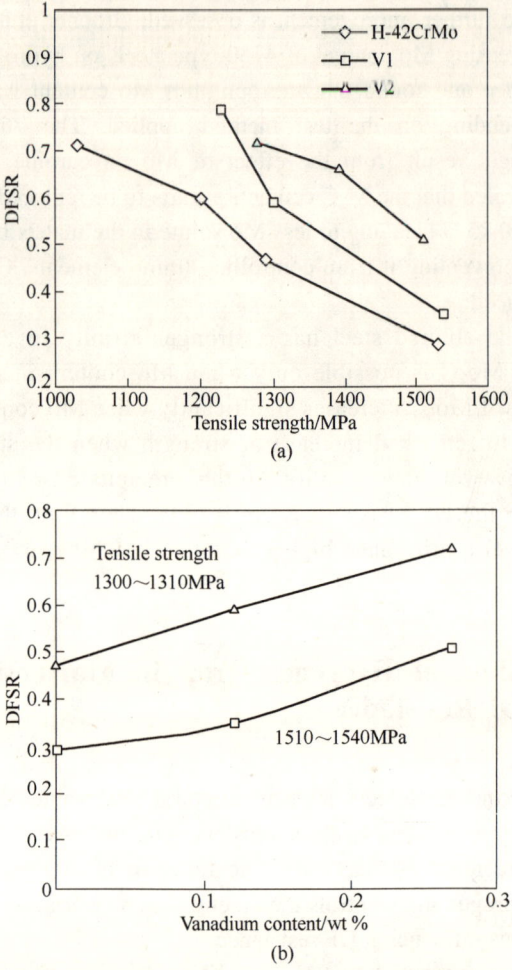

Figure 6.27   Variations of delayed fracture strength ratio (DFSR) with tensile strength(a) and vanadium content (b) of 42CrMo steel with different vanadium content

(H-42CrMo: base steel with high purity; V1: base steel +0.12%V; V2: base steel+0.27%V)

Figure 6.29 shows fractographs in the DF crack initiation area of specimens fractured in Walpole solution of 42CrMoV steel and 42CrMo steel. At similar tensile strength, i.e. 1280 MPa and 1300 MPa respectively, the failure mode is transgranular for 42CrMoV steel, whilst mixed mechanism of intergranular and transgranular for 42CrMo steel, compare Figure 6.29(b) and (c). At similar tempering temperature, the failure mode is same for both steels: mixed mode of transgranular and intergranular at low tempering temperature (470~500℃), whilst transgranular at high tempering temperature (580~600℃). 42CrMoV steel shows higher applied fracture stress than that of 42CrMo steel when their tensile strength and failure time are similar.

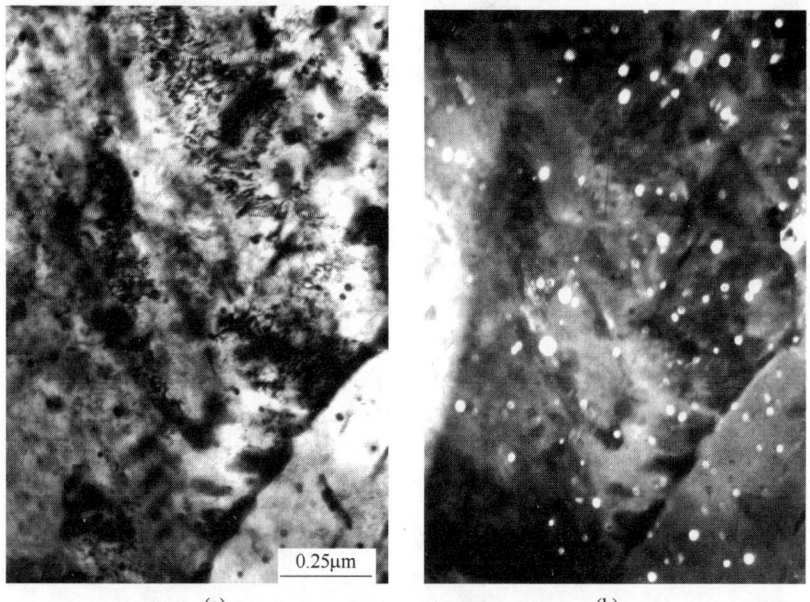

(a)   (b)

Figure 6.28 VC carbide morphology of 42CrMo+0.27 %V steel tempered at 600 ℃
for 2 h (TEM, bright field (a) and dark field (b))

Thermo-Calc calculation and TEM observation show that a considerable amount of VC precipitates does not resolve and still remain in the solution when V-microalloyed steel is soaked at normal austenization temperature of 920~940 ℃ (Hui et al,2003). Therefore, the absorbed hydrogen content in the V-microalloyed steel is obviously higher than that in the steel without V after cathodic hydrogen charging(Figure 6.30). When the steel was tempered at around 600 ℃, the absorbed hydrogen content was markedly increased for the precipitation of nano-scale VC coherent particles. When the steel was as tempered at 700 ℃, the absorbed hydrogen content was decreased but was still as high as that of the as-quenched condition duo the spherical VC incoherent precipitates (Tsuchida et al, 2002).

Is the hydrogen trapped in VC precipitates beneficial to DF resistance for the martensitic steel? This question can be analyzed by the following two aspects: (1)when the V-microalloyed steel was subject to DF test immediately after hydrogen charging, the hydrogen in the specimen is mainly corresponding to the conventional low temperature(100 ℃) desorption peak. Its failure exhibited a typical intergranular fracture and the critical hydrogen content for DF(H_C) is relatively low. When the steel was subject to DF test after hydrogen charging and holding at the ambient temperature for 96 hours, the hydrogen is corresponding to high temperature(200 ℃) desorption peak, as shown in Figure 6.31, implying the existence of strong hydrogen traps. Consequently, the failure mode is mainly transgranular cleavage and H_C increases remarkably (Tarui et

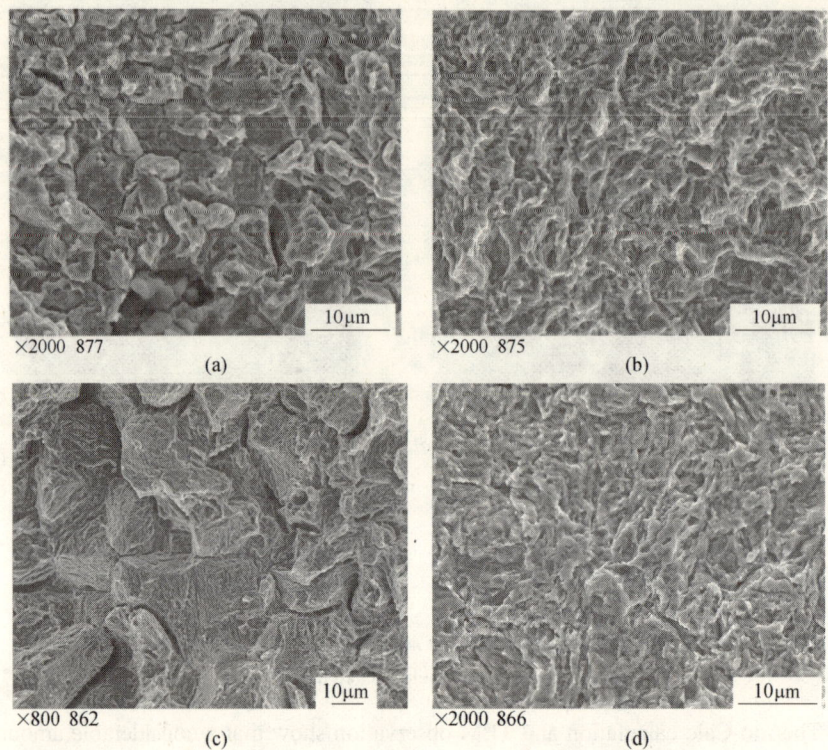

Figure 6.29   Fracture surfaces in crack initiation area of sustained load tensile DF specimens of
42CrMo+0.27%V steel (a,b) and high clean 42CrMo steel (c,d)

(a) 500℃, R_m=1390MPa, σ_a=1660MPa, t=92h;   (b)600℃, R_m=1280MPa, σ_a=1660MPa, t=140h;
(c)470℃, R_m =1300MPa, σ_a=1390MPa, t=88h;
(d)580℃,R_m =1030MPa, σ_a=1530MPa, t=141h

R_m—tensile strength; σ_a—applied stress; t—failure time

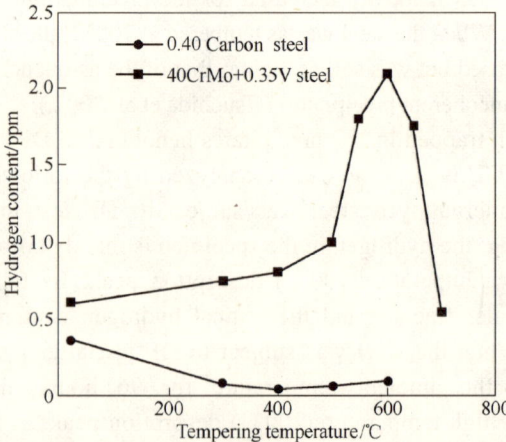

Figure 6.30   Variations of absorbed hydrogen content with tempering temperature
for the V-bearing and 0.40 carbon steels (Tsuchida,Matsumoto,Kuratomi,1996)

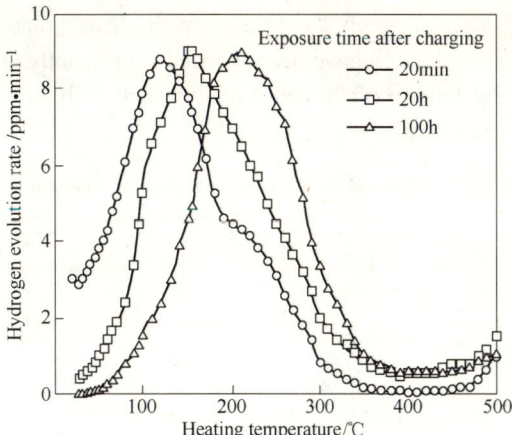

Figure 6.31   Dependence of rate curves for hydrogen evolution on atmospheric exposure time after charging hydrogen and Cd plating for steel V-bearing steel (0.30C-0.98Si-0.51Mn-1.99Cr-0.39Mo-0.35V) tempered at 510℃

al,2002). (2) Results of the electrochemical hydrogen permeation testing show that hydrogen diffusivity in V-microalloyed steel is lower by magnitude of one order than that of SCM440 and plain carbon steels (Kushida et al,1996). Since crack initiation plays an important role on the delayed fracture for high strength martensitic steel, lower diffusivity in V-microalloyed steel leads to the retardation of hydrogen enrichment at the tip of microcrack or notch and hence extends DF life, so the susceptibility to hydrogen-induced DF is reduced.

When tempering temperature is higher than 500℃ for V-microalloying steel, the dispersed precipitation of VC not only acts as strong hydrogen trap, but also leads to precipitation hardening. Therefore, the tempering temperature for V-microalloyed 42CrMo steel is higher than that of non-microalloyed 42CrMo steel at the same strength level. This is also one of the main reasons for improved DF resistance of V-microalloying steel.

6.5   Effect of Cleanliness on the Fatigue Performance of High Strength Martensitic Steels

As mentioned in 6.1, prevention of fish-eye fracture would certainly improve the fatigue property of high strength steels. SEM examination on 200 fatigue fractured specimens of commercial spring steels reveals that most of them are caused by coarse and brittle non-metallic inclusions in high-cycle fatigue especially in very high-cycle fatigue, as listed in Table 6.2. Therefore, controlling of these inclusions is a key to improve fatigue fracture resistance of high strength martensitic steels. With the rapid development of technologies for steelmaking and refining in the recent years, high strength steels are getting much cleaner than before; both the size and quantity of inclusions have been reduced significantly, which would thus greatly influence the fatigue performance of the steels in both high-cycle fatigue and very high-cycle fatigue.

Table 6.2   Statistical results of fatigue fracture surface of commercial spring steels (Number of specimens)

Number of specimens	Surface matrix	Internal matrix	Internal inclusion
High-cycle fatigue ($N_f \leqslant 10^7$ cycle)	61	0	39
Ultrahigh-cycle fatigue ($N_f > 10^7$ cycle)	23	6	71

The following approaches are usually applied to control harmful nondeformable inclusions in high strength steels (Hui et al,1998): 1. To lower the oxygen content in steel so that the quantity of oxides could be reduced; 2. To reduce the inclusion size; 3. To control the composition of oxide inclusions to lower its melting point and be deformable.

The early effort mainly focused on lowering the oxygen content to reduce the quantity of inclusions. At the same time, the size of inclusion is also reduced. Figure 6.32 gives typical results of the fatigue strength of commercial and low-oxygen spring steels (Iikubo et al,1986). Obviously, the fatigue strength of is noticeably increased for the low-oxygen spring steels, which is in the up-band of the statistical data of fatigue strength of commercial spring steels.

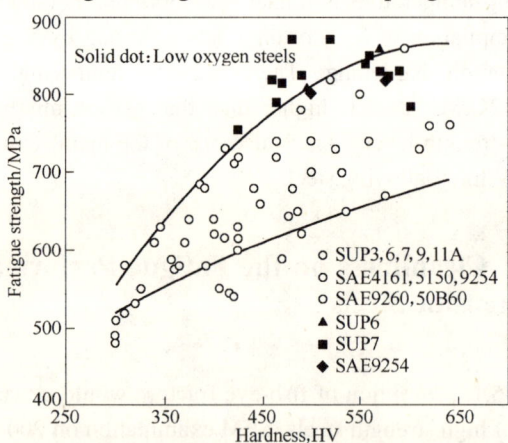

Figure 6.32   Variations of fatigue strength with hardness for commercial and low oxygen spring steels (Iikubo et al,1986)

It should be noted that attention must be paid to avoid the formation of large size inclusions even though the oxygen content in steel is reduced to rather low values. For an example, although the oxygen content decreases from 42 ppm to 12 ppm in the 42CrMo steel, its fatigue strength is not improved as much as expected due to the existence of coarse inclusions(Figure 6.33(a)). Further analysis of inclusion particles extracted from bulk specimen by electrolysis shows that there are two peaks observed in the size distribution of inclusion particles, one is particles with the average size of about 3 μm and the other is about 50 μm(Figure 6.33(b)) (Nie et al,2007). The measurements on the inclusion particles from the commercial 38Si7 spring steel with extremely low oxygen content(<6 ppm) has also proved this finding. As shown in Figure 6.34, almost all fatigue failures initiate from the large oxide inclusion.

The aforementioned experimental results indicate that the size of inclusion plays very important role on fatigue performance of high strength steels. In fact,

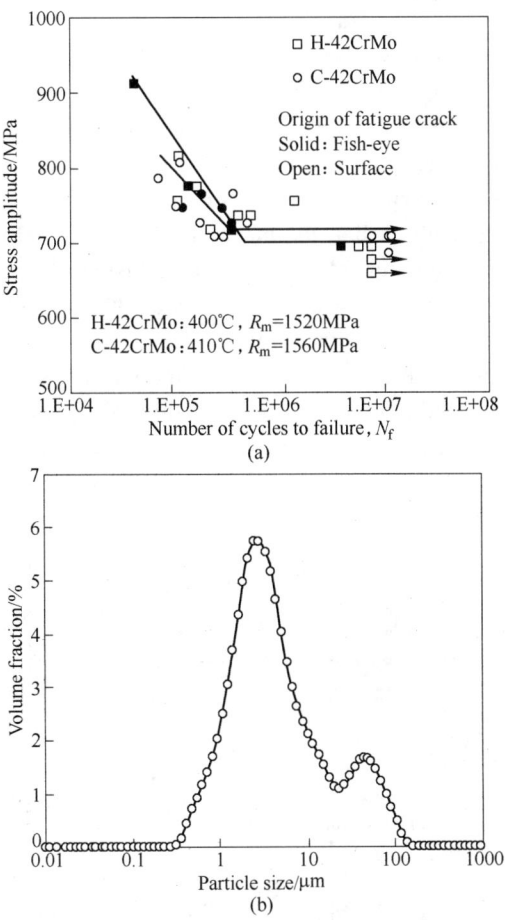

Figure 6.33 S-N curves of rotating bending fatigue test for 42CrMo steels (a) and granulometric distribution of inclusion for H-42CrMo steel (b)
(H-42CrMo: high cleanliness with [O]=13 ppm; C-42CrMo: commercial with [O]=42 ppm)

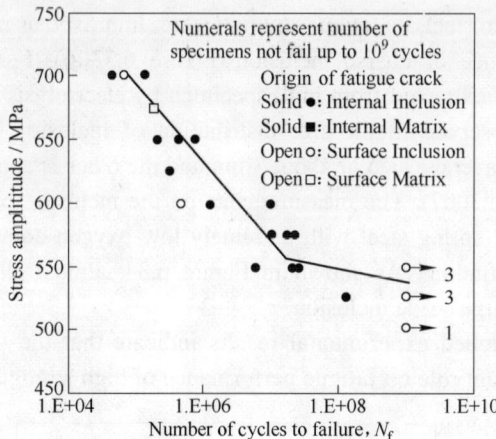

Figure 6.34   S-N curve of very high-cycle fatigue for 38Si7 spring steel with
extremely low oxygen content [O]<6 ppm

a reduction of inclusion size could significantly improve the fatigue strength of high strength steels according to equation 6.2 presented by Murakami. Figure 6.35 summarizes the experimental results of very high-cycle fatigue for commercial spring steels. When the mean size of oxide inclusion is 35.6 μm, fatigue crack always initiates from the coarse inclusion(only one exception) no matter whether low or high stress is applied; when the oxide inclusion is refined to about 4 μm, fatigue crack initiates from specimen surface at the high stress amplitude, whilst it initiates from the fine inclusions at the lower stress amplitude. The size reduction of oxide inclusions shifts the S-N curve to the up-right corner, correspondingly, fatigue strength increases from 632 MPa to 725 MPa, i.e. by 15 %.

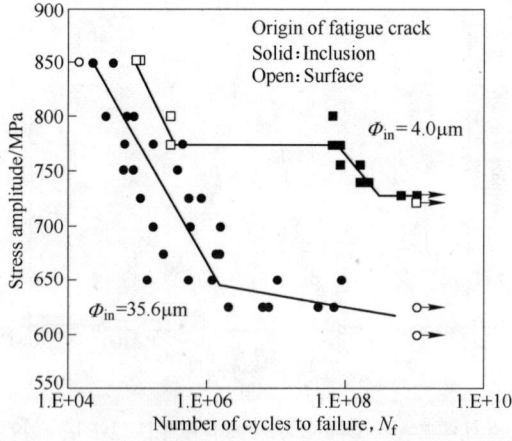

Figure 6.35   S-N curves of very high-cycle fatigue for 50CrV4 spring steels
with different inclusion sizes

Fatigue life, N_f, may be divided into two periods:(1) the crack initiation period(N_i); and (2) the crack propagation period(N_p). The results of fatigue life prediction demonstrated that the initiation period covers the larger part such as >90% of the fatigue life in the high-cycle especially very high-cycle regime for high strength steels (Wang et al,1999). Therefore, the size reduction of inclusions can effectively delay the crack initiation period, resulting in prolonged fatigue life and higher fatigue strength(Figures 6.35 and 6.36) (Zhang et al,2007). When inclusions are refined below a certain size, i.e. below which the fatigue fracture origins will not initiate from them, so that the inclusion-caused fatigue fracture could be avoided.

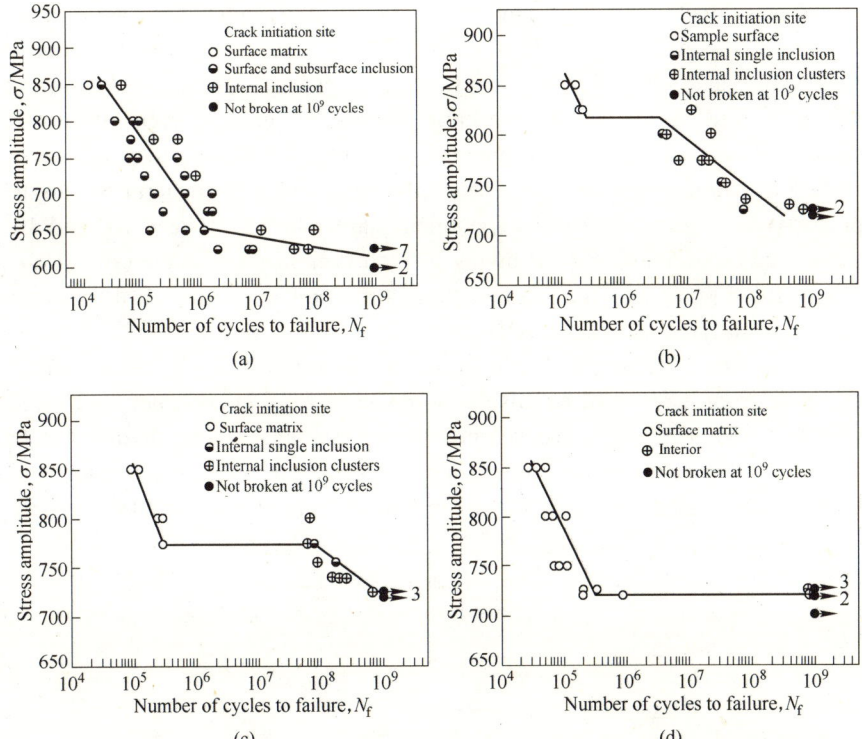

Figure 6.36 S-N curves of four high strength spring steels with different cleanliness and inclusion size, showing that plentiful fracture initiated from inclusions between 10^6 and 10^9 cycles for commercial 50CrV4 (a), clean 54SiCrV6 (b) and clean 50CrV4 (c) steels, but the specimens hardly broke between 10^6 and 10^9 cycles for clean 54SiCr6 steel (d) owing to inclusion size below the critical size. The oxygen contents of the four steel are 29, 27, 24 and 22 ppm, respectively (Zhang et al,2007)

It is worthy of pointing out that the size reduction of inclusions in steels can not only improve fatigue life and fatigue strength, but also greatly improve the reliability of the fatigue life. In Figure 6.36, three clean or super-clean spring steels exhibit the same fatigue strength ($\sigma_{-1p} \approx 720$ MPa) at 10^9 cycles; but the reliability of their fatigue lives changes a lot with the cleanness of the steels. At low stress amplitude level (close to the fatigue strength), the specimens could frequently break between 10^6 and 10^9 cycles for the commercial steel in which the average inclusion size of about 29 μm, while the specimens hardly break between 10^6 and 10^9 cycles for the clean steel in which the inclusion size is small than 1 μm. This finding is further supported by the investigation on the 42CrMo steels with various levels of cleanness (Yang et al,2004).

It is impossible to completely remove all the oxide inclusions from steels, and especially due to the constraint of production cost, Kawahara et al (1992) in Nippon Steel adopted a new tactic of making inclusions harmless by lowering their melting point through controlling their composition by special deoxidation and synthetic slag treatment in secondary refining. Inclusion can be made fine in the plastic working process by making their plastically deformable and stress concentration can be relieved by making the hardness of inclusions similar to that of the steel and thus will not do harm to fatigue property. In Figure 6.36(d), the specimens hardly broke between 10^6 and 10^9 cycles for clean 54SiCr6 steel owing to inclusion size below the critical size due to the adoption of the aforementioned method, even though the oxygen content in the steel is as high as 22 ppm.

As discussed before, fish-eye fractures in high strength steels mainly originate from inclusions, but also in some cases from microstructural defects (Figure 6.37). Therefore, matrix microstructure strengthening should also be taken besides inclusion controlling, otherwise fatigue performance cannot be improved because fatigue cracks may initiate from the weak part of the matrix.

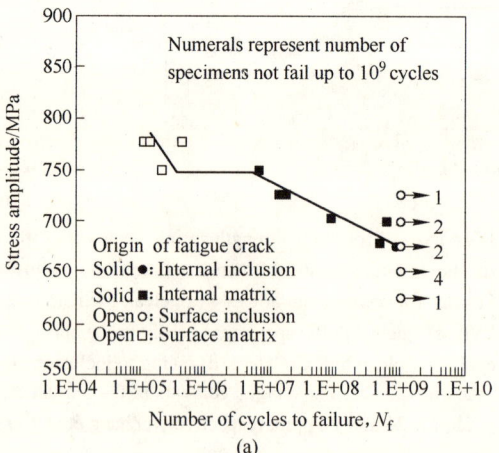

(a)

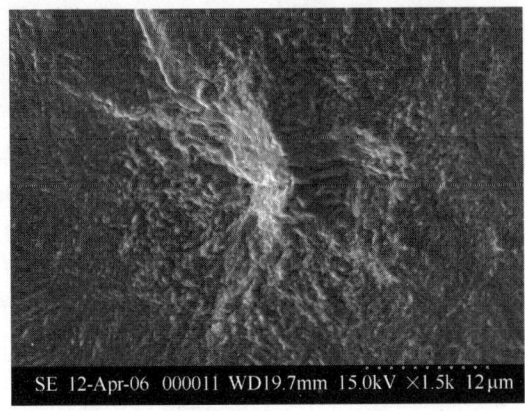

(b)

Figure 6.37   S-N curve of 60Si2MnA spring steel (a) and an example of fatigue
crack initiated from internal matrix defect

6.6 New Developed High Strength Martensitic Steels and Their Industrial Application

Based on the aforementioned understanding of the fundamentals of the DF behavior
of high strength martensitic steels, the proposed concept to improve DF resistance
comprises the combination of grain refinement, grain boundary strengthening and
hydrogen trap controlling. ADF series high strength structural steels have been
developed with excellent DF resistance, which are characterized by:

1. The tensile strength increases to 1500 MPa grade by Mo/V precipitation
   hardening and grain refinement;
2. Grain boundary bonding is strengthened by Mo segregation, and hydrogen
   diffusivity is delayed and its enrichment at grain boundary is weakened
   through the introduction of hydrogen traps of carbides/carbonitrides;
3. Grain refining through microalloying and heat treatment to improve strength,
   toughness and DF resistance at the same time (Hui,2003).

Grain growth in ADF1 steel is much slower than that in 42CrMo steel, the
active energy for migration of austenite grain boundary in ADF1 steel is higher
than that in 42CrMo steel by 158.8 kJ/mol, and consequently, the austenite grain is
as fine as less than 10 μm, when the steel is austenitised at 950℃. ADF1 steel
possesses rather fine microstructure, in which V/Mo alloy carbides are dispersed
extensively and the carbides at grain boundaries are not continuous and
spheroidized after tempering at high temperature (Figure 6.38).

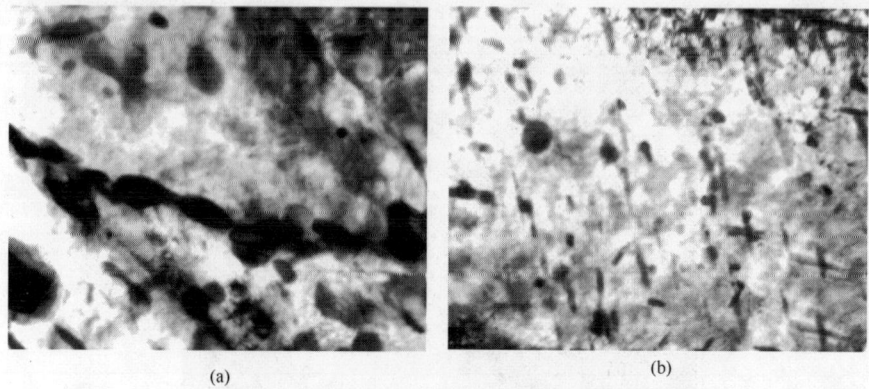

(a)   (b)

Figure 6.38   TEM microstructures of ADF1 steel tempered at 600℃, showing the
broken and spheroidized carbide at prior austenite grain boundary (a)
and the dispersed alloy carbide precipitates (b)

　　Variations of tensile properties of ADF1 steel with tempering temperatures are
shown in Figure 6.39. With the rise of tempering temperature from 400℃ to 650
℃, the strength of 42CrMo steel decreases monotonously largely due to the rapid
coarsening of cementite. There are a significant secondary hardening of ADF1
steel when the tempering temperature is higher than 500℃ and this secondary
hardening reaches a peak at temperatures around 600℃. The addition of strong
carbide forming vanadium and higher molybdenum content not only significantly
retards softening but also forms fine alloy carbides,which produce a hardness and
strength increase at high tempering temperatures.

　　Figure 6.40 shows the variations of toughness with tempering temperature for
ADF1 steel. Optimized alloy design leads to only a slight decrease in toughness at
the secondary hardening peak. With increasing tempering temperature, alloy
carbides gradually lose their coherent relation the matrix and begin to coarsen,
accompanying with a re-increasing of toughness.

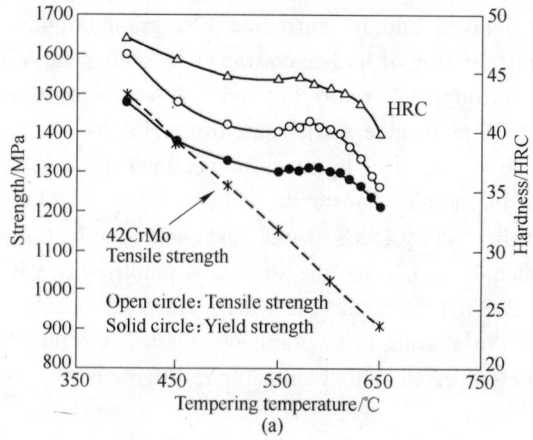

(a)

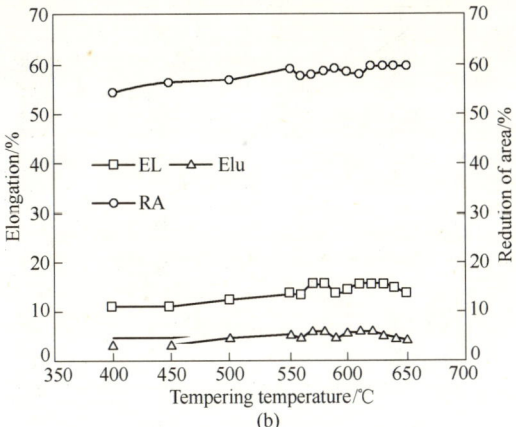

Figure 6.39 Variations of hardness, strength (a) and elongation, reduction of area (b) with tempering temperature of ADF1 steel (El: elongation; Elu: uniform elongation; RA: reduction of area)

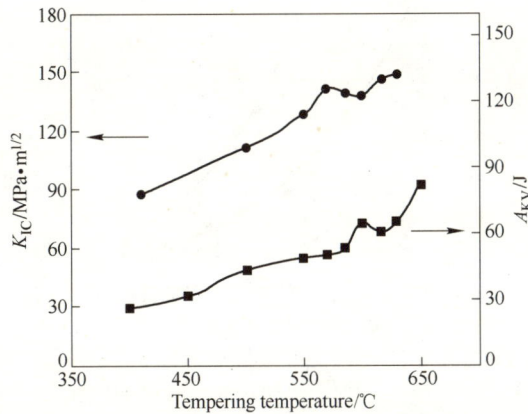

Figure 6.40 Variations of fracture toughness K_{IC} and impact energy absorbed A_{KV} with tempering temperature of ADF1 steel

At the same strength level, both DFSR and K_{ISCC} of the ADF1 steel are noticeably higher than that of 42CrMo steel (Figure 6.41). SEM observation of the fracture surfaces of DF specimens reveals that the failure is mainly transgranular for ADF1 steel whilst mainly intergranular for 42CrMo steel (Figure 6.42).

Owing to the good combination of strength, toughness and DF resistance, the ADF series high strength steels may be used to produce high strength bolts, crafts and connectors et al. Some Chinese automobile makers are now producing these components made from the ADF steels, and some of them have been industrialized for massive production.

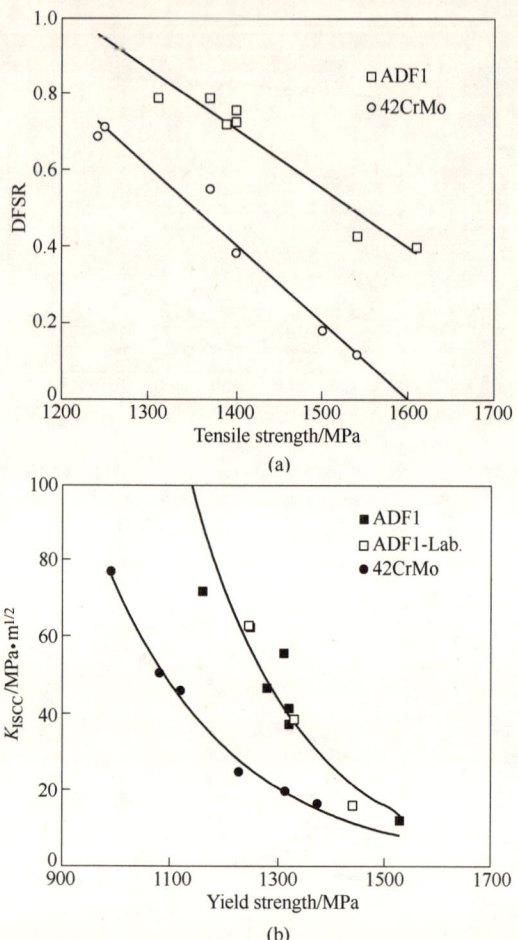

Figure 6.41   Variations of DFSR (a) and K_{ISCC} (b) with strength of ADF1 steel

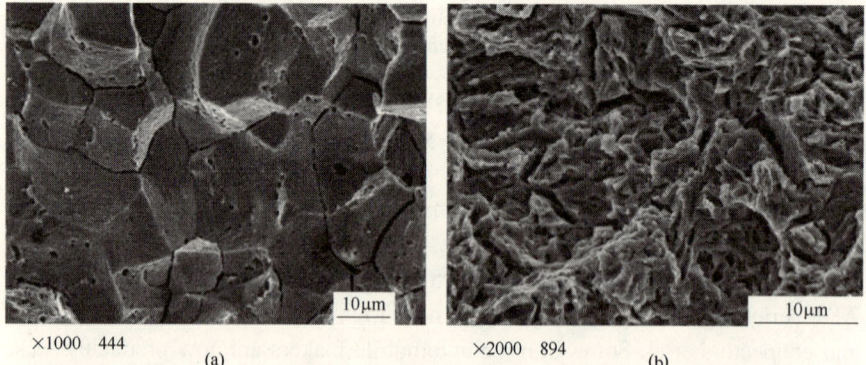

Figure 6.42   Fracture surfaces in crack initiation area of sustained load tensile DF specimens of 42CrMo steel (a) and ADF1 steel (b), showing intergranular fracture for 42CrMo steel and transgranular fracture for ADF1 steel (tensile strength of both steels is 1500 MPa)

References

Abe T, Kanazawa K (1996) Influences of non-metallic inclusion and carbide on high-cycle fatigue strength of tool steel. J Soc Mat Sci Japan, 45(1):9-15

Archer R S, Briggs J Z, Loeb, Jr. C M (eds) (1970) Molybdenum—Steels, Iron and Alloys. Climax Molybdenum Co., New York

Banerji S K, McMahon Jr. C J, Feng H C (1978) Intergranular fracture in 4340-type steels: Effects of impurities and hydrogen. Metall. Trans. A, 9A(2):237-247

Briant C L, Feng H C, McMahon Jr. C J (1978) Embrittlement of a 5 pct nickel high strength steel by impurities and their effects on hydrogen-induced cracking. Metall. Trans. A, 9A(5):625-633

Choi H C, Lee D L, Choo W Y (2001) Development of 1300MPa-grade bolt steels with high delayed fracture resistance. In: Workshop on the new generation steel-NG steel'2001. The Chinese Society for Metals, pp 75-78

Chu W Y et al (eds) (2000) Fracture and Environmental Fracture. Science Press, Beijing

Craig B D (1982) The effect of phosphorus content on the hydrogen stress cracking of high strength 4130 steel. Metrall. Trans. A, 13A(5):907-912

Chu W Y (ed) (1988) Hydrogen Damage and Delayed Fracture. Chinese Metallurgical Industry Press, Beijing

Chu W Y et al (1981) Mechanism of Stress Corrosion Cracking of Low Alloy Steel in Water. Corrosion, 37(6): 320~323

Davis R A, Dreyer G A, Gallaugher W C (1964) Stress corrosion cracking study of several high strength steels. Corrosion, 20(3):93-103

Dumoulin P, Guttmann M, Foucault M et al (1980) Role of molybdenum in phosphorus-induced temper embrittlement. Metal Science, (1):1-15

Furuya Y, Matsuoka S, Kimura T, et al (2005) Effects of inclusion and ODA sizes on gigacycle fatigue properties of high-strength steels. Tetsu-to-Hagane, 91(8): 630-638

Gojic M, Kosec L (1997) The susceptibility to the hydrogen embrittlement of low alloy Cr and CrMo steels. ISIJ Inter., 37(4): 412-418

Grobner P J, Sponseller D L, Diesburg (1979) Effect of Molybdenum content on the sulfide stress cracking resistance of AISI 4130-type steel with 0.035Cb. Corrosion, 35(6): 240-250

Hsu T Y (ed) (1999) Martensitic Transformation and Martensite. Science Press, Beijing

Hui W J, Dong H, Chen S L (1998) Effects of non-metallic inclusions and surface conditions on the fatigue properties of high strength spring steels. J of Special Steel, 19(6): 8-14

Hui W J, Dong H, Weng Y Q, et al (2006) Stress corrosion cracking behavior of Cr-Mo-V high strength steel. Trans of Mater and Heat Treatment, 27(6):37-42

Hui W J, Dong H, Weng Y Q, et al (2005) Delayed Fracture Behavior of Titanium-Containing Cr-Mo Type High Strength Steel. J. of Iron & Steel Research Inter.,12(1): 43-49

Hui Weijun, Dong Han, Weng Yuqing, et al (2004) Delayed fracture behavior of ultrafine grained high strength steel. Acta Metall Sinica, 40(6):561-568

Hui W J, Dong H, Weng Y Q, et al (2004) Effect of molybdenum on delayed fracture behavior of high strength steel. Acta Metall Sinica, 40(12):1274-1280

Hui W J, Dong H, Weng Y Q (2003) Delayed Fracture Behavior of CrMo Type High Strength Steel Containing Vanadium. J. of Iron and Steel Research Inter., 10(4):63-67

Hui W J (2003) Study of Delayed Fracture Behavior of High Strength Bolt Steel. Dissertation, Central Iron & Steel Research Institute

Hui W J, Dong H, Weng Y Q (2002). Effect of Molybdenum on mechanical property and delayed fracture resistance of high strength steel. In: Proceedings of First International Conference on Advanced Structural Steels(ICASS 2002), May 22-24, Tsukuba Inter. Congress Center, Tsukuba, Japan, pp.243-244

Hui W J, Dong H, Weng Y Q (2001) Development of high strength bolt steels with high delayed fracture resistance. Iron and Steel, 36(3):69-73

Iikubo T, Ito Y, Hayashi H, Saito T, Takagi N (1986) Effects of non-metallic inclusions on fatigue properties of ultra-clean spring steels. Electric Furnace Steel(Denki-Seiko), 57(1):23-32

Isokawa K, Namiki K (1983) Effect of sulphur contents on delayed failure susceptibility of high strength steels for bolts. Electric Furnace Steel(Denki-Seiko), 54(2):75-83

Kawahara J, Tanabe K, Banno T, Yoshida M (1992) Advance of valve spring steel. Wire J International, (11):55-61

Kawasaki K, Chiba T, Koga H, et al (1987) Effect of austenite grain size on mechanical properties in spring steel austenitised, quenched and tempered by induction heating. Tetsu-to-Hagane, 73(16): 2298-2305

Komazazki S, Watanabe S, Misawa T (2003) Influence of phosphorus and boron on hydrogen embrittlement susceptibility of high strength low alloy steel. ISIJ Inter, 43(11):1851-1857

Kushida T, Matsumoto H, Kuratomi N, et al (1996) Delayed fracture and hydrogen absorption of 1.3GPa grade high strength bolt steel. Tetsu-to-Hagane, 82(4): 297-302

Kushida T, Matsumoto H, Nakasato F (1998) Study on delayed fracture of high strength steels by thermal hydrogen analysis technique. Sumimoto Metals, 50(3): 25-30

Lee W P (2000) Development of high performance structural steels for 21st century in Korea. In: Ultra Steel 2000, Proceedings of the International Workshop on the

Innovative Structural Materials for Infrastructure in 21st Century. January 12-13, Tsukuba, Japan pp33-63

Lei T Q et al (eds) (1979) Ausforming of Steels. Machinery Industry Press, Beijing

Li G F, Wu R G, Lei T C (1992) Carbide-matrix interface mechanism of stress corrosion cracking behavior of high-strength CrMo Steels. Metall. Trans. A, 23A(10):2879-2885

Li G F, Wu R G, Lei T C (1990) Effect of prior austenite grain size on stress corrosion cracking of a high-strength steel. Metall. Trans. A, 21A:503-505

Maropoulos S, Paul J D H, Ridley N (1993) Microstructure-property relationships in tempered low ally Cr-Mo-3.5Ni-V steel. Mater. Sci. Tech., 9(11):1014-1019

Matsumoto H, Nakasato F, Kushida T (1996) Delayed fracture and culprit hydrogen in steel. Sumimoto Metals, 48(4):128-131

Matsuyama S (ed) (1989) Delayed Fracture. Nikkan-Kogyo Press, Tokyo

McDarmaid D S (1978) Effects of different austenitization treatments on K_{IC}, K_{ISCC}, and other mechanical properties of 300M steel bar. Metals Technology, 5(1):7-16

Murakami Y, Kodama S, Konuma S (1989) Quantitative evaluation of effects of non-metallic inclusions on fatigue strength of high strength steels. I : Basic fatigue mechanism and evaluation of correlation between the fatigue fracture stress and the size and location of non-metallic inclusions. Int J Fatigue, 11(5):291-298

Murakami Y, Usuki H (1989) Quantitative evaluation of effects of non-metallic inclusions on fatigue strength of high strength steels II : fatigue linit evaluation based on statistics for extreme values of inclusion size. Int J Fatigue, 11(5):299-307

Nagumo M (2001) Function of hydrogen in embrittlement of high-strength steels. ISIJ International, 41(6):590-598

Nagumo M, Nakamura M, Takai K (2001) Hydrogen thermal desorption relevant to delayed-fracture susceptibility of high-strength steels. Metall Mater Trans A, 32A(2):339-347

Nakayama T (1999) Corrosion protection technology for improvement of strength on steels. Zairyo-to-Kankyo, 48(8):484-489

Namiki K, Isokawa K (1984) Effect of sulphur and phosphorus on the delayed fracture resistance and mechanical properties of SAE 1541. Electric Furnace Steel(Denki-Seiko), 55(2):101-109

Nie Y H, Hui W J, Fu W T, et al (2007) Effect of cleanliness on fatigue fracture behavior of 42CrMo steel. Chinese J of Materials Research, 21:123-128 Suppl.

Omura T, Kushida T, Nakasato F, et al (2005) Hydrogen absorption into high strength bolts under atmospheric exposure and delayed fracture susceptibility evaluation. Tetsu-to-Hagane, 91(5):478-484

Padmanabhan R, Wood W E (1983) Hydrogen induced cracking in a low alloy steel. Metall. Trans. A, 14A(11):2347-2356

Perkins K M, Bache M R (2005) The influence of inclusions on the fatigue performance of a low pressure turbine blade steel. Int J Fatigue, 27:610-616

Porter L F, Dabkowski D S (1970) Grain-size control by thermal cycling. In: Burke J J, Weiss V (eds) Ultra-fine Grain Metals. Syracuse University Press, New York

Proctor R P M., Paxton H W (1969) The effect of prior-austenite grain-size on the stress-corrosion cracking susceptibility of AISI 4340 steel. Trans. Am. Soc. Metals, 62(4):989-999

Sato A (2000) Research project on innovative steels in Japan (STX-21 Project). In: Ultra Steel 2000, Proceedings of the International Workshop on the Innovative Structural Materials for Infrastructure in 21st Century. January 12-13, Tsukuba, Japan pp1-10

Smith D W, Hehemann R F (1971) Influence of structural parameters on the yield strength of tempered martensite and lower bainite. J Iron Steel Inst, 209:476-481

Suzuki N, Ishii N, Miyagawa T,et al (1993) Estimation of delayed fracture property of steels. Tetsu-to-Hagane, 79(2):227-232

Swarr T, Krauss G (1976) The effect of structure on the deformation of as-quenched and tempered martensite in an Fe-0.2 pct C alloy. Metall. Trans. A, 7A(1):41-48

Tarui T, Yamasaki S (2002) Evaluation method of delayed fracture property and overcoming techniques of delayed fracture of high strength steels. Tetsu-to-Hagane, 88(10):612-619

Terasaki S (2001) Delayed fracture properties of SCM440 steel with various strength levels derived through modified ausforming. CAMP-ISIJ, 14:1309

Tien J K (1976) Diffusion and the dislocation sweeping mechanism for hydrogen transport. In: Thompson A W, Bernstein I M (eds) Effect of Hydrogen on Behavior of Materials, Met. Soc. AIME

Tsuchida T, Hara T, Tsuzaki K (2002) Relationship between microstructure and hydrogen absorption behavior in a V-bearing high strength steel. Tetsu-to-Hagane, 88(11):771-778

Wang Q Y, Berad J Y, Dubarre A, et al (1999) Gigacycle fatigue of ferrous alloys. Fatigue Fract Engng Mater Struct, 1999, 22:667-672

Wang Q Y, Berard J Y, Rathery S, Bathias C (1999) High-cycle fatigue crack initiation and propagation behaviour of high-strength spring steel wires. Fatigue Fract Engng Mater Struct, 22:673-677

Wei F G, Hara T, Tsuchida T, Tsuzaki K (2003) Hydrogen trapping in quenched and tempered 0.40C-0.30Ti steel containing biomodaly dispersed TiC particles. ISIJ Inter., 43(4):539-547

Weng Y Q (2003) Microstructural refinement of structural steels. Iron and Steel, 38(5):1-11

Weng Y Q (2000) New generation of Iron and steel material in China. In: Ultra Steel 2000, Proceedings of the International Workshop on the Innovative Structural Materials for Infrastructure in 21st Century. January 12-13, Tsukuba, Japan pp 11-32

Weng Y Q (1984) Grain boundary segregation and intergranular brittle fracture of ferrous alloys. Dissertation, University of Pennsylvania

Weng Y Q, McMahon Jr. C J (1987) Interaction of phosphorus, carbon, manganese, and chroumium in intergranular embrittlement of iron. Mater. Sci. and Engin., 3(3):207-216

Wittig J E, Joshi A (1990) High-resolution auger electron spectroscopy of grain boundary phosphorus segregation in NiCrMoV and NiCr steels. Metall. Trans. A, 21A(10):2817-2821

Wu R G, Li R S (1984) Effect of quenching from intercritical temperature on hydrogen-induced cracking in 30CrMnSiA steel. J of Chinese Society of Corrosion and Protection, 4(1):22-28

Yamasaki S (1998) Improvement of delayed fracture property of high strength steel by TMCP. CAMP-ISIJ, 11:1242

Yamasaki S, Takahashi T (1997) Delayed fracture mechanism in high strength steels by acoustic emission source wave analysis. Tetsu-to-Hagane, 83(7):460-465

Yang Z G, Li S X, Zhang J M, et al (2004) The fatigue behaviors of zero-inclusion and commercial 42CrMo steels in the super-long fatigue life regime. Acta Materialia, 52(18):5235-5241

Yu J, McMahon Jr C J (1980) The effects of composition and carbide precipitation on temper embrittlement of 2.25Cr-1Mo steel: Part II the effects of Mn and Si. Metall. Trans. A, 11A(2):291-300

Zhang J M, Li S X, Yang Z G, et al (2007) Influence of inclusion size on fatigue behavior of high strength steels in the gigacycle fatigue regime. International J of Fatigue, 29(4):765-771

Zhang J M, Yang Z G, Li S X, et al (2006) Ultra high cycle fatigue behavior of automotive high strength steels 54SiCrV6 and 54SiCr6. Acta Metall Sinica, 42(3):259-264

Zhang X Z, Ma Y, Zhou H H (2001) Electron energy-loss spectroscopy study of grain boundaries in ultrahigh strength CrMo steel. In:Workshop on New Generation Steel, Nov.13-16, 2001, Beijing, China, pp 185-188

Zhong P, Gu B Z, Jin J J, et al (1995) Mechanical properties and stress corrosion cracking of 16Co14Ni10Cr2Mo steel. J of Aeronautical Materials, 15(4):41-46

7

Carbide-free Bainite/Martensite (CFB/M) Duplex Phase Steel[1]

To achieve energy and raw materials conservation, the world focuses attention upon researching and developing structure steel with ultra high tensile strength. Compared with ordinary structure steel, ultra-high strength low alloy (UHSLA) steel has higher tensile strength ($R_m \geqslant 1500$ MPa) but lower toughness. Because of low alloy elements, simple hot working process and relative low cost, UHSLA is widely used in spaceflight, aviation and conventional weapons industries. The process of ultimate heat treatment of this type of steel involves "quenching + tempering" or "austempering + tempering", Austempering + tempering produces tempered martensite or low bainite + tempered martensite duplex phase microstructure, usually used for making component under a larger stress at room temperature (like aircraft undercarriage, gun barrel and bulletproof steel plate). However, during the process of application, because UHSLA steel has not high enough toughness, brittle fracture often occurs, which results in short service life (Fan et al ,2006). The components made of UHSLA steel for dynamic and huge impact load have higher requirement of fatigue life. But medium or high carbon ultrahigh strength low alloy steel is usually low in toughness. It is shown in the recent research that UHSLA steel with tempered martensite structure often breaks in brittle manner due to insufficient toughness. When fatigue cycle is about 10^7 or more, the initiation of fatigue fracture change to inside materials and produce model ladder S-N curve, which results in further lowering fatigue limit (Wang et al ,2002).The delayed fracture is a sudden brittle fracture of material under static load for a long period. This phenomenon is a kind of environmental embrittlement arising from interactions among material, environment and stress. If the tensile strength is higher than 1200MPa, the delayed fracture resistance reduces with the

---

[1]The experimental materials used in Chapter 7 are listed in a appendix at the end of Chapter 7.

increase of strength. In natural environmental condition, the delayed fracture may occur in the bolt with high strength over 1200MPa. Hereby, the low level of toughness, delayed fracture resistance and ultra-high cycle fatigue limit are the key factors to restrict the type of steel from being application for civilian industry products and large-scale application. Along with accelerating processes of "Automobile Weight Lighting" and "Railway High-speed", it is urgent for countries in the world to apply UHSLA steels for civilian industry. Therefore, material scientists optimize alloy design and deeply research the combination of strength and toughness, ultra high-cycle fatigue property and delayed fracture resistance. Research shows that alloying elements, like V and Ti, can improve delayed fracture resistance (Hui et al,2002a); microstructure of low bainite can show higher delayed fracture resistance (Hui et al,2002b); and CFB/M(Carbide Free Bainite/ Martensite)duplex phase microstructure can show higher strength and toughness, fatigue resistance and delayed fracture resistance than the martensite steel (Liu et al, 2003; Gu et al, 2003; Liu et al, 2004).

7.1 CFB/M Duplex Phase Structure

In 1960s', it was found that the combination of strength and toughness of bainite/martensite duplex phase microstructure are superior to the single-phase martensite mirostructure in some HSLA steels. From then on, people have paid more attention to the bainite/martensite duplex phase microstructure.

Austempering based on steel components are heated up to austenizing temperature then quenched into heat-treatment bath (molten nitrate bath, metal bath or floating particle furnace) for a long time, which makes the whole or partial super-cooling austenite be transformed into low bainite microstructure, and then cooled in air to room temperature. Tomita et al modified austempering technology, above the M_s point holding certain time, for receiving partial lower bainite microstructure; and later quenched it and transformed the rest super-cooling austenite into martensite. Utilizing this technique, Tomita et al studied the influence of the isothermal temperature and holding time on the strength and toughness of steel, based on JIS SNCM439, JIS SCM440 and 4330Si and 300M steels. The research on JIS SNCM439 and JIS SCM440 steels(Tomita et al,1985; 1983) shows that the lower bainite/martensite duplex phase microstructure is capable of improving the strength and toughness of the steel, and the steel of lower bainite/martensite duplex phase microstructure with 25 percent lower bainite has the optimal combination of strength and toughness. But the mixed mirostructure of the upper bainite/martensite deteriorates the strength and toughness. Experimental results of modified isothermal treatment on 4330Si steel and 300M steel show that the CFB/M duplex phase microstructures with different contents of carbide-free bainite after isothermal treatment at different periods can improve the strength and toughness, and can also increase the fracture toughness. Furthermore, the lower the temperature of the isothermal treatment is, the more the apparent improvement of the strength and toughness of the steel is (Tomsta et al,1995a ;Tomita et al,1995b).

Many researches (Bhadeshia et al, 1979;Kang et al, 1990) showed in the condition of austempering, low alloy steels with silicon and aluminum involved two processes: in the first process, it produces carbide free bainite with film retained austenite; and in the second process, carbide is precipitated and produce typical bainite; and in the conditions of steel heat treating into carbide free bainite, steel shows higher strength and toughness. In 1970s', Fang Hongsheng et al invented Mn-B series of bainitic steels, applied in some fields. To develop new type of steels with high strength and toughness, based on the former research, Tsinghua University Bainitic Steel R&D Center for Research and Popularization designed CFB/M duplex phase steel with 1500MPa.

7.2 Alloy Design of CFB/M Duplex Phase Steel by Tsinghua University Bainitic Steel R&D Center

7.2.1 . *Alloy design of CFB/M duplex phase steel and its structure*

Alloy design principle of CFB/M duplex phase steel with 1500MPa as follows:
1. Through design of alloy elements and process, CFB/M duplex microstructure should be obtained after air-cooling to improve combination of strength and toughness, as well as the delayed fracture resistance.
2. Depending upon technical progress, vacuum remelting, refining and other purification measures could be adopted, so as to improve inclusion morphology further enhance performance of steel, especially fatigue properties.
3. Paying attention on economy, low carbon Mn-B Bainitic steels were improved to avoid from producing granular bainite microstructure in the condition of air cooling; add silicon alloy to restrain carbide precipitation and enable the retained austenite steadily in the microstructure.
4. Simplifying heat treatment process, CFB/M microstructure is easily be obtained after air-cooling for the steel bar with $\phi 8 \sim 30$mm after austenizing.

Under direction of alloying principle above-mentioned, low carbon Mn-Si-Cr steel is decided to adopt. Carbon plays the role of ensuring steel strength; Manganese is the important element to get bainite microstructure in air cooling condition; combination of Carbon and Chromium can ensure to avoid producing granular bainite and upper bainite in consecutive air cooling processes; Silicon is the unique element to produce carbide free bainite. Combination of Mn, Cr and Si can further improve hardenabilities of steel.

While researching Mn-B Bainitic steels, Fang Hongsheng et al worked out the proper element range of Mn. During designing CFB/M steel, the content of Mn isn't altered. It was found that transforming temperature of low bainite transformation (L_s) could be raised by adding amount of C within some certain carbon content range. Along with considering the tensile strength of the designed steel should be the level about 1500MPa; carbon content is selected to be within range of 0.18~0.25 percent. A certain amount of Cr could further lower the bainite forming temperature (B_s) to avoid producing granular bainite microstructure in the process of air-cooling. With regard to instability of boron steel, present authors firstly made study of the possibility of canceling B element. Effect of B on CCT curve of the experimental steel is seen in Figure 7.1, which shows it is more in favor of producing CFB/M duplex phase microstructure through canceling B.

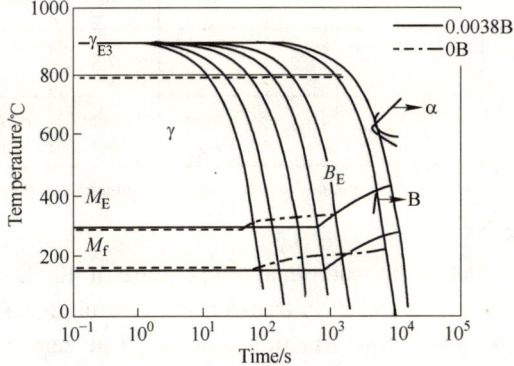

Figure 7.1   Effect of B on experimental steel CCT curve

According to principle above-mentioned, a low carbon Mn-Si-Cr CFB/M duplex phase steel was designed—steel "A". Phase transformation temperature and critical points of the A steel are shown in Table 7.1. Present authors firstly experimented isothermal temperature effects on bainitic morphology and retained austenite content. Steel "A" specimen is kept in certain isothermal temperature for three minutes; then water-cooled. In order to observe microstructure transformation and determine the retained austenite content so as to examine effect of isothermal temperature on carbide free bainitic transformation and retained austenite content, X ray diffraction was conducted and the result is seen in Table 7.2. Steel "A" after higher isothermal temperature treatment, the produced carbide free bainite takes on the gathered featheriness distribution, similar to the typical upper bainitic morphology, seen Figure 7.2. Carbide free bainite isothermal transformed at lower temperature possesses the morphology of independent plate distribution, similar to typical lower bainite, seen Figure 7.3. The critical temperature of carbide free bainitic transformation from the gathered featheriness to independent plate is more than 350℃. After treatment at the temperature of 350℃, TEM morphology of carbide free bainite is shown in Figure 7.4. Original cementite among bainitic ferrite plate and inside plate for ordinary bainite is replaced by filmy retained austenite. Through deeply and extensively observation on the sample by TEM, massive retained austenite has not been found.

Table 7.1　Phase transformation temperature and critical points of steel A

Ac_1	Ac_3	Ar_1	Ar_3	M_s	M_f
725℃	845℃	537℃	720℃	325℃	160℃

Table 7.2[①]　Effect of isothermal temperature on bainitic morphology and retained austenite content (Ar)

Temperature / ℃	273	300	330	350	385	400	420	430
Ar content / %	4.8	4.0	7.8	8.2		7.3		3.9
Bainitic morphology			plate	plate	Feather-iness	Feather-iness	Feather-iness	Feather-iness

① Heat treatment process: 890℃, 15 minutes' austenizing; after isothermal temperature treatment for 3 minutes, water quenching.

Analysis shows that at the isothermal temperature of 400℃, which is in the upper bainitie range, the steel A is transformed to a platform at 27 minutes. The maximum of bainitic transformation is about 14 percent. Incubation stage of bainitic transformation is 32 seconds at the isothermal temperature of 330℃, then after 15 minutes' transformation, the bainite is basically transformed to the end.

In the processes of wind or air-cooling, the sample is cooled at high speed in higher temperature range. For instance, bar with ϕ 40mm is cooled to 400℃ from 890℃ for about 12 minutes. In the process of consecutive cooling, incubation stage of bainitic transformation becomes long and C curve transfers to the right down(Hu et al,1995). So in practice in the condition of air-cooling, the sample can avoid producing a large number of featheriness carbide free bainite and but mainly generate plate of CFB/M duplex phase microstructure, which are seen in Figure 7.2 and Figure 7.3, respectively.SEM image of CFB/M duplex phase microstructure in air cooling condition is shown in Figure 7.5,and Figure 7.6 shows the SEM image of CFB transformed after air-cooling.

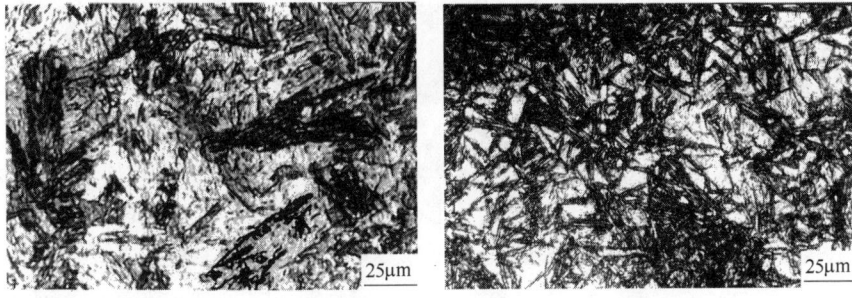

Figure 7.2 CFB morphology through treatment at isothermal temperature of 400℃

Figure 7.3 CFB morphology through treatment at isothermal temperature of 350℃

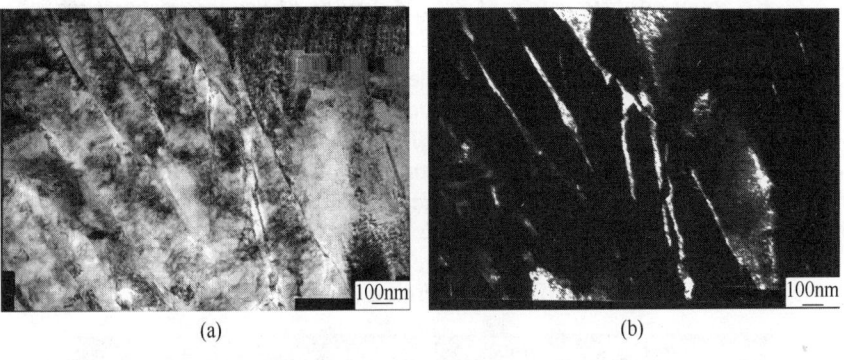

(a)   (b)

Figure 7.4 Carbide free bainitic morphology through treatment at isothermal temperature of 350℃ for 3 minutes

(a) bright field image; (b) centred dark field image

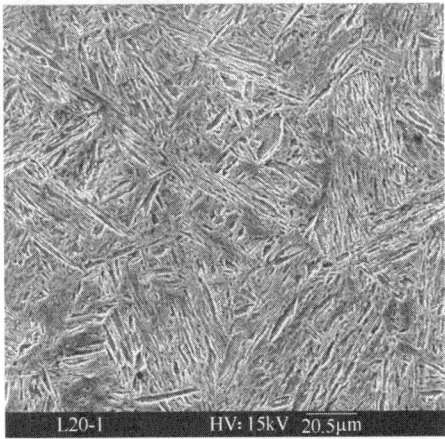

Figure 7.5 Scanning electron microscopy image of CFB/M duplex phase microstructure in air cooling condition

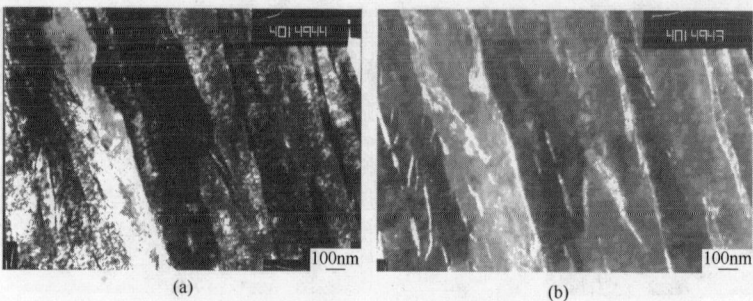

Figure 7.6 SEM Image of CFB transformed after air-cooling
(a) Lighting field image; (b) dark field image

7.2.2 *Effect of cooling rate on CFB/M duplex phase microstructure*

Thermo-mechanical simulation experiments were made with Gleeble 1500D equipment. After keeping at 960℃ air-cooling condition of ϕ10mm, ϕ20mm, ϕ30mm and ϕ50mm bars were simulated. Through microstructure examination and XRD analysis, it was shown that microstructure of round bar with ϕ10~30mm indicates(CFB+M)duplex phase structure after air cooling(AC). But as for round bar with diameter of 50mm in the same way, it is found that there is a less of proeutectoid ferrite, which microstructure indicates complex microstructure with ferrite+CFB/M(F+CFB+M), seen in Figure 7.7.

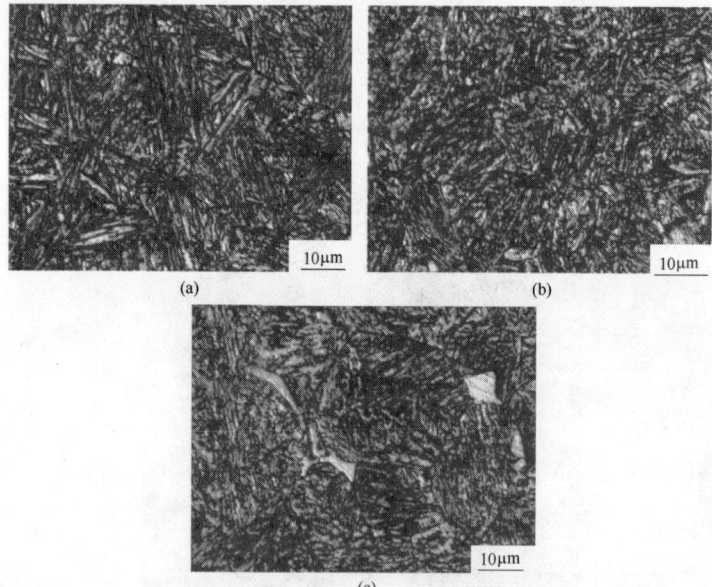

Figure 7.7 Microstructures of the experimental steel in different air cooling conditions
(a) Stimulating round bar(CFB+M)with ϕ20 in AC condition; (b) Stimulating round bar (CFB+M) with ϕ30 in AC condition; (c) Stimulating round bar (F+CFB+M) with ϕ50 in AC condition

Through X-ray diffractometer, by direct contrasting method, determine the content of austenite in the steel, which calculation formula as the following:

$$f_\gamma = \frac{1}{1 + \dfrac{I_\alpha C_\gamma}{I_\gamma C_\alpha}} \tag{7.1}$$

where, C_α and C_γ are constant of α and γ phases proportion respectively, I_α and I_γ is integral strength of α phase (211)diffraction peak and γ phase(311)diffraction peak, respectively; Its experimental results are seen in Table 7.3. It is obvious that as the diameter increasing of round bar, the content of retained austenite will increase. However, when diameter is larger than 40mm, the amount of retained austenite does not have much change.

Table 7.3 Retained austenite contents of round bars with different diameters after AC

Cooling rate	$2\theta\|_\alpha$ /(°)	$2\theta\|_\gamma$ /(°)	I_α	I_γ	C_α	C_γ	f_γ /vol.%
Water cooling	82.3330	—	212.1	0	63.53	—	0
ϕ20 bar in AC (CFB+M)	82.1975	89.5716	129.2	7.2	63.29	50.63	6.5
ϕ30 bar in AC (CFB+M)	82.2698	89.8265	140.2	10.1	63.42	51.11	8.2
ϕ40 bar in AC (CFB+M)	82.2798	89.8041	136.7	10.0	63.44	50.96	8.3
ϕ50 bar in AC (F+CFB+M)	82.2550	89.7774	134.6	10.5	63.39	51.02	8.8

7.2.3 *Effect of CFB/M duplex phase microstructure on strength and toughness of the steel*

As quenched, the strength of low carbon martensite is consisted of three parts: the strength generated by high dislocation density, the solution strengthening of carbon and alloying element and the strength generated by martensite boundary. In the first stage of lower tempering, because the effect of dispersion strengthening owing to the precipitate of ε-carbide, which is coherent to the matrix, offsets the loss of solution strengthening effect due to the separation of carbon and alloying element, and the elimination of first kind and the second kind of inner stresses, the toughness of the steel is improved under the condition of no drop of the strength. As the rise of the tempering temperature, the dislocation density in the matrix decreases, the coherent relation between ε-carbide and the matrix eliminates and the cementite is separated. Therefore, the strength of the steel will decrease. The alloying element Si not only plays a role in the solution strengthening function, but also restrains the separation of cementite during the course of tempering so as to remain the dispersion strengthening effect of ε-carbide at the higher temperature and to enhance temper resistance at the low temperature (shih et al, 1956;Nam et al,1997).

In CFB/M duplex phase microstructure, the strength of no-tempered or lower tempered CFB is lower than that of martensite. Because CFB has relatively strong temper resistance after tempering at medium temperature, the strength of CFB is relatively high. The size of CFB plate and that of low carbon martensite lath are on the same order of magnitude and the main component of CFB are the bainitic ferrite plate, the bainite can be regarded as the same phase approximately. According to the plastic deformation theory of polymerization two phase alloys, the strength of the duplex phase microstructure is the weighted average of the strength of two phases. That is:

$$\sigma = \sigma_1 V_1 + \sigma_2 V_2 \tag{7.2}$$

where, σ is strength of duplex phase microstructure, σ_1 and σ_2 are strengths of CFB and M respectively, and V_1 and V_2 are volume fractions of CFB and M, respectively.

It can be known that the strength of CFB/M duplex microstructure tempered at relatively low temperature is lower than the strength of the martensite tempered at the same temperature, but the strength of CFB/M duplex microstructure tempered at medium temperature is higher than the strength of the martensite tempered at the same temperature.

It is known in the above-mentioned part that as the diameter increasing of air-cooled round bar, cooling rate of round bar will lower, and content of carbide free bainite will increase. As diameter of round bar increase to a certain extent, pro-eutectoid ferrite will generate. What about effect of microstructure change on strength and toughness of steel? Experiment showed that through tempering at the temperature of 280℃, hardness and impact toughness of air cooled round bar with diameter of 10~30mm are higher than that in the condition of water quenching (WQ) or tempering. Therefore, it is obvious that CFB/M duplex phase structure has higher strength and toughness. Once pro-eutectoid ferrite occurs in the microstructure, hardness of steel will obviously lower, which details are seen in Tables 7.4 and 7.5.

Table 7.4 Hardness / HRC of air cooled and quenched round bars[①] with different diameters

Hardness/HRC	Water quenched	Air cooled			
		ϕ 10mm	ϕ 20mm	ϕ 30mm	ϕ 50mm
Before tempering	48.0	48.4	47.6	48.2	44.6
After tempering[①]	46.6	47.7	47.3	47.5	42.6

① Tempering at 280℃.

Table 7.5 Impact toughness of air cooled and quenched round bars[①] with different diameters

Impact toughness	Water quenched	Air cooled			
		ϕ 10mm	ϕ 20mm	ϕ 30mm	ϕ 50mm
A_{KV} / J	55.12	60.64	61.94	66.53	71.91

① Notes: Tempering at the temperature of 280℃.

7.3 Effect of Tempering on Strength and Toughness of CFB/M Duplex Phase Steel

Experimental steel was treated into martensite and CFB/M duplex phase microstructures, respectively. Through tempering at different temperatures, the change of strength, plasticity and impact toughness of steel are shown in Figure 7.8, Figure 7.9 and Figure 7.10. It can be seen from Figure 7.8 that the tensile strength will lower slowly as the increasing of the tempering temperature, but will decrease sharply after the tempering temperature is higher than the critical tempering temperature. However, the strength of CFB/M duplex phase structure is higher than that of the martensite in the critical tempering temperature. Yield strength of the steel increases at first, and then decrease with the rising of tempering temperature. The tempering temperature at which maximum yield strength occurs for CFB/M duplex phase steel is higher than that for the martensite microstructure. It can thus be seen that CFB/M duplex phase steel has relatively high tempering resistance. Figure 7.11 illuminates the yield-tensile ratio variation of different kinds of structural steels with tempering temperature. The duplex phase steel possesses higher yield-tensile ratio after tempered at 340~400℃. It can be seen from Figure 7.9 that the elongation of CFB/M duplex phase microstructure and single martensite microstructure are identical, but the reduction in area of the duplex phase steel is relatively low. It implies that the stage of homogeneous deformation of CFB/M steel is relatively long. It can be seen from Figure 7.10 that the initial temperature for the appearance of first kind temper embrittleness is higher for the steel with CFB/M microstructure than that for martensite microstructure. The impact toughness after being tempered at high

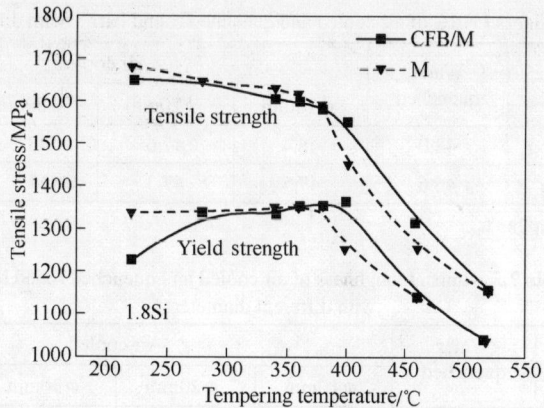

Figure 7.8   Effect of tempering temperature and microstructure on strength of experimental steel

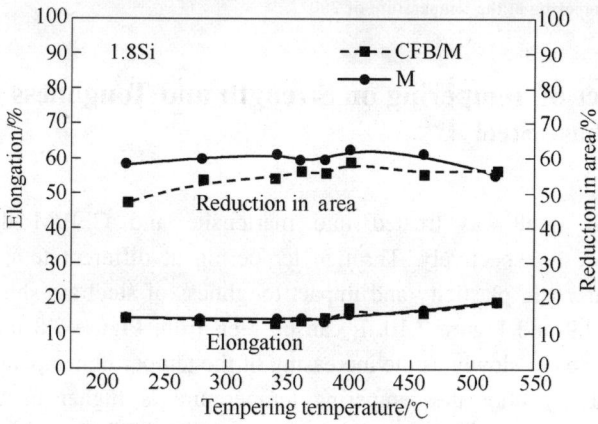

Figure 7.9   Effect of tempering temperature and microstructure on plasticity of experimental steel

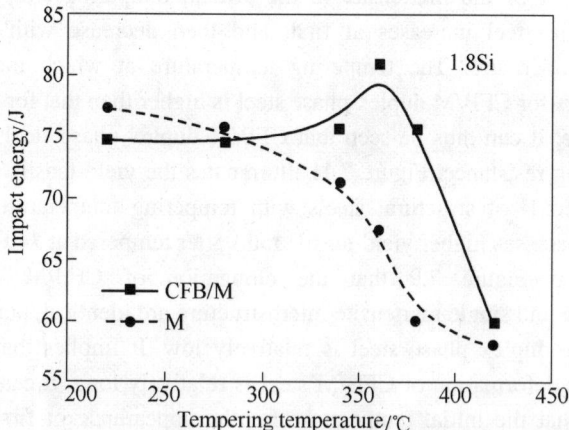

Figure 7.10   Effect of tempering temperature and microstructure on impact toughness of experimental steel

temperature for CFB/M steels is relative high. Similarly, as the rise of temper temperature from 280℃ to 350℃, the fracture toughness of the steel with CFB/M duplex phase microstructure ascends, while the fracture toughness of the steel with martensite microstructure falls, see Tables 7.6 and 7.7 for details. It can be thus seen that CFB/M duplex phase has relatively high toughness after being tempered at the moderate temperature. In addition, it is shown in Tables 7.6 and 7.7 that as increasing content of Silicon (A-0 steels without silicon; A-1 steel with silicon of 1.4 percent; and A-2 steel with silicon of 1.8 percent), toughness of steel will be improved.

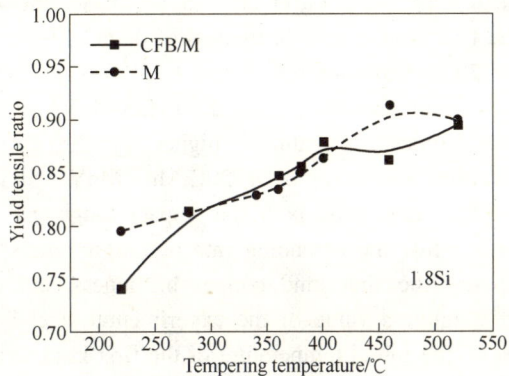

Figure 7.11　Effect of tempering temperature and microstructure on yield-tensile ratio of experimental steel

Table 7.6　Fracture toughness of A-1 steel

Structure	Fracture toughness	280℃ Tempering	350℃ Tempering
M	K_{IC} /MPa・m$^{1/2}$	104.2	93.7
CFB/M	K_Q /MPa・m$^{1/2}$	103	117.5
	K_{max} /MPa・m$^{1/2}$	170	179

Table 7.7　Fracture toughness of A-2 steel

Structure	Fracture toughness	280℃ Tempering	350℃ Tempering
M	K_{IC} /MPa・m$^{1/2}$	—	98
CFB/M	K_Q /MPa・m$^{1/2}$	112	123
	K_{max} /MPa・m$^{1/2}$	150	188.5

7.3.1　Effect of CFB/M duplex phase microstructure on the initial temperature of temper embrittleness the first kind

After being tempered at the temperature range of 250～400℃, the most of hardened steels appear as martensite brittleness, that is, the impact toughness A_K and the fracture toughness K_{IC} decrease. The alloying element Si pushes the temper brittleness of the ultra-high strength medium carbon and low alloy steel from the low temperature to the relatively high temperature, so that the temperature range of the low temperature temper is enlarged and the low temperature temper resistance is enhanced. For instance, 2.2%Si not only can increase the initial temperature of the first kind temper embrittlement of 0.4C-3.44Ni-0.82Mn from 205℃ to 315℃, but also can ensure the steel with relatively high hardness. After the temper at 205~315℃, the softening rate of steel drops. Research by Qiu (Fu et al,1988) and etc. shows that the initial temperature of the first kind temper brittleness of 0.36C-1.91Si-1.88Mn- 0.02Mo steel increases to 320℃. However, research of Li (1982) and etc, on strength and toughness of low carbon martensite steel 20CrMnSiMoVA and 20SiMn2MoVA suggests that if the temper temperature is higher than 200℃, as the rise of the tempering temperature, the strength of 20CrMnSiMoVA and 20SiMn2MoVA decreases, and at the same time both the impact toughness and the fracture toughness decrease, while the extending rate of fatigue crack da/dN increases. Though Si postpones the first kind temper brittleness and consequently the minimum impact toughness value of the experimental steel is the temperature range of 400~500℃, the initial temperature of the first kind temper brittleness is not enhanced. 20CrMnSiMoVA and 20SiMn2MoVA contain higher strength and toughness after being tempered at 200℃. The experiment in the project showed that the initial temperature of temper brittleness of CFB/M duplex phase steel containing 1.4~2.5 percent of Si is higher than 360℃ (shown in Figure 7.12). It can be seen that the first kind tempering embrittlement occurs at relatively higher temperature is a character of the CFB/M duplex phase steel.

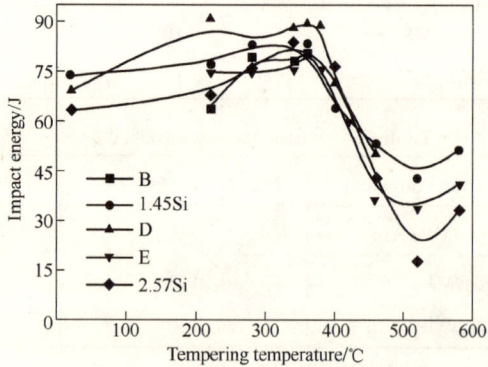

Figure 7.12   Effect of tempering temperature on impact toughness of low carbide CFB/M duplex phase steel

What's the reason to cause the phenomenon? Whether referring to effect of duplex phase microstructure or the retained austenite in carbide free bainite? It can be known the reason from Figure 7.13 that ordinary B/M duplex phase microstructure does not enhance the initial temperature of the first kind temper brittleness. Present authors treat with the experimental steel 1.45Si and 1.86 Si to be CFB/M duplex phase structure and single martenste structure. The effect of temper temperature and microstructure on the strength and toughness is shown in Figure 7.13. Compared with martensite, CFB/M structure can increase the initial temperature for the appearance of the first kind of temper brittleness. No matter the experimental steel contains 1.4%Si or 1.86%Si, the initial temperature of the first kind temper brittleness increases from 280℃ to 360℃. The effects of temper temperature and microstructure on the strength and the toughness of Si-free experimental steel are showed in Figure 7.13. It can be seen that the reason of the rise of initial temperature of the first kind temper brittleness is not the duplex phase microstructure itself, but is the CFB/M duplex phase microstructure, which is maybe related to the retained austenite of CFB/M duplex phase structure.

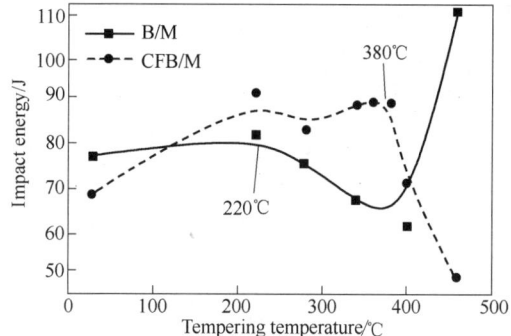

Figure 7.13 Effect of tempering temperature and structure on impact toughness of steel

Compared with Figures 7.14 and 7.15, an interesting experimental phenomenon can be found. After lower tempering, the impact toughness of the steel containing Si and the air-cooled CFB/M duplex phase microstructure is less than that of the quenched martensite microstructure. The superiority of the air-cooled CFB/M duplex phase microstructure shows off only when the temper temperature is higher than 280℃. However, the impact toughness of Si-free steel with B/M duplex phase microstructure is always higher than that of the quenched martensite microstructure no matter that the low temperature temper is conducted. Tomita (1983) holds the opinion that during the course of microstructure transformation, the lower bainite early formed splits the former austenite grain, consequently the size of martensite formed refined. When the crack passes through the large angle phase boundary between the bainite plate and the martensite lath and through the martensite domain interface, the direction changes, the crack propagation work increases, a part of strain energy is consumed and the stress concentration in the

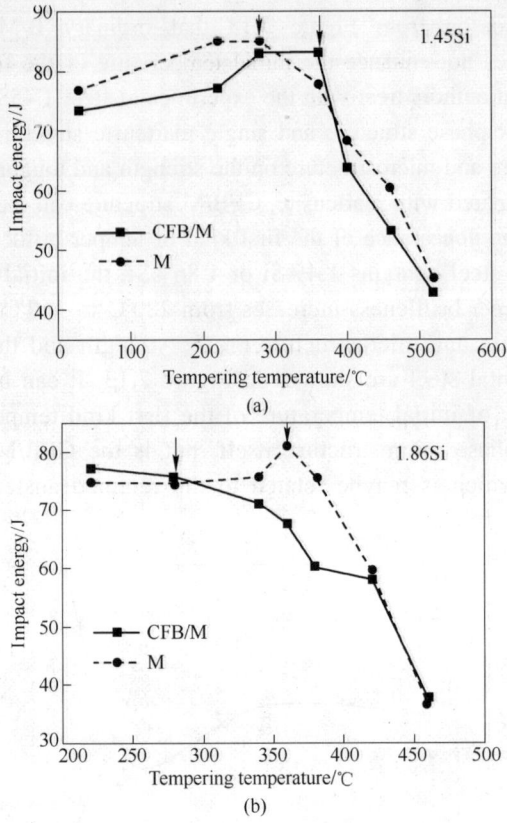

Figure 7.14 Effect of tempering temperature and microstructure on strength and toughness of experimental steel

(a) Containing 1.45Si steel, CFB/M duplex phase microstructure generated in air cooling condition; and martensitic structure generated in oil quenching condition;
(b) Containing 1.86Si steel, CFB/M duplex phase microstructure generated in air cooling condition; and martensitic structure generated in water quenching condition

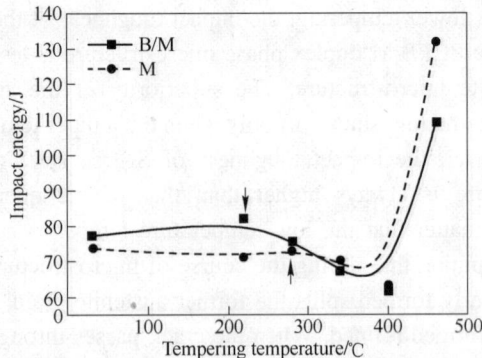

Figure 7.15 Effect of tempering temperature and microstructure on impact toughness of experimental steel without addition of silicon

top end of the crack is delayed. Therefore, the toughness of steel is improved. The optical metallography shows that CFB, which is formed at relatively low temperature, is similar with the lower bainite in shape and distribution, see Figure 7.16. The CFB also splits the former austenite grain, but the superiority of CFB/M duplex phase microstructure appears only after the temper at the relatively high temperature. The reason is that the CFB/M duplex phase microstructure is different from the lower bainite/martensite duplex phase microstructure, for the carbide in the bainite plate is replaced by the filmy retained austenite between the plates and in the plates.

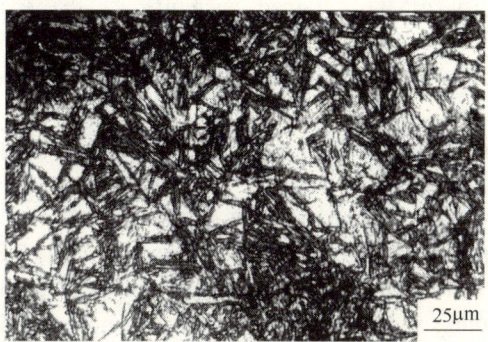

Figure 7.16　Appearance of carbide-free bainite
(Heat treatment process: austenitized at 890℃, isothermal treating at 350℃ for 3min, water cooling(the volume percentage of retained austenite is 8.2 percent))

Effect of retained austenite on the impact toughness of steel is related to its stability. Generally, the stability of the retained austenite is expressed by the thermal stability and the mechanical stability.

Thermal stability of retained austenite refers to the degree of still retained austenite at different temper temperature, which can be expressed by the relative quantity of the still retained austenite after the temper at different temperature.

Namely

$$TS = A_T / A_0 \times 10\% \tag{7.3}$$

where, TS is thermal stability of retained austenite; A_T is quantity of still retained austenite after temper; A_0 is quantity of retained austenite before temper.

Mechanical stability of retained austenite refers to the degree of deformation inducing phase change under load, which can be expressed by the relative percentage of still retained austenite after certain amount of plastic deformation at room temperature.

Namely:

$$MS = A_M / A_T \times 100\% \tag{7.4}$$

where, MS is mechanical stability of retained austenite; A_M is quantity of still retained austenite after the plastic deformation at room temperature; A_T is percentage of the retained austenite after temper at corresponding temperature.

High strength steel with tensile strength over 1500MPa shall be put into application after temper at certain temperature. Therefore, the relative high thermal stability is the prerequisite of the toughening action of retained austenite. Zhang(1993) shows that the primary reason of the improvement of steel impact toughness is that the strain of retained austenite induces the phase transformation of martensite and the energy absorption. The lower the mechanical stability of the retained austenite is, the easier the induced deformation of martensite is. Whether the retained austenite with high mechanical stability improves the impact toughness or the retained austenite with lower mechanical stability deforms to induce the deformation of martensite and correspondingly improve the impact toughness shall be confirmed by further research.

The effect of the tempering temperature on the content of retained austenite in the air-cooled impact sample of A-2 steel is shown in Table 7.8. The effect of 3 percent plastic deformation on the content of retained austenite in A-2 steel through the air-cooling and tempering at different temperature is shown in Table 7.9. When the tempering temperature increases from 220℃ to 380℃, the quantity of retained austenite decreases from 7.2 to 5.9 percent. Therefore, the retained austenite appears the relatively high thermal stability (seen in Figure 7.17). It can also be known from Figure 7.17 that the mechanical stability of the retained austenite takes on the change pattern of rising at first and falling later with the rise of temper temperature. After the temper at 280~360℃, the retained austenite processes the relatively high mechanical stability. The retained austenite in ·carbide-free bainite belongs to the high carbon retained austenite. When the mechanical stability is weak, the high carbon martensite induced in the course of deformation can otherwise generates the second crack in the top end of the crack. The powerful example is that there are certain numbers of second cracks in the fracture of the impact sample tempered at the low temperature. The reason is that after being tempered at the low temperature, the mechanical stability of the retained austenite is lower, and the high carbon martensite transformed from unstable retained austenite in deformation induces the second cracks. Therefore, the superiority of the duplex phase microstructure cannot display, but on the contrary, the impact toughness of the steel falls. When the temper temperature is higher than 280℃, the mechanical stability of the retained austenite is enhanced and it is hard to generate the high carbon martensite during deformation, so no crack is induced and the superiority of the duplex phase structure can show off. Therefore, the CFB/M duplex phase microstructure steel has higher impact toughness than the martensite microstructure steel. After tempering above 380℃, the thermal stability and the mechanical stability drop sharply, so the retained austenite with poor stability.

Table 7.8 Variation of retained austenite content (Ar) with tempering temperature in the air-cooled impact sample of steel A-2

Tempering temperature / ℃	Not tempering	220	280	340	360	380	420
Ar / %		7.2	7.3	7.3	6.0	5.9	4.4

Table 7.9 Effect of 3 percent plastic deformation on retained austenite content of air-cooled A-2 steel after being tempered at different temperature (Ar)

Tempering temperature / ℃		Not tempering	220	280	340	360	380
Ar / %	Before deformation	8.7	8.2	7.2	7.3	5.9	5.8
	after deformation	—		5.2	6.9	7.2	5.9	3.8

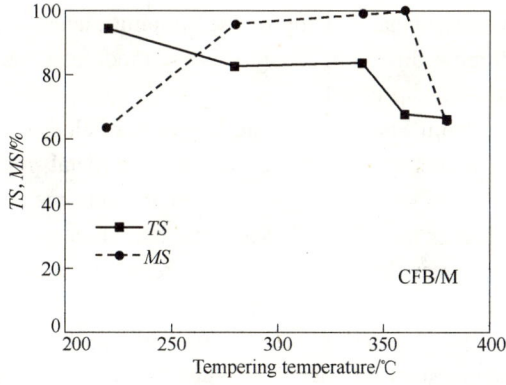

Figure 7.17 Thermal stability (*TS*) and mechanical stability of retained austenite in air-cooled A-2 steel

7.3.2 Effect of CFB/M duplex phase microstructure on yield-tensile ratio of steel

The effect of microstructure and tempering temperature on yield-tensile ratio of steel A is shown in Figure 7.11. Experiment shows no matter how Si content changes at the range of 1.3~2.5 percent at the temper temperature below 340℃, the yield strength of the air-cooled CFB/M duplex phase microstructure is lower than that of the martensite and the yield-tensile ratio is much lower. While tempering temperature is higher than a certain one, not only its tensile strength and its yield-tensile strength of CFB/M duplex phase microstructure are higher than those of the tempered martensite, but also the yield-tensile ratio is higher than that of the tempered martensite. After the temper at the medium temperature, the CFB/M duplex phase microstructure has the higher yield strength than the tempered martensite. The primary analysis of this issue suggests that the yield strength represents the stress to broaden the slip band caused by the occurrence of dislocation multiplication and movement in the macroscale range for polycrystal. Therefore, for the polycrystal as steel, the yield strength depends on the resistance to the movement of dislocation in the crystal. For the pure metal monocrystal, the resistances are the lattice resistance, the resistance of the interaction of dislocations, the resistance of the interaction between dislocation and other crystal defect, and there exists the retained inner stress in the quenching state steel.

As for the lattice resistance, when the dislocation moves in the perfect crystal, a force is needed to overcome the lattice resistance as so to make the dislocation cross the potential barrier. This kind of force is generally called P-N force, expressed as τ_p.

$$\tau_p = \frac{2G}{1-v}\exp\left(-\frac{2\pi a}{b(1-v)}\right) \tag{7.5}$$

where, a is to the interplanar spacing of the slipping plane, b is the interatomic distance in the slipping direction, G and v is the modulus of elasticity for shear and the poisson's ratio, respectively.

It can be known from Formula 7.5, the bigger the value of a, the smaller the value of b and τ_P. Therefore, the face-centered cubic metal possesses lower P-N force, so as lower yield stress. The body-centered cubic metal possesses higher P-N force, so as higher yield stress. When the hardened steel contains retained austenite, the yield stress drops. The more the retained austenite amount is, the lower the yield stress is.

With regard to the interaction of the dislocations (friction resistance), the dislocation movement shall interact with other dislocation in the crystal, so the resistance generated by the dislocations shall be overcome. The resistance includes two aspects: the one is the resistance generated when the dislocation passes through the vicinity of other dislocation (the effect of the dislocation field); the other is the resistance when the dislocation intersects the dislocation of the slip plane. In the crystal with relatively high dislocation density, the two resistances of the interaction between the dislocations are all related to the dislocation density and increase as the rise of the dislocation density. Refer to Formula 7.6 for details.

$$\tau_i = \tau_p + A\rho^{\frac{1}{2}} \tag{7.6}$$

where, τ_i refers to friction resistance, ρ refers to the dislocation density, A refers to the coefficient related to the crystal nature, dislocation structure and the distribution.

The dislocation density is higher than that of CFB for the martensite no tempered or lower tempered. Therefore, the friction resistance of the martensite is higher than that of the CFB/M.

Dislocation cannot slip over grain boundary or sub-boundary. The dislocation will obstruct and accumulate in the vicinity of the boundary. Consequently, the dislocation source in the adjacent grains is activated to make the slip transmit into the adjacent grains. In many metals, the slip crosses through the boundary and transmits the required shear stress τ_B. Refer to Formula *Hall-Petch* for the relation between the shear stress τ_B and grain size as the following:

$$\tau_B = \tau_i + k_y d^{-\frac{1}{2}} \tag{7.7}$$

where, d refers to the grain size and k_y to the constant.

Formula 7.7 indicates that within certain range of grain size, the less the grain size, the larger the value of τ_B. CFB splits the former austenite, so as τ_B becomes large.

Below certain tempering temperature, although the τ_B of CFB/M microstructure is higher than that of martensite, the yield strength of CFB/M is lower, because τ_i and τ_P of CFB/M are lower than those of the martensite. With the rise of the tempering temperature, the retained austenite in the CFB decomposes and decreases. In addition, the relatively high temper resistance CFB results in the increase of τ_i and τ_P of the CFB. Therefore, the yield strength of the CFB/M is higher than that of martensite over certain tempering temperature range, so that the yield-tensile ratio of the CFB/M tempered at the medium temperature is higher than that of the tempered martensite.

In a word, toughness of low carbon CFB/M steel is improved, owing to carbide free bainite. The designed low carbon CFB/M steel has the following properties:

1. Low carbon CFB/M microstructure can postpone the initial temperature of tempering brittleness of the first kind, so that the steel could be tempered at higher temperature and its yield-tensile ratio could be increased.
2. Low carbon CFB/M microstructure has higher tempering resistance, so it can have higher strength and toughness after tempering at intermediate temperature.

7.4 Susceptibility to Hydrogen Embrittlement for CFB/M Duplex Phase High Strength Steel

A large amount of research indicates that the mechanism of stress corrosion and delayed fracture of high or ultrahigh strength steel is the hydrogen-induced fracture. Therefore, the research on susceptibility to hydrogen embrittlement for high strength steel can be regarded as the reference to judge properties of the delayed fracture of the high strength steel. The steels with about 1500MPa high strength, widely used at present, are very susceptible to hydrogen embrittlement. There are some factors as strength (Bandyopadhyay et al, 1983; Sandz, 1972; Peterson et al,1967), alloy element (Steigerwald et al,1971) and microstructure (Watkinson et al,1973) to influence the susceptibility. Among these factors, effect of microstructure is the most significant. Hence, research on the effect of microstructure is being paid more attention. With regard to microstructure effect, some scientists have done much work (Lee et al,2007;Tsay et al,2006;Lunarska et al,2004). It was indicated that different microstructures have different effects on hydrogen embrittlement. In general, the susceptibility to hydrogen embrittlement for martensite is higher than that for pearlite and austenite. Embrittlement indexes of different microstructure become smaller, which is in turn martensite-troostite –sorbite–ferrite+ pearlite (Xu et al,1981). In a general way, the susceptibility to hydrogen embrittlement for metastable microstructure is higher than stable microstructure. The fine grain can improve not only strength and toughness of steels, but also the resistance of environment-induced hydrogen embrittlement. It was shown above mentioned that bainite / martensite duplex phase high strength steel can obviously improve strength and general roughness of materials (Liu et al,2003;Huang et al,1997), which is a novel steel with unique microstructure and up-and-coming market. Hydrogen embrittlement and delayed fracture of this kind of steel are shown as follows.

7.4.1   *Effect of hydrogen content on susceptibility to hydrogen embrittlement for CFB/M duplex phase high strength steel*

Select steel "B" with major alloying elements of C, Si, Mn, Cr, Mo and Ni, for examing the effect of hydrogen content on susceptibility to hydrogen embrittlement. Heat treatment process of B steel is austenizing at the temperature of 900℃ for 10 minutes and then air cooling; tempering at the temperature of 280℃ for two hours and then air-cooling. The original microstructure of B steel is shown in Figure 7.18, which shows that through air cooling treatment, its microstructure is: carbide free bainite(CFB)+ martensite(M)+ retained austenite(γ_R). Earlier formed CFB partitions the grain of the original austenite(A), which makes the subsequently obtained martensite sheaf size smaller.

Excessive hydrogen in the steel is inducted through cathodic charging hydrogen method, which charging hydrogen electrolyte involves 5% of H_2SO_4+0.25g/L As_2O_3. As_2O_3 effect is to resist hydrogen ion synthesizing hydrogen molecule during electrolysis charging hydrogen. Before charging hydrogen, perchloric acid

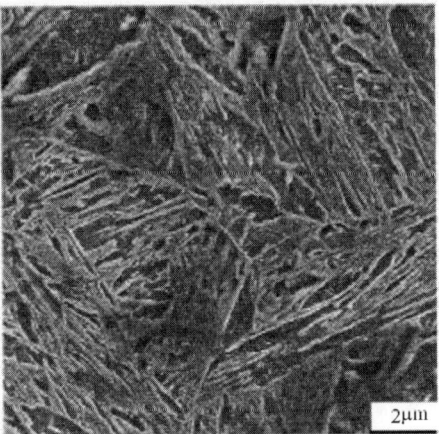

Figure 7.18 The original microstructure of steel B

and glacial acetic acid solution with 1 to 9 was used to activate the surface. Adopt Model RH-404 Hydrogen Determinator, made by USA LECO Company, to determine hydrogen content in the original steel B and the sample charged hydrogen for four hours with current density of 1mA/cm², which is 1.65 ppm and 3.49 ppm, respectively. It shows that charging hydrogen can induct excessive hydrogen into materials. To study the effect of hydrogen content on susceptibility to hydrogen embrittlement for CFB/M steel, charging hydrogen to steel B process was with 0.2 mA/cm², 1mA/cm² and 10mA/cm² of current density for 4h. After natural aging for half an hour, tensile test of the charging hydrogen sample was conducted at room temperature. Tensile specimen with diameter of 6.4mm is standard short gauge length, and tensile speed is 0.5mm/min. Use embrittlement index E_H to evaluate susceptibility to hydrogen embrittlement.

$$E_H = (\psi_0 - \psi_H) / \psi_0 \% \tag{7.8}$$

where, ψ_0 and ψ_H are the percentage reduction of area before and after hydrogen charging respectively. The larger the E_H is, the higher susceptibility to hydrogen material. Relationships among R_m, Z, E_H and hydrogen current density "i" are drawn in Figure 7.19, which shows that the bigger of current density to charge hydrogen is, the lower R_m, σ_f and Z are, but the higher the E_H is.

Just like what's indicated in many literatures (Gu,1985;Wang,1979) that charging hydrogen has less effect on material yield strength, but it can lower the plastic properties. Literature (Zhang et al,1988) shows the relations between levels of steel reduction of area and hydrogen content for the different strength steels, which are shown in Figure 7.20. Namely, the higher the material strength is, the bigger the linear slope between reduction of area and hydrogen content is. It shows

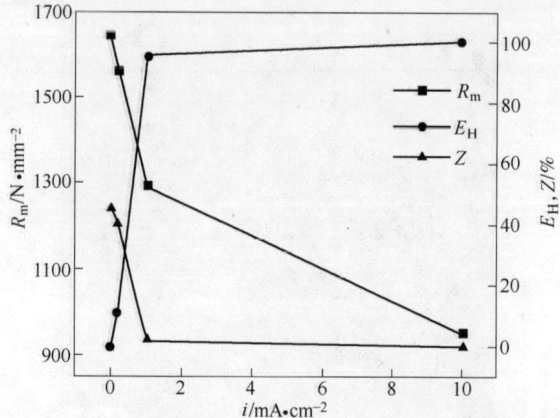

Figure 7.19   Effect of current density of charging hydrogen on the properties of steel B

the higher susceptibility to hydrogen embrittlement. At the same time, experimental result of B steel is also shown in the Figure 7.20, which means when tensile strength of B steel is $R_m=1640MPa$, the value of the linear slope is even smaller than one of 1500MPa high strength steel. Therefore, it shows that resistance to hydrogen embrittlement for steel B is higher than that of high strength steels in the literature (Zhang et al,1988). In addition, it also shows that in the condition of same hydrogen content, Z of steel B is far higher than that of the same strength steels, so it is related to microstructure of steel B different from that of the high strength steels.

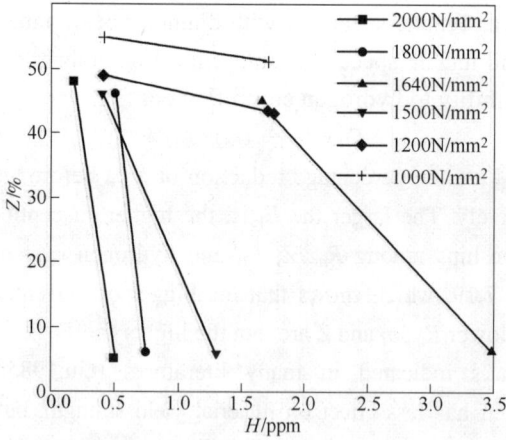

Figure 7.20   Relation between reduction of area and hydrogen content (Kang,Guo,1992)

Figure 7.21 is tensile fracture SEM photograph of steel B specimen with charging hydrogen in current density of $i=0.2mA/cm^2$. Figure 7.21(a) is to its overall perspectives. Because of charging hydrogen, although overaging after charging hydrogen, the hydrogen concentration near surface is still bigger; shear lip in fracture is incomplete and one fish eye crack is on the upper on the left, arisen from hydrogen; Figure 7.21(b) is to its appearance, and Figure 7.21(c) is the enlarged photograph of the fish eye crack, indicating the exact quasicleavage appcarance. Energy spectral analysis shows that the elements at the initial area may be Mn, S, Al and O, which may be compound inclusion of MnS and Al_2O_3(seen in Figure 7.21(d)). Research showed (Chattoraj et al,1995) MnS inclusion was a hydrogen trap with more hydrogen concentration around, possessed the smaller value of critical stress to generate crack initiation, crack was firstly generated nearby.

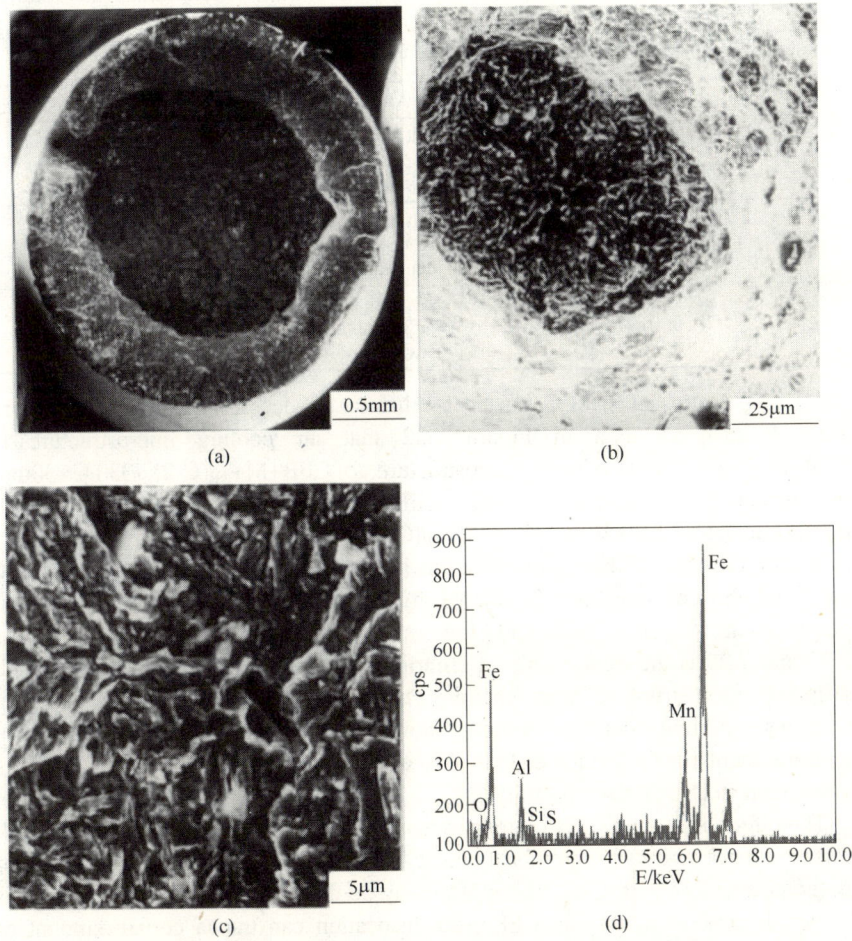

Figure 7.21 Tensile fracture SEM photograph and inclusion energy spectrum of steel B specimen charging hydrogen at current density of 0.2 mA/cm^2
(a) Overall fracture surface; (b) Appearance of fish eye; (c) Enlarged fish eye;
(d) Energy spectrum of the inclusion on the fish eye

7.4.2   *Effect of heat treatment process on susceptibility to hydrogen embrittlement for CFB/M duplex phase high strength steel*

Steel C with major alloying elements of C, Si, Mn and Cr is used to research the effect of heat treatment process on susceptibility to hydrogen embrittlement for CFB/M duplex phase high strength steel. Namely, four types of heat treatment process are adopted to generate the different CFB/M duplex phase microstructures, and the technical parameters are as shown in Table 7.10.

Table 7.10   Heat treatment process of steel C
(Metallographic microstructures of C steel, based on different heat treatment)

Serial number	Heating temperature /℃	Holding time /min	Cooling technology	Tempering temperature /℃	Tempering time /h
C-1	900	10	Air cooling	280	2
C-2	900	10	Salt bath at 330℃ for 3 minutes, then water cooling	280	2
C-3	900	10	Salt bath at 330℃ for 30 minutes, then water cooling	280	2
C-4	900	10	Salt bath at 400℃ for 3 minutes, then water cooling	280	2

Microstructures of steel C treated by different processes are shown in Figure 7.22. It can be seen in Figure 7.22 that air cooling microstructure is CFB+M+γ_R(C-1),330℃×3min microstructure to CFB+M+γ_R(C-2), 330℃×30min microstructure to CFB+γ_R(C-3), which CFB is relatively coarser, and 400℃×3min microstructure is upper bainite(B_U)+M+γ_R(C-4), which B_U is also relatively coarser.

As for the steel C based on different heat treatment processes, with 0.2 and 1mA/cm^2 current densities to charge hydrogen, respectively, the mechanical properties are shown in Table 7.11.

Figure 7.23 is the relationship of embrittlement indexes of the specimens with different microstructure after charging hydrogen with the different charging hydrogen current density, which shows that susceptibility to hydrogen embrittlement for C-2 is lower than that of C-3 and C-4. In addition, C steel is lower than steel B in susceptibility.

The effect of B_U and CFB on the susceptibility could be seen from Figure 7.24. The resistance to hydrogen embrittlement of CFB is obviously higher than that of B_U(compared C-2 with C-4). The reason may be that as for C-2 specimen, there is higher dislocation density in CFB, and dislocation can trap a certain amount of hydrogen so as hydrogen more evenly distributes in materials. It plays a good role in lowering susceptibility to hydrogen embrittlement. However, there is coarser microstructure for the B_U in C-4 specimen, and the consecutively generated coarser martensite structure. The coarser microstructure can easily result in brittle fracture.

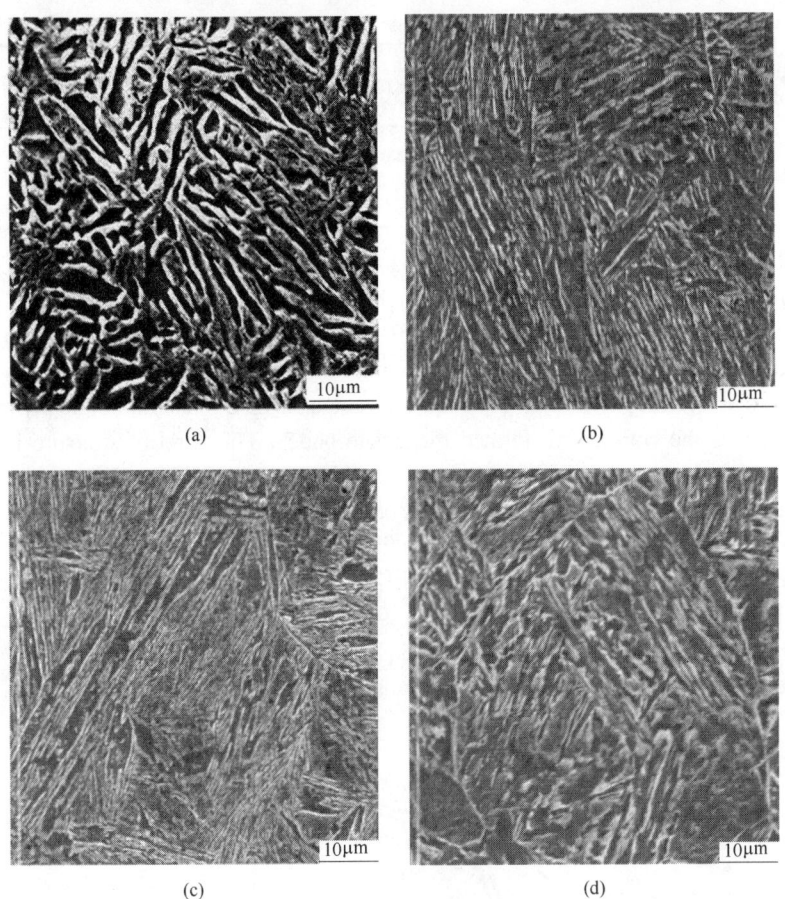

(a)   (b)

(c)   (d)

Figure 7.22   Microstructures of steel C treated by different processes
(a) Air cooling microstructure (CFB+M+γ_R); (b) 330℃×3min Microstructure (CFB+M+γ_R);(c) 330℃×30min
Microstructure (CFB+γ_R); (d) 400℃×3min Microstructure (B$_U$+M+γ_R)

Table 7.11   Susceptibility to hydrogen embrittlement for steels with different microstructures

Serial number	i/mA · cm^{-2}	R_m/ N ·mm^{-2}	σ_f/ N · mm^{-2}	A_5/%	Z/ %	E_H/%	γ_R /%
	0	1510	3580	14.5	57.8	0	
C-1	0.2	1480	1850	8.0	21.4	63	6
	1	950	950	0	0	100	
	0	1510	3860	14.4	60.9	0	
C-2	0.2	1490	1890	7.8	21.3	65	7
	1	1060	1060	0	0	100	
	0	1450	3720	14.2	61.1	0	
C-3	0.2	1410	1680	7.5	15.9	74	10
	1	740	740	0	0	100	

| | | | | | | | Table 7.11(continued) |
Serial number	i/mA $\cdot$ cm^{-2}	R_m/ N $\cdot$ mm^{-2}	σ_f/ N $\cdot$mm^{-2}	A_5/%	Z/ %	E_H/%	γ_R /%
	0	1470	3720	15.6	60.5	0	
C-4	0.2	1410	1630	7.1	13.3	78	7
	1	790	790	0	0	100	

The effect of the CFB content could be also shown in Figure 7.23. The resistance to hydrogen embrittlement of steel C-2 is higher than that of C-3, which indicates that there should be appropriate content of CFB. Excessive amount of CFB could result in the decrease of the resistance to hydrogen embrittlement. The reason is that based on isothermal treatment with 330℃×3min, the generated CFB splits the original γ grain and refines the consecutive formed martensite bunch. This kind of structure is not conductive to crack forming and propagation. However, as isothermal time prolongs through isothermal treatment of 330℃×30min, lower bainite content increases and microstructure becomes coarser, susceptibility to hydrogen embrittlement also increases. Based on result of Watkinson(1973), the microstructure with large amount of bainite or complete bainite possessed higher susceptibility to hydrogen embrittlement. The reason is that its bainitic bunch takes on the same direction, so as it is easy for the crack to form and to propagating along bainitic bunch.

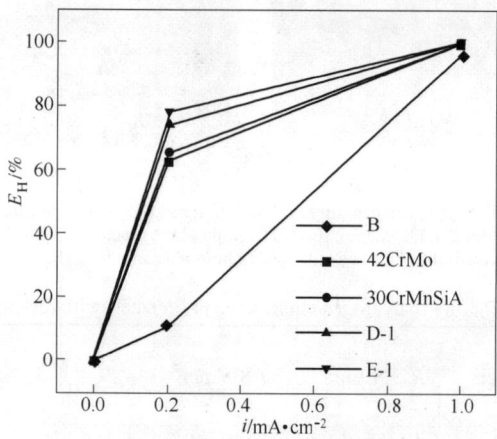

Figure 7.23　Relationships between embrittlement index (E_H) and charging hydrogen current density "i" A: air cooling; C-1: air cooling; C-2: 330℃×3min; C-3: 330℃×30min; C-4: 400℃×3min

Through observation of charging hydrogen fracture of four types of steel C specimens, based on different heat treatment processes, it can compare effects of upper B (B_U), CFB and content of CFB.

7.4.2.1　Effect of B_U and CFB

Figure 7.24 is SEM fracture topography of steel C, based on isothermal treatment with 330℃×3min and 400℃×3min and charging hydrogen with current density of i=0.2mA/cm^2.

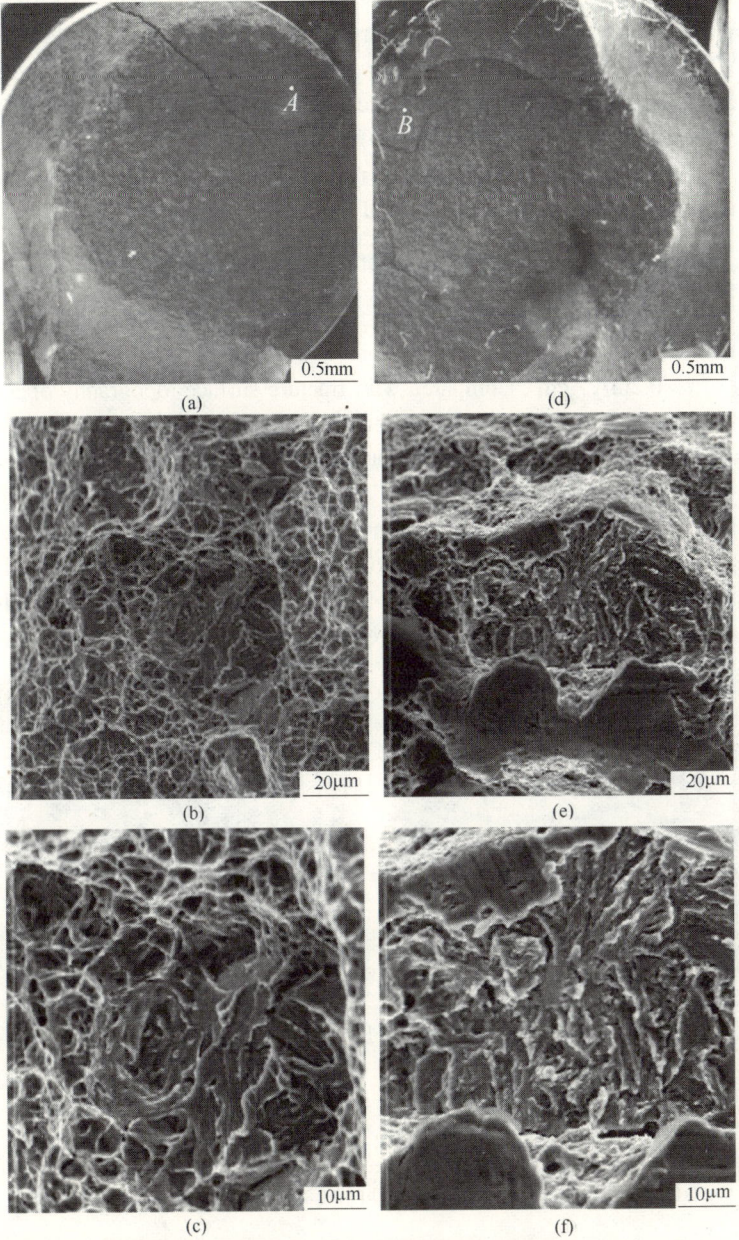

Figure 7.24　SEM fracture topography of steel C, based on charging hydrogen (i=0.2mA/cm^2)
(a) 330℃×3min overall topography; (b) Detail of "A" position in "(a)";
(c) Higher magnification of (b); (d) 400℃×3min overall topography;
(e) Detail of "B" position in (d); (f) Higher magnification of (e)

It is seen from Figure 7.24 that after charging hydrogen, tensile fracture surfaces of B_U and CFB show a certain embrittlement, incomplete shear lip; shear lip proportion of CFB tensile fracture surface is bigger than that of upper one(Figures 7.24 (a) and (d)). After charging hydrogen, fracture surfaces of B_U and CFB in the same distance away from the edge of specimen are all quasi-cleavage fracture. The facet of quasi-cleavage fracture surface of CFB is smaller than that of B_U(Figures 7.24 (b),(c), (e) and (f)), which reason is that higher isothermal temperature of B_U results in coarser microstructure, and embrittlement is more obvious than that of CFB.

7.4.2.2   Effect of CFB quantity on fracture surface topography

Figure 7.25 indicates SEM fracture surface topography of steel C, based on isothermal temperature with 330℃×30min and charging hydrogen with current density of i =0.2mA / cm^2. Compared with fracture surface topography of 330℃× 3min, the fracture surface of C position in the same distance away from the specimen edge is also quasi-cleavage fracture surface. Its facet is larger(shown in Figure 7.25(b)), which reason is that the longer the isothermal temperature time is, the more quantity of bainite, the coarser the size of bainite becomes. It reflects tensile fracture surface, namely, the facet of quasi-cleavage fracture surface is bigger than that based on treatment of 330℃×3min. So its susceptibility to hydrogen embrittlement is more obvious than that treated of 330℃×3min.

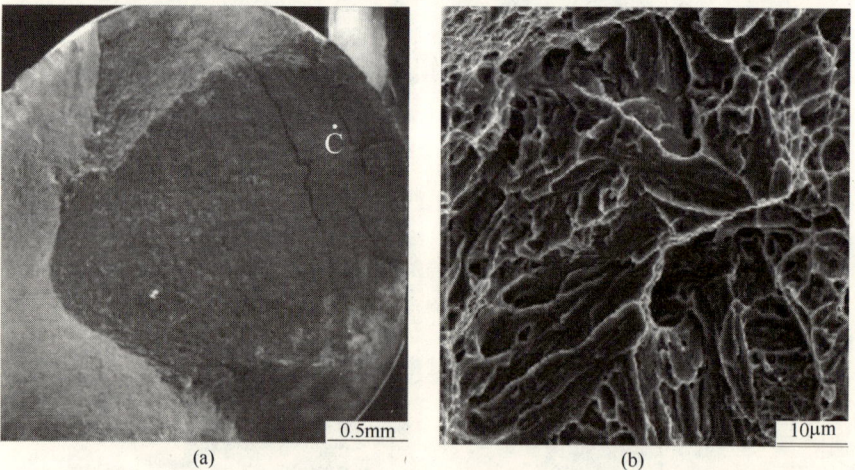

0.5mm	10µm
(a)	(b)

Figure 7.25   SEM fracture topography of C steel, based on charging hydrogen (i=0.2mA/cm^2)
(a) 330℃×30min overall topography; (b) 330℃×30min higher magnification

In a word, compared with high strength steels with the same strength, the susceptibility to hydrogen embrittlement for C-2 is lower than that of C-1. The susceptibility to hydrogen embrittlement for (CFB + M + γ_R) microstructure, transformed based on isothermal temperature with short time, is lower than that of longer time and higher temperature. Hence, further optimizing microstructure of CFB+M+γ_R steel may obviously improve resistance to hydrogen embrittlement.

7.4.3 *Influence of microstructure refinement and retained austenite on susceptibility to hydrogen embrittlement for CFB/M steel*

Research materials are steels with major alloying elements of C, Mn, S and Cr, smelted in the condition of vacuum. Microstructure refinement is based on thermomechanical treatment before austenite phase transformation. The technology is that deformation is based on heating up steel to austenite stabile area(more than Ac_3), and then through air cooling to obtain bainite /martensite duplex phase microstructure. Based on changing Si content in the steel, adjust the retained austenitic quantity of CFB/M steel. High strength 30CrMnSiA steel provided by Fushun Steel Plant and high strength 42CrMo steel provided by Dalian Steel Plant are adopted as the comparison steel. For the details, chemical compositions of all types of steels are shown in Table 7.12.

Table 7.12   Chemical compositions of all types of high strength steels

Materials	Composition/mass%						
	C	Si	Mn	Cr	Mo	S	P
30CrMnSiA	0.33	0.97	0.88	0.90	0.02	0.003	0.012
42CrMo	0.42	0.30	0.60	0.95	0.22	0.01	0.022
D-1	0.23	0.2	2~3	0.75	—	—	—
D-2	0.23	1.74	2~3	0.66	—	—	—
E-1	0.25	1.45	2~3	0.52	—	—	—
E-2	0.23	0.2	2~3	0.75	—	—	—

Heat treatment process is shown in Table 7.13. Hydrogen charging current densities are 0.2 mA/cm^2, 0.5 mA/cm^2, 0.7 mA/cm^2, 0.9 mA/cm^2 and 1mA/cm^2, and the charging time is 4h. After hydrogen charging, the specimen is placed with natural aging for 0.5h, and then conducts the tensile test. According to the classification in Xiao's paper (1990), hydrogen charging condition adopted in the paper belongs to the type of harshness. The tensile test is conducted in the AG-75TA universal electronic testing machine made by Japan Daojin. The tensile strain rate is 0.5 mm/min at the ambient temperature.

Figure 7.26 is the original microstructures of 42CrMo and 30CrMNSiA, those are all tempered troostite, composed of ferrite before generating recrystallization and thin cementite grains, taking on dispersion distribution look. Microstructure of

CFB/M steel is seen in Figure 7.22(a), composed of carbide free bainite, martensite and less retained austenite.

Table 7.13   Heat treatment technological parameters of several kinds of materials

Steels	Austenizing temperature /°C	Holding time /min	Cooling way	Tempering temperature /°C	Retained γ(vol.)/%	Remarks
42CrMo	860	10	Oil cooling	380		
30CrMn-SiA	880	10	Oil cooling	440		
D-1	900	10	Air cooling	280	3	Lower Si CFB/M microstructure
D-2	900	10	Air cooling	280	9	CFB/M microstructure
E-1	900	10	Air cooling	280	6	CFB/M microstructure
E-2	860	18(0.36 strain at 5s^{-1})	Air cooling	280	6	Refined CFB/M microstructure

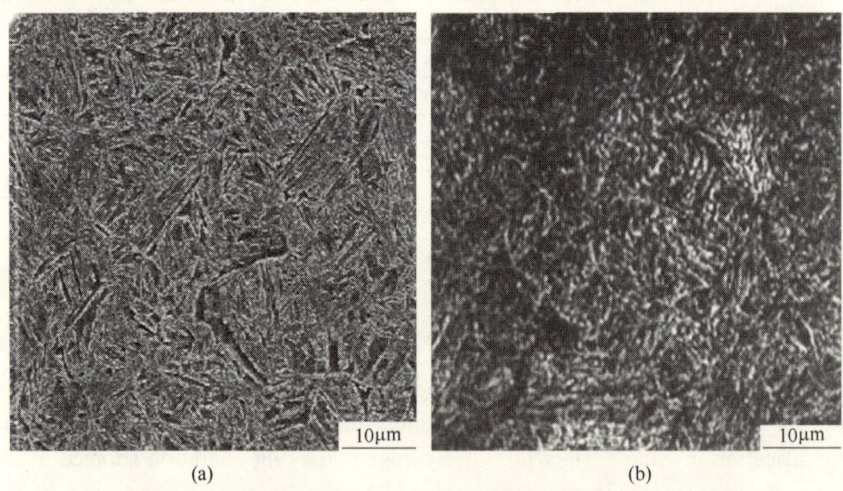

(a)   (b)

Figure 7.26   Original microstructures of 42CrMo and 30CrMnSiA
(a) 30CrMnSiA; (b) 42CrMo

It is seen in Figure 7.27 that compared with CFB/M duplex phase high strength steel; 42CrMo and 30CrMnSiA steels show the higher susceptibility to hydrogen

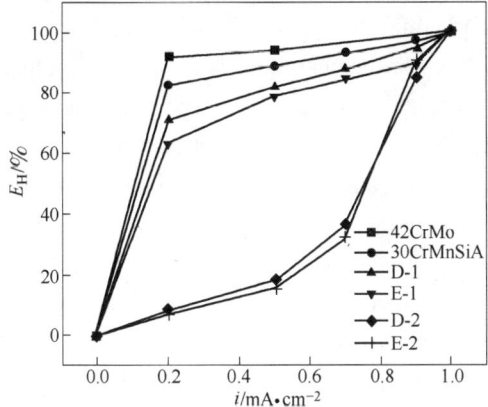

Figure 7.27 Relations between embrittlement index E_H and hydrogen charging current density i of several steels

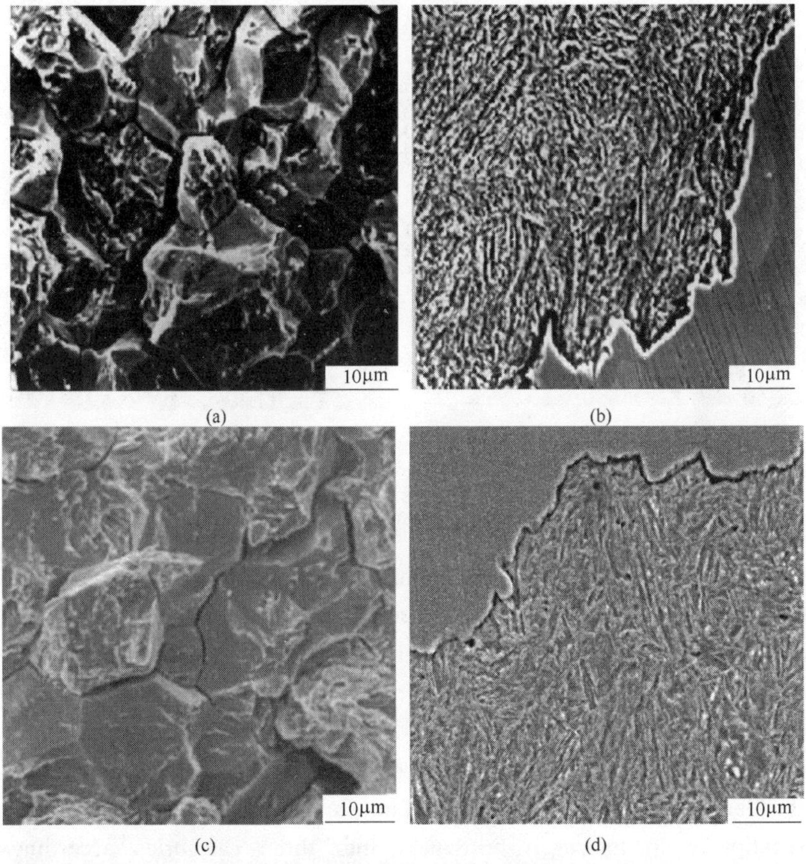

Figure 7.28 SEM fracture surface topographies of two materials charging hydrogen
(a) 42CrMo tensile fracture surface topography ; (b) 42CrMo fracture metallography;
(c) 30CrMnSiA tensile fracture surface topography; (d) 30CrMnSiA fracture metallography

embrittlement after thermal treatment. When i=0.5mA/cm^2, the reduction of area sharply drops and the embrittlement index is far higher than that of CFB/M duplex phase steel. Tension fracture surface of charging hydrogen specimen shows the fracture along grain boundary (Figures 7.28 (a) and (c)); and the fractography indicates the crack propagates along austenite grain boundary after charging hydrogen (Figures 7.28 (b) and (d))

The original microstructures of steel E both without (E-1) and with thermomechanical treatment (E-2) are shown in Figure 7.29, which are all CFB/M duplex phase microstructures with less retained austenite. The amount of retained austenite could be seen in Table 7.13. The size of martensite lath in

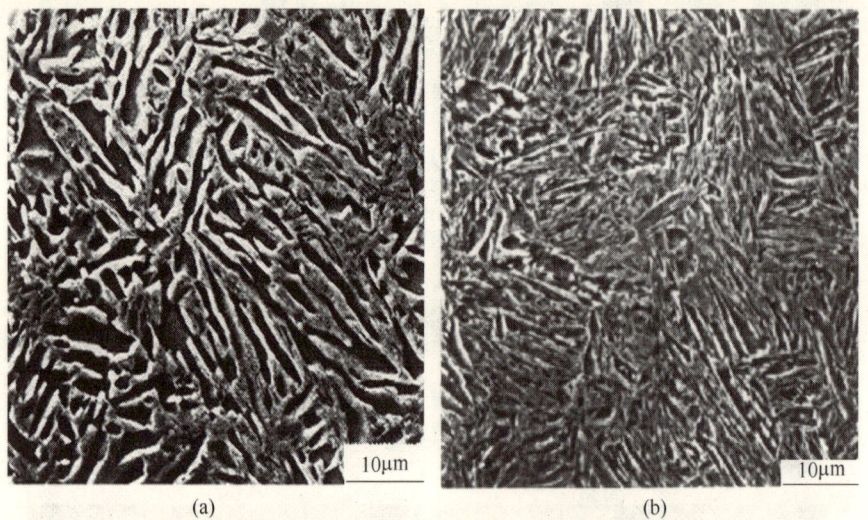

(a)   (b)

Figure 7.29   Original microstructures of two kinds of CFB/M duplex phase high strength steel specimens, based on different heat treatment .
(a) General heat treatment; (b) Thermomechanical treatment

E-2, based on thermomechanical treatment, is reduced up to 5μm in length and 0.6μm in width from the original E-1 average 10.6μm in length and 0.7μm in width, respectively. Figure 7.30 shows the relation between reduction of area (Z) and embrittlement index(E_H)of the specimen with different charging hydrogen current density based on E-1 and E-2 processes. It is shown that for the hydrogen charging E-2 steel, the reduction of area changes slightly, and the embrittlement index is very small. Tan Zhiwen et al (1988) classified the susceptibility to hydrogen brittleness into three categories according to embrittlement index (E_H). He believed that E_H below 25% was safe, E_H over 35% was brittle failure. When charging hydrogen current density is 0.5mA/cm^2, the E_H of the steel E-2 is only 15%. Therefore, it is safe to say that the susceptibility to hydrogen brittleness is not high. However, the steel E-1 shows the relatively high susceptibility to hydrogen brittleness. When $i=0.2\text{mA/cm}^2$, the reduction of area will sharply reduce, the curve will become rather steep, and the embrittlement index will be far bigger than that of the thermomechanical treatment. Hence, the difference is mainly arisen from the factor of microstructure.

Figures 7.31 (a) and (b) are quasi-cleavage fracture surface topographies of specimens, respectively based on general heat treatment and thermomechanical

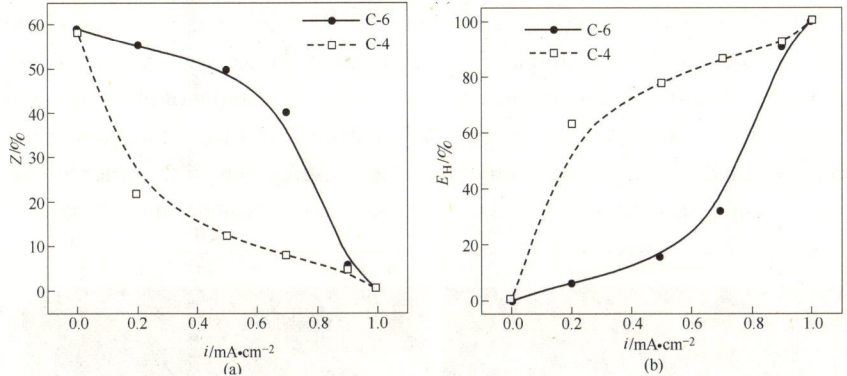

Figure 7.30 Variation of reduction of area and embrittlement index with current density for two kinds of CFB/M duplex phase high strength steel specimens based on different heat treatment
(a) relation between reduction of area Z of the specimen with different charging hydrogen current density "i";
(b) relation between embrittlement index E_H with different charging hydrogen current density "i"

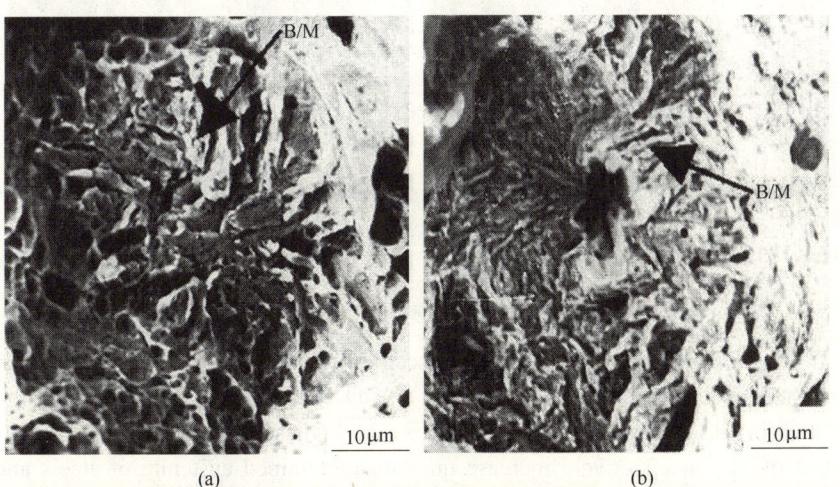

Figure 7.31 Tensile fracture surface topographies of specimens, respectively based on general heat treatment and thermomechanical treatment, charging hydrogen current density of $i=0.2 \text{ mA/cm}^2$
(a) General heat treatment; (b) Thermomechanical treatment

treatment, with current density of i–0.2mA/cm^2 and after charging hydrogen for 4 hours. It could be shown that quasi- cleavage facet on tensile fracture surfaces of specimens, based on general heat treatment, is bigger than that through thermomechanical treatment, namely, it is small, which is likely corresponding to the size of its unit microstructure.

Fracture metallography shows that most of cracks after charging hydrogen propagate along bainitic laths or martensite lath boundary, which is shown in Figure 7.32(a); sometimes also through bainite and martensite, which is shown in Figure 7.32(b). It is in accordance with experimental result of Kikutu(Kikutu et al,1981). After thermomechanical treatment, CFB/M duplex phase microstructure becomes fine, and the unit of quasicleavage fracture surface also becomes small. The fine CFB/M duplex phase microstructure results in disorder of microstructure in orientation, and there is the effect of lower bainite on stress relaxation in the crack top, and cracks change direction when coming across the interface of bainite/ martensite (Fang et al,1988). All these factors consume more energy, so the fracture stress is improved.

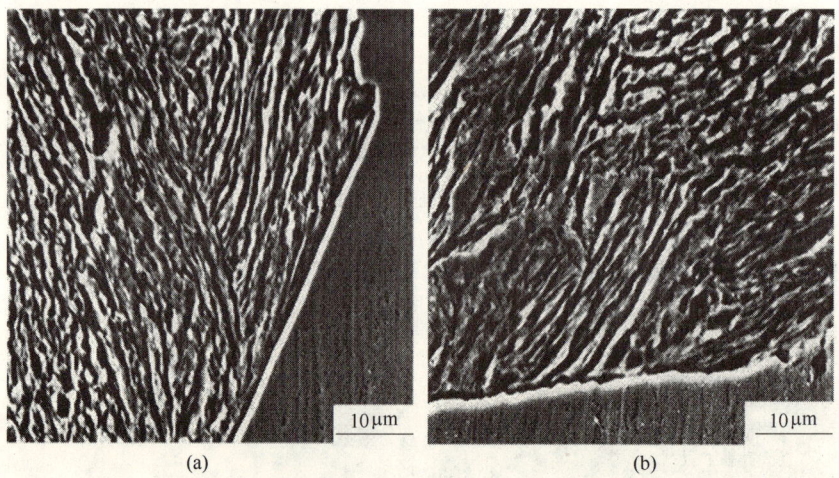

(a)   (b)

Figure 7.32   Tensile fracture metallography of specimen, based on thermomechanical treatment, charging hydrogen with current density of i=0.2mA/cm^2
(a) , (b) Fracture metallographies in different areas

It is seen from Figure 7.27 that the susceptibility to hydrogen embattlement for D-2 steel is far smaller than that of E-1 and D-1. It is arisen from the different content of Si, namely, Si content of D-2 is the biggest, and the smallest of D-1; effect of Si can effectively increase quantity of retained austenite of steels and then improve strength and toughness of steels. Figure 7.33 is TEM bright and dark field images of the retained austenite of D-2 steel, which indicates that in the CFB/M duplex phase steel, the retained austenite is distributed into refinement microstructure in the shape of membrane with higher thermal stability and mechanical stability (Fang et al,2001). It is the reason that susceptibility to hydrogen embattlement for D-2 steel is far lower. On the one hand, high toughness retained austenite resists crack propagation; on the other hand, retained austenite, as hydrogen trap (He et al,1989), can decrease hydrogen diffusion rate and make difficult for hydrogen local enriching. So it obviously improves the resistance to hydrogen embrittlement.

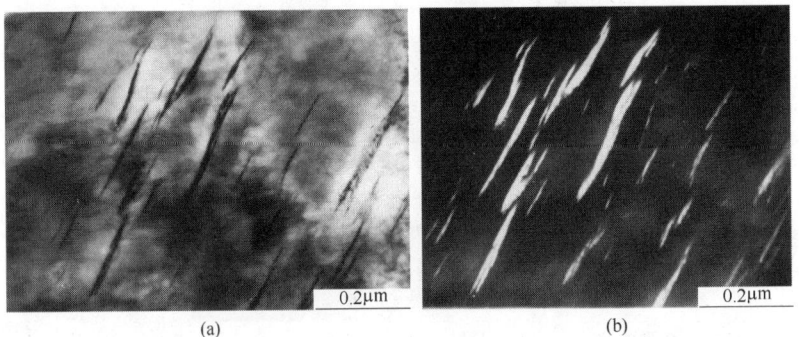

| 0.2μm | 0.2μm |
| (a) | (b) |

Figure 7.33　The filmy retained austenite in D-2 steel
(a) Bright field images of the retained austenite; (b) Dark field image of the retained austenite

7.5　Stress Corrosion of CFB/M Duplex Phase High Strength Steel

7.5.1　*Stress corrosion cracking property of CFB/M duplex phase high strength steel*

Specimens developed from CFB/M duplex phase high strength steel D-2, E-2, E-1 ,D-1 and 30CrMnSiA high strength steel are conducted stress corrosion experiment. Sample loading as for stress corrosion fracture experiment is processed based on two methods. As for D-2, E-2, E-1, D-1 and 30CrMnSiA high strength steels, the specimens are with thickness of B=15mm and improve Model WOL constant displacement, and determine crack threshold K_{ISCC}, which is shown in Figure 7.34. Because E-2 steel was processed through thermomechanical treatment, it is difficult in processing internal thread. Wedge loading method was adopt to determine K_{ISCC} , as shown in Figure 7.35. The experimental procedure is to add a heavy load to generate crack, then to discharge the load and to add a light load, after that to soak in the aqueous solution of 3.5 percent of NaCl and to measure the length of the crack by the reading microscope at the fixed time. If the crack propagation size is smaller than 0.1mm within 24h (da/dt<1×10^{-9}m/s), it can be regarded that the crack stops propagation. The standing time of the specimen in the medium in this experiment is bigger than 300h. The stress corrosion threshold level K_{ISCC} shall be calculated in accordance with the load displacement and the final length of the crack. The formula of K_I is as follows:

$$K_I = \frac{EVF(a/w)}{\sqrt{w}C(a/w)}$$ (7.9)

where, E is the Young's modulus, V is the open displacement, a is the length of the crack, $F(a/w)$ and $C(a/w)$ can be looked up in the Literature (Chu et al,1980).

Figure 7.34   WOL constant displacement stress corrosion specimen for D-2,
E-1, D-1 and 30CrMnSiA steels

Figure 7.35   WOL constant
displacement stress corrosion
specimen for E-2 steel

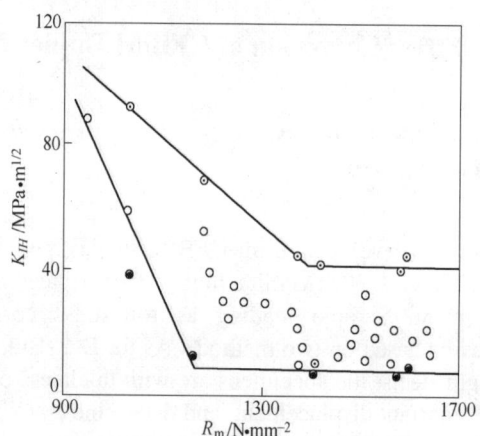

Figure 7.36   Relation between K_{IH} and R_m of some
types of steels

The results of stress corrosion experiment are shown in Table 7.14. It can be known that the K_{ISCC} of the new CFB/M duplex phase high strength steel is higher than that of 30CrMnSiA under the condition of the same strength. The relation between K_{IH} and strength of some alloy steels is shown in Figure 7.36. It can be known when R_m is more than 1500MPa, the maximum of K_{IH} is about

40MPa •m$^{1/2}$. Moreover, the minimum K_{ISCC} of the new CFB/M duplex phase high strength steel shown in Table 7.14 is 40.5MPa • m$^{1/2}$, it will increase with the increase of the number of the retained austenite. When the content of retained austenite is up to 9 percent, the value of K_{ISCC} is 51.5MPa • m$^{1/2}$. When the content of retained austenite is 6 percent after the microstructure refinement, the value of K_{ISCC} is 53.8MPa • m$^{1/2}$. These experiment results indicate that the anti-delayed fracture property of the new CFB/M duplex phase steel is greatly improved. Moreover, it might be further improved through optimizing the amount and configuration of retained austenite, as well as refining microstructure.

Table 7.14 Mechanical properties of materials

Experimental conditions	Materials	$R_m / N • mm^{-2}$	K_{ISCC} / MPa • m$^{1/2}$	$da/dt(10^{-5})$/mm • s^{-1}
3.5%NaCl 25±1℃	30CrMnSiA	1510	36.2	3.2
	D-1	1530	40.5	2.7
	D-2	1520	51.5	1.2
	E-1	1510	45.6	1.8
	E-2	1520	53.8	1

Relation curve between crack propagation rate and stress intensity factor are shown in the Figure 7.37. It was pointed out in the reference (Zhou et al,1998;Chu,1988) that the curve was divided into three parts. The second part is not related to the value of K_I but only depends on diffusion rate of hydrogen towards crack tip. Its value only shows capabilities of materials to resist hydrogen induced crack propagation. The lower the value of $(da / dt)_{II}$ is, the lower the susceptibility to the hydrogen delayed fracture for the materials. It is seen from

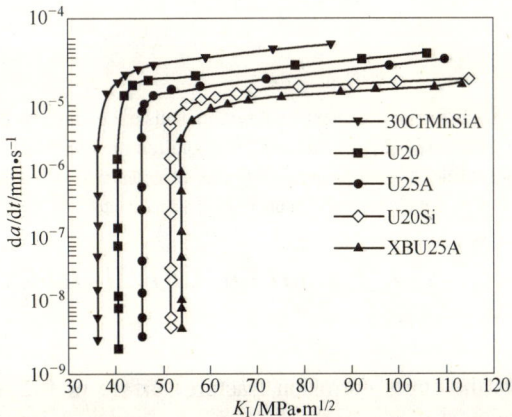

Figure 7.37 Relation curve between da/dt and K_I of several materials

Figure 7.37 that $(da/dt)_{II}$ value of steel(E-2)based on thermomechanical treatment and steel(D-2) with more Si content so as more filmy retained austenite are lower than that of steel(E-1) and (D-1) with lower Si content, and more lower than that of traditional high strength 30CrMnSiA steel. Hence, it is drawn conclusion that capabilities of resistance to hydrogen induced fracture is ranked to be E-2, D-2, E-1, D-1 and 30CrMnSiA from strong to weak, which is in accordance with rank of susceptibility to hydrogen embrittlement.

It can be seen from Figure 7.38 that effect of the quantity of retained austenite on K_{ISCC} and da/dt indicates the linear relationship within the experimental scope. That is, if the quantity of retained austenite increases 1%, the stress corrosion threshold (K_{ISCC}) will increase about 4.5%, and crack propagation rate $(da/dt)_{II}$ will decrease about 20%. The above analysis indicates that the retained austenite can improve the properties of the delayed fracture obviously. It can be found in Table 7.14 and Figure 7.37 that the microstructure refinement is rather effective in improving the properties of the delayed fracture. The microstructure refinement adopted in the paper for the rise of K_{ISCC} and the reduction of $(da/dt)_{II}$ is even more effective than the function by increasing 3% retained austenite. Hence, the effect of microstructure refinement on the steel with more retained austenite will be made further exploration.

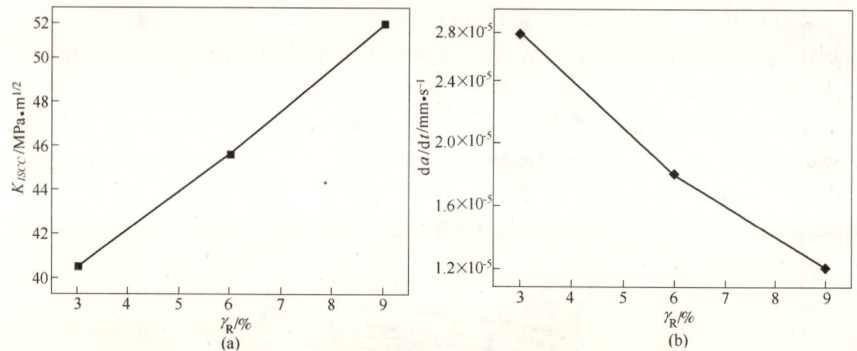

Figure 7.38   Effect of the quantity of retained austenite on stress corrosion threshold (K_{ISCC}) and crack propagation rate(da/dt)

(a) Relation between K_{ISCC} and the quantity of retained austenite; (b) Relation between da/dt and the quantity of retained austenite

7.5.2   *Stress corrosion fracture of CFB/M duplex phase high strength steel*

Figure 7.39 shows the stress corrosion fracture surface of E-2 and 30CrMnSiA steels. Figure 7.39(a) is E-2 crack propagation area; Figures 7.39(b) and (c) are E-2 crack arrest area; it is shown that stress corrosion fracture surface of new CFB/M

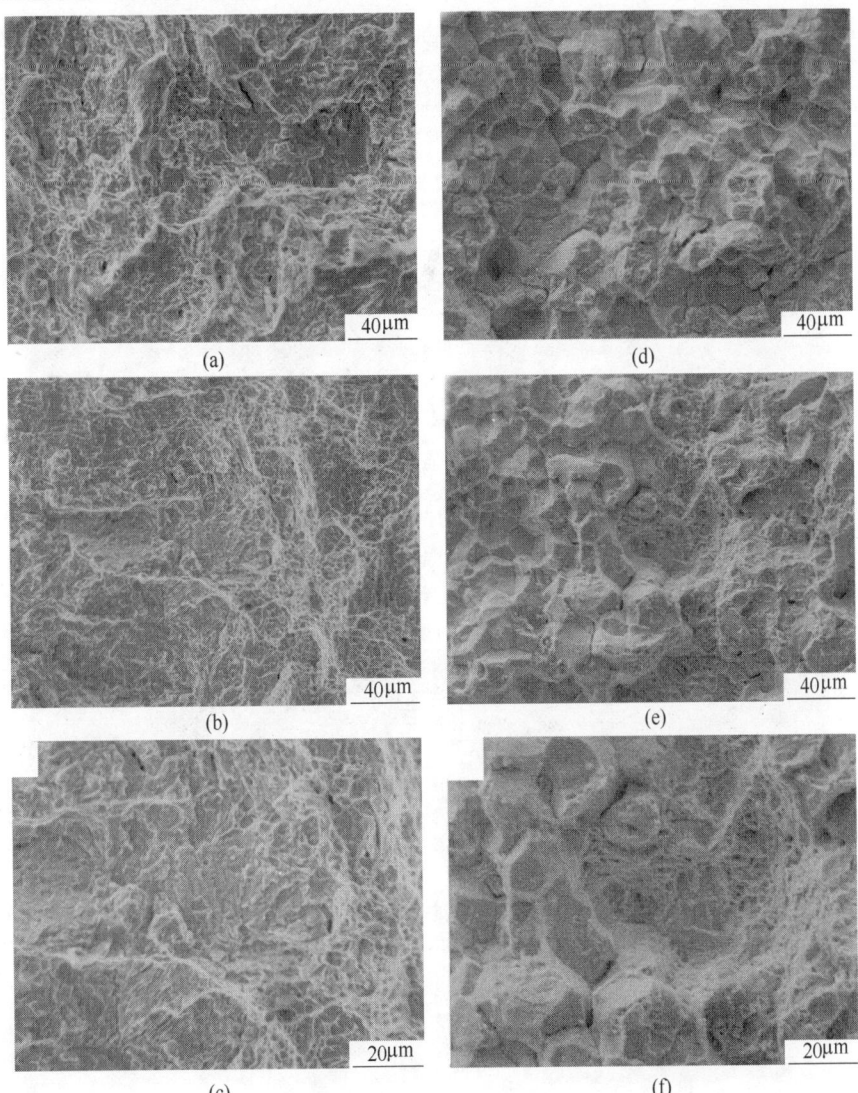

Figure 7.39   Stress corrosion fracture surface of E-2 and 30CrMnSiA steels
(a) E-2 steel crack propagation area (K=71.7MPa • m$^{1/2}$); (b) E-2 steel crack arrest area (K=53.8MPa • m$^{1/2}$);
(c) The enlarged E-2 steel crack arrest area   (K=53.8MPa • m$^{1/2}$); (d) 30CrMnSiA steel crack propagation
area (K=38.7MPa • m$^{1/2}$); (e) 30CrMnSiA steel crack arrest area (K=36.2MPa • m$^{1/2}$); (f) The Enlarged
30CrMnSiA steel crack propagation area (K=36.2MPa • m$^{1/2}$)

duplex phase high strength steel takes on mixing fracture, composed of
transgranular fracture and toughness tearing range, and secondary crack. It is
shown through observation in Figure 7.39 that stress corrosion fracture of several
CFB/M duplex phases high strength steels all takes on a look of transgranular

fracture. Figure 7.39(d) is crack propagation area of 30CrMnSiA steel, Figures 7.39(e) and (f) are crack arrest area of 30CrMnSiA steel. It is shown that stress corrosion fracture of 30CrMnSiA steel is all intergranular fracture in crack propagation and arrest areas.

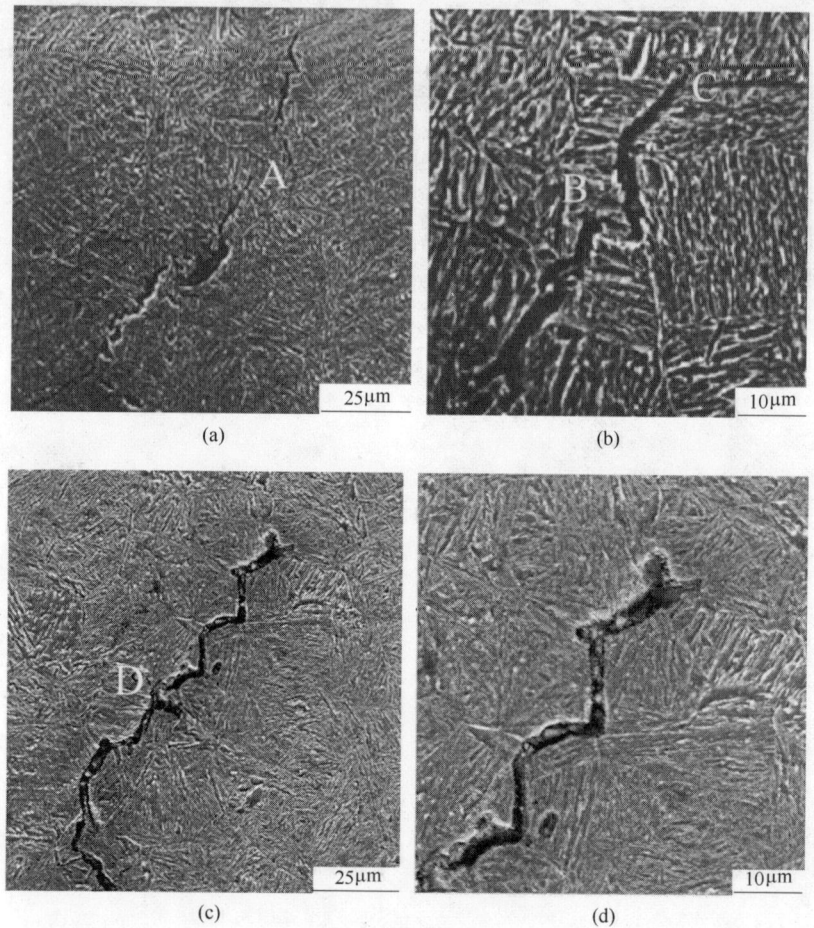

(a)

(b)

(c)

(d)

Figure 7.40   Crack propagation path of CFB/M duplex phase high strength steel and 30CrMnSiA SCC specimen
(a) Overall crack propagation topography of CFB/M duplex phase high strength steel; (b) Higher magnification topography of crack tip in a; (c) Overall crack propagation topography of 30CrMnSiA steel; (d) High multiply topography of crack tip in (c)

Figure 7.40 shows the crack propagation path of the researched CFB/M duplex phase high strength steel and 30CrMnSiA SCC steel specimen. It is seen that discontinuous propagation is in front of the crack tip in two kinds of specimens ("A" in Figure 7.40(a) and "D" in Figure 7.40(c)), which sufficiently indicates stress corrosion mechanism is hydrogen induced cracking. It is shown in Figures

7.40(a)and(b)that cracks can propagate along lath boundary of bainite/martensite, as well as also through lath. But crack usually stops propagation after through the interface of bainite /martensite, which is seen in the "B" and "C" in Figure 7.40(b). The reason is that it may consume more energy through the interface of bainite /martensite. It is shown in Figures 7.40 (c) and (d) that the cracks of 30CrMnSiA steel propagate along grain boundary.

Microstructure of 30CrMnSiA steel is mainly composed of lath martensite and less retained austenite. After tempered at 300℃, the martensite is decomposed into ferrite and cementite. For the microstructure after tempered at 440℃ the laboratory, precipitation cementites, increase ,concentrate and grow up. These interfaces between the carbide and matrix can trap a mass of hydrogen. When hydrogen content increases to a level higher than critical hydrogen content value, crack will initiate and propagate. Congregated hydrogen in grain boundary decreases the strength of grain boundary and obviously induces grain boundary embrittlement. Intergranular fracture could appear. The resistance to stress corrosion should be lower.

The primary reason possessing the excellent resistance to stress corrosion for CFB/M duplex phase high strength steel is the improvement of the microstructure. Composition design of this kind of steel ensures to obtain CFB/M duplex phase microstructure after the air-cooling process. A certain amount of Si in steel restrains the precipitate of carbide, substituted by the filmy retained austenite with relatively high mechanical, thermal and chemical stability. Under the conditions of electrochemical charging hydrogen and loading external stress, no transformation from austenite to martensite occurs. Therefore, the microstructural factors resulting in hydrogen inducing fracture in 30CrMnSiA are avoided. In addition, because the retained austenite has good toughness, it can prevent crack propagation. Filmy retained austenite could also be act as hydrogen trapping (He et al,1989), it can decrease the diffused hydrogen concentration, to make it difficult for hydrogen to enrich in crack tip. Moreover, through thermomechanical treatment, CFB/M microstructure could be refined. Lath boundary area increased. Lath boundary is also a kind of hydrogen trap (Parvathavarthini et al,2001), so the resistance to stress corrosion improves more.

7.6   Hydrogen in CFB/M Duplex Phase High Strength Steel

If hydrogen concentration in local area is higher than the critical level through diffusion, crack will initiate (Pressouyre,1980). The crack would propagate under the external force until fracture happens. Therefore, it is very important to study the diffusion behavior of hydrogen in steel. Because the electrochemical permeation technique invented by Devanathan and Stachurski (1962) is simple, highly effective and flexible, the technique becomes a useful tool in the research of behavior of hydrogen in metal alloy. Generally speaking, crystal defects such as dislocation, grain boundary, inclusion interface and carbide interface co-exist in metals or alloys. The defects are called as hydrogen trap (Prossouyre et al,1978;Gu,1985;Pound et al,2003), which lower diffusion coefficient of hydrogen to the different degree (Brass et al,2004;Asahi et al,2003).

Through research on hydrogen diffusion and trap of CFB/M duplex phase high strength steel, the mechanism of the delayed fracture could be understood more clear.

7.6.1 Measure hydrogen diffusion coefficient using double electrolysis cell

The samples are developed from CFB/M duplex phase high strength steels(D-2, E-2, E-1 and D-1), 30CrMnSiA and 42CrMo steel. The compositions and details of thermal treatment processes of the steels are as above-mentioned.

Figure 7.41 is a schematic diagram of double-electrolysis cell and permeation mechanism. And the hydrogen permeation experiment is conducted in self-made double electrolysis cell; the process of electrochemical permeation is shown in Figure 7.42. The experimental temperatures are 298K，323K，353K respectively. Before experiment, every specimen should be polished until the thickness is 0.88mm. A thin layer of Ni was coated in the anode aside of specimen. The electroplating solution was a kind of aqueous solution, containing $0.2g/LNiSO_4+0.01g/LNaCl+0.03g/L H_3BO_3+0.07g/LNa_2SO_4+0.06g/L MgSO_4$, and the current density was 10mA/cm^2 and was electroplated for 4h.

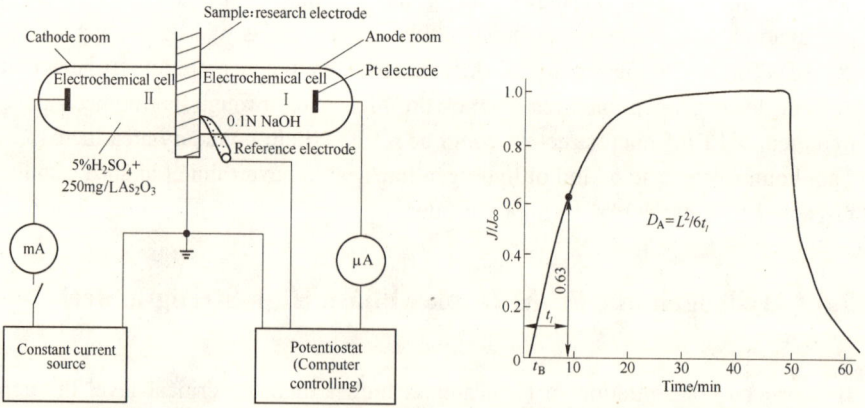

Figure 7.41　Schematic diagram of double-electrolysis cell and permeation mechanism

The electrolyte in anode aside was the 0.1N sodium hydroxide solution (The impurity was eliminated though low current electrolysis in the electrolytic bath before experiment), the electrolyte in cathode aside was the solution of 0.05N H_2SO_4+0.25g/LAs$_2O_3$, and the constant current was 10mA/cm^2. The constant electrical potential in the anode aside was +100mV (compared with saturated Hg/HgO electrode) and platinum sheet acted as the assistant pole. The constant electrical potential added in anode aside can eliminate the retained hydrogen in the specimen. At the same time, a retained current existed in the measurement circuit decreases gradually to the stable value ($i<2\mu A/cm^2$). And then the constant current was added in the cathode aside, hydrogen permeation began, which was shown in Figure 7.42.

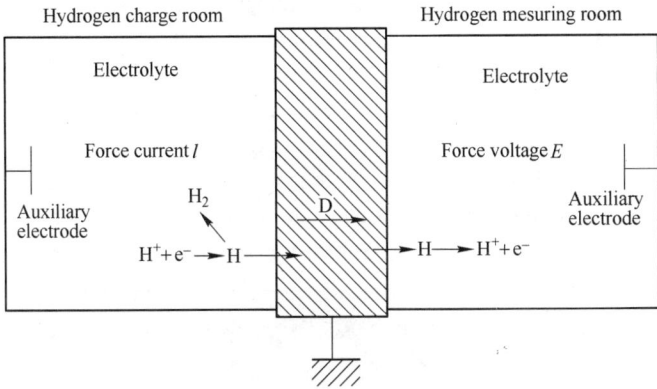

Figure 7.42 Mechanism of double- electrolysis cell

Constant voltage source was used to automatically record the relation curve of "J" (permeation current density) with "t" (time), which was controlled by a computer mounted PS168 electrochemical permeation software. Take the point J/J_∞=0.63 on the curve as the lag time t_l and calculate the apparent diffusion coefficient in accordance with Formula 7.10.

$$D_A=L^2/6t_l \tag{7.10}$$

where, D_A is the apparent diffusion coefficient, L is the thickness of the sample,and t_l is the lag time.

Utilize saturation permeation current density (J_∞) and the apparent diffusion coefficient (D_A, based on formula 7.11 and 7.12, calculate penetration value (p) and the solid solubility (S):

$$p=J_\infty L/ZF \tag{7.11}$$
$$p=D_A S \tag{7.12}$$

where, Z is the reacted electric charge , and F is Faraday constant.

It is shown in Figure 7.43 that electrochemical permeation curve of several materials at 298K. It is seen from Figure 7.43 that penetration time for D-2, E-2, E-1and D-1 to reach the same J/J_∞ value is bigger than that of 30CrMnSiA and 42CrMo steels. Based on formulas 7.10, 7.11 and 7.12, the calculated values of D_A, p and S are listed in Table 7.15. At the same time, it is seen from Table 7.15

that the fined CFB/M duplex phase steel and CFB/M duplex phase steel with filmy retained austenite have the lowest diffusion coefficient and the highest solid solubility S. "S" is related to trap hydrogen performance in the materials. The higher trap density in materials is, the larger trap binding energy is, the performance to arrest hydrogen will be stronger, S will be bigger. It is seen in Table 7.15 that the effect of the microstructure on diffusion coefficient is higher than that of the solid solubility.

It is shown in Table 7.16 that value of diffusion coefficient of hydrogen in several materials at 298K, 323K and 353K. Figure 7.44 shows the relation between apparent diffusion coefficient and reciprocal of absolute temperature for several materials. It is seen that curves of four kinds of CFB/M steels are all steeper than that of 30CrMnSiA and 42CrMo. Based on method of least square, relation between the calculated hydrogen apparent diffusion coefficient and temperature of several materials, as well as hydrogen diffusion activation energy, are shown in Table 7.17. It can be seen that hydrogen diffusion activation energy of CFB/M steels is bigger than that of 30CrMnSiA and 42CrMo steel. So it shows more powerful hydrogen trapping effect for CFB/M steels.

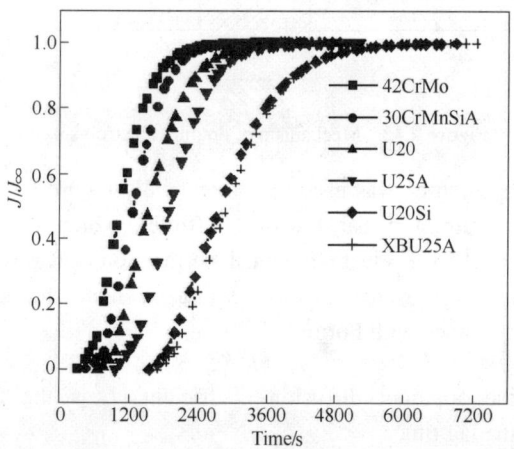

Figure 7.43　Relation between penetration current and time of several steels at 298K

Table 7.15　Hydrogen diffusion coefficient of several materials

Materials	L/cm	J_∞/μA $\cdot$ cm^{-2}	p/mol $\cdot$ (cm $\cdot$ s)$^{-1}$	D_A/cm^2 $\cdot$ s^{-1}	S/mol $\cdot$ cm^{-3}
42CrMo	0.08	48.09	3.99×10^{-11}	0.781×10^{-6}	5.11×10^{-5}
30CrMnSiA	0.08	46.18	3.83×10^{-11}	0.710×10^{-6}	5.39×10^{-5}
D-1	0.08	43.31	3.59×10^{-11}	0.613×10^{-6}	5.86×10^{-5}
D-2	0.08	36.62	3.04×10^{-11}	0.348×10^{-6}	8.74×10^{-5}
E-1	0.08	39.49	3.27×10^{-11}	0.423×10^{-6}	7.73×10^{-5}
E-2	0.08	35.99	2.98×10^{-11}	0.335×10^{-6}	8.90×10^{-5}

Table 7.16　Diffusion coefficient of hydrogen of several materials at different temperatures

Materials	$D_A /cm^2 \cdot s^{-1}$		
	Temperature / K		
	298	323	353
42CrMo	0.781×10^{-6}	1.33×10^{-6}	2.29×10^{-6}
30CrMnSiA	0.710×10^{-6}	1.28×10^{-6}	2.26×10^{-6}
D-1	0.613×10^{-6}	1.17×10^{-6}	2.17×10^{-6}
D-2	0.348×10^{-6}	0.821×10^{-6}	1.89×10^{-6}
E-1	0.423×10^{-6}	0.942×10^{-6}	2.09×10^{-6}
E-2	0.335×10^{-6}	0.810×10^{-6}	1.81×10^{-6}

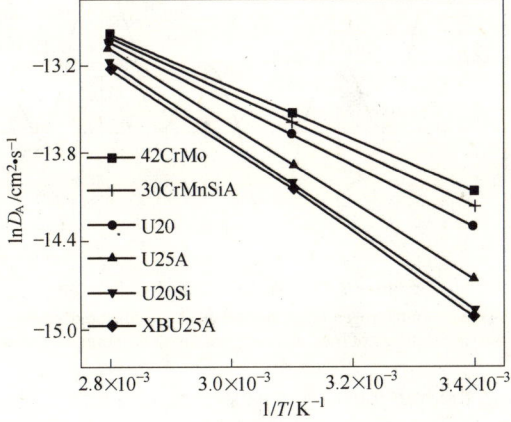

Figure 7.44　Relation between apparent diffusion coefficient and absolute
temperature reciprocal of several materials

Table 7.17　Expression of apparent diffusion coefficient of several materials

Materials	$D_A/cm^2 \cdot s^{-1}$	Activation energy of diffusion / kJ $\cdot$ mol^{-1}
42CrMo	$D_A = 1.963 \times 10^{-4} exp(-13.39/RT)$	13.39
30CrMnSiA	$D_A = 2.972 \times 10^{-4} exp(-14.64/RT)$	14.64
D-1	$D_A = 4.560 \times 10^{-4} exp(-16.03/RT)$	16.03
D-2	$D_A = 5.057 \times 10^{-3} exp(-23.42/RT)$	23.42
E-1	$D_A = 3.653 \times 10^{-3} exp(-22.17/RT)$	22.17
E-2	$D_A = 8.362 \times 10^{-3} exp(-24.85/RT)$	24.85

7.6.2   *Hydrogen trap in CFB/M duplex phase high strength steel*

McNabb and Foster(1963) indicated the relation between apparent diffusion coefficient (D_A) and lattice diffusion coefficient (D_L) below 400°C , as the Formula 7.13:

$$D_L = D_A (1+\alpha) \tag{7.13}$$

In the formula, $\alpha=N k / p$, N is trap density, k and p are the captive rate of trap and the escape rate of trap, respectively. Based on equation 7.13, trap parameter can be calculated out.

Figure 7.45 shows the model of trap location.

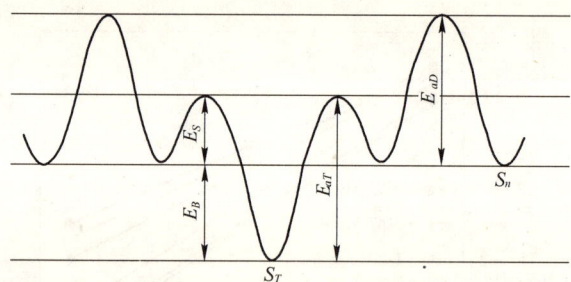

Figure 7.45   Model of trap location

E_{aD}: diffusion activation energy of hydrogen in normal lattice; E_S: saddle point energy; E_B: binding energy of trap; E_{aT}: activation energy of trap; S_T: trap location of; S_n: normal location of lattice

If energy level in the trap location is as shown in Figure 7.45, the captive rate k and the escape rate p of hydrogen trap can be expressed as the following formulas:

$$k=v_0\exp(E_s/RT) \tag{7.14}$$

$$p=v_1\exp(-(E_s+E_B)/RT) \tag{7.15}$$

If the vibration frequency v_0 is equal to v_1, the trap parameter can be expressed as the following formula:

$$\alpha =Nk/p=N\exp(E_B/RT) \tag{7.16}$$

After calculating α at the temperature of from above formula 7.13, suppose α varies with temperature and E_B doesn't vary with the temperature, the trap binding energy E_B will be expressed in the following formula (Choo et al,1982):

$$\alpha_{T_2} / \alpha_{T_1} = \exp(E_B / R(T_2^{-1} -T_1^{-1})) \tag{7.17}$$

Where, α_{T_2}, α_{T_1} are the trap parameters of the same specimens at different temperatures of T_1 and T_2. To obtain α, D_L must be given, which is expressed in formula (7.18); α value is calculated as shown in Table 7.18.

$$D_L =7.23\times10^{-4}\exp(-5.69/RT) \tag{7.18}$$

Table 7.18 Apparent trap parameters of several materials at the different temperatures

Materials	Temperature / K		
	298	323	353
42CrMo	92.1	64.3	44.4
30CrMnSiA	101.4	66.9	45.0
D-1	117.6	73.3	46.9
D-2	207.9	104.8	54.0
E-1	170.9	91.3	48.8
E-2	216.0	106.3	56.5

Trap density(N_T) is calculated out by Formula 7.19 (Zakroczymski,1999); In the formula, S is solid solubility .

$$\frac{D_L}{D_A} = 1 + \frac{3N_T}{S} \tag{7.19}$$

According to formulas 7.16 and 7.19, the average trap binding energy(E_B)and the average trap density(N_T) of E-2, D-2, E-1, D-1, 30CrMnSiA and 42CrMo steels are listed in Table 7.19.

Table 7.19 Average trap binding energy(EB)and trap density(NT)of several high strength steels

Materials	42CrMo	30CrMnSiA	D-1	D-2	E-1	E-2
E_B / kJ $\cdot$ mol^{-1}	11.60	12.92	14.62	21.44	19.93	21.32
N_T/cm^3	0.94×10^{21}	1.1×10^{21}	1.4×10^{21}	3.6×10^{21}	2.7×10^{21}	3.9×10^{21}

It is obvious that the trap binding energy of CFB/M high strength steel is higher than that of 30CrMnSiA and 42CrMo, and the trap effect is stronger than that of 30CrMnSiA and 42CrMo. The N_T values of D-2 and E-2 are about 3~4 times that of 30CrMnSi and 42CrMo. To sum up, the refined CFB/M high strength steel and CFB/M steel with more filmy retained austenite possess not only a strong function of trap effect, but also a large amount of traps.

Because there are many hydrogen traps in material, it is impossible to measure the one specific trap effect from one kind of material. However, effect of a certain trap can be obtained from difference of two kinds of material with distinct trap density in the average trap parameter (α), but other traps in the two kinds of materials are identical. The trap difference can be obtained from formula 7.20.

$$D_L / D_{A1} - D_L / D_{A2} = \Delta\alpha_i = \Delta N_{iki} / p_i = N_i \exp(E_{Bi} / RT) \tag{7.20}$$

where, D_{A1} and D_{A2} are apparent diffusion coefficients of material 1 and material 2, respectively. Material 1 and material 2 have different amount of trap (i). ΔN_i is the difference in amount of the trap density between two kinds of materials. Suppose the trap density won't vary with the temperature in the selected temperature range, trap parameter difference $\Delta\alpha_i$ of the same type of trap (i) of the different material can be obtained from formulas 7.16 and 7.20. And then the value of $\Delta\alpha_i$ is used to calculate the binding energy of this kind of trap. See formula 7.21 for details.

$$\Delta\alpha_{iT_2} / \Delta\alpha_{iT_1} = \exp(E_B/R(T_2^{-1} - T_1^{-1})) \tag{7.21}$$

Predecessors have done researches on hydrogen traps, such as grain boundary and dislocation. There are two main kinds of hydrogen traps in CFB/M duplex phase high strength steel, lath boundary and filmy retained austenite, the study about them is as follows.

7.6.2.1   Bainitic/martensite lath boundary

Take two kinds of materials, namely, unrefined CFB/M steel (E-1) and CFB/M steel (E-2) thermomechanical treated, according to the results measured by the electrochemical permeation system, $\Delta\alpha_i$ can be calculated at different temperatures, as shown in Table 7.20. Then the biding energy E_B=28kJ/mol of lath boundary of CFB/M can be calculated from formula 7.21.

Table 7.20   Trap parameter difference between E-2 and E-1 ($\Delta\alpha_i$)

Temperature / K	$\Delta\alpha_i$
298	45.15
323	15.0
353	7.70

7.6.2.2   Retained austenite

Take CFB/M steels with high silicon (D-2) and low silicon content (D-1) to study trapping effect of retained austenite. There is more filmy retained austenite as hydrogen trap in the D-2 steel, and is less in the D-1. Therefore, the difference in hydrogen traps between them is the difference in quantity of retained austenite. According to the former calculation method, $\Delta\alpha_i$ of the two kinds of materials at different temperatures can be obtained, as shown in Table 7.21.

Table 7.21   Trap parameter difference between D-2 and D-1 ($\Delta\alpha_i$)

Temperature / K	$\Delta\alpha_i$
298	90.3
323	31.5
353	7.10

Trap binding energy of the filmy retained austenite can be obtained from formula 7.20 as E_B=40kJ/mol. The value is bigger than the binding energy of dislocation (19.2kJ/mol), cavity (27.6kJ/mol) (Choo et al,1982) and grain boundaries (20.5kJ/mol) with hydrogen (Lee et al,1986). Therefore, the trap effect of the retained austenite is higher than that of dislocation, cavity and grain boundary.

Interaction between hydrogen and metal is based on hydrogen entry into metal. In normal conditions, hydrogen is entry into metal through a series of processes, including physical adsorption, chemical adsorption, dissolution and diffusion through the metal surface, but not in the form of molecule. The processes of hydrogen entry into metal can be shown in Figure 7.46 (Zhou et al,1998) in details. Firstly, hydrogen molecule in gas phase is in collision with metal surface through irregular thermal motion. Because atomic coordination number in metal surface is different from the internal metal, which results in mutual polarization each other and products attraction force. As a result, partial hydrogen molecule enriches in the metal surface, called physical adsorption, which is shown in the first process in Figure 7.46.

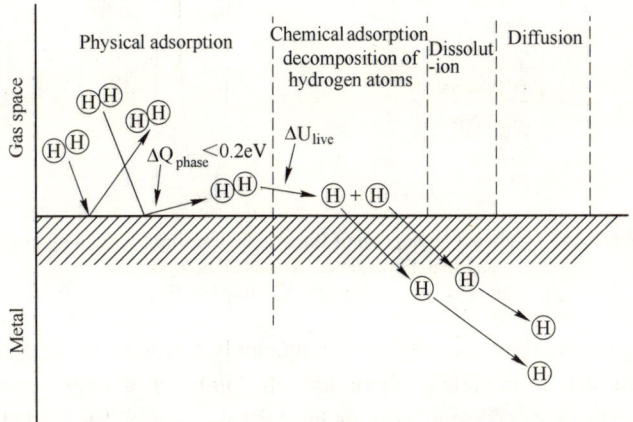

Figure 7.46 Schematic diagram of processes of hydrogen entry into metal

Under the action of activation energy, hydrogen molecule, based on physical absorption, is split up into atoms of hydrogen, which outer electrons react with electrons of metal atoms to generate ionic bond, covalent bond or mixing bound, and they are absorbed, namely, chemical absorption, which is shown in the second process in Figure 7.46.

In metal surface, hydrogen atoms, based on chemical absorption, under the action of chemical affinity, enter metal interstitial void or grain boundary, namely, dissolution process, which is shown in the third process in Figure 7.46.

Hydrogen atoms or ions, dissolved into metal are gradually removed into the depth of metal through concentration diffusion or stress-induced diffusion, namely, called hydrogen diffusion, which is shown in the fourth process in

Figure 7.46.

After entry into the metal, hydrogen is not only in the normal lattice site, but also in the microstructure defect site. For instance, pore space, solid solution atom, dislocation, grain boundary and the second phase grain interface, and these defects are called hydrogen traps. Under normal conditions, hydrogen in the lattice site and one in the trap are all in dynamic equilibrium (Alfons et al,2000), which is seen in Figure 7.47.

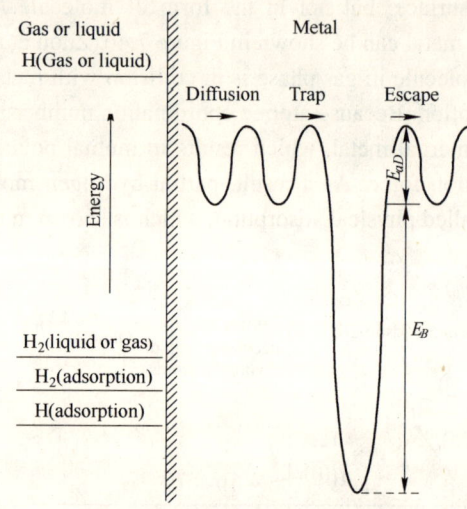

Figure 7.47   Schematic diagram of Energy relationship between hydrogen and metal in balance (Alfons et al,2000)
E_{aD}: lattice activation energy; E_B : trap binding energy

In ideal crystal, there is not any defect, and hydrogen is in crystal lattice interstice; in actual materials, there are all kinds of defects, which lowers hydrogen diffusion coefficient more or less. Pressouyre(1978) divided traps into reversible traps and irreversible traps based on the trap depth; the former had less interact with hydrogen, but the later strong interact with hydrogen; at low temperature, irreversible trap always trapped hydrogen atom, so the bigger the trap binding energy was, the more the trapped hydrogen content was; but reversible traps not only released hydrogen as hydrogen sources, but also trapped hydrogen as hydrogen trap.

Figure 7.48 indicates penetration curve of materials, in which P, P_1 and P_2 show ideal penetration curves, the first penetration curve and the second penetration curve, respectively; t_1 and t_2 indicate the first and second breakthrough times; D_1 is degassing process (Manolatos et al,1988). To compare difference between two penetrations, move P_2 to the starting point, mark P_2'. Based on existence and movement of hydrogen of materials above-mentioned, in the Figure the area enclosed by P_1 and P_2', is decided by the quantity of irreversible traps in materials. Because, in the first penetration, reversible and irreversible traps of materials are demanded to fill out, lag time is longer than that of ideal crystal so far. After the first penetration, based on dehydrogenation of sample, residual current in the return circuit is less than $2\mu A/cm^2$. Here hydrogen in reversible trap of material escapes out, but hydrogen in irreversible trap still reserves in it. Subsequently, secondly penetrate is conducted, it is

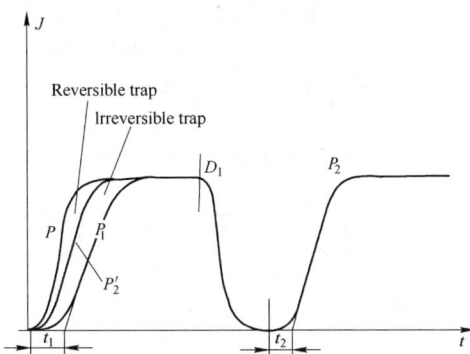

Figure 7.48 Illustration of penetration curve
P is ideal penetration curve; P_1 is first penetration;
P_2 is second penetration

known from the Figure 7.48 that the lag time is shorter than that in the first penetration. The reason is as following: In the first penetration irreversible traps of materials are demanded to fill up. In the second penetration, only reversible traps needed to fill. It means that trap quantity in material becomes less, so diffusion velocity of hydrogen accelerates. The phenomenon is that lag time is shorter than that in the first penetration.

Based on principle above-mentioned, with computer- controlled electrochemical penetration device, penetration experiments were made twice for the D-2 and D-1 steels, which results are shown in Figure 7.49. It could be seen that total trap quantity in D-2 (M)(direct proportion to area, enclosed by P and P_1)and quantity of irreversible trap (M_1)(direct proportion to area, enclosed by P_1 and P_2')are all higher than that in D-1.

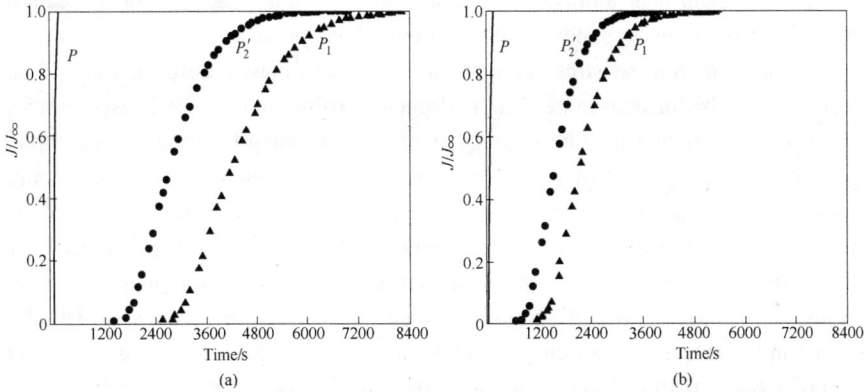

Figure 7.49 Contrast with hydrogen traps of several materials
(a) D-2; (b) D-1
P is ideal penetration curve(Manolatos et al,1988); $P1$ is the first penetration curve;
$P2$ is the second penetration curve

Total trap quantity ratio of the two steels and irreversible trap quantity ratio of the two steels could be calculated through weighing method, which is shown in Table 7.22. It is seen that total hydrogen trap quantity and irreversible trap quantity in D-2 are 1.6 times and 1.9 times to that in D-1, respectively. The difference in filmy retained austenite quantity results in the difference between total trap quantity and irreversible trapping quantity for the two steels.

Table 7.22   Hydrogen trap quantity in D-2 and D-1

Materials	$M/$ g	$M_1/$ g	M_{D-2}/M_{D-1}	M_{1D-2}/M_{1D-1}
D-2	0.4236	0.1022		
D-1	0.2613	0.0550	1.6	1.9

7.7   Mechanism of Resistance to Delayed Fracture of CFB/M Steel

7.7.1   *Relationship between susceptibility to hydrogen embrittlement and hydrogen trap for CFB/M steel*

Reversible hydrogen embrittlement of steel arises from enrichment of hydrogen in the partial area through diffusion. The enrichment is based on two ways:
1. Stress inducing hydrogen diffusion to enrich in area with the highest stress.
2. Dislocations transfer—hydrogen is enriched due to dislocation pile-up.

During tensile, smooth specimen generates necking and there is the triaxial stress area due to the local plastic strain. So a large number of dislocations are concentrated in the location. Due to the interaction between hydrogen and dislocations, hydrogen atoms tend to concentrate in this area around dislocation line. The trapping hydrogen has great pinning effects on dislocation movement. So it is difficult to release stress concentration through plastic deformation. Crack sources could be formed. In general, hydrogen distribution in steels is asymmetric. The hydrogen content may be higher in hydrogen trapping location (for example, in front of crack tip, micro-pore, grain boundary and inclusion location), and could cause hydrogen embrittlement of steel. Hydrogen embrittlement of the steel is directly related to characteristic of hydrogen traps. It is shown in the Figure 7.21 that after tensile fracture, hydrogen-charging specimen generates crack in inclusion location. Through analysis of energy spectrum, it is MnS or Ti(C,N) compound inclusion, which is a kind of hydrogen trapping (Reu et al,2007;Chattoraj,1995;Liou et al,1993).Because of stronger interaction of the inclusions with hydrogen, a large amount of hydrogen is enriched around inclusions. Based on "weak bond" theory, additional stress and enriched hydrogen together cause separation of these inclusions from matrix interface. Crack initiates in the interface, and constantly propagates and finally fracture occurs. Hence, improving purity and avoiding the harmful phases of steels can lower the susceptibility to hydrogen embrittlement for steels.

In addition, capacity of hydrogen diffusion in the steel directly influences on the segregation speed and degree of hydrogen. Based on the research above-mentioned, it is known that trap kinds and quantity have great effects on hydrogen diffusion. Therefore, controlling kind, quantity and distribution of hydrogen traps in the steel is a major measure to improve susceptibility to hydrogen embrittlement. Bainite/martensite lath boundary is a kind of trap. After thermomechanical treatment the microstructure is refined and boundaries of bainite/martensite laths increase, which makes hydrogen more evenly be distributed. Under the effect of external force, the microstructure can lower hydrogen segregation speed and resist hydrogen from further enriched, as well as improve resistance to fracture.

Increasing silicon content and obtaining more filmy retained austenite are also a good measure. Because solubility of hydrogen in austenite is bigger than that in ferrite, but diffusion coefficient is smaller, the retained austenite is also a kind of trap. The retained austenite in CFB/M duplex phase steel does not transform with charging hydrogen, so it has higher chemical stability. In addition, the conference (Fang et al,2001) showed that thermal and mechanical stabilities of retained austenite in CFB/M duplex phase steel are also good. However, massive retained austenite is unstable, it isn't beneficial to the property (Bhadeshia et al,1983). In addition, the retained austenite is a tough phase, crack propagation within it consumes more energy. Therefore, stabile retained austenite can improve the resistance to hydrogen embrittlement.

7.7.2 *Relationship between stress corrosion and hydrogen trap in steel*

Mechanism of stress corrosion of high strength steel is hydrogen-induced fracture, which is a diffusion process of hydrogen atoms. Under the loading condition, hydrogen atom diffuses into high stress region of crack tip. When the local hydrogen concentration is higher than critical value, crack will occur. Because there is a small distance between the crack tip and the biggest triaxial stress in front of crack tip, in the process of hydrogen diffusion, peak value of hydrogen concentration is in some position less far away from crack tip, where hydrogen crack is easily formed(Liu et al,1993). Therefore, the location of initial crack is in a certain distance away from the front of main crack, every process of fracture only goes within a certain distance. When crack propagates to the location where hydrogen content is lower than critical value, it will temporarily stop. And then hydrogen atoms are enriched through diffusion; like it again and again, crack propagates in the discontinuous forms. The experiment result of present authors also proves the phenomenon (Figure 7.40).

Infiltrating into steel from the surface and concentrating in high stress location, hydrogen atoms make steel bonding strength lower, so as crack occurs. Therefore, It depends upon both hydrogen segregation degree and decohesion effect whether stress corrosion crack occurs or not. Hydrogen traps can reduce transfer of hydrogen in materials, and evenly distributed hydrogen traps can effectively prevent segregation of hydrogen in crack tip and reduce embrittlement. On the contrary, if some irreversible hydrogen traps with higher bonding energy are unevenly distributed, owing to their strong effect on capturing hydrogen, hydrogen constantly accumulates around these areas. While the accumulated hydrogen is higher than critical concentration value, crack will occur. For instance, MnS, TiC inclusions and some carbides are irreversible hydrogen trap with great trap bonding energy (Gojic et al,1997;Hirth et al,1980;Pressouyre,1979). Under the action of environmental medium, it is easy to initiate crack in these trap locations, showing strong trend of environmental fracture. Microstructural refinement can increase lath boundary of bainite/martensite. Boundary is a kind of hydrogen trap(E_B=28kJ/mol). Increasing lath boundary can increase the number of hydrogen trap and make the traps more evenly distribute. Diffusion rate of hydrogen becomes much lower. Diffusion coefficient decrease from 0.423×10^{-6}cm^2/s to 0.335×10^{-6}cm^2/s through deformation. It can more effectively reduce diffusion of hydrogen towards crack tip and lower velocity of hydrogen concentration in crack tip towards critical value. In view of kinetics, it is difficult for hydrogen to reach high segregation concentration. Hence, it is seen from Table 7.15 that K_{ISCC} nearly increases by 18 percent, and $(da/dt)_{II}$ about reduces by 80 percent. Trap bonding energy of retained austenite is E_B=40kJ/mol, which is a medium-strength hydrogen trap, more than that in dislocation (19.2kJ/mol), cavities (27.6 kJ/mol)(Choo et al,1982) and grain boundary (20.5 kJ/mol)(Lee et al,1986), as well as more than retained austenite trapping bonding energy(E_B=30kJ/mol) determined by He Jianhong (He,1988) in ferrite and austenite duplex phase stainless steel, but less than that (E_B=52kJ/mol) determined by Turnbull(Turnbull et al,1994). Increasing silicon content can obtain more retained austenite. With increasing by 1 percent of retained austenite, K_{ISCC} will about increase by 4.5 percent, and $(da/dt)_{II}$ reduces by about 20.8 percent. In addition, as for analysis of stress corrosion fracture surface, in CFB/M duplex phase high strength steel, it should be quasi-cleavage fracture, and not find relatively fragile intergranular fracture, which shows that grain boundary strength in CFB/M duplex phase steel is higher. This is reason that susceptibility to stress corrosion for CFB/M duplex phase high strength steel is lower than that of 30CrMnSiA steel.

7.7.3 *Crack propagation model of CFB/M duplex phase steel*

Based on crack propagation path in Figure 7.40, crack propagation model of CFB/M duplex phase steel is built, as Figure 7.50. It shows the effect of microstructure refinement of CFB/M on crack propagation. It could be seen from Figure 7.50(a) that crack does not propagate along a beeline, but zigzag, constantly along or through bainite/martensite lath boundary. Through thermomechanical treatment lath of bainite/martensite is obviously refined and more desultory distributed. When a crack is propagating, it must be often changed direction, which results in large energy consumption and improve delayed fracture resistance. It is shown in Figure 7.50(b) shows the effects of filmy retained austenite on crack propagation. When crack meets with filmy retained austenite during propagation, cracks sometimes cut it and sometimes pass by it. Retained austenite is a kind of tough phase. Cracks mostly cut the retained austenite in the way of propagation, absorbing a certain amount of energy. Whether passing by or cutting it, it demands certain energy consumption. Hence, it also improves stress corrosion resistance.

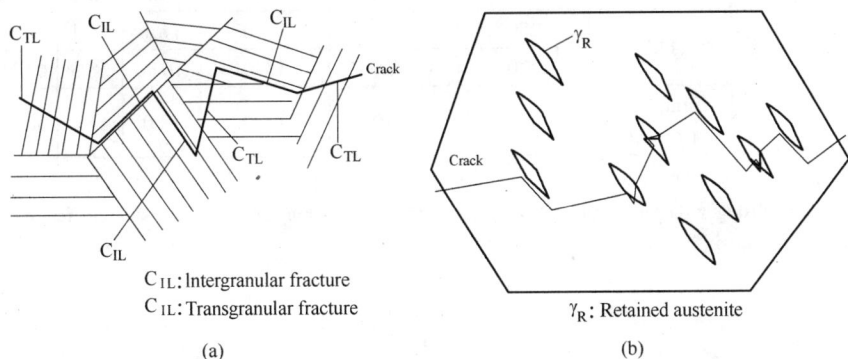

Figure 7.50 Crack propagation model of CFB/M duplex phase high strength steel
(a) Effect of refined CFB/M; (b) Effect of film retained austenite

7.8 Fatigue Behavior of 1500MPa CFB/M Duplex Phase High Strength Steel

7.8.1 *Fatigue behavior of CFB/M duplex phase steel*

7.8.1.1 Fatigue strength of CFB/M duplex phase steel

To compare mechanical properties of CFB/M duplex phase steel with other types of high strength steels, we listed data of general mechanical properties of CFB/M high strength steel, FM high strength steel and 30CrMnSiA steel into Table 7.23, and their fatigue behaviors are shown in Figure 7.51. At the same time, it is known from Figure 7.51 that based on electroslag remelting (ER) and different tempering temperatures (280℃or 370℃), fatigue strength $\sigma_{-1}(N_f=10^7)$of CFB/M(ER) steel is higher than 725MPa; fatigue strength $\sigma_{-1}(N_f=10^7)$of CFB/M steel at different tempering temperatures (280℃or 370℃) is higher than 700MPa; Fatigue strength σ_{-1} of FM steel (with the same composition of CFB/M steel) is higher than 635 MPa. σ_{-1} of 30CrMnSiA steel is higher than 600 MPa. It is obvious that for the steels with similar strength level, fatigue strength of CFB/M(ER) and CFB/M steels is higher than that of FM and 30CrMnSiA steels.

Table 7.23   Mechanical properties of D-2 steels with different microstructures and 30CrMnSiA

Materials	Microstructure	Tempering temperature / ℃	$R_m/N \cdot mm^{-2}$	$R_e/N \cdot mm^{-2}$	$A/\%$	$Z/\%$	a_K/J
D-2	CFB/M (ER) [1]	280	1570	1360	17.20	64.08	116
		370	1550	1340	17.35	67.03	121
	CFB/M	280	1560	1360	15.7	54.7	68.7
		370	1540	1340	16.5	55.6	79.5
	FM	280	1570	1370	16.1	56.1	70.3
		370	1540	1340	16.9.	58.3	63.7
30CrMnSiA [2]	Tempered troostite	440	1510	1350	12.0	45.2	58.0

[1]ER_Electroslag remelting;

[2]Austenising at the temperature of 890℃, and then oil quenching and tempering at temperature of 440℃ for 2h.

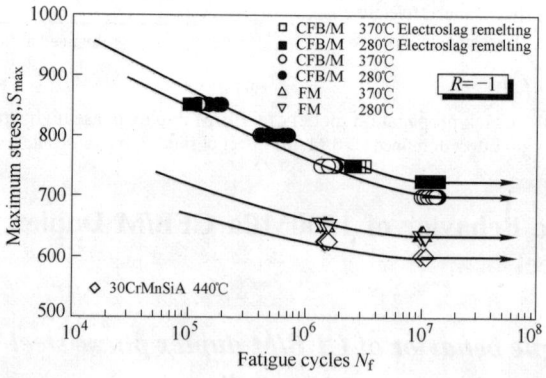

Figure 7.51   Fatigue strength of three kinds of high strength steels

7.8.1.2 Fatigue crack propagation behavior

Fatigue threshold value (ΔK_{th}) is an index to indicate fatigue crack propagation resistance of materials; fatigue crack propagation (da/dN) shows fatigue behavior during fatigue crack propagation process. Figure 7.52 shows da/dN- ΔK Curve of

30CrMnSiA high strength steel at tempering temperature of 440℃ under different stress ratio (R=0.1 or R=0.3). Figures 7.53 and 7.54 indicate da/dN- $\triangle K$ Curve of FM and CFB/M high strength steel at tempering temperature (280℃ or 370℃) under different stress ratio (R=0.1or R=0.3).

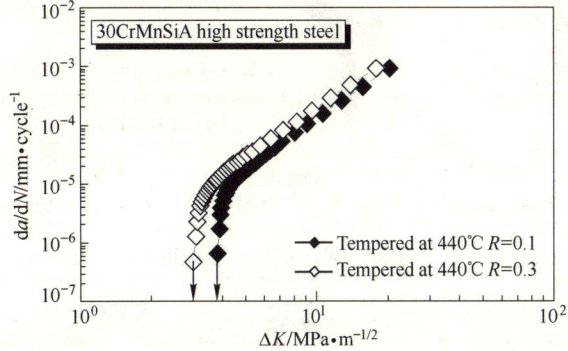

Figure 7.52 da/dN- $\triangle K$ Curve of 30CrMnSiA high strength steel

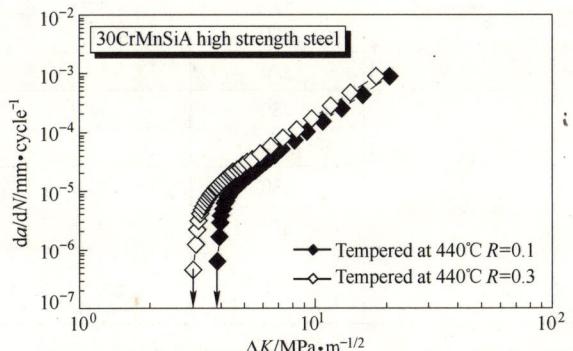

Figure 7.53 da/dN- $\triangle K$ Curve of FM high strength steel

$\triangle K_{th}$ data of three kinds of high strength steels are shown in Table 7.24, which indicates that in the conditions of different tempering temperature (280℃ or 370℃) and fatigue stress ratio (R=0.1or R=0.3), $\triangle K_{th}$ value of CFB/M high strength steel is the highest, and tempering temperature has less effects on the value of $\triangle K_{th}$. In case of R=0.1, $\triangle K_{th}$ value at different tempering temperatures can reach 12.7 MPa / $m^{1/2}$; and in case of R=0.3, $\triangle K_{th}$ value at different tempering temperatures can reach 10.0 MPa / $m^{1/2}$. As a result, the stress ratio has a more obvious effect on $\triangle K_{th}$ value. $\triangle K_{th}$ values of FM high strength steel at different conditions are smaller than that of CFB/M high strength steel; and effect of R and tempering temperature on $\triangle K_{th}$ value of FM high strength steel is similar to that of CFB/M high strength steel. But the $\triangle K_{th}$ value of 30CrMnSiA steel is far smaller than that of CFB/M and FM high strength steels.

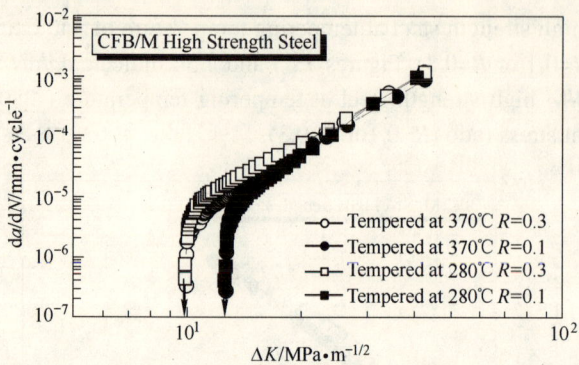

Figure 7.54 da/dN - ΔK curve of CFB/M duplex phase high strength steel

Table 7.24 Fatigue threshold value (ΔK_{th}) of high strength steels in the different conditions

Materials	Microstructure	Tempering temperature / ℃	ΔK_{th}/MPa • m$^{-1/2}$	R
D-2	CFB/M	280	12.7	0.1
		370	12.5	
		280	10.3	0.3
		370	10.0	
	FM	280	11.3	0.1
		370	10.6	
		280	8.40	0.3
		370	8.36	
30CrMnSiA	TS	440	3.80	0.1
			3.00	0.3

Based on the same stress ratio and da/dN-ΔK curve at different tempering temperatures in Figures 7.52 , 7.53 and 7.54, Figure 7.55, da/dN-ΔK curve of CFB/M duplex phase high strength steel, can be drawn. It is obvious that in case

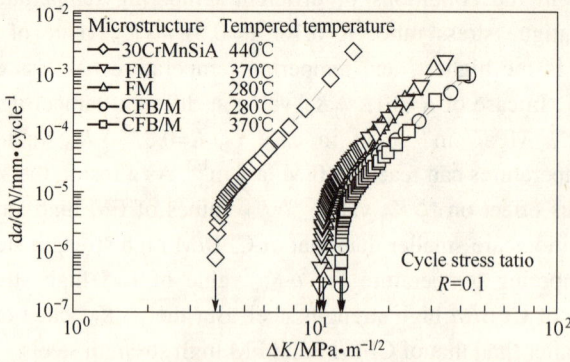

Figure 7.55 da/dN - ΔK curve of CFB/M duplex phase high strength steel

of $R=0.1$, the value of da/dN of 30CrMnSiA is the biggest; the next is FM. However, the value of da/dN of 30CrMnSiA at tempering temperature of 370℃ is slightly bigger than that at tempering temperature of 280℃; the value of da/dN of CFB/M duplex phase steel is the smallest, but the value at tempering temperature of 370℃ is slightly smaller than that at tempering temperature of 280℃. In case of $R=0.3$, da/dN - ΔK curve varying law of three kinds of high strength steels is similar to that in case of $R=0.1$. At the same tempering temperature, da/dN value will increase with the increase of stress ratio.

Figure 7.56 shows SEM photos of fatigue crack propagation paths in the near-threshold and propagation regions of CFB/M high strength steel; it is observed from Figure 7.56 (a), (b), (c) and (d) that in the near-threshold and propagation regions of fatigue crack, fatigue crack propagation path is mainly through B(M) lathing or along B(M) lath boundaries; near-threshold region with

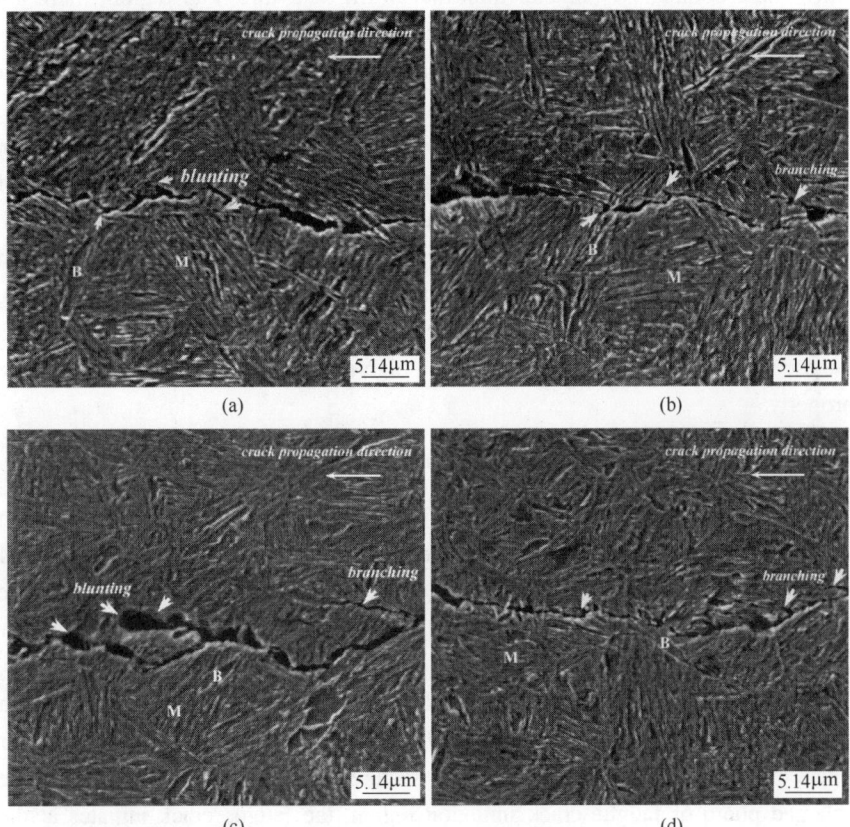

(a) (b)

(c) (d)

Figure 7.56 Fatigue crack propagation path of CFB/M high strength steel (280℃ tempering)
(a), (b), (c) indicate near threshold region of fatigue crack;
(d) indicates propagation region of fatigue crack

lower value of K, probability of through B(M) lath bundles in CFB/M high strength steel's fatigue crack propagation path is higher than that of along B(M) lath boundaries. During the process of fatigue crack propagation, it takes on a large number of turns and braches. At the same time, passivation occurs in crack branch tip, and it mostly occurs within bainite ferrite or lath interface. It can be seen from Figure 7.56(a) that fatigue crack is flexure with more turns, branches and passivation in branch tip. Fatigue crack shown in Figure 7.56 (b) is relatively straight, but crack branches and its tip passivation are more distributed. Figure 7.56 shows fatigue crack is flexure with obvious branches and passivation. In fatigue crack propagation region with a higher ΔK *value*, the probability of fatigue crack through B(M) lath bundle of CFB/M high strength steel is higher than that in near-threshold region; But the probability of propagation along B(M) lath bundle boundary is smaller than that in the near threshold region; there are turns, branches in the fatigue crack propagation path, as well as passivation occurs in crack branch tip, but degree of turns is relatively smaller than that of near threshold region (Figure 7.56(d)).

Compared fatigue crack propagation path in the near threshold and propagation regions of CFB/M high strength steel with that of FM high strength steel, turns of fatigue crack are more obvious, and quantity of branches is obviously increased, because CFB/M high strength steel has difference in microstructure with FM high strength steel. At the same time, passivation occurs in fatigue crack branch tip, which increases resistance in the process of fatigue crack propagation, lowers fatigue crack propagation rate. So CFB/M high strength steel has excellent fatigue property.

7.8.1.3　Fatigue fracture of CFB/M duplex phase high strength steel

Figure 7.57 (a), (b), (c) and (d) show fatigue fracture surface of 30CrMnSiA high strength steel; Figure 7.58 (a), (b), (c) and (d) show fatigue fracture surface of FM high strength steel; and Figure 7.59 (a), (b), (c) and (d) show fatigue fracture surface of CFB/M high strength steel; all of these results were obtained after tension and compression fatigue tests.

It can be seen from Figure 7.57(a) that fracture surface of 30CrMnSiA high strength steel is not very fluctuant, and fatigue crack propagation region area is rather small, only about 50 percent of the whole fracture surface. Figure 7.57 (b) shows the enlarged photo of fatigue crack initiation region; the fatigue crack initiates at the inclusion near the specimen surface (based on analysis of energy spectrum, it is $MgO\text{-}Al_2O_3\text{-}CaO$ series of metal oxide), and then propagates in the radial direction and insides. Tearing edge takes on radiation distribution in the radial direction. Fracture mode of this fatigue fracture is quasi-cleavage crack through grains.

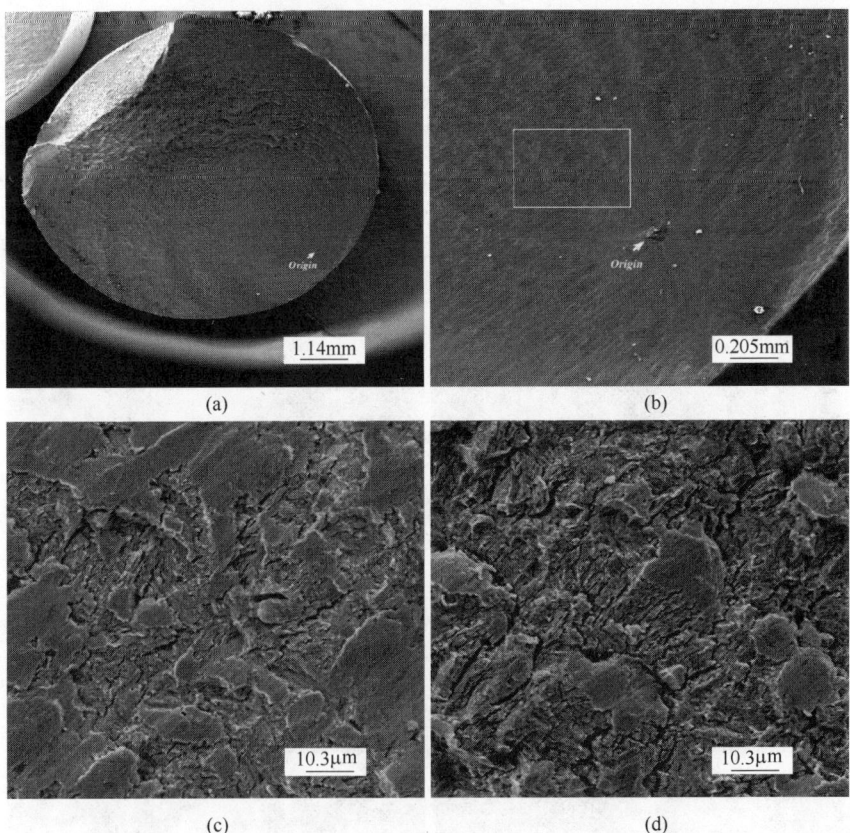

Figure 7.57 Scanning electronic microscope photos of fatigue fracture surface of
30CrMnSiA high strength steel (SEM)(440℃ tempering);
stress amplitude σ_a=700MPa, and fatigue cycle number N_f=1.136×10^6

(a) fatigue macro-fracture; (b) fatigue crack source region;
(c) multiply of "□" in (b); (d) fatigue crack propagation region

Figure 7.58(a) shows, as for FM high strength steel, shear lip region is
relatively wide, and fatigue crack propagation region is relatively small, nearly
accounting for 35 percent of the whole fracture section area; in addition, two
fatigue crack initiations exist in the surface and near the surface. Figure 7.58(b)
shows fatigue initiation region is in inhomogeneous microstructure near the
surface of specimen, and the other fatigue crack initiates in the surface of
specimen. Fracture way of fatigue fracture is still quasi-cleavage fracture
through grains.

It is found in Figure 7.59(a) that as for CFB/M high strength steel, fracture
surface is obviously fluctuant, and fatigue crack propagation region area is
larger; two fatigue crack initiations also exist in the fracture section, both of

which propagate in the different locations. Figure 7.59(b) is an enlarged photo of one fatigue crack initiation region, which initiates in the defect location near the surface, and then propagates outsides by irradiation shape; while the other initiates in the specimen surface. Figure 7.59(c) shows further enlarged fatigue crack initiation of Figure 7.59(b), and it is easy to see that there is no inclusion. Fracture way of fatigue fracture is still quasi-cleavage fracture through grains. As for CFB/M and FM high strength steels, after tempering at temperatures of 370℃ and 280℃ respectively, their fatigue fracture are very similar.

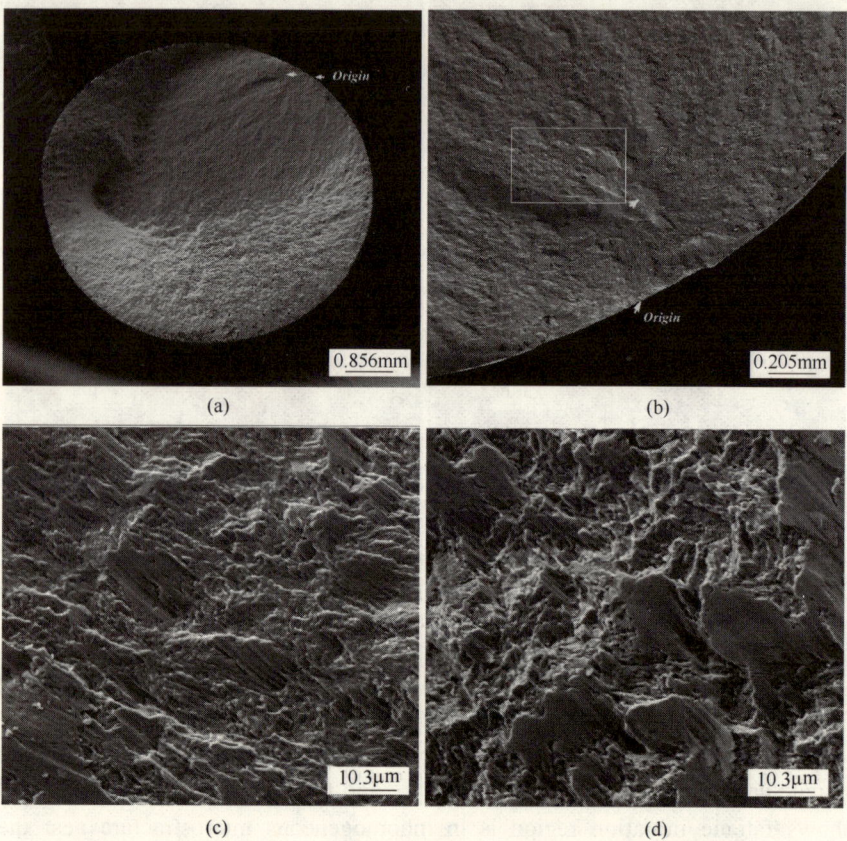

Figure 7.58   SEM photos of fatigue fracture of FM high strength steel   (tempering at 280℃),
stress amplitude σ_a=650MPa; fatigue cycle number N_f=3.271×10^6
(a) macro-fatigue fracture; (b) fatigue crack initiation region
(c) multiply of "□" zone in (b); (d) fatigue crack propagation region

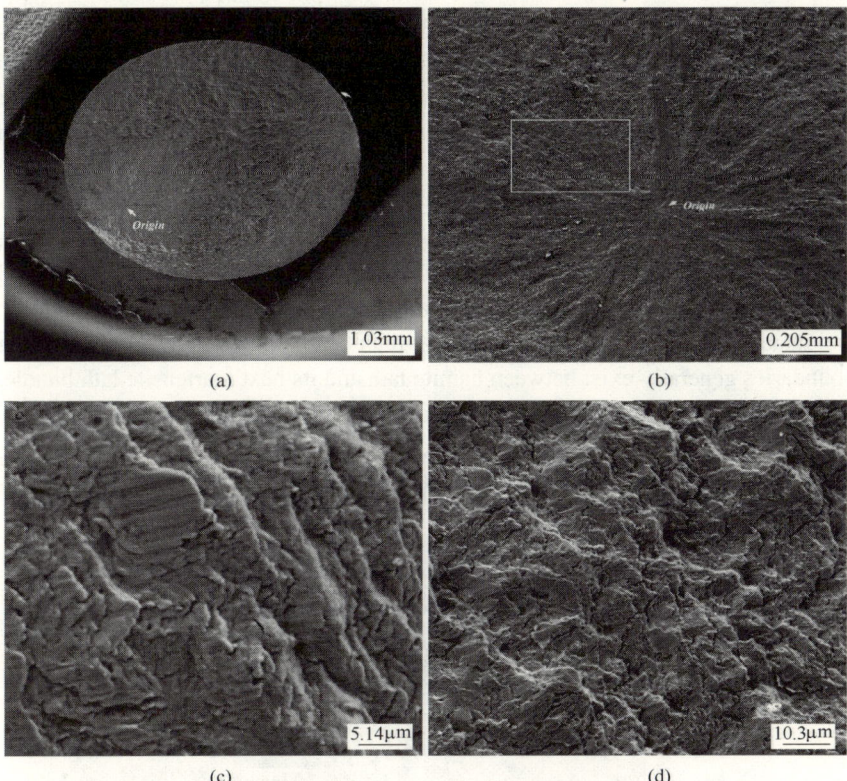

(a)   (b)

(c)   (d)

Figure 7.59 SEM photos of fatigue fracture of CFB/M high strength steel (tempering at 280℃), stress amplitude σ_a=750MPa; fatigue cycle number N_f=3.739×10^6
(a) macro-fatigue fracture; (b) fatigue crack initiation region; (c) multiply
of "□" zone in (b); (d) fatigue crack propagation region

7.8.2 Effect of microstructure characteristics of CFB/M duplex phase steel on fatigue behaviors

7.8.2.1 Effect of microstructure characteristics on fatigue strength

Experimental result shows that the fatigue strength of several kinds of steels at the same strength level and in the same conditions of experiment are obviously different. Fatigue strength σ_{-1} of CFB/M high strength steel is higher than 700MPa, σ_{-1} of FM high strength steel is higher than 635 MPa, and σ_{-1} of 30CrMnSiA high strength steel is higher than 600MPa, which shows the effect of their microstructures on σ_{-1} is indispensable.

Figure 7.60 shows SEM photos of microstructures of three kinds of high strength steels; of which, Figure 7.60(a) is tempering troostite microstructure of 30CrMnSiA high strength steel, after austenitizing at temperature of 890℃ and then tempering 440℃; Figure 7.60(b) refers to complete tempering lath martensite microstructures (FM) of D-2 steel, after austenitizing at temperature of 900℃ and oil quenching, as well as tempering at 280℃. Figure 7.60(c) refers to CFB/M duplex phase microstructure of D-2 steel, after austenitizing at temperature of 900℃, and then air cooling, as well as tempering at 280℃. And small angle grain boundaries exist between the next laths for tempering troostite and FM microstructures. As for CFB/M high strength steel in Figure 7.60(c), after austenitizing, and then air cooling to room temperature from high temperature, lower bainites of low carbon content are firstly precipitated inside the original austenite, splitting grain of the original austenite, and refines martensite lath. At the same time, inside grains of CFB/M high strength steel, large angle grain boundaries generally exist between bainite lath and its next martensite lath bundle, while small angle grain boundaries exist between martensite lath bundles.

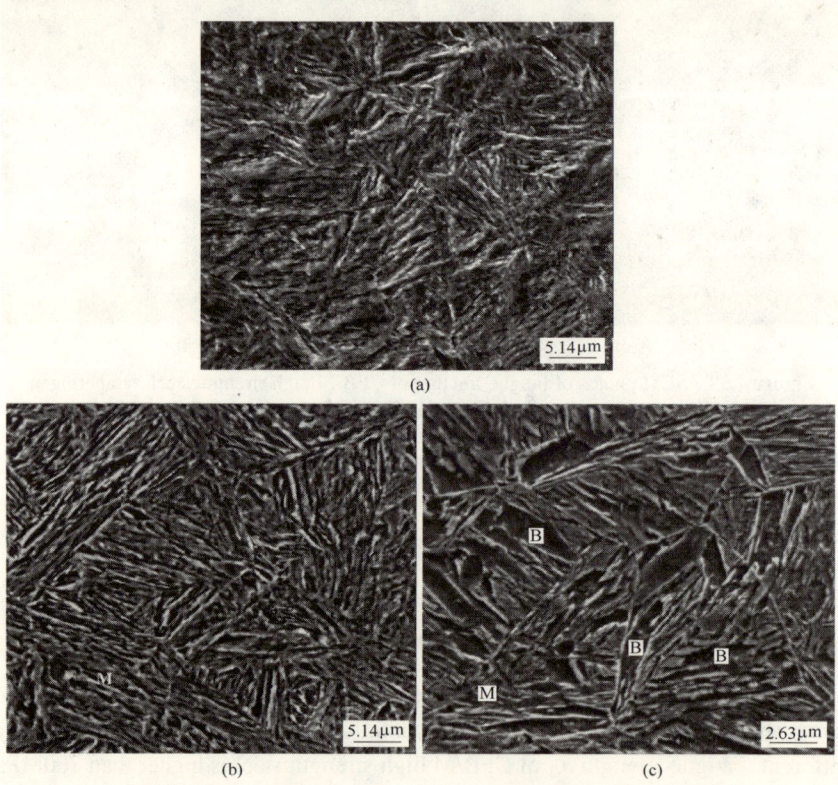

(a)

(b)   (c)

Figure 7.60   SEM photos of high strength steel's microstructure
(a) tempering troostite microstructure (30CrMnSiA);(b) full martensite microstructure (FM);
(c) CFB/M duplex phase microstructure; (D-2): B-Bainite; M-Martensite

Figure 7.61 is TEM photos of CFB/M high strength steel; Figure 7.61 (a) is duplex phase microstructure of lower bainite and martensite laths of CFB/M high strength steel, whose accordant dark field photo is showed in Figure 7.61(b). It is found that a certain thickness of retained austenite membrane is distributed between lower bainite laths, as well as lower bainite lath and martensite lath boundary; it is found in Figure 7.61(c) that a certain thickness of retained austenite film is also distributed between sub-laths inside lower bainite; and Figure 7.61(d) is dark field photo of Figure 7.61(c), which further proves the existence of the retained austenite film in Figures 7.61(c), (e) and (f)are TEM photos of bainite lath splitting martensite lath, of which Figure 7.61(e) shows double bainitic laths and Figure 7.61(f) shows single bainitic lath. As for CFB/M high strength steel, after tempering at temperature of 370℃ and 280℃, respectively, their microstructure characteristics are very similar.

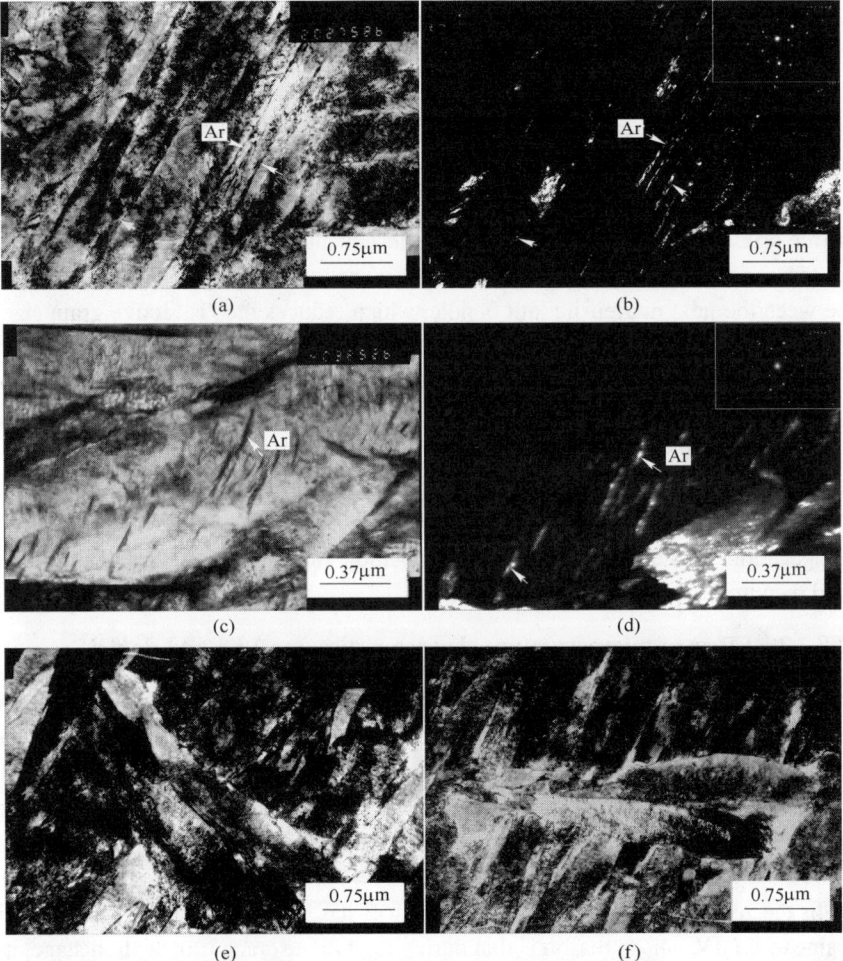

Figure 7.61　TEM photos of CFB/M high strength steel (280℃ tempering)

(a,) , (c) bright field photos; (b), (d) dark field photos; (e), (f) photos of B lath splitting M lath

Note: B-Bainite; Ar- Retained austenite

Microstructure characteristics of D-2 and 30CrMnSiA high strength steels directly depend upon their chemical compositions. Although strength is in the same level of 1500MPa, but the C element content in two high strength steels is different. Namely, 30CrMnSiA steel is medial carbon high strength steel, while D-2 steel is lower carbon high strength steel. After different technical treatments, for the microstructure of generated CFB/M and FM high strength steels, the lath martensite and bainite have better cooperation of strength and toughness than that of tempering troositie microstructure. As for CFB/M and FM high strength steels, strength and toughness of CFB/M duplex phase microstructure (B_L+M+A_r) is better than that of single microstructure of FM high strength steel(Murakani et al,1990;Tomita Y et al,1985). CFB/M high strength steel is a kind of high strength steel containing Mn-Si-Cr elements, of which, Si(1.8 percent) content is higher, so it has an effect on phase transition point (B_s and M_s) of bainite and martensite. B_s of CFB/M high strength steel in the research is at the temperature of 330℃; and M_s is 295℃. Therefore, as for CFB/M high strength steel, after austenitizing and then air cooling to room temperature from high temperature, lower bainite of low carbon content is firstly precipitated inside the original austenite, splitting grains of the original austenite and refining the subsequently precipitated martensite lath; at the same time, this splitting effects also make large angle bundle boundary between the next martensite lath bundle, which reduces the "Effective grain size" in fatigue facture. While for FM and 30CrMnSiA high strength steels' microstructure, small angle bundle boundaries exist between the next laths of martensite and tempering troostite; therefore, by comparison, the "effective grain size" in fatigue facture is relatively bigger. Microstructure characteristics above-mentioned result in orientation changes of fatigue crack during the propagation stage, which increases resistance force against fatigue crack propagation, reduces fatigue crack propagation rate, increases propagation life, and then improves the fatigue strength.

7.8.2.2   Effect of microstructure characteristics on ΔK_{th} and da/dN

As is reported in the relatively early papers, low carbon lower bainite microstructure, ferrite / martensite duplex phase microstructure has higher value of ΔK_{th} and lower value of da/dN (Ramage et al,1987;Suzuki H et al,1979); especially in ferrite / martensite duplex phase microstructure, if ferrite is enclosed by the continuous martensite, the value of ΔK_{th} will be high; even in case that R is lower, the value of ΔK_{th} can reach more than 20 MPa·m$^{1/2}$ (Dutta et al,1984).

In the research, CFB/M high strength steel has high value of ΔK_{th} and lower value of da/dN, whose reason is that during the fatigue crack propagation stage, its unique microstructure can improve crack tip closure resistance and induce closures in fatigue crack tip(Kontt J F,1984). In the near-threshold region of fatigue with lower ΔK, ΔK_{th} value determines the fatigue crack propagation rate

(Fleck N A,1984). And the value of ΔK_{th} involves two components: the intrinsic resistance force (ΔK_{th}^{i}) against fatigue crack propagation and the crack closure resistance force (ΔK_{th}^{c}). In addition, there are three fatigue crack tip closure mechanisms in the near-threshold region and propagation region, including "Plasticity induced crack closure"(Beevers C J et al,1984), "Oxide induced crack closure"(Stewart A T,1980) and "Roughness induced crack closure" (Ritchie R O et al,1979). As a result, these factors will have effects on the value of ΔK_{th} and da/dN.

CFB/M high strength steel has good toughness and its "Effective grain size" as fracture unit is relatively small. So in the near-threshold region, more turns and branches exist in fatigue crack propagation path, which makes the fracture surface rough; in addition, the crack tip endures loads of model Ⅰ and Ⅱ; dislocation proportion of Model Ⅱ / Ⅰ is big, which makes crack surface rouch more earlier. So it results in "roughness induced crack closure" and actually effective value of ΔK_{th}^{i} in fatigue crack tip decreases while the value of ΔK_{th}^{c} obviously increases. Hence, ΔK_{th} value of CFB/M high strength steel increases. In addition, in the near-threshold region of fatigue crack, increasing roughness results in "roughness induced crack closure" showed by the crack fracture surface, which makes ΔK_{eff} value in crack tip decrease and da/dN value obviously lower. Observation by SEM shows, in the near-threshold region, a number of friction and extrusion trails are found in the fracture surface, which greatly proves that the mechanism of "Roughness Induced Crack Closure" exists. It must be mentioned that in the crack fracture surface of near-threshold region, it is also found that in some ΔK value range, micro-cleavage plane exists. King thought that actually these cleavage planes were close packed plane of matrix phase (crystal slip plane); when the size of plastic zone in crack tip was smaller than that of the material grain, again and again slips in crack tip plastic zone resulted that atomic binding force of the material became weak, and finally the material fractured along slip plane.

In general, effect of "roughness induced crack closure" on values of ΔK_{th} and da/dN depends upon propagation path of fatigue crack in different propagation stages. In the near-threshold region, dislocation proportion of Model Ⅱ / Ⅰ is big, so the effect of "roughness induced crack closure" is dominant. In case of crack propagation beyond the near-threshold region, the crack propagates in the way of Model Ⅰ and the dislocation proportion of Model Ⅱ / Ⅰ greatly decreases in the crack tip so that it can be omitted, so effects of "roughness induced crack closure" and "oxides induced crack closure" decreases, and "plasticity induced crack closure" is dominant. In different stress states, the "Plasticity induced crack closure" is different. In general the closure contribution of plane stress state is lower than that of plane strain state. In plane stress state, residual plasticity track in crack surface of material comes from the specimen surface; while in plane strain state, the size of plastic region in front of the crack tip and residual plastic deformation of crack tip track are the largest in the specimen surface(Suzuki H et al,1979). In addition, the contribution of "plasticity induced crack closure" to values of ΔK_{th} and da/dN will increase with the increase of strain hardening rate, yield strength and constraint (Fleck N A , 1982).

When material is in active environment, oxide film will exist in fracture surface. And periodical model Ⅱ dislocation will result in the corrosion damage of the oxide film. Here "oxides induced crack closure" has certain effect on the value of ΔK_{th} and da/dN. Experimental result of low strength steel in the active environment, researched by Suresh, etc.(1983), showed when thickness of oxide film δ_0=0.2μm and representative value l=0.2 μm, K_{cl} value in crack tip was about 2.3 MPa·m$^{1/2}$. In the near-threshold region of fatigue crack, the effects of "roughness induced crack closure" and "oxides induced crack closure" are dominant, the effect of "plasticity induced crack closure" is not very obvious; as for CFB/M high strength steel, in the whole fatigue crack fracture, XPS measuring result shows oxygen content is low, so the effect of "oxides induced crack closure" less contributes to the value of ΔK_{th} and da/dN. As for fracture characteristics, attention should be paid to the different effects of "roughness induced crack closure" and "plasticity induced crack closure" in different stages of fatigue crack propagation.

As for FM and 30CrMnSiA high strength steels, their values of ΔK_{th} are obviously smaller than that of CFB/M high strength steel, and their values of da/dN are bigger than that of CFB/M high strength steel. Similar to CFB/M high strength steel, FM and 30CrMnSiA high strength steels also have crack closures effects, but the effects are weak during fatigue crack propagation stages. The microstructure of FM high strength steel is full martensite, and small angle grain boundary exists between the next lath bundle in general; in case of tempering at temperature of 370℃, there will be a little carbide to precipitate, so when fatigue crack propagates in the near-threshold region, turns, branches, and passivation in the crack tip obviously decrease less than that of CFB/M high strength steel in the propagation path of the fatigue crack. As for the effect of crack tip closure on values of ΔK_{th} and da/dN, the roughness of fracture surface in fatigue crack propagation path of near-threshold region of FM high strength steel, is relatively small; the conditions of surface oxide film are similar to that of CFB/M high strength steel, so the effect of "roughness induced crack closure" and "oxides induced crack closure" on FM high strength steel is relatively lower. "plasticity induced crack closure" has certain contribution effect on values of ΔK_{th} and da/dN in the near-threshold and propagation regions of fatigue crack, especially in fatigue crack propagation region since here crack propagation of model Ⅱ are dominant. In addition, a little carbide exists in FM high strength microstructure; in the process of fatigue crack propagation, micro-crack initiates in carbide location, which can increase the driving force to the fatigue crack propagation, and consequently result in decreasing value of ΔK_{th} and increasing da/dN value.

As for 30CrMnSiA high strength steel, its microstructure is tempering troostite and a little carbide, whose toughness is weaker than that of CFB/M and FM high strength steels; its fatigue crack propagation path is relatively flat; and turns and branches of the fatigue crack are obviously much less than that of CFB/M and FM high strength steels. Therefore, there is few passivation in the fatigue crack tip. In addition, the roughness of fatigue fracture in fatigue crack propagation path is lower than that of CFB/M and FM high strength steel; its surface oxidizing condition is similar to that of CFB/M and FM high strength steels, so "roughness induced crack closure" and "oxides induced crack closure" make less contribution to the values of ΔK_{th} and da/dN; only "plasticity induced crack closure" has certain effect on the values of ΔK_{th} and da/dN in the propagation process of the fatigue crack. However, because strain hardening rate and yield-strength are smaller than that of CFB/M and FM high strength steels, the effect of "plasticity induced crack closure" is lower.

7.8.3 Effect of retained austenite on fatigue behaviors of CFB/M duplex phase steel

7.8.3.1 Retained austenite content and cyclical stability

Retained austenite content and cyclical stability have great effect on fatigue performance of the CFB/M duplex phase steel. Based on measurement by magnetometer, average content of retained austenite, in CFB/M high strength steel after treatment of tempering at 280℃, reaches 8.7vol percent; after treatment of tempering at 370℃, its average content reaches 8.3vol percent; at the tempering temperatures of 280℃ or 370℃, variation of retained austenite, in CFB/M high strength steel, is less than 5 percent of the original content. It shows that retained austenite film in CFB/M high strength steel has good tempering stability. And as for FM high strength steel, based on treatment of tempering at 280℃ or 370℃, as well as 30CrMnSiA high strength steel, based on treatment of tempering at 440℃, average contents of retained austenite are all less than 1vol percent.

Figure 7.62 shows Retained austenite content in CFB/M high strength steel at different tempering temperatures, based on different stress cycles; In Figure 7.62, 0.0 point in the abscissa is retained austenite content in CFB/M high strength steel at different tempering temperatures, not based on stress cycle, whose value is about 8.7Vol percent. In fatigue experiment, the factors, influencing on retained austenite stability in CFB/M high strength steel, mainly focus on fatigue cycle number N_f and stress amplitude σ_a. It is found in Figure 7.62 that based on 10^7 cycles, the lowest retained austenite content is 8.2vol percent. In addition, stress amplitude value increased to 750MPa from 500 MPa; although in the conditions of different tempering temperature and stress cycle number, retained austenite content only reduces to 8.3 vol percent from 8.7Vol percent. As a result, in the process of fatigue cycle, there is no obvious variation in retained austenite content. And so it shows the retained austenite in CFB/M high strength steel has good cyclical stability.

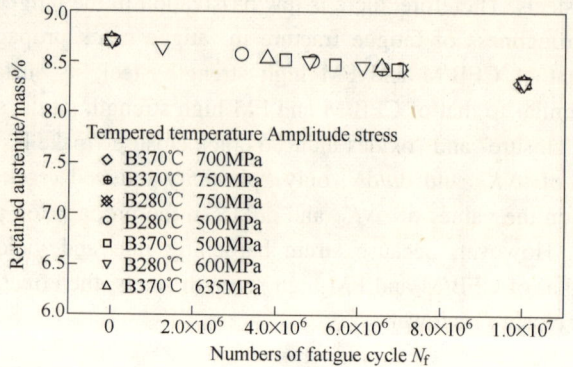

Figure 7.62   Schematic drawing of retained austenite's cyclical stability in CFB/M high strength steel

7.8.3.2   Effect of retained austenite and its cyclical stability on fatigue strength

Compared microstructure of CFB/M high strength steel with that of FM and 30CrMnSiA high strength steels, there is obvious difference that the interior of the CFB/M high strength steel contains a certain film of retained austenite. The reason of retained austenite existence is that as an element to form non-carbide, an amount of alloying element Si is added to the steel; when bainite forms, Si can prevent carbide to precipitate. And so austenite around lower bainite and ferrite becomes austenite with rich carbon, and is stably preserved at room temperature. Therefore, retained austenite with certain thickness exists in the original austenite grain boundary, lower bainite and martensite lath boundary and sub-lath boundary(Tan Zhunli et al,2005;Gui Zhou et al,2006;Fang Hongsheng et al,2005). Membrane-shaped or film retained austenite can not only clear up the danger of carbide, split ferrite plate and refine microstructure, but also result in passivation in fatigue crack tip(Miihkinen VTT et al,1987), relaxing stress concentration in fatigue crack tip, consuming energy in the process of fatigue crack propagation, and increasing fatigue resistance of high strength steel. The effect of retained austenite on fatigue strength of CFB/M high strength steel, depends upon its fatigue cyclical stability. If in fatigue cyclical process, the stability of retained austenite is weak, here retained austenite will be decomposed and transformed into martensite, whose effect on passivation in fatigue crack tip will disappear, which will accelerate the propagation of fatigue crack, and lower fatigue strength of CFB/M high strength steel. Just because retained austenite of CFB/M high strength steel has relatively high stability, while fatigue crack initiates and enter fatigue crack propagation stage in CFB/M high strength steel, its fatigue crack propagation rate will be obviously smaller than that of FM and 30CrMnSiA high strength steels. And so fatigue life with the same stress amplitude will be prolonged; and at the same fatigue life, stress amplitude will increase. In addition, adding Si also has effect on the first kind of tempering brittle temperature range of low and medial   carbon high strength steel; less Si has less effect on the first kind of tempering brittle temperature range, while more Si (1.8%) makes temperature interval transfer. In the research, based on treatment of tempering at temperature of 370℃, CFB/M high strength steel has good toughness, and there is no tempering brittleness. As a result, it has good fatigue property.

7.8.3.3   Effect of retained austenite film on fatigue crack propagation

In CFB/M high strength steel, an amount of alloying element Si is added into it. In bainitic transforms, Si can prevent carbide to precipitate. And so austenite around lower bainite and ferrite becomes austenite with rich carbon, and is stably preserved at room temperature. Therefore, retained austenite with certain thickness exists in the original austenite grain boundary, lower bainite and martensite lath bundle boundary and sub-lath boundary (Beaehem C D et al,1973). Because the retained austenite film has good mechanical stability, tempering stability (Miihkinen VTT et al,1987), chemical stability (Liu Dongyu,2002), as well as cyclical stability, the retained austenite film in CFB/M high strength steel plays a significant role in improving the fatigue property.

It is shown in the relevant document research (Chang Kaidi,2002;Cui Wenlong et al,2007;Bai Bingzhe et al,2006) that retained austenite can change plasticity in fatigue crack tip, which results in passivation in fatigue crack tip, and relaxes stress concentration in crack tip. In addition, under the action of crack tip stress, retained austenite also absorbs energy in the process of fatigue crack propagation which results in "stress induces matensitic transformation" in the retained austenite, and so fatigue crack tip stress is decreased.

The experimental results above-mentioned show that in the process of fatigue crack propagation, there are the phenomena that retained austenite in the original austenitic grain boundaries, lath bundle boundaries, and lower bainitic and martensitic lath boundaries, makes the fatigue crack tip passivate, which reduces stress concentration in fatigue crack tip; but, "stress induced retained austenite transformation to martensite" is not found in fatigue crack tip region of CFB/M high strength steel. Because of the microstructure and refinement characteristics of CFB/M high strength steel, more turns and branches exist in fatigue crack propagation path, which makes threshold region of fatigue crack be of larger roughness, and form closure effect in fatigue crack tip (Ritchie R O et al,1979). Consequently, this kind of characteristic can not only raise ΔK_{th} value, lower da/dN value in the near-threshold region of fatigue crack, but also cause da/dN value, in near-threshold region of fatigue crack of CFB/M high strength steel, to become obviously smaller than that of FM and 30CrMnSiA high strength steels.

7.8.4　*Fatigue fracture mechanism of CFB/M duplex phase steel*

CFB/M duplex phase high strength steel has good fatigue properties. Based on electroslag remelting, fatigue strength of CFB/M high strength steel σ_{-1} is higher than 725MPa, which accounts for σ_b of 48.3 percent. Not based on electroslag remelting, fatigue strength of CFB/M high strength steel σ_{-1} is higher than 700MPa, which accounts for σ_b of 46.7 percent. CFB/M high strength steel has high threshold value, namely, ΔK_{th}, as well as lower fatigue crack propagation rate da/dN. In normal condition, in case of stress ratio R=0.1, its ΔK_{th} value will be 12.7MPa·m$^{1/2}$; in case of stress ratio R=0.3, its ΔK_{th} value will be 10MPa·m$^{1/2}$. The reason that CFB/M high strength steel has higher ΔK_{th} value and lower da/dN value is due to closure resistance force in fatigue crack tip, especially due to "Roughness induced crack closure" and "Plasticity Induced Crack Closure" which cause the increase of the closure resistance force in fatigue crack tip. Besides, the reason also involves the effect of "Roughness induced crack closure" in the near-threshold region of purely mechanical fatigue crack. Microstructure of CFB/M high strength steel is a kind of carbide free bainite and martensite duplex phase microstructure. At the same time, retained austenitic film with certain thickness exists in the original austenitic grain boundary, low carbon bainite lath interior, lath boundary and martensitic lath boundary. Because the firstly formed bainite lath splits the original austenitic grain, it can refine the martensitic lath, and subsequently form smaller "Effective grain size" of fatigue fracture unit. Therefore, the fatigue property is improved as for CFB/M high strength steel. CFB/M high strength steel's retained austenitic film has good cyclical stability, which causes passivation in fatigue crack tip during fatigue crack propagation, reduces stress concentration in fatigue crack tip, and is very significant to increase ΔK_{th} value and lower da/dN value. In the course of corrosion fatigue, retained austenite, as hydrogen trap, can improve delayed fracture resistance property of CFB/M high strength steel, which is because hydrogen has most small coefficient of diffusion D and penetration capability, and larger solubility.

7.9　Application Prospect of CFB/M Duplex Phase Steel

The CFB/M duplex phase steel, designed and developed by R&D Center on Bainitic Steels, affiliated to Tsinghua University, has been used for high-speed and heavy-load rail frog, as well as the large-scale 14.9 grade high strength bolt.

High manganese steel has been used for railway frog for many years. However, frog fails frequently due to crack and contact fatigue. During average service life, carrying capacity can reach 60~80Mt. Recent years the speed of train is getting higher and higher, its load is getting heavier and heavier, frequency of passing train is getting higher and higher. High manganese steel can't meet the demand.

The steel used in the high manganese steel frog is mostly ZGMn13. The mechanical properties are: $R_m \geqslant 735MPa$, $A_5 \geqslant 35\%$, $a_{KU} \geqslant 147J/cm^2$ and the hardness is 170~230HB. The mechanical properties of frog made from CFB/M duplex phase steel are: $R_m \geqslant 1400MPa$, $A_5 \geqslant 13\%$, $a_{KU} \geqslant 90J/cm^2$ and the hardness is 42~45HRC. The CFB/M duplex phase steel railway frog developed by this project has been applied in the busy sectors in JingGuang Railway and JinPu Railway over 2 years. Due to the low carbon content, this steel has good welding property. Therefore, frog and train switch can be welded together, and train runs more stably.

The British standard BS 3692: 1967 stipulates that the mechanical properties of 14.9 grade high strength bolt are: $R_m \geqslant 1373MPa$, $A_5 \geqslant 7\%$, $a_{KV} \geqslant 29.4J/cm^2$ and hardness $\geqslant 40HRC$. The mechanical properties of high strength bolt made by CFB/M duplex phase steel are: R_m is 1385MPa, A_5 is 11.3%, a_{KV} is 67.4J/cm^2 and hardness is 44HRC. The properties exceed the requirements in BS3692. The large-scale bolt with the length of 1.44m and the diameter of 56mm can be applied in the equipment installation in a certain major harbor. Because of high environmental requirement for stress corrosion resistance properties of materials in the harbor, the CFB/M duplex phase steel with film retained austenite is a favorable option.

Appendix: Experimental materials in Chapter 7

Steel code	Composition (mass%)						
	C	Mn	Si	Cr	Ni	Mo	Ti
A	0.22	2~3	1.62	0.52			
A-1	0.22	2~3	1.45	0.52			
A-2	0.22	2~3	1.86	0.52			
B	0.31	2~3	1.5	0.60	1.0	0.25	0.02
C	0.22	2~3	1.86	0.52			
42CrMo	A kind of commercial steel						
30CrMnSiA	A kind of commercial steel						
D-1	0.23	2~3	0.2	0.75			
E-1	0.25	2~3	1.45	0.52			
D-2	0.23	2~3	1.74	0.66			
E-2	0.23	2~3	0.2	0.75			

References

Alfons H M Krom , Bakker A D (2000) Hydrogen Trapping Models in Steel. Metall. Trans. 31B(12):1475-1482

Asahi Hitoshi, Hirakami Daisuke, Yamasaki Shingo (2003) Hydrogen trapping behavior in vanadium-added steel. ISIJ International 43(4):527-533

Bai Bingzhe, Cui Wenlong, Gu Jialin, Liu Dongyu (2006) Fatigue properties of carbide-free bainite and martensite mixed microstructure high strength steel. In: The 3rd International Conference on Advanced Structural Steels. Gyeongju, Korea, August 22-24, 2006

Bandyopadhyay N, Kameda Jun, Mcmahon CJJR. (1983) Hydrogen Induced Cracking in 4340-Type Steel: Effect of Composition, Yield Strength and H2 Pressure. Metall. Trans. A. 14(5):881-888

Beachem C D, Yoder G R (1973) Elastic-Plastic Fracture by Homogeneous Microvoid Coalescence Tearing Alone Alternation Shear Planes. Metallurgical Transactions 4(4):45-1153

Beevers C J, Carlson R L (1984) A Consideration of the Significant Factors Controlling Fatigue Thresholds. In: Fatigue Crack Growth 30 Years of Progress, Proceedings of Conference on Fatigue Crack Growth Cambridge,UK,20 September 1984, Pergamon Press, 89-101

Bhadeshia H K D H, Edmonds D V   (1979) The Bainite Transformation in a Silicon Steel. Metall. Trans. A 10:895-907

Bhadeshia H K D H, Edmonds D V (1983) Bainite in Silicon Steels. New Composition-Property Approach Part2. Metal Science 17(9):420-425

Brass A M, Guillon F, Vivet S (2004) Quantification of hydrogen diffusion and trapping in 2.25Cr-1Mo and 3Cr-1Mo-V steels with the electrochemical permeation technique and melt extractions. Metallurgical and Materials Transactions A: Physical Metallurgy and Materials Science, v 35 A, n 5, May, 2004, p 1449-1464

Chang Kaidi (2002) Study on Delayed Fracture Mechanism of Bainite/Martensite Duplex Phase High Strength Steel [Doctoral Thesis], Beijing: Tsinghua University , April , 2002

Chattoraj I, Tiwari S B , Ray A K , A Mitra, S K Das (1995) Corrosion Science 37(6):885-896

Choo W Y, Lee J Y (1982) Hydrogen Trapping Phenomena in Carbon Steel. Journal of materials Science 17:1930-1938

Choo W Y, Lee J Y (1982) Thermal Analysis of Trapped Hydrogen in Pure Iron. Metall.Trans. 13A:135-140

Chu Wuyang, Li Shiqiong, Xiao Jimei (1980) Study on High Strength Liquid Steel

Medium Stress Corrosion. Journal of Metallkunde 16(2):179-189

Chu Wuyang (1988) Hydrogen Damage and Delayed Fracture. Beijing: Metallurgical Industry Press,1988, 214

Cui Wenlong, Gu Jialin, Bai Bingzhe, Fang Hongsheng (2007) Study of ultra-long life fatigue of high strength steel with duplex-phase of carbide-free bainite and martensite. Materials Science Forum 539-543, 3: 4532-4537

Liu D Y, Yang Z G, Bai B Z, Fang H S, Yang W Y (2003) The properties of 1500MPa grade alloy steel with carbide free bainite/martensite mixed microstructures. ISIJ International 43(3): 433-437

Devanathan M A V, Stachurski Z (1962) The Adsorption and Diffusion of lectrolytic Hydrogen in Palladium, Proc. Roy. Soc. A270:90-102

Dutta V B, Suresh S, Ritchie R O (1984) Fatigue Crack Propagation in Dual-Phase Steels: Effects of Ferritic-Martensitic Microstructures on Crack Path Morpholigy. Author Affiliation: Lawrence Berkeley Lab, Materials & Molecular Research Div, Berkeley, Calif, USA Source: Metallurgical Transactions A. Jun 1984,vol.15(6): 1193-1207

Fan Changgang, Dong Han, Yong Qilong, Weng Yuqing, et al (2006) Research Development of Ultrahigh Strength Low Alloy Steels. Materials for mechanical engineering 30(8):1-4

Fang Hongsheng, Liu Dongyu, Bai Bingzhe (2001) Latest Development of CFB/M Duplex Phase Steel. Thermal Treatment of Metals 26(10): 6-11

Fang Hongsheng, Tan Zhunli, Bai Bingzhe (2005) Characteristics of Mn-series Bainitic Steels and Its Recent Development. Iron & steel supplement Vol.40: 259-263

Fang Hongsheng, Zheng Yankang, Chen Xiuyun(1988). Air-cooled Bainite Steel. New Materials and Technology 5:3-8

Fleck N A (1984) Fatigue crack Growth-the Complications. Fatigue Crack Growth 30 Years of Progress, Proceedings of Conference on Fatigue Crack Growth Cambridge,UK,20 September 1984: Pergamon Press 76-78

Fleck N A, Smith R A (1982) Crack Closure is it Jest a Surface Phenomenon? International Journal of Fatigue 1982:157-160. Correction in International Journal of Fatigue. October, 1982:234-238

Fu Ming, Qiu Yaojian (1988) Effect of Molybdenum on Tempering Martensitic Brittleness of Medial Carbide Silicon-manganese Steel. Iron and Steel 23(7):36-41

Gojic Mirko, Ladislav Kosec (1997) The Susceptibility to the Hydrogen Embrittlement of Low Alloy Cr and CrMo Steels. ISIJ International 37(4):412-418

Gu Jialin (1985) Discussion on Body-centered Cubic(BBC) Alloy Induced Hydrogen Fracture Process: [Doctor's degree Themes]; Beijing: Tsinghua University Department of Materials Science & Engineering, 1985

Gu J L, Wei D Y, Chang K D, Liu D Y, Fang H S, Bai B Z, Yang Z Y, Zhang W Z (2003) A Novel 1500MPa Economic High Strength Steel. Materials Science Forum 426-432: 1475-1480

Gui Zhou, Tan Zhun li, Bai Bing zhe (2006) Effect of Silicon on Microstructure and Properties of Low-Carbon Si-Mn-Cr-Mo Bainite Steel. Heat Treatment of Metals 31(5):4-6

He Jianhong, Tang Xiangyun, Chen Nanping (1989) Diffusion of Hydrogen in （α+γ） Duplex Stainless Steel. Journal of Metallkunde 25(1):A42-A47

He Jianhong (1988) Study on Hydrogen Induced Crack of Ferrite-Austensite Duplex Stainless Steel, [Doctor's degree Themes]; Beijing: Tsinghua University Department of Materials Science & Engineering,1988

Hirth J P, Mehl Medalist R F (1980) Effects of Hydrogen on the Properties of Iron and Steel. Metall. Trans. 11(6): 861-890

Hu Daxin, Wang Jiajun, Yang Zhigang (1995) Transformation Dynamics and Structural Study on Mn-B Air Cooled Bainite Steel. Automobile Technology (1):27-30

Huang Weigang, Xu Rong, Fang Hongsheng (1997) Impact Roughness of Low & Medial Carbon Silicon Air-cooled Bainite Steel. Journal of Iron and Steel Study (2):31-34

Hui Weijun, Donghan, Wang Maoqiu, Chen Silian, Weng Yuqing. (2002) Effect of Vanadium on delayed fracture resistance properties of high strength steel. Metal heat treatment 27(1):10-12

Hui Weijun, Donghan, Wang Maoqiu, Chen Silian, Weng Yuqing (2002) Effect of thermal treatment on delayed fracture resistance properties of 42CrMo steel. Acta Metallurgica Sinica 38(7):715-719

Kang M K, Sun J L, Yang Q M (1990) High-Temperature Transmission Electron Microscopy In Situ Study of Lower Bainite Carbide Precipitation. Metall. Trans. A 21: 853-858

Kikuta Yoneo Araki Takao (1981) Microscopic Redistribution Behaviours of Hydrogen and Fracture Morphology of Hydrogen-Assisted Cracking in High Strength Steel. Hydrogen Effects in Metals. Edited by I M Bernstein and Anthonyw. Thompson. New York, The Metallurgical Society of AIME.,1981, 309-318

Kontt J F (1984) Models of Fatigue Crack Wrowth Fatigue Crack Growth 30 Years of Progress. Proceedings of Conference on Fatigue Crack Growth Cambridge,UK,20 September 1984: Pergamon Press. 31-52

Lee S M, Lee J Y (1986) The Trapping Transport Phenomena of Hydrogen in Nickel. Metall. Trans. 17A:181-187

Lee Yongwon, Gangloff Richard P (2007) Measurement and modeling of hydrogen environment-assisted cracking of ultra-high-strength steel. Metallurgical and Materials

Transactions A: Physical Metallurgy and Materials Science, v 38 A, n 13:2174-2190

Li Helin, Zhangyi, Luo Baohuai (1982) Study on Tempering Temperature of 20CrMnSiMoVA and 20SiMn2MoVA steels. Metal heat treatment (8):20-26

Li Huilu,Gao Kewei,Qiao Lijie,et al (2001) Threshold Stress Intensity of Hydrogen-Induced Cracking and Stress Corrosion Cracking of High   Strength Steel. J. Iron and Steel Res., Int. 8(2):42-46

Liou H Y, Shieh R I, Wei F I, et al (1993) Roles of Microalloying Elements in Hydrogen Induced Cracking Resistant Property of HSLA Steels. Corrosion 49(5):389-398

Liu Cheng , Zhao Zhenbo, Bhole S D (2006) Lathlike upper bainite in a silicon steel. Materials Science and Engineering A 434:289–293

Liu Dongyu (2002) Study on 1500MPa Low Carbon CFB/M Duplex Phase High Strength Steel [Doctoral Thesis]. Beijing: Tsinghua University , April , 2002

Liu Dongyu, Xuhong, Yangkun, Bai Bingzhe, Fang Hongsheng (2004) Effect of Bainite /Martensite Duplex Phase Structure on Strength and Roughness of Low-carbon Alloy Steel. Acta metallurgica Sinica 40(8):882-886

Liu Xiaokun, Wang Jianjun, Lu Minxu (1993) Corrosion Fatigue Crack Growth of Martensite and Bainite Structure GC-4 Ultra-High Strength Steel. Journal of Metallkunde B,29(12):533-539

Lunarska E, Nikiforow K, Sitko E (2004) Stress corrosion cracking of bainite 0.3C-1Cr-1Mn-1Si-1Ni type steel in acid rain simulated solution. Materials and Corrosion v 55, n 5:373-380

Manolatos P,Unirec C Duret Coze J,et al (1988) Electrochemical Permeation of Hydrogen in Pure Iron and Low Alloy Steels. Influence of the Passive Layer Formed on the Exit Side, 4th International Conference, Edited by Pierre Azou, Chen Nanping,Beijing, 1988, May,9-13

McNabb A, Foster P K (1963) A New Analysis of the Diffusion of Hydrogen in Iron and Ferritic Steels. Trans. Aime 227,618-627

Miihkinen V T T, Edmonds D V (1987) Fracture Toughness of two Experimental High-Strength Bainite Low-Alloy Steel Containing Silicon. Materials Science and Technology 6(3):441-449

Murakami Yukitaka, Uemura Yujiro, Natsume Yoshitaka, Miyakawa Susumu (1990) Effect of mean stress on the fatigue strength of high-strength steels containing small defects or nonmetallic inclusions Source. Nippon Kikai Gakkai RonbunshuA.Hen/Transactions of the Japan Society of Mechanical Engineers Part A v 56 n 525: 1076-1581

Nam W J, Choi H C (1997) Effects of Silicon, Nickel, and Vanadium on Impact Toughness in Spring Steels. Mater. Sci. &Tech. 13(7): 568-574

Parvathavarthini N, Saroja S, Dayal R K, et al (2001) Studies on Hydrogen Permeability of

2.25%Cr-1% Mo Ferritic Steel: Correlation with Microstructure. Journal of Nuclear Materials 288:187-196

Peterson M H, Brown B F, Newbegin R L, et al (1967) Stress Corrosion Cracking of High Strength Steels and Titanium Alloys in Chloride Solutions at Ambient Temperature. Corrosion 23(5):142-148

Pound, Bruce G (2003) Irreversible hydrogen trapping in high-strength alloys. Proc. of the International Conference on Hydrogen Effects on Material Behaviour and Corrosion Deformation Interactions, 2003, p 93-103, Sep 22-26 2002, Moran, WY, United States

Pressouyre G M (1979) A Classification of Hydrogen Traps in Steel. Metall.Trans. 10A:1571-1573

Pressouyre G M, Bernstein I M (1978) A Quantitative Analysis of Hydrogen Trapping. Metall. Trans. 9A:1571-1579

Pressouyre G M (1980) Trap Theory of Hydrogen Embrittlement. Acta Metall. 28(7):895-911

Ramage R M, Jata K V, Shiflet G J, et al (1987) Effect of Phase Continuity on the Fatigue and Crack Closure Behavior of a Dual-Phase Steel. Author Affiliation: Univ of Virginia, Charlottesville, VA, USA Source: Metallurgical Transactions A. Jul 1987,vol.18A(7): 1291-1298

Ren Xuechong, Chu Wuyang, Li Jinxu, Qiao Lijie, Su Yanjing (2007) Effect of MnS inclusions on hydrogen diffusion in steel. Beijing Keji Daxue Xuebao/Journal of University of Science and Technology Beijing, v 29, n 2:232-236, Language: Chinese

Ritchie R O, Castrocedeno M H, Zackay V F, Parker E R (1978) Effect of Silicon Addition and Retained Austenite on Stress-Corrosion Cracking in Ultrahigh Strength Steel. Metallurgical Transactions A-Physical Metallurgy and Materials Science 9(1):35-40

Ritchie R O, Chang V A, Paton N E (1979) Influence of Retained Austenite on Fatigue Crack Propagation in HP9-4-20 High Strength Alloy Steel. Fatigue of Engineering Materials and Structures Vol.1(1):107-121

Sandoz G (1972) A Unified Theory for Some Effects of Hydrogen Source, Alloying Elements and Potential on Crack Growth in martensitic AISI 4340 Steel. Met. Trans. 3:1169-1176

Shih C H, Averbach B L, Cohen M (1956) Some Effect of Silicon on the Mechanical Properties of High Strength Steels. Transactions of the A.S.M. 48:66-118

Steigerwald E A , Benjamin W D (1971) Effect of Composition on the Environmentally Induced Delayed Failure of Precracked High-strength Steel. Metall. Trans. 2(2):606-608

Stewart A T (1980) The Influence of Environment and Stress Ratio on Fatigue Crack Growth at Near Threshold Stress Intensities in Low-Alloy Steel. Engineering Fracture Mechanics 13(3): 463-478

Suzuki H, Mcevily A J (1979) Microstructural Effects on Fatigue Crack Growth in A low-Carbon Steel. Metall Trans A 10 (4): 475-481

Tan Wenzhi, Du Yuanlong Fuchao (1988) Cathodic Protection Induced Hydrogen Embrittlement of ZC-120 Steel in Seawater. Material Protection 21(3):10-13

Tan Zhunli, Bai Bingzhe, Fang Hongsheng, et al (2005) The Effect of Si on the Toughness of High Strength Mn-Si-Cr Series Bainitic Steels. Materials science forum (475-479): 213-216

Thomas Richard L S, Li Daoming, Gangloff Richard P., Scully John R. (2002) Trap-governed hydrogen diffusivity and uptake capacity in ultrahigh-strength

Tomita Y, Okabayashi K (1985) Mechanical Properties of 0.40 Pct C-Ni-Cr-Mo High Strength Steel Having a Mixed Structure of Martensite and Bainite. Metall.Trans. 16A(1):73-82

Tomita Y, Okabayashi K (1983) Improvement in Lower Temperature Mechanical Properties of 0.40Pct C-Ni-Cr-Mo Ultrahigh Strength Steel with the Second Phase Lower Bainite. Metall.Trans. 14A:485-492

Tomita Y (1995) Mechanical Properties of Modified Heat Treated Silicon Modified 4330 Steel. Mater. Sci & Technol. 11:259-263

Tomita Y, Okawa T (1995) Effect of Modified Heat Treatment on Mechanical Properties of 300M Steel. Mater. Sci & Technol. 11:245-251

Tsay L W, Chi M Y, Wu Y F, Wu J K, Lin D Y (2006) Hydrogen embrittlement susceptibility and permeability of two ultra-high strength steels. Corrosion Science, v 48, n 8:1926-1938

Turnbull A, Hutchings R B (1994) Materials Science and Engineering A177:161-171

Wang Qingyuan (2002) fatigue study on ultra-high strength steel with one billion frequencies. Mechanical Strength 24(1):81-83

Wang Xiaojing (1979) Metal Brittleness. Material Protection (2-3):11-25

Watkinson F, Boniszewski T (1973) Effect of Weld Microstructures on Hydrogen-Induced Cracking in Transformable Steels: Part 1. Metals and Materials 2:90-96

Wu-Yang Chu, Chi Mei Hsiao,Wen-Xue Li, et al (1984) Investigation of Stress Corrosion Cracking of the Cast and Forged Steel in Water. Metall.Trans. 15(11):2087-2092

Wu-Yang Chu, Chi Mei Hsiao, Bai Ji Xu (1986) Stress Corrosion Cracking in High Strength Steel under Mode III Loading. Metall. Trans. 17(4):711-716

Xiao Jimei (1990) Metal Corrosion under the Action of Stress. Beijing: Chemical Industry Press,1990,372

Xu Jian, Dai Xinmin, Xia Yuzhu (1981) Corrosion Metallkunde and Anti-corrosion Metal Materials. Zhejiang: Zhejiang Science and Technology Publishing House. 1981,77

Zakroczymski Tadeusz (1999) Electrochemical Determination of Hydrogen in Metals.

Journal of Electroanalytical Chemistry 475:82-88

Zhang Mingxing, Kang Mokuang (1993) Relation between mechanical stability and strength and roughness of granular bainitic retained austenite. Journal of Metal Thermal Treatment 14(1):14-19

Zheng Wenlong, Yu Qing (1988) Environmental Susceptive Fracture of Steel. Beijing: Chemical Industry Press, 1988,145

Zhou Dehui, Tan Yun (1998) Environmental Hydrogen Embrittlement and Testing Technology of Metal. Beijing: National Defence Industry Press, 1998,6-10/19

8
Extra Low Sulfur and Non-metallic Inclusions Control for Ultra Fine Grain High Strength Steels

In the past twenty years, cleanliness of steel products has been significantly increased, by which properties of steel products have been largely improved. Among the extra fine grain high strength steels, the HSLA steel grades for hot rolled heavy plates request extra low sulfur and the high strength alloying special steel grades for gears, springs, shafts, etc. demand extra low oxygen and non-metallic inclusions control. In this chapter, technologies for producing extra low sulfur heavy plate grades are introduced, including hot metal desulfurization pretreatment, measures against S (Sulphur) element content increase during BOF (basic oxygen furnace) steelmaking, extra low S secondary refining, etc. For extra low oxygen special steels, technologies of deoxidation of liquid steel, high basicity slag secondary reefing, non-metallic inclusion control, etc. are introduced.

8.1　Introduction

Properties of steel products, e.g. the ductility, toughness, workability, welding, anti erosion property, etc. can be greatly improved by increasing cleanliness of steel, i.e. decreasing contents of impurities like S, P, O, etc. As shown in Figure.8.1, in the past of thirty years, cleanliness of steel has been increased remarkably. Taking [C], [P], [S], [N], T[O] for instance, in 1970s, they could only be eliminated mostly to 0.006%, 0.01%, 0.0022%, 0.0027% and 0.0024% respectively. However, in 1990s, their minimum concentrations could be lowered to 0.0009%, 0.0011%, 0.0002%, 0.0011% and 0.0006% respectively. In future, as the requests of customers for property control of steel products will be more strict, further increasing cleanliness of steels will be of more importance.

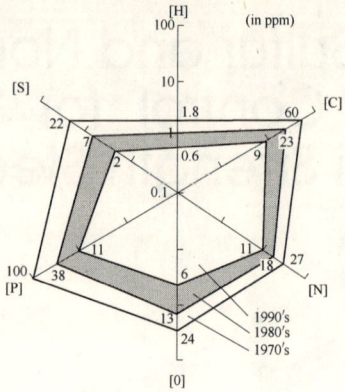

Figure 8.1 The elimination limits of the impurities in steels in 1970s, 1980s and 1990s respectively

There is no unique definition for the term of "Clean Steel". The following concept has been widely accepted that, when the cleanliness of one steel does not lower its fabrication capability or in-service properties, then the steel is considered clean and no need to pursue extra cleanliness for saving cost. Among the extra fine grain high strength steels, the HSLA steel grades for hot rolled plates request extra low sulfur control for guarantee the ductility, welding, anti HIC properties, etc. and the high strength alloying special steel grades for gears, springs, shafts, etc. demand extra low oxygen and non-metallic inclusions control for getting good fatigue properties.

In this chapter, technologies in two respects will be mentioned. One is the refining technology for the extra low sulfur steels for high strength hot rolled steel plates and another one is the technology for extra low oxygen and non-metallic inclusions control of high strength alloying steels.

8.2　Refining Technology for Extra Low Sulfur Steels

Sulfur in most of steels exits in form of MnS. The detrimental influences of sulfur on properties of the high strength steel plates are:
1. Lowering the ductility and low temperature toughness.
2. Increasing the direction difference of the mechanical properties, i.e., the ductility of the steel in not rolling direction is lower than that in rolling direction.
3. Resulting in severe segregation in the cast slabs.
4. Decreasing properties of welding, anti SCC, anti HIC, etc. of the steels.

As shown in Figure 8.2(Kozawa K, 1977), [S] largely lowers the ductility of the steel plates on direction of thickness of the plates. Taking the low temperature impacting toughness (vE$_0$) for instance, even when [S] is eliminated to about 0.0030%, the difference of vE$_0$ between the direction of length and thickness of the plates is still 4kg·m. Only when [S] content is decreased to less than 0.0010%, can the difference of vE$_0$ be largely decreased. Now, sulfur in high strength steel plates of important uses, e.g. for high buildings, big bridges, ocean structures, etc., has to be controlled below 0.0060%. Sulfur in line pipe steels should be less than 0.0030%. For anti HIC line pipe steels, [S] is requested to be at least less than 0.0010%.

In integrate steelworks, methods of hot metal desulfurization pretreatment, BOF blowing and ladle refining are used for producing the extra low sulfur steels.

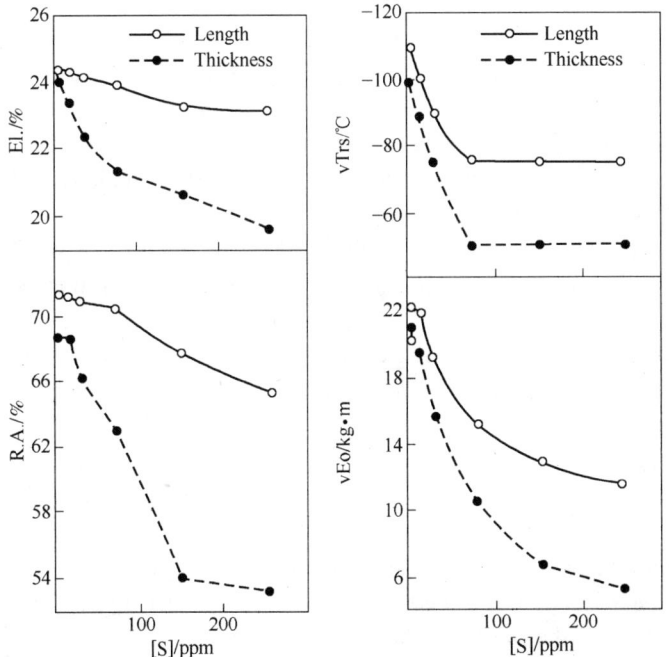

Figure 8.2   Influence of [S] on properties of 800MPa strength hot rolled steel plates

8.2.1 *Hot metal De-S pretreatment*

The history of hot metal desulfurization pretreatment has been more than 50 years. Comparing with desulfurization in basic oxygen converter steelmaking (BOF), the activity of sulfur is high and oxygen is low in the hot metal. So, the desulfurization efficiency is higher in hot metal desulfurization pretreatment. Previously, soda ash, Mg-coke, lime, CaC$_2$, etc. were used as desulfurization fluxes in hot metal pretreatment. Now, owing to environment regulation, uses of soda ash and CaC_2 are decreasing. The main fluxes used currently are CaO-CaF_2, CaO-CaC_2, Mg, Mg-CaO, etc.

The reactions of CaO, CaC_2 and Mg in desulfurization fluxes with [S] in the pretreatment are

$$CaO(s) + [S] + [C] = (CaS) + CO \qquad (8.1)$$
$$\Delta G^{\ominus} = 350266 - 182.15T(\text{Turkdogan E T, 1996})$$
$$CaC_2(s) + [S] = (CaS) + 2[C] \qquad (8.2)$$
$$\Delta G^{\ominus} = -333125 + 66.56T(\text{Turkdogan E T, 1996; Kubaschewiski O et al, 1967})$$
$$Mg(g) + [S] = MgS(s) \qquad (8.3)$$
$$\Delta G^{\ominus} = -325950 + 98.77T(\text{Turkdogan E T, 1996})$$

It is known that Mg and CaC_2 have stronger desulfurization abilities than CaO by comparing $\Delta G^{\ominus}$ values of reaction 8.1 ~ 8.3. Although $\Delta G^{\ominus}$ value of reaction 8.1 is positive, as hot metal contains higher carbon and silicon which largely increase the activity of [S], high enough De-S efficiency can also be obtained when lime is used as De-S flux. Now, there are mainly two types of fluxes used in De-S pretreatment. One is lime based flux and another is Mg based flux. [S] in hot metal after the treatment can be eliminated from 0.02%~0.035% to less than 0.005% or even less.

Mainly two hot metal desulfurization processes are used now. One is the powder injection method and another is the mechanical stirring method (KR). In powder injection De-S process, N_2 of high pressure is used as carrying gas to inject powders of lime, Mg, CaF_2, etc. into the hot metal contained either in ladles or in torpedo cars (Figure 8.3).   The advantage of the injecting method is:

1. Large reaction interfaces owing to the fine powders.
2. Relatively simpler equipments and less investment.
3. Able to inject powders of Mg deeply into the metal which decreases the vaporization loss of Mg.

The main weakness of the injection method is the insufficient stirring for the hot metal in large capacity torpedo containers. When the injected powders float up to the top surface of the metal, as the stirring is not strong, desulfurization of the metal by the top slag is influenced.

In KR desulfurization pretreatment, which was developed by Nippon Steel in 1980s, fluxes of CaO-CaF_2 or CaO-CaF_2-CaC_2 are added on top surface of the hot metal. A mechanical stirrer lined with refractory is inserted into the hot metal and rotated to agitate the metal (Figure 8.3). Comparing with powder injection process, in KR treatment, the stirring to the interface between the top slag and the metal is stronger so that higher De-S efficiency can be obtained (Figure 8.4). Recently, many Japanese steel works which used to use injection De-S methods have changed to use KR. Many newly installed steel plants in China recently tend to adopt KR for hot metal desulfurization pretreatment.

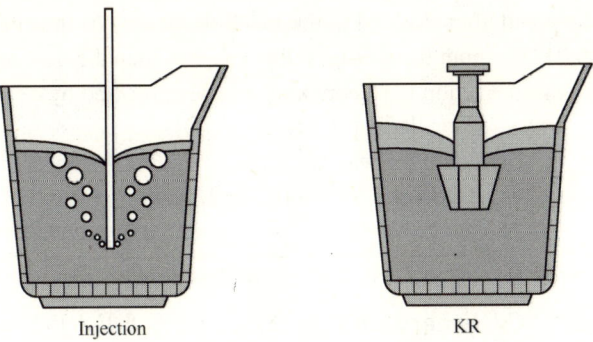

Figure 8.3 Illustration of injection De-S and KR De-S pretreatment

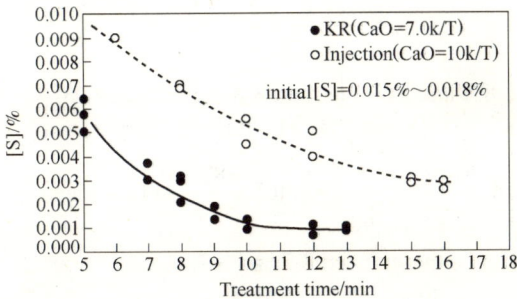

Figure 8.4 Relationship between treatment time and [S]
after treatment(Ueki T, Fujiwara K et al,2004)

8.2.2 *Reducing [S] pick up in BOF steelmaking*

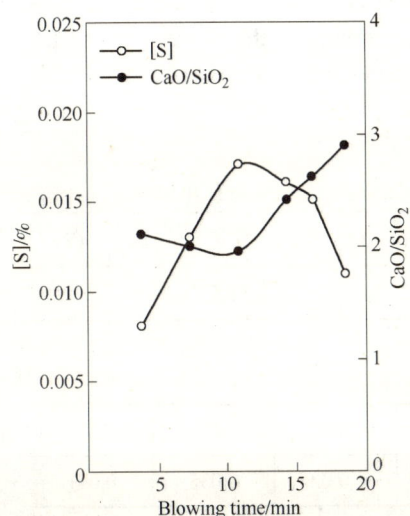

Figure 8.5 Change of [S] content
and slag basicity during BOF blowing

In BOF steelmaking, if the hot metal has not been subjected to De-S pretreatment, desulfurization of the liquid metal can take place and the desulfurization degree is between 25% to 40%. However, when De-S pretreated hot metal is blown in BOF, no desulfurization can be expected. Usually, [S] content of the liquid steel after BOF blowing is higher than [S] in the pretreated hot metal.

Figure 8.5 shows an example of [S] change during BOF steelmaking. The sulfur content of the hot metal after De-S pretreatment is 0.0050%. After O_2 blowing starts, [S] in molten metal rapidly increases. The increase of [S] reaches maximum at 12 min blowing time and after that, [S] in the metal decreases. At the end of blowing, [S] is around 0.012%, about 0.007% of sulfur increase than the hot metal.

Reaction of desulfurization in steelmaking can be expressed by

$$[S]+(O^{2-})=(S^{2-})+[O] \qquad (8.4)$$

Equilibrium of the reaction 8.5 was investigated by F.D. Richardson(1954).

$$1/2S_2(g)+(O^{2-})=(S^{2-})+1/2O_2(g) \qquad (8.5)$$

$$K_S = \frac{a_{S^{2-}}}{a_{O^{2-}}} \cdot \sqrt{\frac{P_{O_2}}{P_{S_2}}} = \frac{f_{S^{2-}} \cdot (\%S)}{a_{O^{2-}}} \cdot \sqrt{\frac{P_{O_2}}{P_{S_2}}} \qquad (8.6)$$

Sulfide capacity Cs(Richardson F D, Fincham C J B,1954) was definited as

$$C_S = \frac{K_S \cdot a_{O^{2-}}}{f_{S^{2-}}} = (\%S) \cdot \sqrt{\frac{P_{O_2}}{P_{S_2}}} \qquad (8.7)$$

From reactions 8.4 and 8.5, reaction 8.8 can be obtained.

$$[S]+1/2O_2(g)=[O]+1/2S_2(g) \qquad (8.8)$$

$$\log K_8 = \log\left(\frac{a_{[O]}}{a_{[S]}} \cdot \sqrt{\frac{P_{S_2}}{P_{O_2}}}\right) = 1.467 - \frac{828.6}{T} \text{ (Turkdogan E T, 1996)} \qquad (8.9)$$

Equation 8.10 can be drawn from 8.7 and 8.9,

$$\log L_S = \log\frac{(\%S)}{[\%S]} = 1.467 - \frac{828.6}{T} + \log f_{[S]} + \log C_S - \log a_{[O]} \qquad (8.10)$$

Where, L_S is sulfur distribution coefficient between slag and steel, C_S is sulfide capacity of slag, $a_{[O]}$ is activity of oxygen in liquid steel, $a_{[S]}$ is activity of sulfur in liquid steel, $f_{[S]}$ is activity coefficient of sulfur in liquid steel.

Table 8.1 shows an example of the chemical compositions of the liquid steel and slag at the end of BOF blowing. The temperature of the molten steel at the blowing end was 1640°C. From the activity interaction parameters shown in Table 8.2, the activity coefficient of [S] is calculated.

$$f_{[S]}=1.012$$

Table 8.1　Chemical compositions of the liquid steel and slag at the end of BOF blowing (%)

[C]	[Si]	[Mn]	[P]	[S]	(MgO)	(Al₂O₃)	(SiO₂)	(CaO)	(T.Fe)	(S)
0.07	<0.015	0.08	0.01	0.019	7.03	1.38	14.18	51.54	14.60	0.15

Table 8.2　Activity interaction parameters in liquid steel at 1600°C (Ishii,Fuwa,1981;Gama,Etwa,1970;Ban,Chipman, 1969)

j	S	C	Si	Mn	P	Al
e_S^j	−0.046	0.111	0.075	−0.026	0.035	0.041

I.D. Sommerville et al. investigated the sulfide capacities in slags and found relations between C_S and the optical basicity (Λ) of slags as shown by equation 8.11. The optical basicity of the slag can be calculated with equation 8.12.

$$\log C_S = \frac{22690 - 54640\Lambda}{T} + 43.6\Lambda - 25.2 \tag{8.11}$$

$$\Lambda = \frac{\sum i X_{A_zO_y} \cdot \Lambda_{A_zO_y}}{\sum i X_{A_zO_y}} \tag{8.12}$$

where, i is oxides in slag, $X_{A_zO_y}$ is mole fraction of oxide A_xO_y in slag, $\Lambda_{A_zO_y}$ is calculated optical basicity of A_xO_y.

From Equation 8.11 and 8.12, the sulfide capacity of the slag shown by Table 8.1 is calculated as

$$\mathrm{Log}C_S = -1.745$$

The activity of oxygen $a_{[O]}$ in liquid steel which contains 0.07% carbon is about 0.035 at the end of BOF blowing. With this $a_{[O]}$ and the above calculated $f_{[S]}$ and C_S, the equilibrated sulfur distribution between the slag and steel is calculated as

$$L_S = (S)/[S] = 5.62$$

In addition, in BOF steelmaking, sulfur is also brought into the melt by scraps, fluxes, etc. Based on the above calculation, it is roughly known that, if the total amount of sulfur carried by all of the raw materials into the furnace makes L_S larger than 5.6, there will be sulfur pick up taking place during the BOF steelmaking. In contrast, if L_S is less than 5.6, there will be desulfurization.

Table 8.3   Sulfur contents of raw materials and the De-S slag

Substances	S/%
Hot metal	0.005
Scrap	0.04
Pig iron	0.03
Lime	0.011
Raw dolomite	0.015
Hot metal De-S slag	1.0~2.2

Table 8.3 shows an example of sulfur contents of raw materials for BOF steelmaking. Based on the data shown in Table 8.3, the quantities of the raw materials and the carried hot metal De-S pretreatment slag, the percentage of sulfur carried into the BOF furnace is calculated as shown in Figure 8.6.

It is known from Figure 8.6 that sulfur in BOF comes mainly from the hot metal, scrap and the hot metal De-S pretreatment slag. In order to decrease [S] pick up, measures should be taken to eliminate as more as possible the slag from the charging ladle after De-S pretreatment and use low sulfur content scrap or reduce the scrap charging ratio.

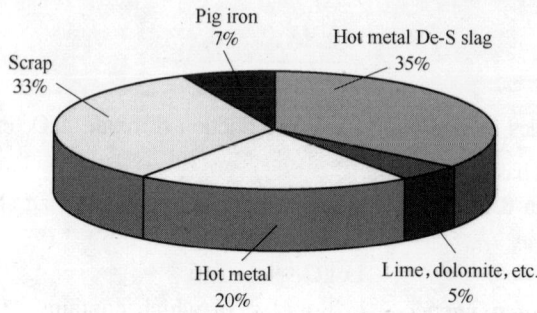

Figure 8.6　Percentage of sulfur brought into BOF by hot metal, scrap, fluxes, De-S slag, etc.

8.2.3　*Desulfurization in secondary refining of liquid steel*

Secondary refining plays an important role for production of extra low sulfur steel. The main secondary refining processes for desulfurization are LF (ladle furnace), TN, KIP, V-KIP, etc.

CaO is mainly used as the desulfurization flux in secondary refining. The desulfurization reaction can be written as

$$[S]+(CaO)=(CaS)+[O] \tag{8.13}$$
$$\Delta G^{\ominus}=371510-143.24T(\text{Turkdogan E T, 1996})$$

The distribution ratio of sulfur between the slag and the molten steel can be obtained from 8.13 as

$$\log[\%S]=\log\frac{[\%O]\cdot a_{CaS}}{a_{CaO}}+\frac{19400}{T}-7.48 \tag{8.14}$$

It is known from equation 8.14 that, in order to get high efficient desulfurization, it is necessary to decrease [O] content of the liquid steel, decrease the activity of S in the slag and use high basicity (CaO/SiO_2) slag.

It is effective and also economic to use Al to lower [O] content of the liquid steel. When liquid steel contains more than 0.015% Al, [O] can be decreased to less than 0.0005%. Actually, in all secondary refinings for desulfurization, deoxidation of the liquid steel by Al has to be carried out firstly. Al contents of steels usually are between 0.02% to 0.05%. The chemical reaction of desulfurization can be written as

$$(CaO)+2/3[Al]+[S]=(CaS)+1/3(Al_2O_3) \tag{8.15}$$
$$\Delta G^{\ominus}=-31688-11.47T(\text{Turkdogan E T, 1996})$$

It is also necessary to decrease FetO content of the slag in desulfurization refining. Al and CaC_2 are usually added into the slag to decrease FetO to about 0.5% or even less. In addition, SiO_2 content of the slag should also be decreased by reducing slag carry over during BOF tapping, using low SiO_2 fluxes and using low SiO_2 ladle linings. If the slag contains more SiO_2, reaction shown by equation 8.16 will take place, which decreases [Al] content and affects the desulfurization efficiency.

$$2[Al]+3/2(SiO_2)=(Al_2O_3)+3/2[Si] \tag{8.16}$$
$$\Delta G^{\ominus} = -325044+49.86T (\text{Turkdogan E T, 1996})$$

The equilibrium constant of reaction 8.15 can be written as 8.17.

$$K_S = \frac{f_{CaS} \cdot (\%S) \cdot a_{Al_2O_3}^{1/3}}{[\%S] \cdot a_{CaO} \cdot [\%Al]^{2/3}} \tag{8.17}$$

Equation 8.18 can be derived from 8.17

$$\frac{(\%S)}{[\%S]} = \frac{a_{CaO}}{f_{CaS} \cdot a_{Al_2O_3}^{1/3}} \cdot [\%Al]^{2/3} \cdot K_S \tag{8.18}$$

When CaS in slag reaches saturation

$$a_{CaS} = f_{CaS} \cdot (\%S)_{sat} = 1 \tag{8.19}$$

$$f_{CaS} = \frac{1}{(\%S)_{sat}} \tag{8.20}$$

Substitute 8.20 into 8.18,

$$\frac{(\%S)}{[\%S]} = \frac{a_{CaO} \cdot (\%S)_{sat}}{a_{Al_2O_3}^{1/3}} \cdot [\%Al]^{2/3} \cdot K_S \tag{8.21}$$

Y. Ogura, et al(1986) and K. Kawakami, et al(Ogura Y, Kiguchi Y et al, 1982) defined the term of Slag Parameter (S.P.) by 8.22

$$(S.P.) = \frac{a_{Al_2O_3}^{1/3}}{a_{CaO} \cdot (\%S)_{sat}} \tag{8.22}$$

Equation 8.23 can be obtained by substituting 8.22 into 8.21.

$$\frac{(\%S)}{[\%S]} = \frac{[\%Al]^{2/3}}{(S.P.)} \cdot K_S \tag{8.23}$$

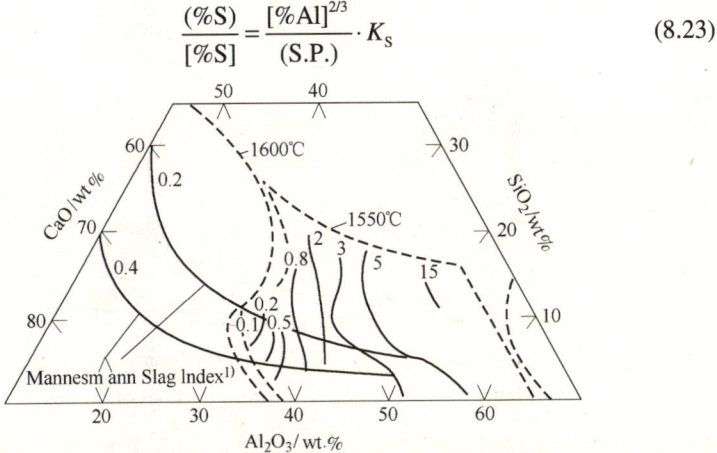

Figure 8.7 Values of (S.P.) in slag at 1550℃

It is known from 8.22 and 8.23 that (S.P.) depends only on slag composition and reaction temperature. Figure 8.7 shows the values of (S.P.) calculated by K. Kawakami, et al (Ogura Y, Kiguchi Y et al, 1982) in $CaO-SiO_2-Al_2O_3$ system slag. It is seen that the slag with minimum values of (S.P.) locates around the place of $60\%CaO-30\%Al_2O_3-10\%SiO_2$, which means that high desulfurization degree can be expected if slag with this chemical composition is used. NKK(Ogura Y, Kiguchi Y et al, 1986) reported that very low sulfur steel ([S]: 0.0002%~0.0005%) was produced by using this type slag and top lance Ar stirring in ladle refining.

When [S] is eliminated to very low in secondary refining, transfer of [S] in liquid steel will be the rate control step of the desulfurization reaction. Thus, in secondary refining of extra low sulfur steel, it is necessary to take measures to increase the stirring of the liquid steel in the ladle. Usually, Ar bubbling is widely adopted to stir the molten steel in secondary refining. The unit stirring energy can be calculated by Equation (8.24)(Fukumoto I, 1988).

$$\bar{\varepsilon} = \frac{0.0285Q \cdot T}{W} \times \log\left(1 + \frac{H}{148}\right) \tag{8.24}$$

where, $\bar{\varepsilon}$ is unit stirring energy (W/t), Q is flowrate of stirring gas (Nl/min), T is temperature of liquid steel (K), H is depth of the steel in the ladle (cm).

The stirring energies of different secondary refining methods are shown in Figure 8.8(Tanizawa K,Okumura H et al, 1990). It is seen that, blowing Ar or injecting powders into steel under vacuum has much stronger stirring energy than that of common LF, RH, etc. So, in Nippon Steel, Dillingen Steel, etc., method of vacuum powder injection (Figure 8.9) are adopted and [S] can be eliminated to less than 0.0005% after the refining.

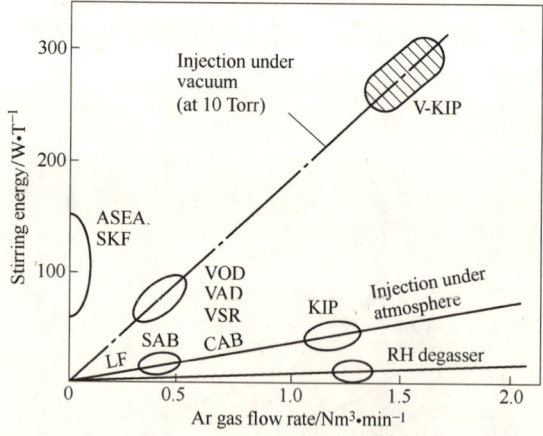

Figure 8.8　Comparison of stirring energies of various secondary refining methods

The technologies of the secondary refining used for extra low sulfur steels mainly are:

1. Desulfurization during BOF tapping.

2. Desulfurization in ladle furnace refining.
3. Injection of powders under vacuum.

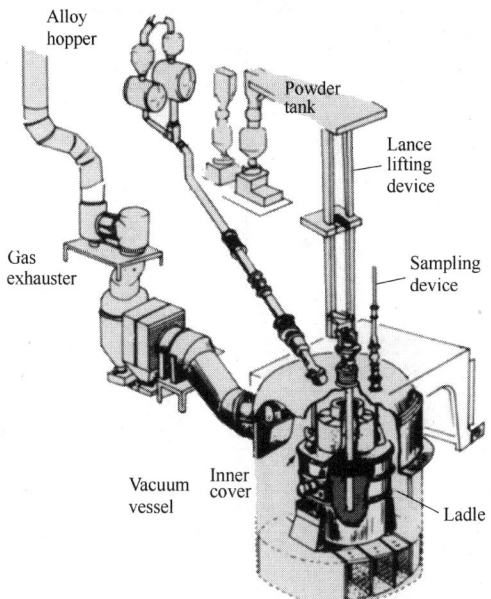

Figure 8.9   Illustration of V-KIP refining process developed by Nippon Steel

8.2.3.1   Desulfurization during BOF tapping

During BOF tapping, liquid steel is tapped from the converter through the tapping hole into the ladle. The stream of the steel strongly agitates the liquid steel bath in the ladle. For producing extra low sulfur steel, this agitation of the molten steel should be taken use of for early slag making and desulfurization.

Desulfurization of the liquid steel during BOF tapping includes the following operations:

1. Deoxidizing the liquid steel with Al during the tapping and [Al] content should be more than 0.015%.
2. Adding desulfurization fluxes (usually using $CaO-CaF_2$ system flux) into the ladle during the tapping.
3. Preventing BOF slag carried into the ladle.
4. The slag in the ladle should be controlled around 60% CaO, 30% Al_2O_3 and 10% SiO_2.

Experiments were carried out by the author to make desulfurization of the liquid steel during BOF tapping, in which, fluxes, Al and Mn-Si alloys were added during BOF tapping and samples of metal and slag were taken before the tapping, immediately after the tapping and when the steel was sent to the location of ladle furnace. It is seen in Table 8.4 and Table 8.5 that desulfurization did take place during BOF tapping and the desulfurization ratio could be 50%~85%.

Table 8.4   [S] contents in liquid steels

Heat	[S] contents/%			De-S ratio/%
	Before tapping	After tapping	After the ladle sent to LF	
1	0.009		0.004	55.56
2	0.01	0.007	0.005	50.00
3	0.008	0.004	0.003	62.50
4	0.008	0.005	0.003	62.50
5	0.007	0.004	0.001	85.71
6	0.008	0.004	0.002	75.00
7	0.008	0.004	0.002	75.00
8	0.008	0.006	0.003	62.50

Table 8.5   Chemical compositions of slags before LF refining (%)

Heat	Al_2O_3	CaF_2	CaO	MgO	MnO	S	SiO_2	T.Fe
1	23.81	4.21	53.58	5.67	1.42	0.16	9.89	0.53
2	25.58	3.29	48.27	6.21	2.96	0.10	10.72	1.12
3	24.77	3.29	49.56	7.02	1.95	0.13	10.06	1.90
4	29.64	5.14	52.94	5.36	0.52	0.15	6.93	0.32
5	36.30	3.80	47.47	5.23	0.46	0.15	6.07	0.39
6	22.02	4.93	54.58	6.19	0.64	0.18	7.12	2.50
7	34.46	3.74	48.43	5.73	0.57	0.21	5.63	1.25
8	24.12	4.93	55.81	5.95	0.73	0.18	8.58	0.95

Figure 8.10 and Figure 8.11 respectively show the relationship between slag basicity CaO/SiO_2, slag T.Fe content and desulfurization degree of steel during the time BOF tapping and transportation of the ladle from BOF to the LF station. It is

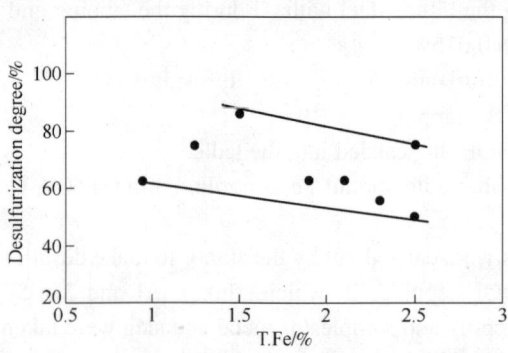

Figure 8.10   Effect of slag T.Fe content on desulfurization degree during the time of BOF tapping and the ladle transportation

seen that desulfurization is largely affected by the slag composition. For getting more than 50% desulfurization degree, slag T.Fe content should be less than 2% and slag basicity should be higher than 6.

Figure 8.12 shows the relationship between the sulfur slag-metal distribution ratio and the Mannesmann Index of the slag ($CaO/SiO_2/Al_2O_3$). It is seen that, when the Mannesmann Index is controlled at about 1.5, higher sulfur distribution ratio is obtained.

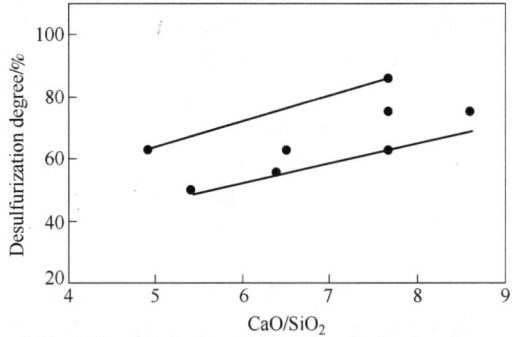

Figure 8.11   Effect of slag Basicity on desulfurization degree during the time of BOF tapping and the ladle transportation

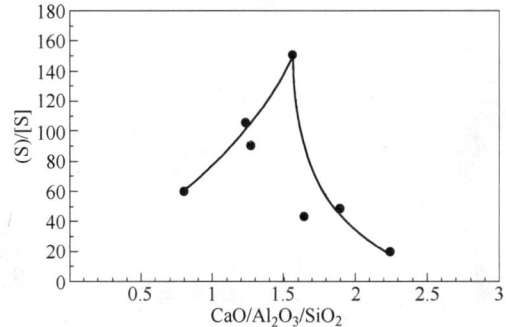

Figure 8.12   Relation between the slag Mannesmann Index and the sulfur partition ratio (S)/[S]

8.2.3.2   Desulfurization in ladle furnace refining (LF)

Ladle furnace refining (LF) was developed by Nippon Steel in 1970s and is now widely used for secondary refining of steels. As external heat can be supplied to liquid steels through electrodes, it is easier to make new slag than other refining processes. In addition, diffusive deoxidation of the liquid steels can also be easily made in LF, through which low T.Fe content slag can be made. Thus, LF is most widely used for producing extra low sulfur steels.

In LF refining of extra low sulfur steels, [Al] contents should be more than

0.015% to decrease [O] (soluble oxygen in liquid steel) to less than 0.0004%. The slag volume should be more than 12kg and the slag T.Fe content should be less than 0.6%. As mentioned above, in order to make low (S.P.) slag, the CaO, SiO₂ and Al₂O₃ contents of the slag should around 60% CaO, 10% SiO₂ and 30% Al₂O₃.

Figure 8.13 and Figure.8.14 illustrate the ladle refining method developed by NKK(Ogura Y,Kiguchi Y et al,1986) for producing extra low S steels ([s]≤ 0.004%) In this praess,method of VSC was used to absorb the top slag on the steel bath in the ladle after BOF tapping. In the ladle reefing (NK-AP), the composition of the slag was controlled around 60% CaO, 8% SiO₂ and 32% Al₂O₃. When [S] was eliminated to low content level, in order to still get fast desulfurization, a lance was inserted from above into the steel bath to blow Ar to stir the molten steel (GI treatment) and the Ar flow rate reached as more as 2000Nl/min. With this method, [S] can be decreased maximum to 0.0002%.

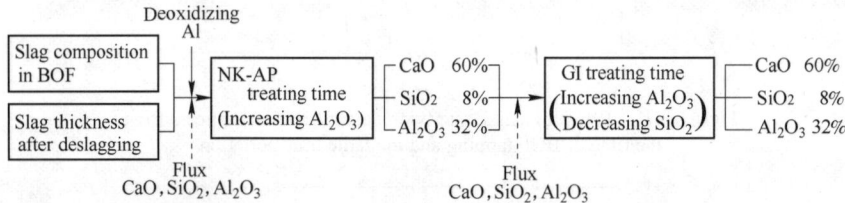

Figure 8.13　Illustration of the ladle refining for extra low S steels by NKK

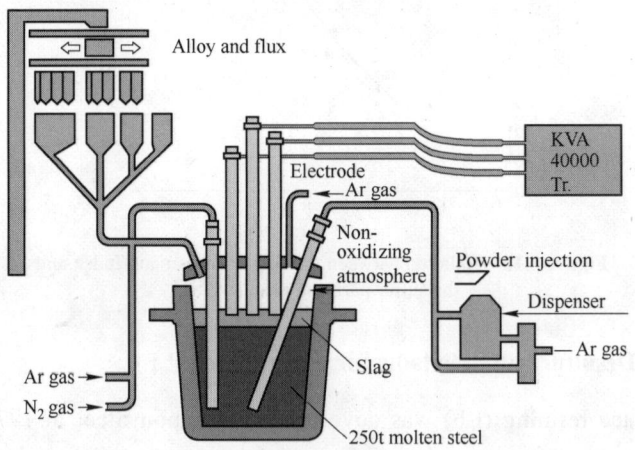

Figure 8.14　Illustration of the ladle refining process used by NKK

8.2.3.3　Powder injection desulfurization methods

As early as in 1970s, powder injection methods like TN, KIP, etc. were developed, in which powders of CaSi, CaO-CaF₂, etc. were injected into liquid steels in ladles and sulfur in steels could be quickly removed to less than 0.0010% owing to the strong stirring of the steel and the large reaction interfaces between steels and the powders. However, in traditional powder injection processes, liquid steels were easily exposed to air due to the strong agitation, which increased [N] content and resulted in serious reoxidation of steels.

In order to avoid the reoxidation and nitrogen absorption of the molten steel, Sumitomo Metal Industry, Ltd(Watanabe Y et al, 1984; 1985). developed a powder injection method (Figure.8.15), in which a large diameter snorkel was inserted into the liquid steel which provided an inert atmosphere during the injection. The desulfurization powders consisted of about 85% CaO and 15% CaF_2 and the flowrate of the carrying gas Ar was 3~4Nm^3/min. After the injection, sulfur in the steel was decreased to less than 0.0005%. Later, Nippon Steel(Inetomi J, Yamashita K et al, 1988) also developed its powder injection desulfurization method also with an inserted snorkel and [S] could be removed to less than 0.0010%.

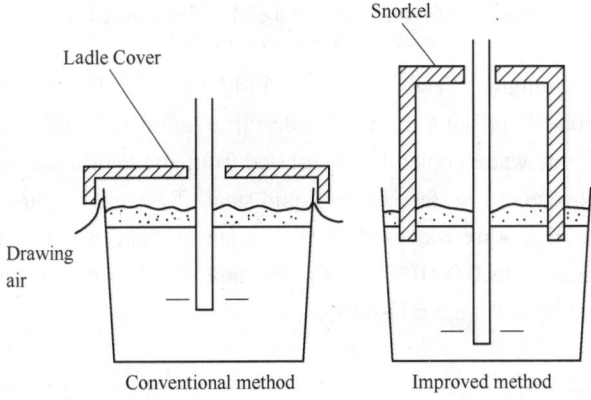

Figure 8.15   Illustration of powder injection with large diameter snorkel

Nippon Steel(Tanizawa K, Okumura H et al, 1990) developed vacuum tank powder injection desulfurization method named as V-KIP. As shown in Figure 8.9, in V-KIP process, the ladle is located inside the vacuum tank and powders of desulfurization fluxes are injected into the liquid steel. As the molten steel can be very strongly stirred in V-KIP, very high desulfurization degree can be obtained. It was reported that, with about 25 minutes treatment by V-KIP, [S] could be eliminated to less than 0.0005%(Tanizawa K, Okumura H et al, 1990). Moreover, elimination of [H] can be done simultaneously with desulfurization, which largely saves the time for the secondary refining compared with the traditional LF desulfurization plus vacuum de-hydrogen secondary refining route.

In some Japanese steelworks, methods of powder injection in RH degassing are used for desulfurization of liquid steel. Figure 8.16 shows the process developed by Nippon Steel(Yagura S et al, 1986) in which the injection lance was inserted into the steel at the place just below the up leg of the snorkel. Powders of 60%CaO-40%CaF$_2$ were injected into the liquid steel and [S] could be eliminated to about 0.0005% .

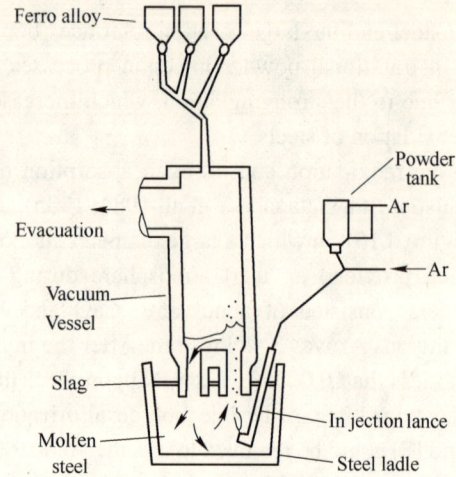

Figure 8.16   Illustration of the RH powder injection
desulfurization method by NSC

In 1990s, Sumitomo Metal Industries, Ltd(Okada Y, 1992). developed top powder injection RH refining method for desulfurization of liquid steel. As shown in Figure 8.17, one water cooled lance inserted from above into the vacuum vessel and injected powders on surface of the liquid steel. [S] could be removed to about 0.0005% when 5kg/t flux was used. If the amount of flux increased to 8kg/t, [S] could be eliminated to 0.00013%~0.00029% and the distribution ratio of sulfur between slag and metal were 600~1100.

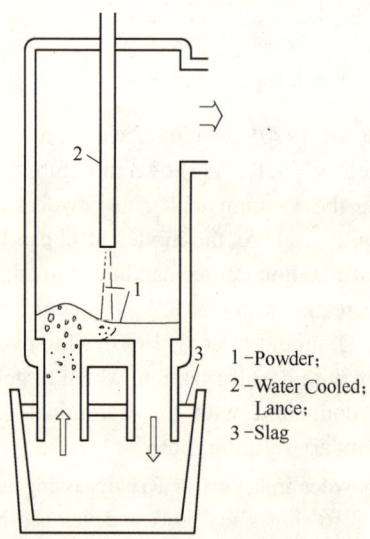

1 –Powder;
2 –Water Cooled;
  Lance;
3 –Slag

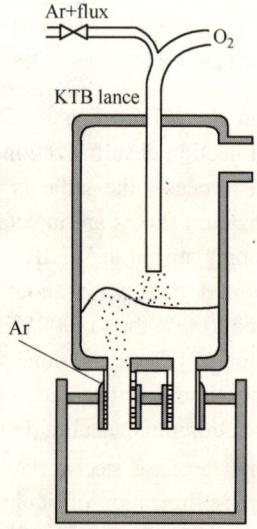

Figure 8.17   RH-TPB desulfurization
method developed by SMI

Figure 8.18   Top powder injection
desulfurization method developed by KSC

Kawasaki Steel(Uehara H, 1992) also developed RH powder injection desulfurization method based on the technology of RH-KTB. As shown in Figure.8.18, the top lance used for blowing O_2 in RH-KTB was also used for injection of powders for desulfurization. They used three types of fluxes of CaO, CaO -10%MgO - 27%CaF$_2$ and CaO -18%Al$_2$O$_3$-18%CaF$_2$ and the desulfurization degree was about 30% when 4kg/t of fluxes were used. When the flux was increased to 7kg/t, the desulfurization degree could be increased to about 60%.

8.3 Extra Low Oxygen and Non-metallic Inclusions Control of High Strength Alloying Steels

Alloying structure steels include a lot of steel grades, which contain 0.18%~1% carbon and some alloying elements like Mn, Si, Mo, Cr, V, Ti, etc. The strength of the alloying structure steels is between 600 ~2000MPa and they are mainly used for making machine parts like shafts, gears, springs, bearings, etc. These parts are subjected to stresses which changed periodically and reversely and failures of these parts are often caused by fatigue fractures.

Figure 8.19(Melander A, Larsson M, 1993) shows the failure probabilities of specimens of steels under five stress amplitudes between 800MPa to 1200MPa. It can be seen that the failure probability of high strength steel is higher than the lower strength steel.B-I,Klevebring (1976) found that, when strength of steel is higher than one definite value (critical strength), non-metallic inclusions in steels will affect their fatigue lives. It is considered that, the higher the strength of the steel, the larger of the influence of the non-inclusions on the fatigue property of the steel.

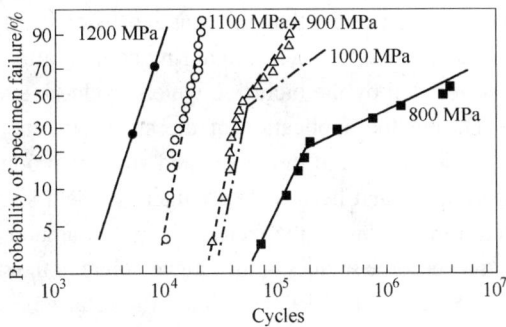

Figure 8.19 Weibull plot of probability of specimen failure at five stress amplitudes loaded at $R=-1$

S. Li et al.(Weng Y Q, 2003) investigated the fatigue property of the 42CrMoVNb steel and found that most of the fatigue fractures were initiated from non-metallic inclusions at high stress amplitude. They also found that the possibility of the initiation of fracture from non-metallic inclusions was high for steels with finer grain (1~2μm) structure. They explained that, in fine grain steels, grain slipping is evener and cracking is difficult to occur. However, once the cracking is generated, the resistance to the expansion of the crack is smaller. So, the initial cracking is easily to develop and can quickly result in fracture failure of the steel.

8.3.1   *Influence of non-metallic inclusions on fatigue property of steel*

D.Brooksbank and K.W.Andrews(Brooksbank D, Andrews K W, 1968; Brooksbank D, 1970; Brooksbank D, Andrews K W, 1970) explained the influences of different types of non-metallic inclusions on properties of steels based on the theory of tessellated stresses. They explained that the non-metallic inclusions constituted tessellate structures in steels. During heating or cooling of steels, tessellated stresses formed owing to the difference of the heat expansion coefficients between steels and the inclusions. The stress depended on the heat expansion coefficients, temperature, shape of the inclusions, etc. as shown by Equation (8.25). The field in which the steel was subjected to the tessellated stress was about four times of the diameter of the inclusion. If there were more inclusions existed, the tessellated stress field caused by individual inclusion would superpose.

$$\sigma_T = \pm\psi(\alpha_m - \alpha_i)\Delta T \tag{8.25}$$

where, σ_T is tessellated stress, α_m and α_i are the heat expansion coefficients of steel and non-metallic inclusions respectively, ΔT is the temperature change and ψ is the coefficient which is related to the elastic coefficient, shape and distribution of the inclusions, location and direction of the stresses.

According to the theory of tessellated stresses, if the heat expansion coefficient of the non-metallic inclusion is less than the heat expansion coefficient of the steel, contraction of the steel around the inclusion during cooling after high temperature deformation will be resisted by the inclusion which produces tensile stress in this zone of the steel. During the application of the steel part, the external stresses which the steel is subjected to and the tessellated stresses produced owing to the inclusions can superimpose and become larger than the yield strength of the steel. Micro cracking may form owing to the increased stresses around the inclusion and these micro cracks may become sources of the fatigue failure of the steel parts.

R. Kiessling and H. Nordberg(1970) defined the relative deformation index v of non-metallic inclusion (equation (8.26)) and used it to explain the influence of the non-metallic inclusions on properties of steels. They explained that, during the deformation of steel at high temperature, the inclusions which were well deformed could keep close contact with steel during and after the deformation. According to S. Rudnik(1966), for the non-metallic inclusions with the relative deformation index v between 0.5 to 1.0, it was difficult for micro cracks to form at the interfaces between the inclusions and steels. For the inclusions with v of 0.03 to 0.5, cone or fishtail typed micro empties were easy to occur. While, when v was zero, occurrence of cone typed empties and hot tearing cracks would be very often.

$$v = \frac{\varepsilon_i}{\varepsilon_s} = \frac{2}{3} \cdot \frac{\ln\lambda}{\ln h} = \frac{2}{3} \cdot \frac{\lg\lambda}{\lg h} \tag{8.26}$$

$$\varepsilon_i = \ln\lambda = \ln\frac{b}{a} \tag{8.27}$$

$$\varepsilon_s = \frac{3}{2}\ln h = \frac{3}{2}\ln\frac{A_0}{A_1} \tag{8.28}$$

In Equation (8.26) ~ (8.28), b is the size of the non-metallic inclusion along the deformation direction, a is the size of the inclusion at the direction perpendicular to the deformation, A_0 is the section area of the steel before the deformation and A_1 is the section area of the steel after the deformation.

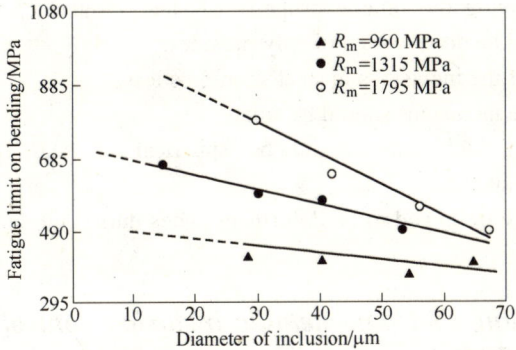

Figure 8.20 Influence of non-metallic inclusions with different sizes on fatigue limit of steel

The detrimental effect of the non-metallic inclusions on the fatigue property of steel largely depends on the number, size, shape, distribution and hot deformation ability of the of the inclusions. Figure 8.20 (Zhang S, 1981) shows the relation between the fatigue limit of steel on bending and the size of non-metallic inclusions. It is seen that the fatigue limit of steel decreases with increasing size of the inclusions. W.E. Duckworth et al.(1963) used the term of "critical size" to explain the influence of the non-metallic inclusions on fatigue properties of steels, i.e., if the inclusions were smaller than the critical size, their detrimental effect on fatigue property of steel could be neglected.

It should be pointed out that value of the critical size depends on the distance of the non-metallic inclusion from the surface of the steel part. Compared with the inclusions locating inside the steels, the detrimental effect of the inclusions locating at the surfaces or sub-surface areas are much severer. Actually, most fatigue fractures are generated owing to the inclusion locating at surface or near surface of the steel part. Therefore, sizes of the non-metallic inclusions which locate at surfaces are not important. Even very small inclusions can be sources of fatigue fracture if they exist at surfaces or near surfaces of steel parts.

Shape of the non-metallic inclusion also largely affects the fatigue property of steel. Stress concentration is easy to occur at places around inclusions with small curvature radius. Fatigue fractures are easier to occur at places around wedge angle shaped inclusions than spherical shaped inclusions and expansion of the fractures around wedge angle shaped inclusions is also faster. So, the detrimental effect of the block and wedge angle shaped inclusions on fatigue property of steel is larger than that of spherical shaped inclusions.

Whether or not the non-metallic inclusions are deformable during the hot deformation of steel also affects the fatigue property of steel. If the inclusions can not be deformed during hot rolling of steel, there will be cone typed empties, micro cracks, etc. formed at the interfaces between steel and the inclusions. These empties and cracks can be the sources of the fatigue fractures of the steel parts.

So, for improving the fatigue property of steel, control of the non-metallic inclusions should be done, which mainly includes:

1. The number of the inclusions in steel should be less.
2. The size of the inclusions should be small.
3. Most of the inclusions should be spherical or near spherical shaped (symmetrical shaped).
4. The inclusions are hoped to be deformable ones during the hot deformation of steel.

8.3.2   *Refining and non-metallic inclusion control of extra low oxygen alloy steels*

Dimension of the non-metallic inclusions is closely correlated to number of the non-metallic inclusions, which means that the inclusions in steels containing more inclusions are larger on average than the inclusions in steels containing less inclusions. Thus, key of the inclusion control for high strength alloy steel is to decrease the number of the inclusions in the steel, i.e. to decrease the T[O] content of the steel.

Figure 8.21 shows the relationship between the T[O] content of bearing steels produced by Sanyo Special Steel(Tsubota K, Fukumoto I, 1990) and the fatigue life of the bearings manufactured. The steel T[O] content largely affects the fatigue life of the bearing. When T[O] is reduced from 0.0020% to 0.0005%, the fatigue life of the bearing increased from about 2×10^6 to $2 \times 10^7.$ Currently, in production of steels for bearings, gearing, shafts, springs, etc., measures of reducing T[O] to decrease the contents of non-metallic inclusions are adopted and the T[O] contents for these steels are controlled to be less than 0.0012%. For bearing steels, T[O] contents have been decreased even to below 0.0005%.

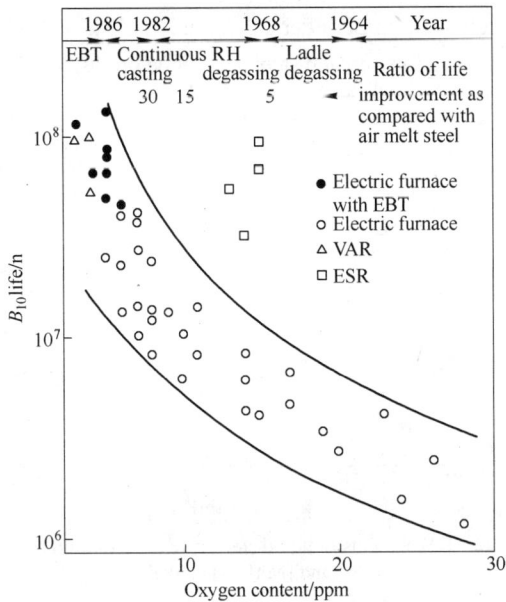

Figure 8.21 Relationship between the T[O] content of the steel and the fatigue life of the bearings

The refining of the extra low T[O] alloying structural steels mainly includes:
1. Deoxidation of the steels by Al.
2. Using high basicity (CaO/SiO$_2$) slag in ladle furnace refining (LF).
3. Diffusion deoxidation in LF refining.
4. Using low SiO$_2$ ladle linings.
5. Well stirring the steel in ladle refining to promote the aggregation and floating up of the inclusions.
6. Vacuum treatment.

The deoxidation reactions of steel by [Si], [Mn], [Al] can be expressed by
$$[Si]+2[O]=SiO_2(s) \tag{8.29}$$
$$\Delta G^\ominus=-589700+230.3T \text{ (Melander A, Larsson M, 1993)}$$
$$[Mn]+[O]=MnO(s) \tag{8.30}$$
$$\Delta G^\ominus=-285334+123.89T \text{ (Melander A, Larsson M, 1993)}$$
$$2[Al]+3[O]=Al_2O_3(s) \tag{8.31}$$
$$\Delta G^\ominus=-1209594+395.31T \text{ (Melander A, Larsson M, 1993)}$$

Assuming the activities of the deoxidation products being 1 and the activity coefficients of [Al], [Si] and [Mn] are 1, the [O] contents in equilibrium with [Si], [Mn]

and [Al] at 1803K can be calculated (Figure 8.22). It is seen that the deoxidation abilities of [Si] and [Mn] are weaker than that of [Al]. Taking the deoxidation by [Si] for instance, at the temperature close to the solidification temperature of steel, there are still several ten ppm oxygen dissolved in the steel if it is deoxidized by Si. The soluble oxygen can no be removed further after solidification of steel. Thus, using [Si], [Mn], etc. for deoxidation, extra low oxygen steel can not be produced.

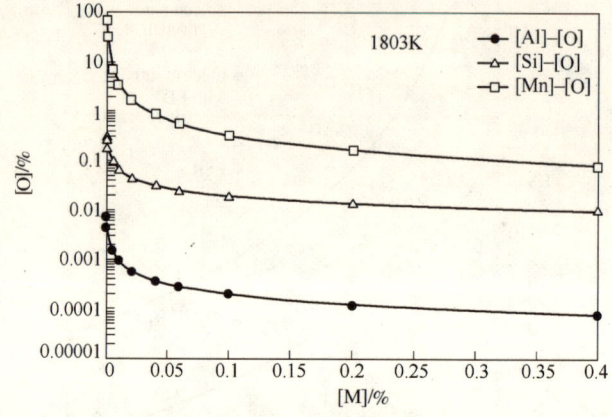

Figure 8.22   [O] contents in liquid steel at 1873K equilibrated with [Al], [Si] and [Mn] respectively

Al is a much stronger deoxidizer than Si and Mn in steels. When liquid steel contains 0.02%~0.05% Al, the soluble oxygen in liquid steel [O] can be decreased to 0.00025%~0.0005%. Most of oxygen in steel before the deoxidation is transferred into Al_2O_3 after Al deoxidation and the main task for decreasing oxygen is changed from chemical deoxidizing reactions to removing the deoxidation products. By properly stirring the liquid steel, making diffusion deoxidation vacuum treatment, etc., steel which contains less than 0.0012% T[O] can be produced.

After the deoxidation by Al, in ladle furnace refining, diffusion deoxidation of the steel has also to be done by adding Al, C, etc. into slag to reduce the contents of FetO, MnO, etc. of the slag. Decreasing FetO content of slag plays two roles:
1. Avoiding the oxidation of [Al] by FetO in the slag which results in increase of T[O] in steel.
2. Accelerating the diffusion deoxidation owing to the low FetO in the slag. Figure 8.23 shows the relation between FetO and MnO contents of slag and T[O] content of steel during LF and RH refinings. It is seen that T[O] could be decreased to less than 0.0010% only after (T.Fe+MnO) in slag was decreased to be less than 0.5%.

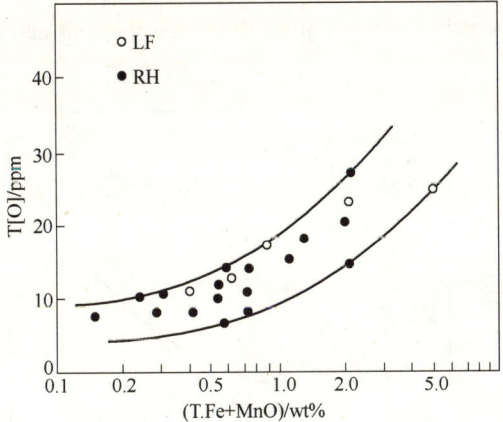

Figure 8.23 The relation between T[O] and (T.Fe+MnO)

During the refining of extra low oxygen steels, if the activity of SiO_2 in the slag is not low, it can be reduced by [Al] as shown by Equation (8.32) and (8.33), which results in increase of T[O] and Al_2O_3 inclusions in steel. Thus, high basicity slag has to be made to decrease the activity of SiO_2 during the refining. In addition, low SiO_2 refractory lining of ladle also has to be used in order to avoid the reaction between [Al] and the SiO_2 in the lining.

$$(FeO)+[Al]=Al_2O_3(s) \tag{8.32}$$

$$3/2(SiO_2)+2[Al]=Al_2O_3(s)+3/2[Si] \tag{8.33}$$

Figure 8.24 and Figure 8.25 show the relations between slag basicity, SiO_2 in slag and T[O] content of steel in LF and RH refining, which was obtained by Sanyo Special Steel(Fukumoto I, 1988). It is seen that, for producing extra low T[O] steel, the slag basicity should be controlled higher than 5 and SiO_2 content of slag should be less than 8%. In order to quickly increase the basicity and decrease FetO content of the slag in ladle refining, it is very

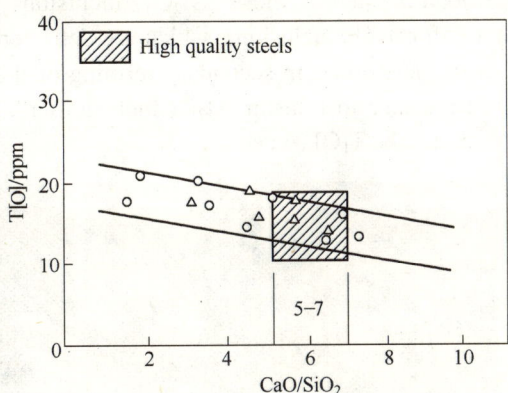

Figure 8.24 Relation between slag basicity and T[O] content

important to reduce the volume of the BOF slag carried into the ladle during BOF tapping. Now, in electric arc furnace steelmaking, eccentric bottom tapping (EBT) is widely adopted to prevent the slag carry over during the tapping. In BOF steelmaking, various devices like hollow ball stopper, dart, gas operated flap gate, thermal image detection, etc. are used to reduce the slag carry over during the tapping.

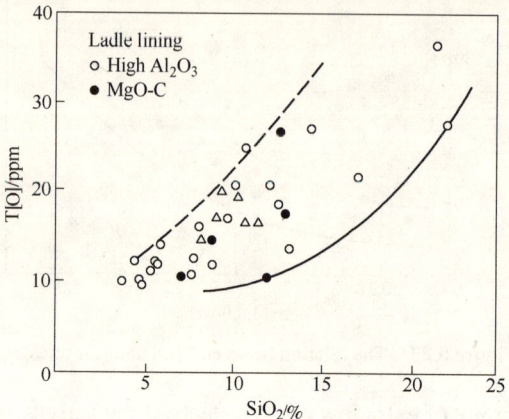

Figure 8.25   Relation between slag SiO_2 and T[O]

When liquid steel is deoxidized with Al, Al_2O_3 is formed either in form of clusters or irregular shaped single Al_2O_3 oxides. Removal of large sized Al_2O_3 products from the liquid steel is fast because of the high surface tension between Al_2O_3 and the molten steel. Thus, after the secondary refining, Al_2O_3 inclusions still remained in liquid steel are small cluster typed or irregular shaped Al_2O_3 inclusions, usually smaller than 25μm (Figure 8.26). For high strength structural steels, these Al_2O_3 inclusions are still too large and are un-deformable inclusions, which are detrimental to the fatigue property of the steels. Therefore, in secondary refining of the high strength alloying steels, it is necessary to transfer Al_2O_3 inclusions (Al_2O_3 modification) in addition to decrease the T[O] content.

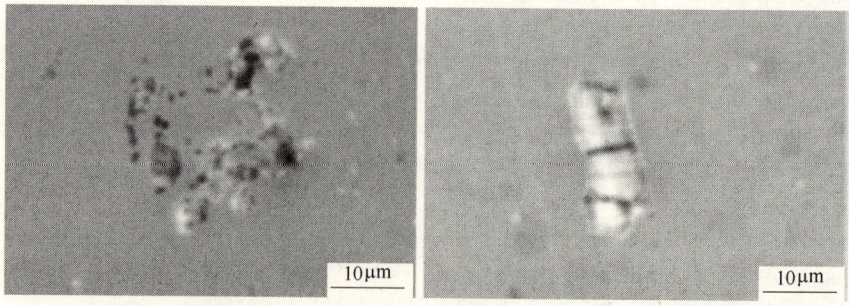

Figure 8.26   Cluster and irregular shaped Al_2O_3 inclusions in Al deoxidized steels

In ladle furnace refining, when high basicity slag is used and the contents of [O] and (FetO) are very low, reactions shown by Equation (8.34) and Equation (8.35) can take place. Once the molten steel contains Ca and Mg, even several ppm, it can make Al_2O_3 inclusions transfer into more stable aluminates of $MgO \cdot Al_2O_3$, $CaO \cdot Al_2O_3$, $12CaO \cdot 7Al_2O_3$, etc.

$$3(CaO)+2[Al]=3[Ca]+(Al_2O_3) \tag{8.34}$$

$\Delta G^{\ominus}=1025856-189.21T$ (Turkdogan E T, 1996; Sponseller D L, Flinn R A 1964)

$$3(MgO)+2[Al]=3[Mg]+(Al_2O_3) \tag{8.35}$$

$\Delta G^{\ominus}=721368-340.86T$ (Turkdogan E T, 1996)

Investigation was done by the author on transfer of non-metallic inclusions in LF refining of gearing steels. Figure 8.27 shows the typical non-metallic inclusions observed in steel samples taken before LF refining. The steel had been deoxidized by Al during BOF tapping. It can be seen that most of the inclusions before LF refining were block or wedge angle shaped Al_2O_3 inclusions.

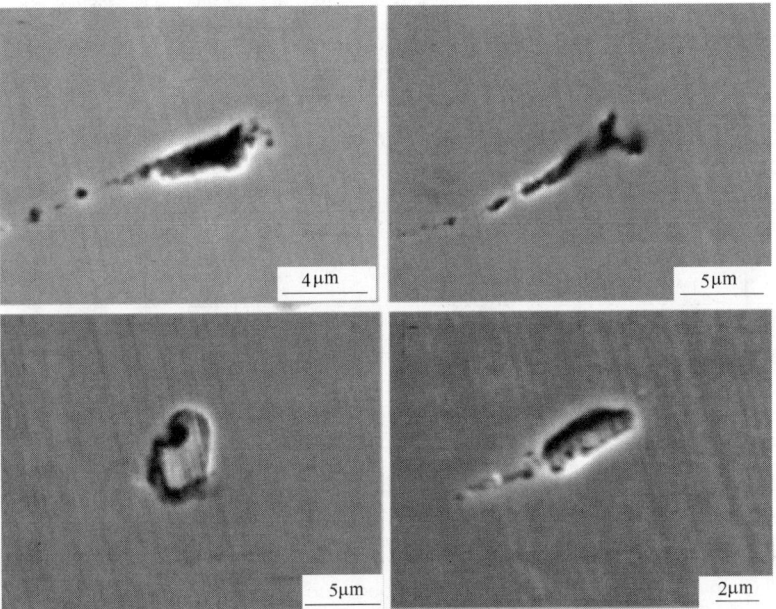

Figure 8.27 Al_2O_3 inclusions in the liquid steel before LF refining

In LF refining in the experiment, high basicity slag was made and enough Al droplets were added into the slag to make strong diffusion deoxidation. At 25min refining time, the slag basicity was about 7 and slag FetO content was 0.6%. Figure 8.28 shows the non-metallic inclusions observed in steel samples which were taken at 25 minutes of LF refining time. As shown by Table 8.6, it did not find Al_2O_3 inclusions and most of the inclusions observed are Al_2O_3-MgO system inclusions spinels which contains about 76%~81% Al_2O_3 and 18%~22% MgO.

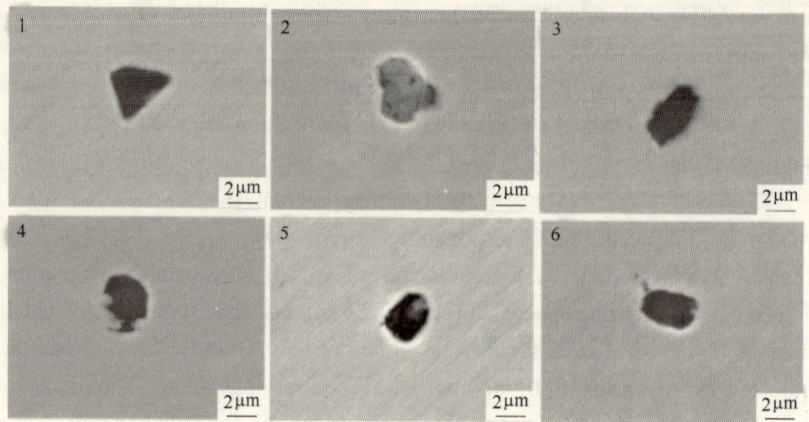

Figure 8.28   Typical non-metallic inclusions in steel specimens taken at 25min after starting LF refining

Table 8.6   Compositions of the non-metallic inclusions shown in Figure.8.28 by SEM-EDS (mass%)

No.	SiO$_2$	MnS	MnO	Al$_2$O$_3$	CaS	TiO$_2$	MgO	Cr$_2$O$_3$	CaO
1				78.73			21.27		
2				77.85			22.15		
3				81.48			18.52		
4		2.63		76.93			20.44		
5				78.36			20.66	0.98	
6				77.88			22.12		

Figure 8.29 shows the non-metallic inclusions observed in specimens taken from the molten steel after LF refining in the experiment. Table 8.7 shows the chemical compositions of the inclusions. It is seen that, after LF refining, content of CaO in the inclusions largely increased and Al$_2$O$_3$ contents decreased. The inclusions are in spherical shape because they are liquid in liquid steels. In addition, as liquid inclusions are easier to be aggregated together and eliminated from the liquid steel, most of the inclusions remained in the steel after LF refining were smaller than 10μm.

It is known from the thermodynamic data that the reduction of MgO in slag by [Al] is easier than the reduction of CaO by [Al] in LF refining of the extra low oxygen steels. This is the main reason why Al$_2$O$_3$ inclusions in liquid steel are firstly transferred to magnesium spinels and then to calcium aluminates. In addition, most of the non-metallic inclusions remaining in molten steel after the refining are small spherical inclusions. They are less detrimental to the fatigue properties of steels.

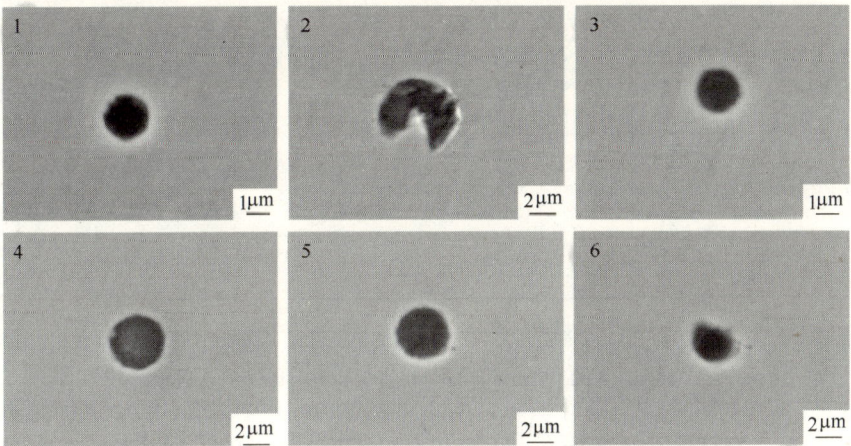

Figure 8.29   Typical non-metallic inclusions in steel specimens
taken at the end of LF refining

Table 8.7   Compositions of the non-metallic inclusions
shown in Figure8.29 by SEM-EDS (mass%)

No.	MgO	Al$_2$O$_3$	CaS	MnS	CaO	MnO	SiO$_2$	Cr$_2$O$_3$	TiO$_2$
1	11.23	44.95	19.12		17.17		2.52	5.01	
2	6.74	:48.42	4.54		40.30				
3	11.61	46.37	2.54		34.52			4.97	
4	25.43	32.43			40.39		1.75		
5	9.96	46.70	8.90		34.44				
6	8.24	36.86	25.53		10.44	17.29		1.63	

Also, it is important to make strong stirring in the ladle refining to promote the aggregation and floatation of the non-metallic inclusions in liquid steel. For extra low oxygen structural steels, the unit stirring power which is calculated by Equation 8.24 should be larger than 100W/t in ladle furnace refining.

In production of high strength alloying steels, usually after LF refining, vacuum degassing treatment by VD or RH has to be done. Figure 30 shows the total oxygen content change in LF and RH treatment of the bearing steel in Sanyo Special Steel(Tsubota K, Fukumoto I,1990). It can seen that T[O] could be decreased to about 0.0015% after LF and 0.0005%~0.0009% after RH.

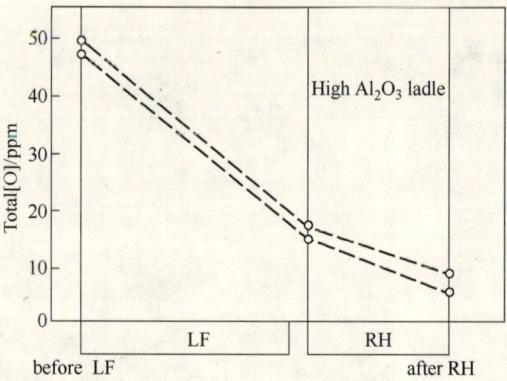

Figure 8.30   Transition of total [O] during the refining

8.3.3   *Deformable non-metallic inclusions for tyre cord and valve spring steels*

As mentioned above, minimizing contents of T[O] and non-metallic inclusions can significantly improve unti-fatigue properties of high strength alloy steels. However, for some steel grades like steels for making tyre cord wires or springs for engine valves of automotives, it is requested that the non-metallic inclusions have to be deformable, i.e., the inclusions can be deformed also during the hot rolling of steels.

Tyre cord steels contain 0.7%~0.95% carbon and the strength of the cord wires are between 2800MPa to 4000MPa. As shown in Figure 8.31, in tyre cord manufacturing, wire rods of about ϕ5.5mm are firstly drawn into thin filaments of ϕ0.15~0.38mm and then, the filaments are stranded with more than 2000r/min rotation speed into the cords. It is known that, if the non-metallic inclusions are larger than 2 percent of the diameter of the filament, the filament is very easy to be broken during cold drawing and stranding. Furthermore, even there is no broken taking place during drawing and stranding, broking of the filament is still easy to occur during the later dynamic fatigue test. Fracture of the tyre cords are also easy to occur during use of the tyre if the inclusions are un-deformable ones. Thus, in tyre cord steels, the non-metallic inclusions should be small (less than 10μm) and deformable ones.

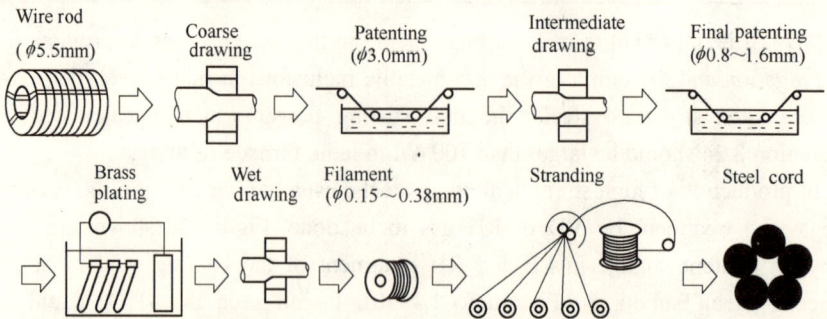

Figure 8.31   Illustration of the tyre cord wire manufacturing

Springs used for engine valves of automotives are made from oil tempered steel wires and their strength is around 1950MPa. It is requested that the fatigue life of the valve springs be more than 10^8 cycles under alternative reverse shearing stress of 700MPa. Recently, the strength of the valve springs has been increased to about 2100MPa. As shown in Figure 8.32, when the strength of the spring wires is lower than 1900MPa, the fatigue limit of the steel increases with the increase of the strength. However, the fatigue limits fluctuate when strength of spring wire is over 1900MPa, which is considered to be aroused by the non-metallic inclusions in steels. It was found that, if the steel contains un-deformable inclusions like Al_2O_3, SiO_2, $CaO \cdot Al_2O_3 \cdot 2SiO_2$ etc., micro cracks are easy to form around the inclusions during the cold drawing of the steel wires. These micro cracks might be sources of fatigue fractures during the application of the springs. Thus, it is necessary to make non-metallic inclusions in form of deformable ones in valve spring steels.

| | Initiation of fracture | | Chemical composition/mass% | | | | |
	Inclusion	Surface	C	Si	Mn	Cr	V
Si Cr steel	●	○	0.55	1.40	0.70	0.70	
Cr V steel	●	△	0.67	0.25	0.75	0.50	0.20
Plan Carbon steel	●	□	0.67	0.25	0.75		

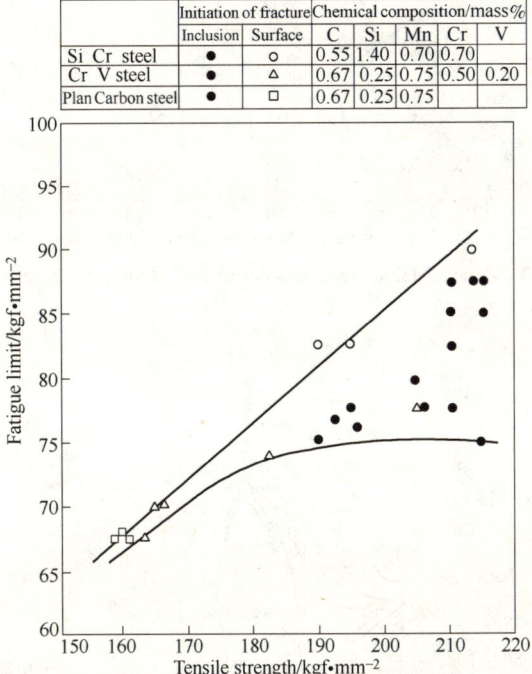

Figure 8.32 Relation between tensile strength and fatigue limit (after shot peening)

8.3.3.1 Deformable non-metallic inclusions

T. Gladman(1992) investigated the deformation indexes of (Fe,Mn)O, Al_2O_3, spinel typed complex oxides, silicates, sulfides, etc. and fund that inclusions of Al_2O_3, calcium aluminates, spinel and cristobalite were un-deformable at hot deformation temperatures of steels. G . Bernard (Malm S, 1976) investigated the deformation properties of inclusions of CaO-Al$_2$O$_3$-SiO$_2$ and MnO-Al$_2$O$_3$-SiO$_2$ system. It is considered that, for MnO-Al$_2$O$_3$-SiO$_2$ system, inclusions which chemical compositions are around 3MnO · Al$_2$O$_3$ · 3SiO$_2$ (shadow areas in Figure 8.33) are deformable inclusions. In CaO-Al$_2$O$_3$-SiO$_2$ system, inclusions around CaO · Al$_2$O$_3$ · 2SiO$_2$ and CaO · SiO$_2$ (shadow areas in Figure 8.34) are deformable ones.

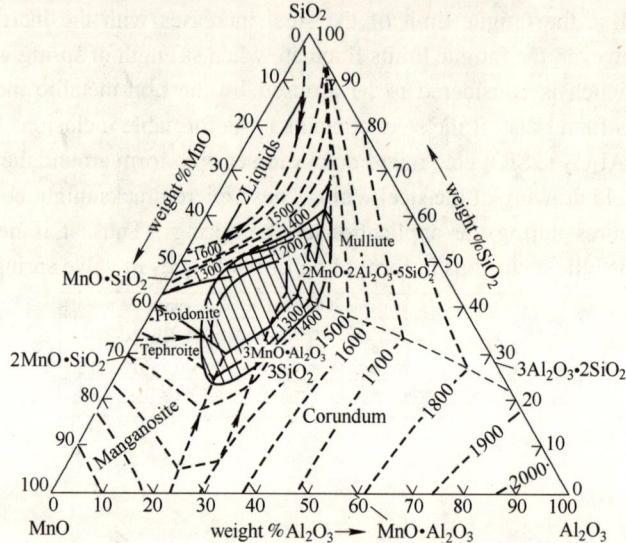

Figure 8.33 Zone of deformable inclusions in MnO-SiO$_2$-Al$_2$O$_3$ ternary system

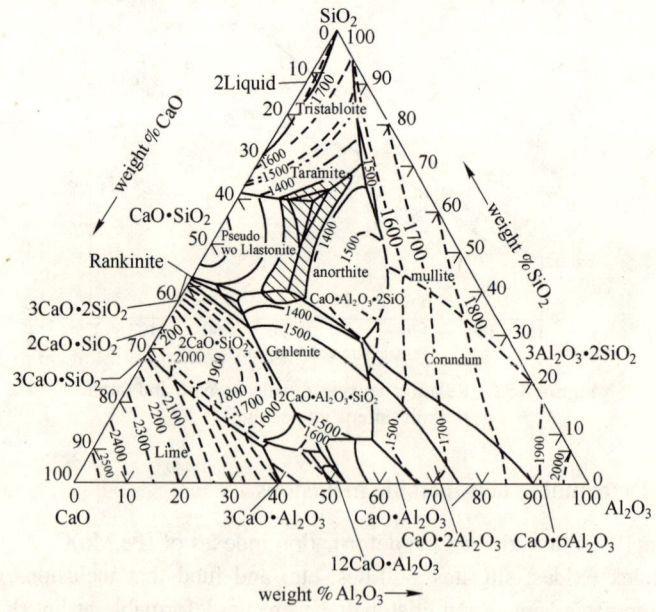

Figure 8.34 Zone of deformable inclusions in CaO-SiO$_2$-Al$_2$O$_3$ ternary system

It can be seen in Figure 8.33 and Figure 8.34 that the chemical composition rang of the deformable inclusions in $MnO-SiO_2-Al_2O_3$ system is 20%~60% MnO, 60%~27% SiO_2 and 12%~28% Al_2O_3. In $CaO-SiO_2-Al_2O_3$ system, the chemical composition rang of deformable inclusions is 20%~45% CaO, 70%~40% SiO_2 and 12%~25% Al_2O_3. Kobe Steel(Okushima I, 1988) investigated the fatigue lives of the valve springs and found that the non-metallic inclusions in the springs which had good fatigue life located in the marked area in Figure 8.35. It is seen that Al_2O_3 contents of the inclusions are 20%~30%.

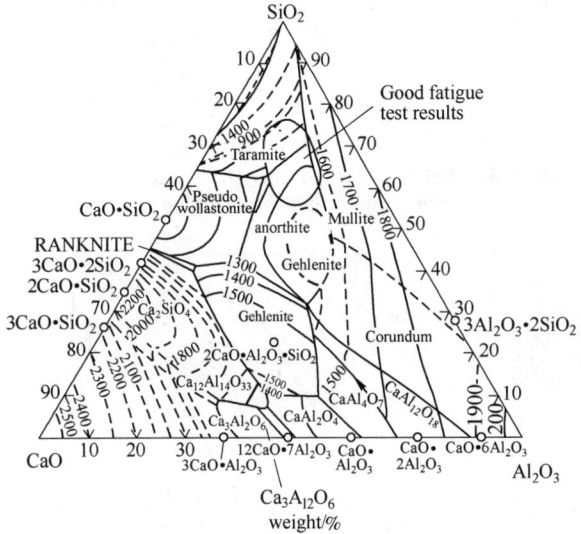

Figure 8.35　Composition of the inclusions in valve springs with good fatigue lifes

8.3.3.2　Control of [Al] in liquid steel

As mentioned above, Al_2O_3 contents of deformable non-metallic inclusions of $CaO-SiO_2-Al_2O_3$ system and $MnO-SiO_2-Al_2O_3$ system are between 12% to 30%. Figure 8.36 shows the influence of Al_2O_3 content on deformability of the inclusions and Figure 8.37 shows the relation between contents of Al_2O_3 of non-metallic inclusions and [Al] in tyre cord steels investigated by Kobe Steel(Okushima I, 1988). It can be seen that [Al] should be controlled within the range of 0.0002% to 0.0006% so that Al_2O_3 content of the inclusions can be controlled between 12% to 30%. If [Al] is less than this range, un-deformable inclusions like SiO_2 will form. On the other hand, if [Al] is higher than this range, un-deformable inclusions containing higher Al_2O_3 will form. Actually, in production of tyre cord steel and valve spring steel, deoxidation of liquid steel can only be done with Si, Mn. Aluminum contents of ferro alloys of Fe-Si, Fe-Mn, etc. have to be very tightly controlled.

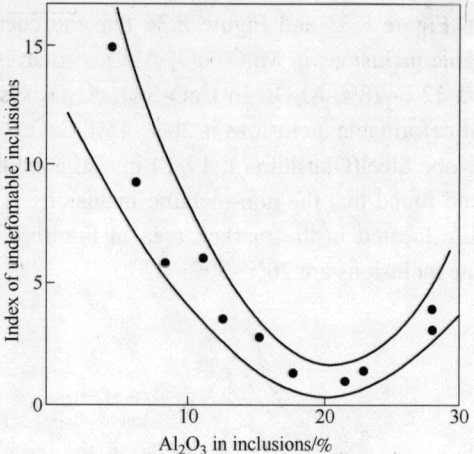

Figure 8.36　Relation between Al_2O_3 in inclusions and the index of the un-deformable inclusions

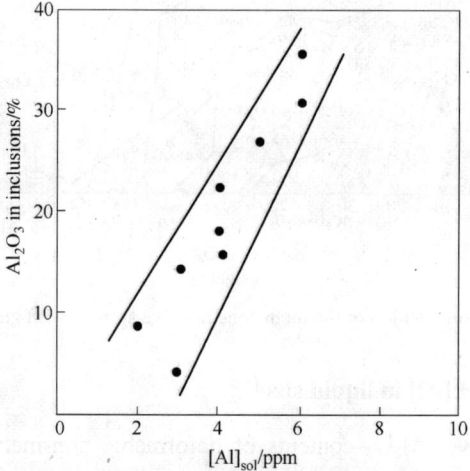

Figure 8.37　Relation between [Al] in steel and Al_2O_3 contents of the inclusions

8.3.3.3　Slag control

For tyre cord steel and valve spring steel, it is of great importance to make almost all of the non-metallic inclusions locate within the narrow composition range of the deformable inclusions. Slag-metal reaction plays a very important role for the inclusion control. Contents of [Al], [Ca], [O], which controls compositions of the inclusions, should be mainly controlled through slag-metal refining other than adding deoxidation agents of Al, Ca, etc. So, the time used for slag-metal refining should be enough to make reactions between slag, metal and inclusions as close as possible to equilibriums.

Investigation was carried out on equilibriums between slag, high carbon steel and non-metallic inclusions by the author. Table 8.8 and Table 8.9 respectively show the chemical compositions of the metal and slag used in the investigation Figure 8.38 and Figure 8.39 show changes of [Al] and $a_{[O]}$ of liquid steels during the experiments. It is seen that [Al] and $a_{[O]}$ did not change after 35 minutes reaction, which indicated that the slag-metal reactions reached or were close to equilibriums.

Table 8.8 Chemical composition range of the steel in the experiment (%)

[C]	[Si]	[Mn]	[P]	[S]	[Al]s	[Ca]
0.65~0.83	0.12~0.24	0.6~0.63	0.008~0.01	0.009~0.012	0.0002~0.0012	0.0002~0.0005

Table 8.9 Chemical composition range of the slag in the experiment (%)

CaO	MnO	SiO$_2$	Al$_2$O$_3$	Fe$_t$O	MgO	CaO/SiO$_2$
24.1~44.8	0.63~1.82	22.9~40.1	4.3~35.0	0.5~2.4	4.9~24.6	0.71~1.36

Figure.8.40 shows the distribution of the chemical compositions of the inclusions in steels in equilibrium with slags which basicities (CaO/SiO$_2$) are between 0.71 to 1.0, in which the chemical composition range of deformable inclusions is roughly marked by the shadow area. It can be seen that, when Al$_2$O$_3$ was controlled between 4% to 12% in the experiment, most inclusions in steels located within or very close to the deformable inclusion zone. When Al$_2$O$_3$ in slag was higher than 12%, Al$_2$O$_3$ contents of the inclusions increased which made them out off the deformable inclusion composition zone.

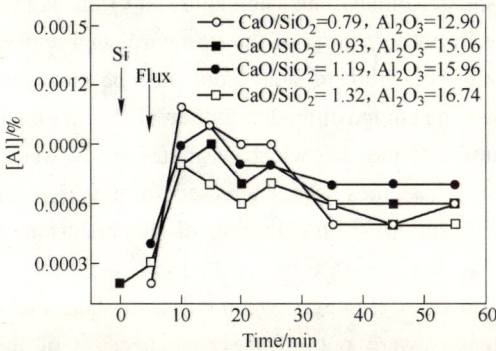

Figure 8.38 Change of [Al] with reaction time

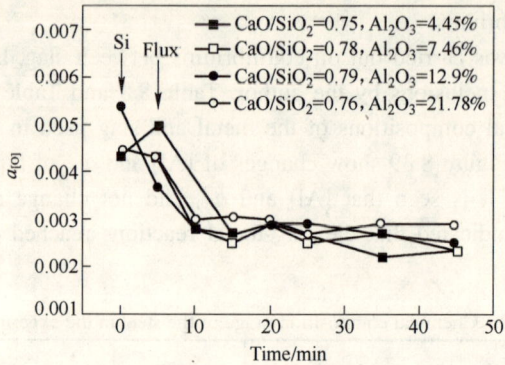

Figure 8.39   Change of $a_{[O]}$ with reaction time

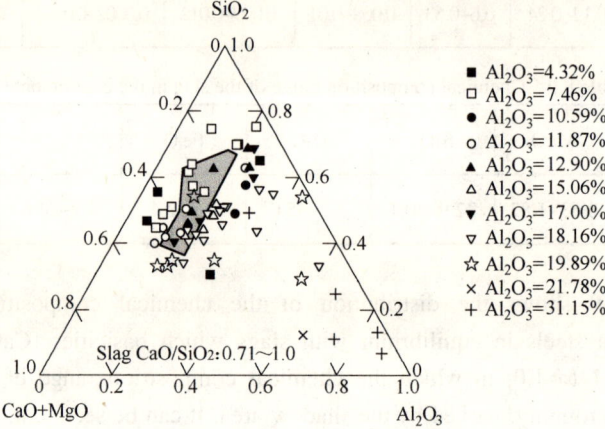

Figure 8.40   Effect of Al_2O_3 in slag on composition of the inclusions
when slag basicity within 0.71~1.0

Al_2O_3 in slag affects content of [Al] in liquid steel, which influences Al_2O_3 contents of the non-metallic inclusions. In order to avoid Al_2O_3 contents of the inclusions out off the deformable inclusion zone, Al_2O_3 in slag should be less than 5%. Thus, in ladle furnace refining of the tyre cord steel and valve spring steel, Al_2O_3 content in lining materials of ladle should also be strictly controlled.

Figure 8.41 shows the composition distribution of the non-metallic inclusions in steels in equilibrium with the slag which basicities are between 1.05 to 1.2. It is seen that, when slag basicities were increased from 0.71~1.0 to 1.05~1.2, the scatteration of the composition distribution of the inclusions increased. When Al_2O_3 of slags was between 5% to 12%, most inclusions were within the deformable inclusion zone. However, when Al_2O_3 of slags was higher than 15%, most of the inclusions were out off the zone because of their higher Al_2O_3 contents.

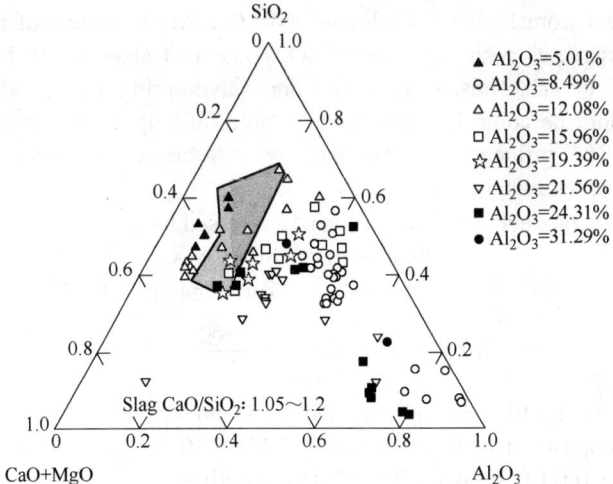

Figure 8.41 Effect of Al_2O_3 in slag on composition of the inclusions
when slag basicity within 1.05~1.2

Figure 8.42 shows the composition distribution of the non-metallic inclusions in steels in equilibrium with the slag which basicities are between 1.23 to 1.36. Compared with the inclusions in steels equilibrated with lower basicity slags, the distribution of the inclusions were even more scattered when the slag basicity was increased to 1.23~1.36. Only when Al_2O_3 in slag was low (between 5% to 8.5%), could the inclusions be within the deformable zone. When Al_2O_3 of slag was higher than 10%, most of the inclusions were out off the zone because of their higher Al_2O_3 contents.

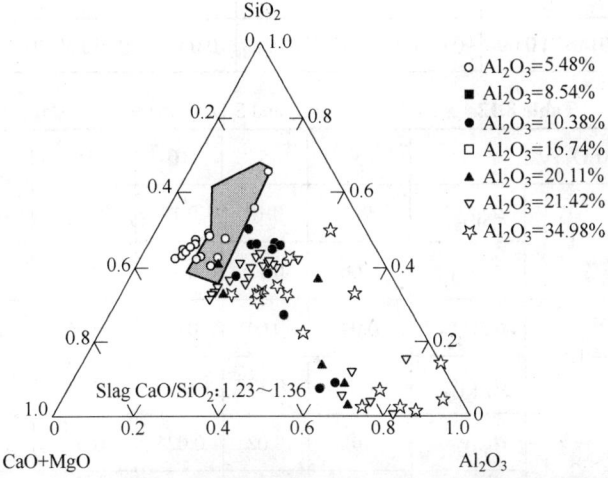

Figure 8.42 Effect of Al_2O_3 in slag on composition of
the inclusions when slag basicity within 1.23~1.36

It is known from Figure 8.40~Figure 8.42 that Al_2O_3 content of non-metallic inclusions increases with increasing Al_2O_3 content of slags which basicities are between 0.7 to 1.3. Thus, in tyre cord and valve spring steel production, slag basicity should be controlled around 1 in ladle refining for making deformable inclusions. The influence of slag basicity will be further explained by the following calculations.

Deoxidation of steel by Si and Al can be expressed by

$$4[Al]+3(SiO_2)=3[Si]+2(Al_2O_3) \tag{8.36}$$

$$\Delta G^{\ominus}=-650088+99.72T \text{(Turkdogan E T, 1996)}$$

$$\log K = \frac{a_{[Si]}^3 \cdot a_{Al_2O_3}^2}{a_{[Al]}^4 \cdot a_{SiO_2}^3} = \frac{33960}{T} - 5.21 \tag{8.37}$$

The activity coefficients of [Si] and [Al] can be calculated based on the chemical composition of steel shown in Table 8.10 and the activity interaction parameters at 1600°C shown in Table 8.11 respectively.

$$f_{[Si]}=1.41$$
$$f_{[Al]}=1.20$$

The activity of [Si] is

$$a_{[Si]}=0.30$$

Table 8.10 Average chemical composition of the steel used in the calculation

C	Si	Mn	S	P	Ca	Al
0.75%	0.21%	0.62%	0.01%	0.009%	0.0004%	0.0006%

Table 8.11 Activity interaction parameters at 1600°C (Turkdogan,1996)

e_{Si}^C	e_{Si}^{Mn}	e_{Si}^P	e_{Si}^S	e_{Si}^{Si}	e_{Si}^{Al}	e_{Al}^C	e_{Al}^P	e_{Al}^S	e_{Al}^{Si}
0.18	−0.0146	0.09	0.066	0.103	0.058	0.091	0.033	0.035	0.056

Table 8.12 Activities of Al_2O_3 and SiO_2 of the selected slag

Al_2O_3 / %		3	5	10	15	20	25
CaO/SiO$_2$=1	a_{SiO_2}	0.2	0.18	0.17	0.16	0.17	0.17
	$a_{Al_2O_3}$	0.06	0.12	0.22	0.25	0.28	0.33
CaO/SiO$_2$=1.5	a_{SiO_2}	0.04	0.04	0.05	0.06	0.065	0.07
	$a_{Al_2O_3}$	0.1	0.13	0.2	0.23	0.26	0.3
CaO/SiO$_2$=2	a_{SiO_2}	0.01	0.02	0.025	0.03	0.035	0.04
	$a_{Al_2O_3}$	0.07	0.1	0.14	0.18	0.22	0.25

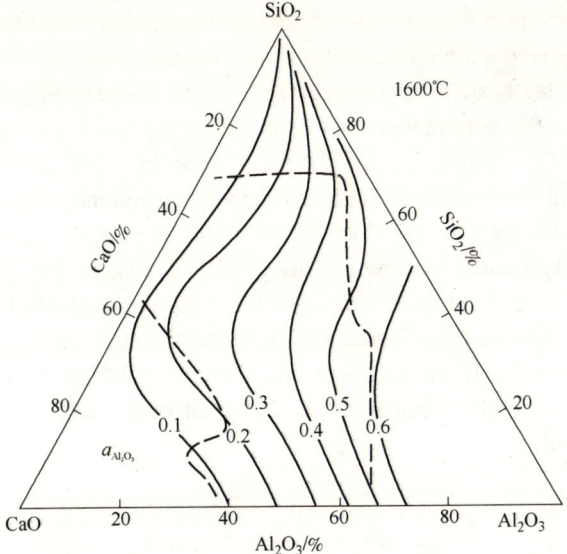

Figure 8.43 Activity of Al_2O_3 in $CaO-SiO_2-Al_2O_3$ system slag

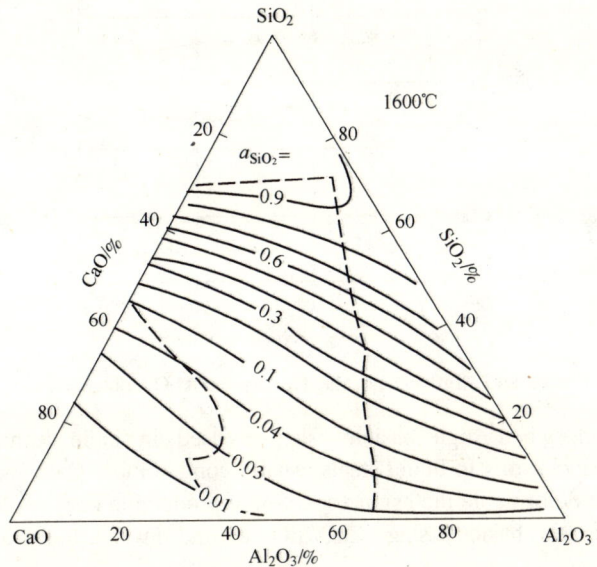

Figure 8.44 Activity of SiO_2 in $CaO-SiO_2-Al_2O_3$ system slag

As shown in Table 8.12, fifteen slags were selected in the calculation, which basicities are 1, 1.5 and 2 and their Al_2O_3 contents are 3%, 5%, 10%, 15% and 20% respectively. The activities of SiO_2 and Al_2O_3 of the slags are obtained from Figure 8.43(Chen J X, 1998) and Figure 8.44(Chen J X, 1998). Substituting the values of, a_{SiO_2} $a_{Al_2O_3}$ $a_{[Si]}$ and $a_{[Al]}$ into Equation (8.37), relationship between [Al] in liquid steel and Al_2O_3 in slag can be obtained as shown in Figure 8.45.

It is seen in Figure.8.45 that, when slag basicity is low ($CaO/SiO_2=1$), [Al] in liquid steel equilibrated with the slag which contains 25% Al_2O_3 is only 0.0005%. While, when slag basicity is increased to 1.5, the equilibrated [Al] increases to more than 0.0010% even though the slag contains only 5% Al_2O_3, which can make the non-metallic inclusions out off the deformable inclusion zone. In the equilibrium experiment carried out by the author as mentioned above, it was found that the composition scatteration of the inclusions increased with increasing slag basicity. This is because that the activity of SiO_2 decreases very much when the slag basicity is increased from 1 to 1.5~2 but the activity of Al_2O_3 changed very little. It is also known from Figure 8.45 that Al_2O_3 content of slag should be less than 5% so that [Al] can be controlled between 0.0003% to 0.0005%. This calculation is in good coincidence with the result of the equilibrium experiment made by the author.

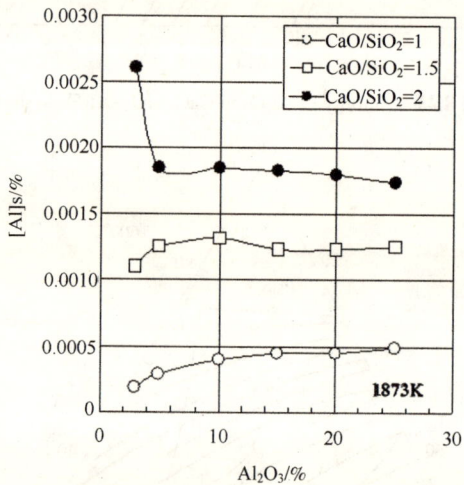

Figure 8.45   Influence of slag basicity and Al_2O_3 content on [Al]

In addition, when high basicity slag is used in ladle furnace refining, non-metallic inclusions in liquid steels usually contain more CaO and are easy to be out off the deformable inclusion zone. So, in production of tyre cord and valve spring steels, low basicity slag (CaO/SiO_2 around 1) is usually used in ladle furnace refining.

8.3.4   Steel with premium cleanliness

As described in 8.3.3, the anti-fatigue property of the high strength alloying steels can be significantly improved by lowering the total oxygen content T[O], i.e. decreasing the number of the non-metallic inclusions in the steels (Figure8.21). However, occasionally, some large size inclusions (about 100μm) could still be found on fracture surfaces of fatigue test specimens of steels which contained very low T[O], even though no inclusions larger than 10μm could be found usually by optical microscope or SEM. So, for steels which request high anti-fatigue property, in addition to reduce the number of the inclusions, efforts should be specially made to reduce the existence of large sizeed inclusions, i.e. to produce the so called "steels with premium cleanliness" （Kawawue K，2005）.

Figure 8.46 shows the size distribution of the non-metallic inclusions in the conventional high clean bearing steels (T[O]: 0.00055%) and the premium cleanliness bearing steels (T[O]: 0.00045%) which were produced by Sanyo Special Steel(Kawawue K,2005). The sizes of the inclusions were obtained by method of ASTM-D. It is seen from this figure that both the content and the size of the inclusions in premium cleanliness steels were significantly less that the conventional clean steels.

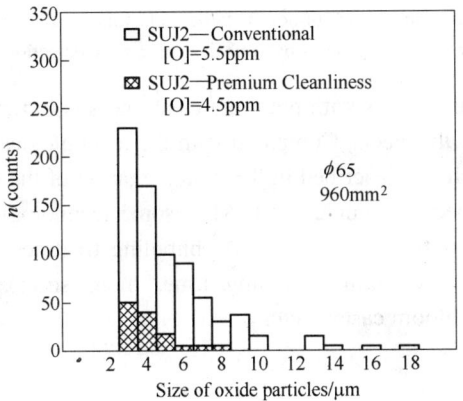

Figare 8.46   Distribution of sizes of non-metallic inclusions in conventional and premium cleanliness bearing steels

For the conventional high clean steels, it is already difficult to find large sized inclusions by optical microscope or SEM because the specimen is small and the number of the large sized inclusions are very few. Compared with the analysis method of optical microscope or SEM, using super sonic detection method, the inspection of large size specimens can be carried out. Recently, researches of using 50~100MHz super sonic analyzers to detect inclusions of 20 ~100μm were reported(Kawawue K,2005).

Figure 8.47 shows the comparison of the inclusion size distributions between the conventional clean bearing steels and the premium cleanliness bearing steels by 100MHz super sonic analyzer(Kawawue K,2005). It can be seen that, even though T[O] of the conventional clean steels was lowered to 0.00055%, there still exited some large sized inclusions (50~55μm). Compared with the conventional clean steels, both the size of the inclusions and the number of the larger sized inclusions in the premium cleanliness steels were greatly reduced.

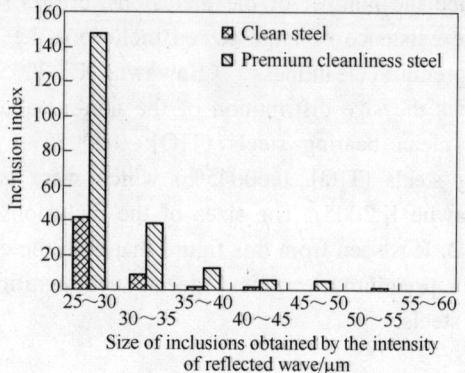

Figure 8.47   Distribution of size of non-metallic inclusions in conventional and premium cleanliness bearing steels by 100MHz supersonic detection method

The key to produce steels with premium cleanliness is to further lower the total oxygen contents of the steels. Compared with the technologies used for extra low oxygen steels which are described in 8.3.2, aggregation of the inclusions in liquid steels should be specially emphasized. Also, some technologies are emphasized, which include the optimization of the Ar bubbling treatment of liquid steels in ladles, increase the vacuum degassing time, more strict protection casting, adopting large size bloom casters, etc.

References

Ban-ya S, Chipman J (1969) Sulfur in Liquid Iron Alloys. PT.2. Effects of Alloying Elements. Trans. Metall. Soc. AIME 245: 133-143

Brooksbank D (1970) Thermal Expansion of Calcium Aluminate Inclusions and Relation to Tessellated Stresses. JISI, 208: 495-499

Brooksbank D, Andrews K W (1970) Stress field around inclusions and their relation to mechanical properties, Production and application of clean steels. In: Production and Application of Clean Steels, The Iron & Steel Insitute, Balatofred, 186-198 1970

Brooksbank D, Andrews K W (1968) Thermal Expansion of Some Inclusions Found in Steels and Relation to Tessellated Stresses. JISI 206: 595-599

Chen J X (eds) (1998) Selected Data for Steelmaking. Metallurgical Industry Press, Beijing

Duckworth W E, Ineson E (1963) The effects of externally introduced alumina particles on the fatigue life of En24 steel. In: Clean steel 77, Iron Steel Inst., 87-103

Eguchi J, Fukunaga M, et al (1990) Manufacture of High Quality Case-Hardening Low Alloy Steel for Automobile Use. In: Proceedings of the 6th International Iron and Steel

Congress, Nagoya, 644-650 1990

Fukumoto I (1988) Clean Steel. In: ISIJ (ed) Nishiyama Memorial Technical Seminar, 1988 Gammal T E, Etwa S (1970) Arch. Eisenhuettenwes 41: 517

Gladman T (1992) Developments in Inclusions Control and Their Effects on Steel Properties. Ironmaking and steelmaking 19: 457-463

Inetomi J, Yamashita K, et al (1988) Application of Powder Injection into Ladle Refining Process. CAMP-ISIJ 1: 233

Ishii F, Fuwa T (1981) Activity of Sulphur in Liquid Iron Alloys. Tetsu-to-Hagane 67: 746-754

Ishii F, Fuwa T (1981) Activity of Sulphur in Liquid Iron. Tetsu-to-Hagane 67: 736-745

Kawakami K, Kikuchi Y et al (1982) Development of a Ladle Desulphurization Process at Nippon Kokan. Stahl. Eisen 102: 227-231

Kawawue K (2005) Technology for Control of Nonmetallic Inclusions and Production of Clean Steels. In: ISIJ (ed) The 182nd and 183rd Nishiyama Memorial Technical Seminar, Tokyo and Osaka; 151-179

Kiessling R, Nordberg H (1970) Influence of Inclusions on Mechanical Properties of Steel. In: Production and Application of Clean Steels, The Iron & Steel Insitute, Balatofred, 179-185 1970

Klevebring B-I (1976) Determination of the Critical Inclusion Size of Plastic Inclusions with Respect to Void Formation during Hot Work. Scand. J. of Metall., 5: 63~68

Kozawa K (1977) Quality Improvement of Ultra Sulfure Steel products. Tetsu-To-Hagane 63: S713

Kubaschewski O, et al (eds) (1967) Metallurgical Thermochemistry. Pergamon Press, London

Malm S (1976) On the Precipitation of Slag Inclusions During Solidification of High-carbon Steel, Deoxidized With Aluminium and Mish Metal. Scand. J. of Metals 15: 248-257

Melander A, Larsson M (1993) Effect of stress amplitude on the cause of fatigue crack initiation in a spring steel. Int.J.Fatigue 15: 119-131

Mimura T (2005) Technology for Control of Nonmetallic Inclusions and Production of Clean Steels. In: ISIJ (ed) The 182nd and 183rd Nishiyama Memorial Technical Seminar, Tokyo and Osaka; 125-150

Ogura Y, Kiguchi Y, et al (1986) Development of secondary refining process and its application to production of clean steel. Tetsu-To-Hagane 72: 1309-1315

Okada Y (1992) Development of Power Top Blowing Desulphurization Method in RH. CAMP-ISIJ 5: 1238-1239

Okushima I (1988) Recent Development of Production Technology for Super-clean Wire Rod, Clean Steel. In: Nishiyama Memorial Technical Seminar, ISIJ, 147- 1988

Richardson F D, Fincham C J B (1954) Sulphur in silicate and aluminate slags. J. Iron Steel Inst 178: 4-15

Rudnik S (1966) Discontinuities in Hot-rolled Steel Caused by Non-metallic Inclusions.

JISI 204: 374-376

Sommerville I D (1986) The Measurement, Prediction and Use of Capacities of Metallurgical Slags. Scaninject IV 8: 1-21

Sponseller D L, Flinn R A (1964) The Solubility of Calcium in Liquid Iron and Third Element Interaction Effects. Trans. Metall. Soc. AIME 230: 876-888

Tanizawa K, Okumura H, et al (1990) The Mass Production Process of High Purity Steel by Vacuum KIMITSU Injection Process. In: Proceedings of the 6th International Iron and Steel Congress, Nagoya, 611-618 1990

Tsubota K, Fukumoto I (1990) Production and Quality of High Cleanliness Bearing Steel. In: Proceedings of the 6th International Iron and Steel Congress, Nagoya, 637-643 1990

Turkdogan E T (eds) (1996) Fundamentals of Steelmaking. The University Press, Cambridge

Uehara H (1992) Development of Desulphurization of Steel Melt by Powder Blasting. CAMP-ISIJ 5: 1240

Ueki T, Fujiwara K, et al (2004) High Productivity Operation Technologies of Wakayama Steelmaking Shop. In: The 10th Japan-China Symposium on Science and Technology of Iron and Steel, ISIJ, Chiba, 116-123

Watanabe Y, et al (1985) Manufacturing of Clean Steel by Injection Refining with Intensive Stirring in Ladle. Tetsu-To-Hagane 71: S191

Watanabe Y, et al (1984) Effects of Intensive Stirring on Characteristics of Injection Refining. Tetsu-To-Hagane 70: S1002

Weng Y Q (eds) (2003) Ultra-fine grained steels—Microstructure refinement theory and controued technology. Metallurgical Industry Press, Beijing

Yagura S, et al (1986) Development of RH Injection Technology. Tetsu-To-Hagane 72: S261

Zhang S (eds) (1981) Alloy Steel. Metallurgical Industry Press, Bejing

9

Fundamental Study on Homogeneity of Solidification Structure of Steel

High purity, high homogeneity and ultra-fine grain size are the features of new generation steels. The solidification process control is much more efficient and economical to get high homogeneity than other methods such as hot deforming and high temperature diffusion annealing. This chapter focused on fundamental studies on the liquid structure of Fe-C alloy, heterogeneous nucleation and formation of fine equiaxed grain structure. It is expected that such knowledge can benefit the improvement of homogeneity of steels.

9.1   The Structure of Liquid Fe-C Alloy

The structures of liquid metals have a close relationship with their solid structures and structural heterogeneity. For example, the structural correlation length and the cluster number of liquid alloys affect the grain size of solid metals. Material scientists have been studying the liquid structures of metals and their heredity in order to control the solid ones. Although steels are most widely used metal, little work on their liquid structure has done because of the technical difficulties involved with the high melting point and severe oxidation at high temperature.

Our work is to investigate the liquid structure of Fe-C alloy in the temperature range near melting point by means of X-ray diffraction. The heredity of liquid metals on the solidified structures and the effect of purity on liquid structures are suggested for the future research.

9.1.1   *Experimental*

The alloy specimen was made from electrolytic 99.97% pure iron which was melted in highly pure graphite crucible to obtain a Fe-C alloy. Then the alloy was remelted in a zirconia crucible under a high purity helium atmosphere. Finally, the Fe-C alloy with 99.54% iron and 0.40% carbon was obtained. The experiment was carried out in the refilled highly pure helium atmosphere at 1.3×10^5 Pa after the chamber was vacuumed to 10^{-6} Pa. The specimen was placed in a 20 mm $\times$ 18 mm $\times$ 10 mm alumina crucible. The temperature was increased to 1600°C, at the rate of 20°C per minute, for 30 minutes isothermal holding, and then decreased to 1580°C, 1560°C and 1540°C respectively. Next, the specimen was held at the specified temperature for 20 minutes and during this period the X-ray diffraction test was carried out and X-ray scattering intensity data was collected.

The X-ray scattering intensity from the liquid alloy was measured using a θ-θ diffractometer (2θ is the scattering angle). The scattering intensity patterns were obtained by Mo a K_α radiation, selected by a graphite monochromator in the diffraction beam. The total scattering intensities were recorded within the range $5 < 2\theta < 90°$ with variable steps (Qin et al,1998a; 1998c; 1998d).

9.1.2   *Data analysis*

The method of analyzing the measured X-ray intensities for noncrystalline systems such as liquids and glasses is now very common (Waseda et al, 1980 and 1995; Zhang et al,2000), but the essential points are given below for convenience of discussion. The scattering intensity measured in arbitrary units can be converted into the coherent scattering intensity per atom in electron units I_{eu}^{coh}, using generalized Krogh-Moe-Norman method (Krogh-Moe, 1956 and Norman, 1957). Compton scattering has been corrected using the values given by Cromer and Mann(Cromer and Mann,1967).

$$I_{eu}^{coh}(Q) = \sum_i c_i f_i^2 + \int_0^\infty 4\pi r^2 \left[\sum_i \sum_j c_i f_i f_j \rho_{ij}(r) - \left(\sum_i c_i f_i\right)^2 \rho_0 \right] \frac{\sin(Qr)}{Qr} dr \tag{9.1}$$

The total structure factor is

$$S(Q) = \frac{I_{eu}^{coh}(Q)}{\left[f^2(Q)\right]} = c_1 k_1^2 S_{11}(Q) + c_2 k_2^2 S_{22}(Q) + 2(c_1 c_2)^{\frac{1}{2}} k_1 k_2 S_{12}(Q) \tag{9.2}$$

where Q is scattering vector, $Q = 4\pi \sin\theta / \lambda$ (2θ is the scattering angle. λ is the wavelength of incident X-ray). N_i and N denote the number of i-type atoms and total atoms in the scattering volume respectively. c_i is the percentage of i-type atoms and equal to N_i/N. f_i is the atomic scattering factor of the type i atom, and $i, j = 1, 2$.

The radial distribution function $4\pi r^2 \rho(r)$ or the pair distribution function $g(r) = \rho(r)/\rho_0$ is calculated by the following Fourier transformation.

$$4\pi r^2 \rho(r) = 4\pi r^2 (c_1 k_1 + c_2 k_2)^2 \rho_0 + \frac{2r}{\pi} \int_0^\infty \left[S(Q) - 1 \right] Q \sin(Qr) dQ$$

(9.3)

where, $\rho(r)$ is the radial density function, ρ_0 is the average number density of atoms. In addition,

$$k_i = f_i < f^2(Q) >^{\frac{1}{2}}, \quad < f^2(Q) >= \sum_i c_i f_i^2$$

The coordination number can be obtained from the following equation

$$N_{min} = \int_{r_0}^{r_{min}} 4\pi r^2 \rho(r) dr$$

(9.4)

where, r_0 and r_{min} are the two points of the radial distribution function. r_0 is the nearest zero point on the left side of the first peak, and r_{min} is the least value point on the right side.

9.1.3   Medium-range order structure in liquid Fe-C alloy

Figure 9.1 shows the X-ray scattering intensity of liquid Fe-C alloy at three different temperatures. Figure 9.2 shows the total structure factor of liquid Fe-C alloy. It can be seen from Figure 9.1 that the first main peak of the diffraction pattern is very distinct, but other peaks are flat. Generally, liquid has short-range order while crystal has both short-range and long-range order. The short-range order is mainly represented by the presence of first main peak at the range from 25 nm^{-1} to 35 nm^{-1} on the scattering intensity curve. At the same time, in real space there is a distinct first peak on the pair distribution function curve.

It can be found from Figure 9.1 that there exists a small peak in the range from $Q = 5$ nm^{-1} to 20 nm^{-1} at 1540℃ and 1560℃ respectively. The small peak is called prepeak. The presence of prepeak in this range indicates that there is a medium-range order in the liquid Fe-C alloy (Maret et al, 1989). However, it is very indistinct at 1580℃. Qin J Y and Bian X F (1998b) studied hypoeutectic Al-Fe alloy melt and confirmed that the prepeak appeared at the small angle part of the total structure factor curve in non-superheat Al-Fe alloy melt, and the prepeak disappeared when the melt was heated to a certain high temperature (375 ℃ above the melting point), which is quite consistent with the results presented in Figure 9.1.

According to our study, the prepeak can still be found in liquid pure iron at 1580 ℃(Luo, 2002), but it can not be found in liquid Fe-C alloy. Obviously, over-superheat is the reason for disappearance of the medium-range order in the liquid metal. Therefore, analysis should be started from the melting point. The melting points of pure iron and Fe-C alloy with 0.4% carbon are about 1539℃ and 1505℃ respectively. That is to say, the degrees of superheat of pure iron and the Fe-C alloy are about 40℃ and 75℃ respectively at 1580℃. Obviously, the degree of superheat of the Fe-C alloy exceeds that of pure iron. Liquid metal becomes more disordered when the degree of superheat is increased, which results in the disappearance of the medium-range order, or prepeak, in the X-ray diffraction intensity curve.

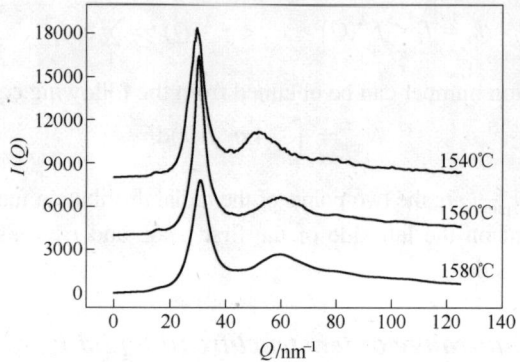

Figure 9.1   The X-ray scattering intensity of liquid Fe-C alloy

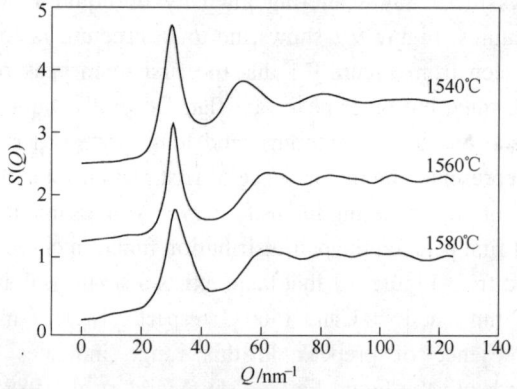

Figure 9.2   Total structure factor of liquid Fe-C alloy

Figure 9.3 shows the pair distribution function of liquid Fe-C alloy. Figure 9.4 is the radial distribution function. The pair distribution function is an interference function that describes the density of atom number fluctuating around the average value. It fluctuates and trends to 1 with the increasing of the radius r. It can be seen from Figure 9.3 that the fluctuation of the curve becomes very little when $r \geqslant 1$ nm. The size of atom cluster r_s can be calculated by the pair distribution function. According to the widely accepted definition, the maximum r is the radius of the atom cluster when $g(r)$ is within the range of 1 ± 0.02. The radius of atom cluster (or the structural correlation length), atom number in an atom cluster, average atom density and so on are listed in Table 9.1. The abscissa of the radial distribution function is the radial distance from the atom on the sphere to the reference atom, and the ordinate denotes the atom number on the sphere. Therefore, the position of the first peak is the distance of the nearest neighbour atoms. The coordination number can be worked out from the area of the first peak on the radial distribution function curve.

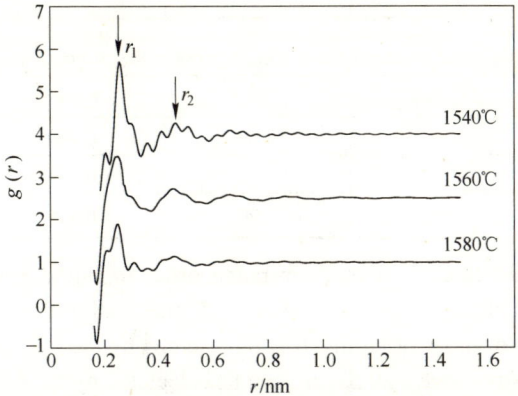

Figure 9.3 The pair distribution function of liquid Fe-C alloy

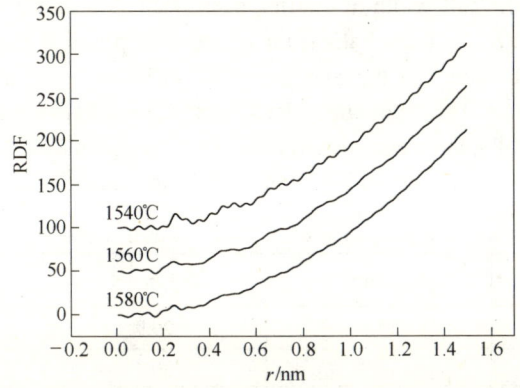

Figure 9.4 The radial distribution function of liquid Fe-C alloy

It is found from Table 9.1 that the distance of the nearest neighbour atoms r is almost the same for all temperatures. The coordination number N, radius of atom cluster r_s and atom number in the atom cluster n_s all decrease with increasing temperature. This indicates that Fe-C alloy melt becomes more disordered with the increasing temperature.

Table 9.2 shows the position and height of the first and second main peak in the pair distribution function curve. The height of the peaks decreases with increasing temperature. The pair distribution function is an interference function denoting that the density of atom number fluctuates around the average value, and the decrease of peak height corresponds to the reduction of the coordination number.

Table 9.1   The main parameters of liquid Fe-C alloy

T /°C	r / nm	N	n_s	r_s / nm
1540	0.255	8.1	506	1.24
1560	0.250	7.7	467	1.23
1580	0.250	7.5	432	1.21

Table 9.2   The place and height of the two main peaks in the pair correlation function curve

T /°C	r_1 / nm	$G(r_1)$	r_2 / nm	$G(r_2)$
1540	0.255	2.69	0.460	1.28
1560	0.250	1.97	0.455	1.24
1580	0.250	1.90	0.455	1.15

Whether or not there is a medium-range order in liquid Fe-C alloy can be testified by calculating topologic order and chemical order. Topologic order reflects the level of order of atoms. It is represented by the first peak of the X-ray diffraction intensity curve, and its size can be calculated by the following formula

$$\xi = 2\pi / \Delta Q \tag{9.5}$$

Here ΔQ is the half-width of the first peak. Table 9.3 shows the half-width of the first peak ΔQ_1. But the half-width of the first peaks at three temperatures varies from each other, so the average value, 6.77 nm^{-1}, is used to calculate topologic order size. The topologic order size calculated from the above formula is 0.928 nm. Generally, the medium-range order size is considered to be 0.5~1.0 nm, therefore, the topologic order of liquid Fe-C alloy is a medium-range order.

Table 9.3   The parameters of the X-ray diffraction intensity curves

T /°C	Q p /nm^{-1}	Q 1 /nm^{-1}	ΔQ_1 /nm^{-1}
1540	14.8	29.9	6.8
1560	15.8	30.4	6.0
1580	—	31.0	7.5

Chemical order or the formation of compound is displayed by the appearance of the prepeak on the X-ray diffraction intensity curve within the range from 10 nm^{-1} to 20 nm^{-1}. The extended range of chemical order can also be calculated from equation 9.5. It should be noted that ΔQ is the half-width of prepeak, while the exact half-width of prepeaks cannot be obtained from Figure 9.1. However, it is for sure that there are Fe-C compounds in liquid Fe-C alloy according to the distance of the nearest neighbor atoms and the coordination number. The position of the prepeak at 1540°C and 1560°C are listed in Table 9.3 (The position of the prepeak at 1580°C is not listed because this prepeak cannot be distinguished from

Figure 9.1). The quasi-period of chemical order can be calculated from the position of prepeak Q_p using the following equation

$$\xi = 2\pi / Q_p \tag{9.6}$$

The average value of Q_p at 1540℃ and 1560℃ is 15.3 nm^{-1}, which is used to calculate the quasi-period of chemical order. The result is 0.410 nm, which is the distance of Fe-Fe atoms in the atom clusters when Fe-C compound is formed. However, it is still difficult to distinguish the type of Fe-C compound or the coordination details from existing experiment data.

Because the content of carbon in this alloy is only 0.40%, which means that most of the coordination atoms should be Fe-Fe atoms, it would be more reasonable to treat the alloy as pure iron. It can be found form Table 9.1 that the coordinated lattice is body-centered cubic lattice (bcc) in the atom cluster. If the distance of the two neighboring body-center atoms is d, the position of the prepeak can be calculated from this equation

$$Q_p = 7.725 / d \tag{9.7}$$

According to Table 9.1, the scattering vector Q_p is about 15.3 nm^{-1}. So the distance d is 0.505 nm. The distance between the nearest neighboring atoms, which is the half-length of the body diagonal line, is 0.255 nm. Therefore, the length of the edge, the body diagonal line and the face diagonal line of the bcc units are 0.294 nm, 0.510 nm and 0.415 nm respectively. If the units are connected into network by occupying the same apex, the distance d is 0.510 nm, which is very close to the experimental result with an error of only 0.98%. If the units occupy the same surface, the distance d is 0.294 nm, which is well below the experimental result. If the units occupy the same edge, the distance d is 0.415 nm, which is different from the experiment one too. Figure 9.5 shows the structure model of the atom cluster in liquid Fe-C alloy. In liquid Fe-C alloy there are both Fe-C atom clusters and Fe-Fe atom clusters. The Fe-Fe atom cluster has bcc structure, which is formed by occupying the same apex. The atoms between the atom clusters are disorderly arranged.

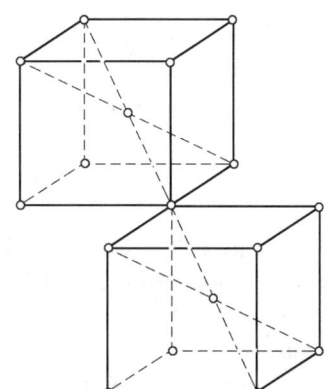

Figure 9.5   The structure model of the atom cluster in liquid Fe-C alloy

9.1.4 Conclusions

1. Near the melting point there is a medium-range order structure in liquid

Fe-C alloy which gradually changes to disorderly structure with increasing temperature. This is because liquid metal becomes more disordered when the degree of superheat increases, resulting in the disappearances of both the medium-range order and the prepeak of the X-ray diffraction intensity curve.

2. The coordination number, the atom cluster size and atom number of the clusters decrease with increasing temperature of the Fe-C alloy melt, indicating that liquid Fe-C alloy becomes more disordered with increasing temperature.

3. Near the melting point there are not only Fe-C atom clusters but also Fe-Fe atom clusters in liquid Fe-C alloy. The Fe-Fe atom cluster has the bcc structure, which is formed by occupying the same apex. The atoms between the atom clusters are disorderly arranged.

9.2   Observation and Analysis of Heterogeneous Nucleation Phenomena

Crystal structure in castings is of vital importance for its processing and properties. Although there have been a lot of researches, formation mechanism of the equiaxed grain structure in castings is still not very clear. In 1954, Winegard and Chalmers first proposed the constitutional undercooling theory, suggesting the origin of equiaxed crystal is attributed to nucleation in the constitutional undercooling ahead of the columnar zone (Winegard et al, 1954). Chalmers (1963) further proposed the free chill crystal theory, pointing out that there were several objections to this early proposal, and introducing the possibility that all the crystals, equiaxed as well as columnar, originate during the initial chilling of the liquid layer in contact with the mould. Based on *in situ* observation in transparent alloys experiments, Jackson (1966) put forward that dendrite fragments, re-melted or broken off from the columnar dendritic arms, act as nuclei for the formation of equiaxed grains. Based on the Al-Cu alloys experiments, Southin (1976) suggested that dendrite branches dislodged from the free surface of the melt are responsible for the formation of equiaxed crystal microstructure. Ohno (1976) proposed the separation theory, which is somewhat similar to the free chill crystal theory, but with some important differences. He emphasized the importance of thermal fluctuations in the melt, suggested that the equiaxed crystals in the melt center actually result from crystal detachment from the mould walls. These crystals nucleate on the mould surface as a result of large thermal undercooling and then separate from the nucleation sites by action of convective currents. Many studies have identified all these mechanisms occurring if the appropriate experimental conditions existed (Cole and Bolling, 1967; Mathiesen, 2006).

Recently, a novel method for nucleation and detachment of a lot of crystals from a vibrating chilling solid surface inserted into the alloy melt is proposed to further increase the proportion of equiaxed grains in steel billet and refine the solidification structure (Gan et al, 2006). This method has been shown very effective in producing fine equiaxed cast microstructure. In our research, in-situ observations of the crystal nucleation and detachment from a vibrating chilling solid surface that was inserted into the liquid of NH_4Cl-70mass%H_2O solution, and the formation of crystals were directly observed to reveal the mechanism of nucleation from a vibrated chilling metal surface. The effects of vibration frequency and amplitude, chilling temperature as well as surface roughness on the nucleation were investigated in details.

9.2.1 *Experimental*

The liquidus of NH_4Cl-70mass% H_2O solution is 307K (Hansen et al, 2002). The experimental apparatus is illustrated in Figure 9.6. A chilling bar made of LY12 aluminum alloy, which acted as a nucleation generator, was inserted into the liquid of NH_4Cl-70mass%H_2O solution in a glass chamber. The chilling aluminum bar, which was cooled by a circulating coolant to achieve an adjustable undercooling from 1K to 50K below the solution liquidus, was rigidly connected to a vibrator, which can exert vibration with frequencies range between 5~10kHz and amplitudes range between 0.001~10mm, respectively. The inner dimensions of the glass chamber, mounted inside a larger column, made of Lexan are 30mm×30mm×60mm. Water from a thermostatic bath circulated in the space between the two columns so that a precise temperature control within 0.1K of the solution inside the chamber was achieved.

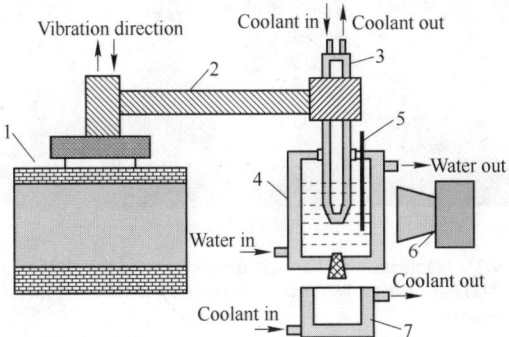

Figure 9.6 Schematic of the experimental apparatus
1—Electric vibrator; 2—Coupling bar; 3—Chilling aluminum bar; 4—Glass chamber;
5—Thermo-couple; 6—Video microscope; 7—Cooling mould

The solution was first heated to a given temperature above the liquidus and retained for a certain period to ensure fully liquid state, and then the vibrating chilling bar with its temperature below the solution liquidus was inserted into the solution. The crystal nucleation and detachment from the vibrating chilling aluminum surface was in-situ observed through a video microscope. When the plug locating in the bottom of the glass chamber was pulled out, the solution with equiaxed crystal grain nuclei was poured into the cooling mould to solidify. The microstructure formation during solidification was also observed through a video microscope.

9.2.2 *Effects of vibration frequency and amplitude*

Figure 9.7 shows crystal nucleation and detachment on the chilling surface of the aluminum bar, with different vibration frequency f and vibration amplitude D exerted on the bar. Temperature of the solution T_m was 310K before the chilling bar was inserted into the liquid, temperature on the surface of the bar T_C was 275K after the chilling bar was inserted into the liquid. It could be seen that, a solidifying dendritic crystal shell was formed on the bottom of the bar in the absence of vibration (Figure 9.7(a)). Exerted vibration prevented the formation of the solidifying shell and promoted the break-off and detachment of dendrites (Figure 9.7(b),(c)). The detached dendrites deposited as "crystal rain" around the chilling surface. Meantime, there exists a crystal agglomeration phenomenon under low-frequency vibration (Figure 9.7(b)). With increase of vibration frequency, the size of crystal grains and their agglomeration decreased, and the number of crystal grains increased.

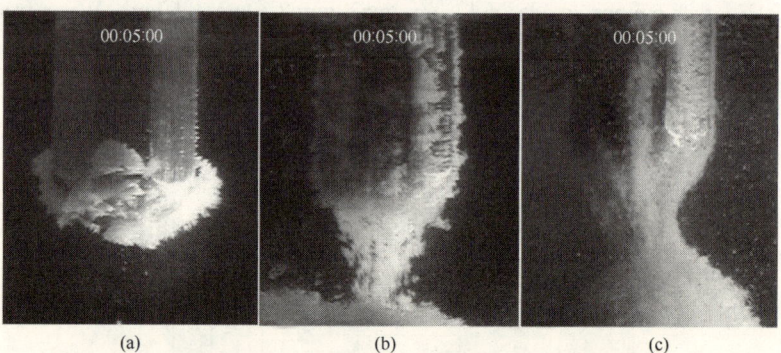

Figure 9.7   Nucleation and crystal detachment on the chilling surface
(a) $f=0$, $D=0$; (b) $f=100$Hz, $D=50\mu$m; (c) $f=2$kHz, $D=20\mu$m

Figure 9.8 shows the solidifying microstructures of NH_4Cl-70%H_2O solution when it was poured into the lower chamber. In the upper chamber a vibration was generated by an aluminum bar with different frequency f and the same amplitude D of 20μm. Under the condition without vibration, corresponding to Figure 9.8(a), the microstructure exhibits a much developed dendritic morphology. With the exerted vibration, the crystal size continuously decreases with increasing vibration frequency, and the dendrites become less developed. In the end, a transition of dendritic-to-equiaxed grains could be observed when vibration frequency was high enough. Fully equiaxed grain microstructure was observed when the vibration frequency was up to 500Hz. Further increasing vibration frequency to 2kHz led to finer and more globular crystals. Moreover, increasing vibration amplitude has similar influence on the morphology of microstructure as increasing vibration frequency.

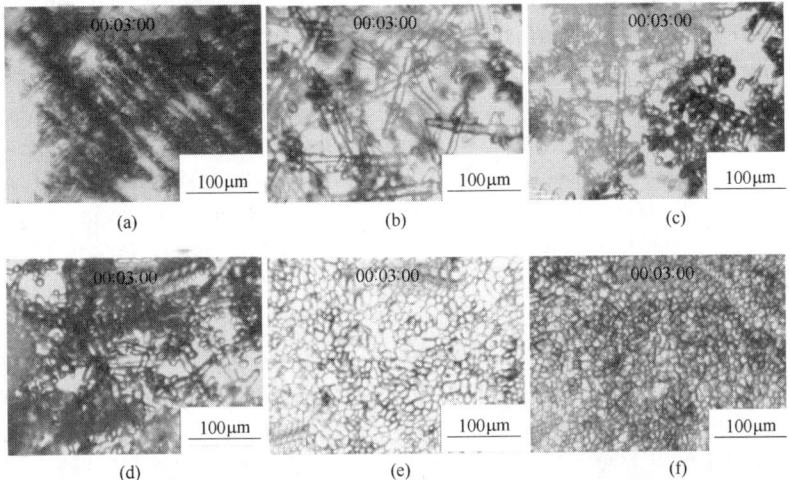

(a)   (b)   (c)

(d)   (e)   (f)

Figure 9.8 Effects of vibration frequency on the microstructure of NH_4Cl-70%H_2O alloy
(a) f=0, D=0, T_S=5.12℃; (b) f=50Hz, D=20μm, T_S=5.20℃ ; (c) f=100Hz, D=20μm,
T_S=5.08℃ ; (d) f=200Hz, D=20μm, T_S=5.02℃; (e) f=500Hz, D=20μm,
T_S=5.12℃ ; (f) f=2kHz, D=20μm, T_S=5.10℃

9.2.3 *Effects of solid substrate temperature and surface roughness*

Figure 9.9 shows the effect of chilling temperature on the nucleation and detachment behavior of crystal grains on the chilling solid surface. It can be seen that, decreasing temperature, i.e. increasing undercooling on the chilling surface, results in increasing nucleation sites and decreasing critical size for crystal detachment.

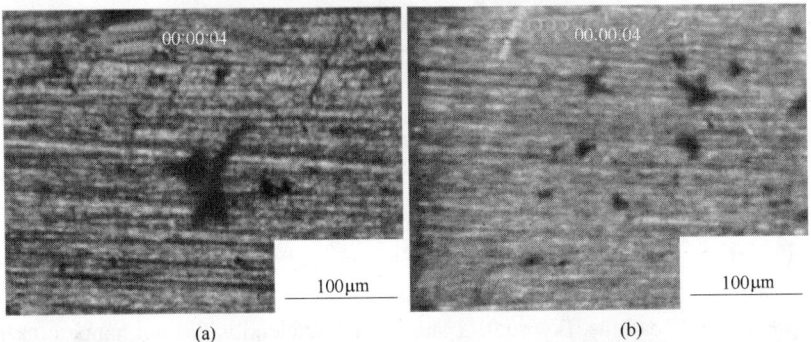

(a)   (b)

Figure 9.9 Effects of chilling temperature on the nucleation and detachment behavior on the chilling solid surface, with the same f=200Hz, D=10μm and T_m=310K.
(a) T_C=275K; (b) T_C=260K

It is interesting to note that nucleation on a chilling solid surface is very much localized. It was observed that dendritic crystals nucleated and then grew to a certain size followed by detachment from some fixed nucleation sites on the chilling surface. These crystals nucleated on the same fixed positions of the chilling solid surface among all experimental runs, while nucleation on the rest part of the solid surface was not observed. When temperature of the chilling surface is lowered, the active nucleation sites increase.

It is often assumed that the localized nucleation sites may be referred to some small notches or pits existing on the position of the active nucleation sites. Therefore, it is believed that the rougher surface should lead to more nucleation sites available. In order to verify this assumption, we investigated the effects of surface roughness on the nucleation behavior. Several chilling bars made of the same aluminum alloy but with different surface roughness were used. The arithmetic profile R_a of these surfaces is ranging from 1.6μm to 0.055μm. The experimental results shows that nucleation on the smoothest surface is as easy as on the most rough surface, in the range of roughness investigated in the experiments. Figure 9.10 shows that nucleation occurs on the surface with very small roughness, $R_a = 0.055$μm. Some notches free of crystal nucleation can be observed just nearby the nucleation sites of crystals on the smooth region.

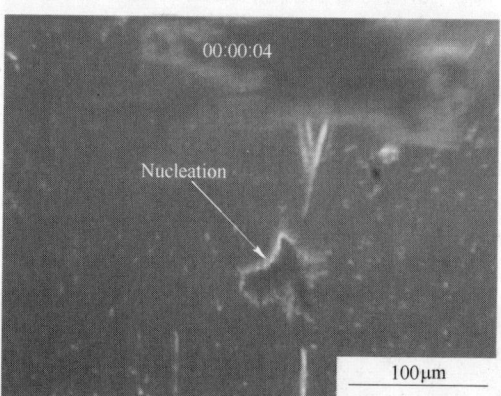

Figure 9.10   Nucleation on the metal surface with roughness of $R_a = 0.055$μm, $f=50$Hz, $D=10$μm, $T_C=275$K, $T_m=310$K

In order to further understand the nucleation characteristics on the chilling metal surface, a series of micro-hardness indentations, with the dimension of 10μm and 1μm, were made on the chilling metal surface, to iniate nucleation at the pre-known locations. Figure 9.11 shows that, nucleation did not happen on the pre-set indentation site, that is to say, the surface roughness R_a greater than 1 micron has little effect on the nucleation. It was also observed that a crystal

nucleated on the smooth region close to the indentations at an undercooling of
45K (Figure 9.11(b)).

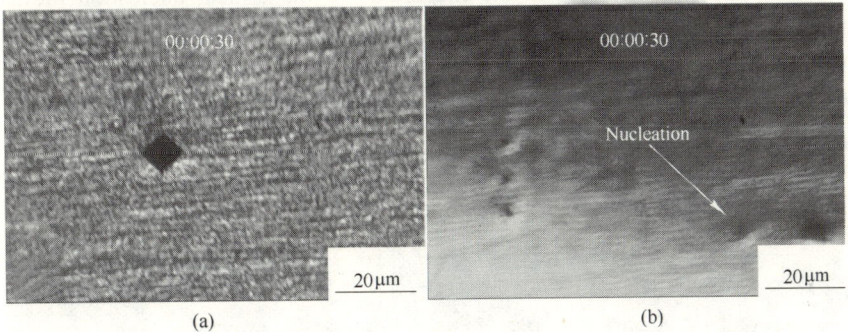

(a)   (b)

Figure 9.11   Effects of surface roughness on nucleation behavior at the chilling metal surface,
f=100Hz, D=20μm, T_m=310K and T_c=262K

(a) R_a=0.295μm, one 10μm indentation; (b) R_a=0.067μm, three 1μm indentations

Figure 9.12 shows calculated critical nucleation radius as a function of
undercooling for NH_4Cl-70%H_2O solution. It can be seen that the critical
nucleation radius is between 20nm and 100nm when the undercooling on the
chilling metal surface is between 10K and 50K, which is the range of the present
experimental conditions. The comparison of the experimental results with the
critical nucleation radius seems to indicate that there is a size match between the
submicro-pits and active nucleation sites on the chilling metal surface.

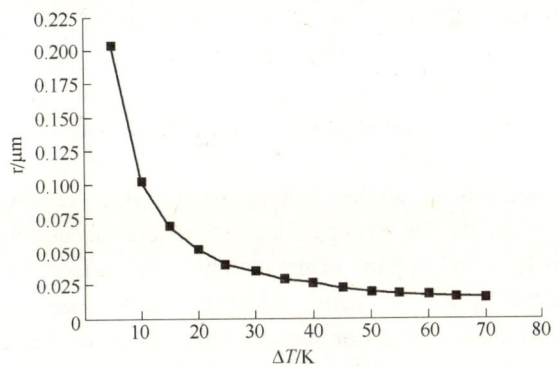

Figure 9.12   Critical nucleation radius as a function of undercooling
for NH_4Cl-70%H_2O alloy

The geometric micro-pattern of the chilling metal surface was examined with an
atomic force microscope to reveal the difference between the area with and
without active nucleation sites. Figure 9.13(a) shows the AFM image of an area
with active nucleation site. There are some submicro-notches and submicro-pits
with the size in the magnitude of the critical nucleation radius, which may serve as

the active nucleation sites. Figure 9.13(b) shows the AFM image of an area without active nucleation site. There are not any submicro-notches and submicro-pits with the size in the magnitude of the critical nucleation radius; otherwise there are many small convex apices. This evidence further supports the above opinion that there is a size match between the small submicro-pits and active nucleation sites on the chilling metal surface.

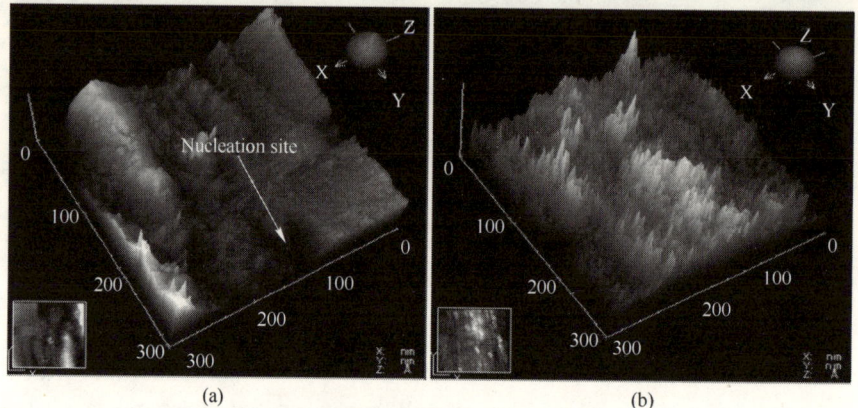

(a)   (b)

Figure 9.13   AFM images of (a) an area with active nucleation site,
(b) an area without active nucleation site

9.2.4   *Conclusions*

1. Vibrating is an effective way to produce a lot of nuclei of equiaxed crystalmicrostructure by preventing formation of the solidifying shell and promoting break-off and detachment of dendrites from the solid substrate surface. The effects are strengthened with increasing vibration frequency and amplitude.
2. Increasing undercooling at the chilling metal surface results in increasing nucleation sites and the decreasing critical size for crystal detachment.
3. Nucleation is localized in parts of the chilling solid surface. Only some fixed positions on the surface are active nucleation sites. There is a size match between the submicro-notches or submicro-pits and active nucleation sites on the chilling metal surface. The active nucleation sites increases at lower temperature of the chilling surface.

9.3   Homogeneity and Equiaxed Grain Structure of Steels

Metallurgists have believed that an equiaxed grain structure can significantly suppress macro segregation and central porosity of billets. However, up to now little direct evidence has been found on the significantly positive influence of the equiaxed grain structure on the macrostructure of as-cast billets.

9.3.1　Relation of segregation and equiaxed grain structure

The traditional method to analyze segregation of elements in a billet is to drill a hole into it and take samples for chemical analysis. The measured points are uncontinuous and the result is a lack of reproducibility and accuracy. OPA is a technology to analyze chemical composition and structure on the original billet surface through continuous scanning (Yang et al, 2000). Millions of signals are recorded and processed with computer. The analysis results are given in several forms, such as 3-dimensionional graphs and probability distribution diagrams.

Two silicon steel billets were cast from the same heat of liquid steel, but from different casting strands. The chemical composition of this steel was: C 0.05%; Si 2.60%; Mn 0.24%; P 0.013%; S 0.020%. Due to the different technical parameters during the casting, their as-cast structures are different, as shown in Figure 9.14. Sample 1 exhibits columnar grains while Sample 2 shows equiaxed grains in the central zone.

The segregation of elements in the samples can be described in terms of the distribution probability of the elements, shown in Table 9.4. It is clear that the element distribution across the billet with equiaxed grains is more homogeneous compared to columnar grains. e.g. in regard to the silicon content, 42.51% of the measured points on Sample 1 are in the range of 2.23%~2.63%, which meets the analysis specification. The other points (57.49%) are out of the range, i.e. the segregation is found in these points. On Sample 2, 71.34% of the measured points meet the specification. That is, the segregation is only found in the remaining 28.66% points.

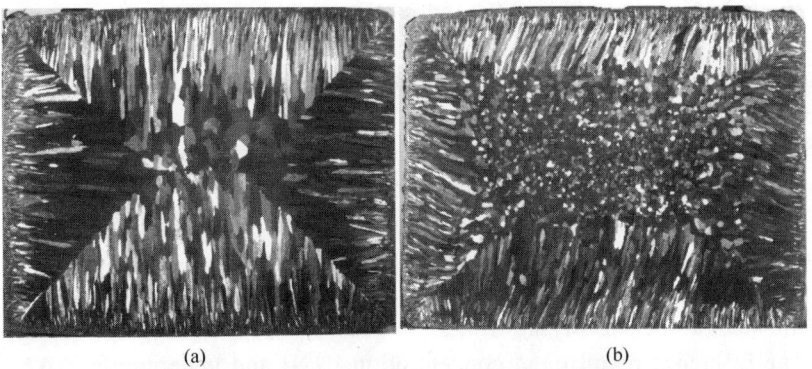

(a)　　　　　　　　　　　　　　　(b)

Figure 9.14　As-cast structures of silicon steel billets
(a) Conventional columnar structure; (b) Equiaxed structure

Table 9.4   Distribution probabilities of elements in Si steel billets

Elements		Sample 1 (columnar)	Sample 2 (equiaxed)
C	Accepted range of mass content / %	0.031 ~0.071	0.043~ 0.083
	Probability / %	81.29	90.21
Si	Accepted range of mass content / %	2.23~ 2.63	2.26~ 2.66
	Probability / %	42.51	71.34
S	Accepted range of mass content / %	0.014 ~ 0.022	0.011~ 0.019
	Probability / %	22.91	55.98

9.3.2   Titanium-based inoculation technology

It is well known that titanium nitrides particles can pin austenite grain boundaries effectively at a very high temperature. So they are used to achieve grain refinement in the heat affected zone after welding. In contrast, our purpose is to refine as-cast structures of steel according to a similar concept. Titanium-based particles can act as effective nuclei where δ-ferrite dendrites may nucleate and grow further. The reasons can be explained in terms of the matching of the lattice parameters and the wetting angle of titanium oxides (Chiang, 2001). A few reports were published on the grain refining by means of titanium-based heterogeneous inoculation for stainless steel. But for commercial plain steels, this technology is still an exploratory and interesting project.

9.3.2.1   Precipitation of TiN particles

In the condition of [%Ti]= 0.02 and [%N] = 0.005, TiN can precipitate only after the solidification ratio f_s exceeds 0.8, as seen in Figure 9.15. At that time, TiN particles contribute little to the formation of equiaxed grains because they precipitate quite late, close to the end of the solidification process. Our new idea is to make TiN precipitate at the early stage of solidification. Two approaches can be made to move the intersection point in Figure 9.16 to the left side. One is to move the curve of log Q upwards through increasing the contents of Ti and N in liquid steel. The other is to move the line of log K downwards through increasing the undercooling in the liquid steel at the solidifying front.

The influence of nitrogen concentration [%N] and undercooling (ΔT) on the precipitation time can also be seen in Figure 9.15. When [%N] = 50ppm and ΔT = 0K, TiN precipitation starts at f_s=0.8. If [%N] is increased up to

137ppm, TiN will already precipitate at the beginning of solidification. The undercooling (ΔT) has a great influence on precipitation, too. When ΔT increases from 0K to 49K, the start of TiN precipitation will move from f_s=0.8 to f_s=0.7. Under simultaneous control of titanium and nitrogen contents as well as of ΔT, TiN precipitation at the early stage of solidification can be obtained. Influence of concentration of [%N] and undercooling (ΔT) on the precipitation time also can be seen in Figure 9.1. In the condition of [%N]=50ppm and ΔT=0,TiN precipitation begins at f_s=0.8. If [%N] is increased up to 137ppm, TiN will precipitate at the beginning of solidification. The undercooling (ΔT) also obviously influences the precipitation beginning time. When ΔT is increased from 0K to 49k , TiN will precipitate from f_s=0.8 to f_s=0.7. If we are able to control the contents of titanium and nitrogen and ΔT simultaneously, it will be easier to obtain TiN precipitates at the early stage of solidification.

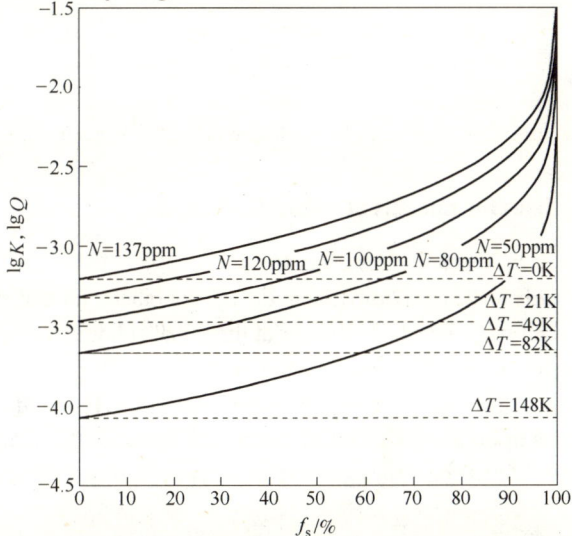

Figure 9.15 Influence of [%N] and undercooling on precipitation time

9.3.2.2 Competitive precipitation between TiN and Ti$_2$O$_3$

There are mainly two kinds of titanium oxides occurring in steelmaking and casting processes: TiO$_2$ and Ti$_2$O$_3$. TiO$_2$ is stable in liquid steel with high oxygen content. Ti$_2$O$_3$ precipitates only if [O] $\leqslant$ 40 ppm. More important, the initial [%N] content has a great effect on the competition of TiN and Ti$_2$O$_3$ precipitation. As shown in Figure 9.16, when initial [%N] content increases from 50ppm to 80ppm at ultra-low oxygen content of 0.5ppm, TiN particles will precipitate ahead of Ti$_2$O$_3$ precipitation. Therefore, the following condition should be met for precipitation of TiN at the early stage of solidification:

1. High nitrogen and adequate titanium contents;
2. Ultra-low oxygen content to prevent precipitation;
3. High cooling strength and high purity of steel to obtain great undercooling.

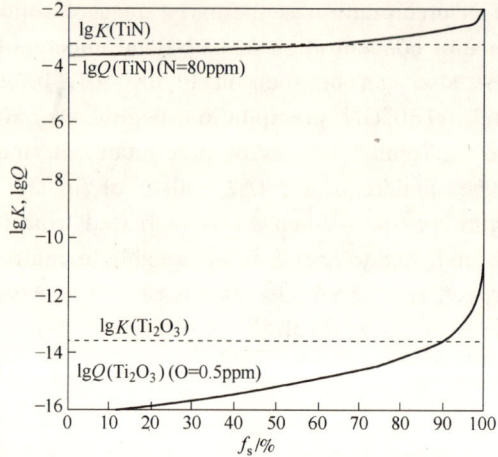

Figure 9.16   TiN particles precipitate before Ti_2O_3 precipitation

9.3.2.3   Particles for nucleus of δ-ferrite dendrites

An experiment was specially designed to get a large number of titanium-based particles in the early stage of solidification. Firstly, the billet with thin shell and liquid in front of the shell was quenched in water at the initial solidification period. Then, a sample was taken and observed with SEM. Two types of TiN particles were found in the sample: the pure TiN and the complex of TiN and Ti_2O_3. The particle size is about 1~2 μm, as shown in Figure 9.17. This is also a clear evidence that the particle acts as nucleus on which δ-ferrite dendrites grow at the early stage of solidification.

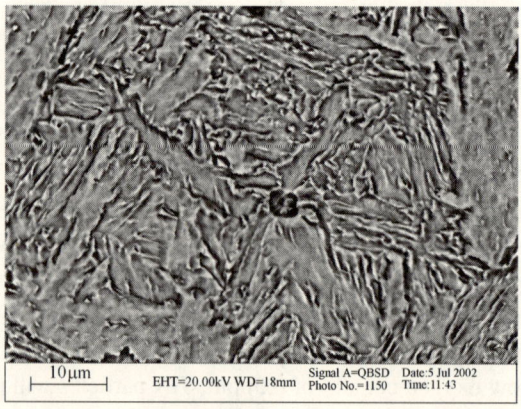

Figure 9.17   δ -ferrite dendrites grow up on combined TiN particle

9.3.3 Small temperature gradient technology

Both liquidus temperature of the silicon steel and temperature gradient determine the constitutional undercooling at the solidifying front, which can subsequently change the morphology of the solidifying structure. It can be seen from Figure 9.18 that the smaller the temperature gradient is, the wider the constitutional undercooling zone is and the greater the constitutional undercooling. Moreover, the morphology of the solidification structure is determined by the constitutional undercooling. Whether the liquid steel transforms to the columnar or the equiaxed grain structure in the front of solid mainly depends on the temperature gradient; whereas the growth rate of the solid phase has less effect on such a transformation, as shown in Figure 9.19.

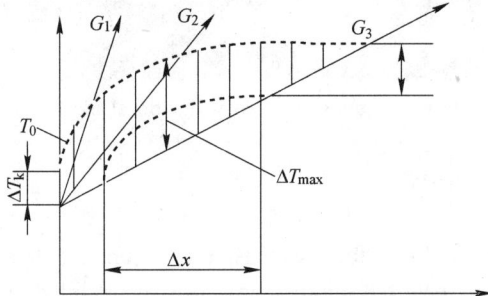

Figure 9.18 Dependence of constitutional undercooling in the solidifying front on temperature gradient. Δx is the width of the constitutional undercooling zone, ΔT_{max} is the maximum constitutional undercooling degree, ΔT_k is the constitutional undercooling degree on the inner wall of the mould, T_0 is liquidus temperature, G_1, G_2, G_3 are different temperature gradients in liquid

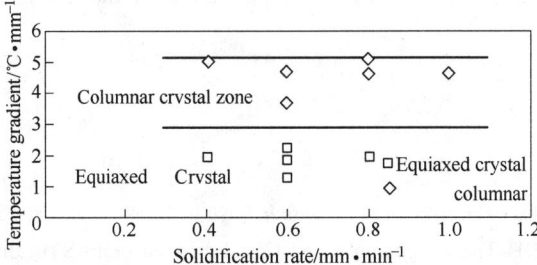

Figure 9.19 Influence of temperature gradient on columnar/equiaxed transformation

In order to achieve a small temperature gradient in the continuous casting, which is such a massive production process, a special compound mould was designed. The upper half of the mould is made of heat-resistant material and the lower half of the mould is made of conventional material. Since heat transfer is retarded in the upper mould, a small temperature gradient can be established. Then, the liquid steel without overheating will solidify in the lower half of the mould. Consequently, not only the equiaxed grain structure is well developed, but also the occurrence of longitudinal cracks is greatly reduced. Macrostructures produced by the traditional and the low gradient moulds are shown in Figure 9.20.

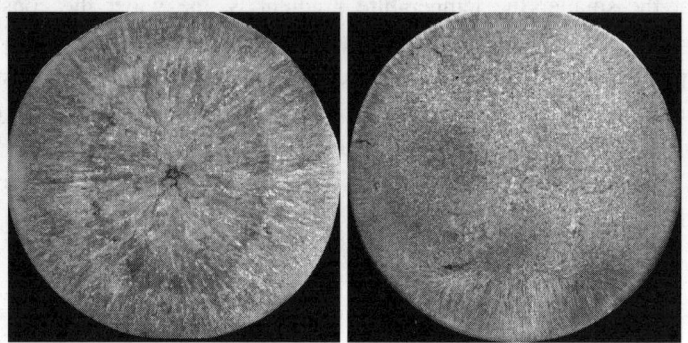

Figure 9.20   Macro structures produced by traditional and low gradient moulds

9.3.4 *Conclusions*

1. By means of Original Position Analysis, it was found that the equiaxed structure could greatly eliminate the micro-segregation in the billet. The equiaxed grain technology is efficient to achieve a high homogeneity of steel materials.
2. TiN and TiN/ Ti$_2$O$_3$ complex particles can precipitate at the early stage of solidification as heterogeneous inoculants of δ-ferrite dendrites if the solidifying condition is properly controlled.
3. The small temperature gradient has a great effect on the fraction of the equiaxed grains in billets.

References

Chalmers B J (1963) The structure of ingots J. Australian Inst Metals 8: 255-263

Chiang L K (2001) The Formation of As-Cast Equiaxed grain Structures in Steel using Titanium-Based Inoculation Technology, In: Proceedings of NG Steel 2001, Beijing, 2001, pp.187-191

Cole G S, Bolling G F (1967) Enforced fluid motion and the control of grain structures in metal castings Trans Metall Soc AIME 239: 1824-1835

Cromer D T, Mann J B (1967) Compton scattering factors for spherically symmetric free atoms J Chem Phys 67:1892

Gan Y, Zhao P, Wang M, Zhang H, Tao H B, Lv Y C (2006) Physical Analogue of Liquid Metal Original Position Nucleation Stirred by Vibration J Iron Steel Res 18(8): 9-13

Hansen G, Liu S, Lu S Z, Hellawell A J (2002) Dendritic array growth in the systems NH_4Cl-H_2O and $[CH_2CN]_2-H_2O$: steady state measurements and analysis Crystal Growth 234: 731-739

Il'inskii A, Slyusarenko S, Slukhovskii O, Kaban I, Hoyer W (2002) Structure of liquid Fe–Al alloys Mater Sci Eng A 325:98

Jackson K A, Hunt J D, Uhlmann D R, Seward T P III (1966) Trans Metall Soc AIME 236(2):149-158

Krogh-Moe J (1956) A method for converting experimental X-ray intensities to an absolute scale Acta Crystallogr 9:951

Luo J (2002) Liquid and high temperature structure of Fe and Fe-C alloy. Dissertation for master degree, University Science & Technology Beijing

Maret M, Pasturel A, Senillou C, et al(1989) Partial structure factors of liquid Al80(Mnx(FeCr)1-x)20 alloys J Phys France 50:295

Mathiesen R H, Arnberg L, Bleuet P and Somogyi A (2006) Crystal fragmentation and columnar to equiaxed transitions in Al-Cu studied by synchrotron X-ray video microscopy Metall Mater Trans 37A: 2515-2524

Norman N (1957) The Fourier transform method for normalizing intensities Acta Crystallography 10:370

Ohno (1976) The solidification of metals. Chijin Shokan Co. Ltd., Tokyo, Japan. p50-104

Qin J Y, Bian X F, Sliousarenko S I, Wang W M(1998a) J Phys Condens Matter 10:1211

Qin J Y, Bian X F, Wang W M, et al (1998b) Chin Sci Bulletin 43:1445

Qin J Y, Bian X F, Wang W M, Sliousarenko S I, Xu C Y, Ma J J (1998c) Sci Chin E 28:97

Qin J Y, Bian X F, Wang W M, Sliousarenko S I, Xu C Y, Ma J J(1998d) Sci Chin E 41:182

Southin R T(1976) Trans Metall Soc AIME 239(2):220-225

Waseda Y (1980) The Structure of Non-Crystalline Materials. McGraw-Hill, New York, p27

Waseda Y, Shinoda K, Sugiyama K, et al (1995a) High temperature X-ray diffraction study of melt structure of silicon J Appl Phys 34:4124

Winegard W C, Chalmers B (1954) Trans Am Soc Met 46:1214-1224

Yang Z J, Ii X J, et al (2000). Original Position Analysis of Material. In: Proceedings of International Conference on Engineering and Technological Sciences 2000, Advanced Materials Session, Beijing, China, Vol 2,p1423

Zhang L, Wu Y S, Bian X F, Li H, Wang W M, Wu S J (2000) Short-range and medium-range order in liquid and amorphous Al90Fe5Ce5 alloys J. Non-Cryst Solids 262:169

10
Welding of Ultra-Fine Grained Steels

Weldability is an important application property of ultra-fine grained steel. The grain growth and microstructure transformation in the HAZ of ultra-fine grained steel are studied in the present chapter. Laser welding and arc welding processes of 400 MPa grade ultra-fine grained carbon steel and 800 MPa grade ultra-fine microstructure Bainitic steel are discussed.

10.1 Introduction

As is shown in the previous chapters and many papers（Kang J H, 2007; Majta J, 2007; Mathis K, 2007; Murty S V S N, 2005）, both the strength and the toughness of steels can be dramatically enhanced by grain refinement. Whether the properties of a welded joint can match those of the base metal is the key issue for the application of these ultra-fine grained steels in engineering structures.

The heat affected zone (HAZ) in the ultra-fine grained steel is the major concern in many studies (Hamatani H, 2007; Kawaguchi Y, 2002; Youn J G, 2002; Tian Z, 2002). In the HAZ, the microstructure of an ultra-fine grained steel will undergo severe transformations due to the effect of the welding thermal cycle. During heating, the base metal will start to transform into austenite when the temperature reaches the Ac_1 point and accomplish at Ac_3 point. The austenite grains will grow to form the coarse grained HAZ, and the size of the austenite grains is dependent on the time of grain growth at high temperature, which is related to the method and parameter of welding (wang et al,2002). During cooling, the austenite transforms into microstructure that is different from the base metal in the heat-affected zone (HAZ) (Lancaster J F, 1980). Welding performance is very important from the view point of joint strength and toughness, and both the softening and the deterioration of

---

❶ The chapter 10 was written by Zhiling Tian and Yun Peng.

toughness are the major concerns in the stability of HAZ.

Another concern is the weld metal. Whereas grain refining improves both the strength and the toughness of the base metal, the weld metal maintains largely a cast structure. With conventional welding materials, the toughness of the deposited metal can hardly match that of the base metal of ultra-fine grained steel when strength matching is required. In order to achieve integrate properties in a welded joint, it becomes necessary to develop new welding materials for the ultra-fine grained steels, especially for the high strength grades.

In section 10.2, the grain growth and microstructure transformation in the HAZ of ultra-fine grained steel is studied. A computational simulation of HAZ grain growth based on the Monte Carlo model generated the grain size distribution across the HAZ, which coincides with to that of actual welded joints.

In section 10.3, the welding of 400 MPa grade ultra-fine grained carbon steel is reported, including laser welding in 10.3.1 and arc welding in 10.3.2. The welding of ultra-fine grained anti-weathering steel and rebar is reported in 10.3.3 and 10.3.4, respectively.

In section 10.4, the welding of 800 MPa grade ultra-fine microstructure Bainitic steel is reported. A welding wire with ultra low carbon bainite (ULCB) microstructure deposited metal is developed, as shown in 10.4.1. Arc welding and laser welding of the steel are respectively reported in 10.4.2 and 10.4.3.

10.2❶　Simulation of Welding of Fine-grained Steel

10.2.1　*Simulation of grain growth in HAZ*

The Monte Carlo (MC) technology has been widely used to simulate grain growth under both isothermal and non-isothermal conditions. This MC methodology for grain structure evolution is based on Potts model and was adopted by Anderson et al(1984; Srolovttz D J, 1984), to simulate grain structure evolution and predict various aspects of grain growth under isothermal conditions.

The principal of MC grain growth simulation of two dimensional or three dimensional monophase structure starts with the initiation of the simulation lattice. This is accomplished by dividing the material into small volume elements, and placing the center of these elements on to the lattice points. Each of the grid points is assigned as random orientation number between 1 and Q, where Q is the total number of grain orientations. A grain boundary segment is defined to lie between two sits of unlike orientation. The kinetics of grain boundary migration are

---

❶ The part 10.2 was written by Xiaoyan Li and Yaowu Shi.

simulated by selecting a site randomly and changing its orientation to one of the nearest neighbor orientations based on energy change due to the attempted orientation change. The successful transitions at the grain boundaries to orientations of nearest neighbor grains thus correspond to boundary migration.

10.2.1.1　The monte carlo model of the HAZ

In order to apply MC technology in simulation of grain growth in the HAZ, the relationship between the MC simulation time step (t_{MCS}), the real time t and the temperature T should be defined previously. Three models were proposed, to correlate the t_{MCS} and the real time t, for different simulation. They are the atomistic model, the experimental data based (EBD) model and the grain-boundary migration (GBM) model. Generally, due to the small size of the atoms and the limitation of computer resources, the atomistic model can only be used to simulate grain growth in a structure with small assemblies of atoms such as nanocrystals. GBM model utilizes the concept that grain boundary migration reduces number of grains, thereby increasing the mean grain size and reducing the total grain boundary energy. GBM mode is a good approach for grain growth simulation when the isothermal grain growth data for a given material are not available. However, the physical and thermodynamic properties of the material must be available. Strictly speaking, the GBM model is only valid for pure material due to the grain growth exponent was assumed to be 0.5 which was theoretically derived and was only suitable for very pure materials at high temperature, in which the effects of solute drag, impurity segregation and second phase particles on grain growth could be ignored. Thus, for metals with relatively high content of impurities, or in alloys the experimental data based (EDB) model should be used, in which sufficient kinetic data for isothermal grain growth at different temperatures are needed. In continuous cooling process, the real time could be subdivided into series time increments. Each time increment could be treated as a isothermal process. The total t_{MCS}, then, is the accumulation of the t_{MCS} at each time increment.

Another important feature to be remembered while applying MC technique to model grain growth in the HAZ is that in the MC technique the choice of grid point for updating the grain orientation number is random. As a consequence, the probability to select each grid point is the same. However, grains must grow at faster rates in regions of higher temperatures in the HAZ and this fact must be included in the calculation scheme. Therefore, the thermal cycle in the weld HAZ, which is a function of the distance from the fusion plane, is represented by gradient of t_{MCS}, which, in turn, is incorporated in the simulation by visiting each site with a probability. In this way, locations with higher t_{MCS} and higher temperature are updated more frequently and the temperature gradient in the HAZ is properly taken into account (Shi Y W, 2004).

10.2.1.2   The EDB model

Based on isothermal experimental data and the grain growth regression analysis, there exists a relation among the grain size (L), initial grain size (L_0), holding time (t), and temperature (T), as follows:

$$L^n - L_0^n = Kt \exp\left(-\frac{Q}{RT}\right) \qquad (10.1)$$

where K is a constant and Q is the activation energy. Both K and Q are obtained from experimental data. In the MC simulation there is an empirical relation between the simulated grain size and the MC simulation time. This is

$$L = K_1 \times \lambda \times (t_{MCS})^{n_1} \qquad (10.2)$$

which may be written as

$$\log\left(\frac{L}{\lambda}\right) = \log(K_1) + n_1 \log(t_{MCS}) \qquad (10.3)$$

where λ is the discrete grid point spacing in the MC network. K_1 and n_1 are the model constants, which are obtained from regression analysis. In addition the MC simulation time is a dimensionless quantity.

Substituting equation (10.2) into equation (10.1), and integrating it over an entire thermal cycle by summing the grain growth in short time intervals at different temperature, a relationship among the MC simulation time, real time and temperature is deduced. That is

$$(t_{MCS})^{nn_1} = \left(\frac{L_0}{K_1\lambda}\right)^n + \frac{K}{(K_1\lambda)^n}\sum\left[\Delta t_i \exp(-\frac{Q}{RT})\right] \qquad (10.4)$$

where T is the mean temperature in a time interval (Δt_i). Thus, t_{MCS} can be related to the real time ($T = \sum_i \Delta t_i$).

It is well known that steep temperature gradient exists in the weld HAZ. Different thermal cycles occur in the different location. Computed values of the t_{MCS} are varied with location where the temperature is a function of time. Thus, the values of t_{MCS} are distributed in gradient form. In addition computed t_{MCS} can not be directly applied to the MC model. Thus, a concept on the site selection probability should be introduced. That is the site selection probability varies with location. The grain orientations at higher temperature locations are updated more frequently by considering a probability gradient. The larger the t_{MCS} at a site, the higher the corresponding site selection probability ($p(r)$).

$$p(r) = \frac{t_{MCS}(r)}{t_{MCS}^{max}} \qquad (10.5)$$

where $t_{MCS}(r)$ is the value at any location with distance of r from the heat source, and t_{MCS}^{max} is the maximum value in the whole region. Thus, the temperature gradient of HAZ is included through the site selection at any location.

10.2.1.3　MC simulation of grain growth in HAZ of fine-grained steels

The fine-grained steels were produced by Baosteel. The thickness of the plate of 400 MPa grade steel is 3 mm with the microstructure mainly consists of ferrite and pearlite. The average ferrite grain size is 7 μm. The thickness of the plate of 800 MPa grade steel is 1.8 mm with the microstructure mainly consists of ferrite and a little of bainite. The average grain size is 2 μm. The characteristic phase transition temperatures of the above steels are shown in Table 10.1.

Table 10.1　Characteristic phase transition temperatures

Steel	Ac_1	Ac_3	Ar_1	Ar_3
400MPa Grade	725℃	840℃	645℃	745℃
800MPa Grade	725℃	845℃	630℃	785℃

The relationship between t_{MCS} and t was established based on EDB model. The thermal physical properties of the above two steels are shown in Table 10.2.

Table 10.2　Thermal physical properties

Steel	ρ /kg·m^{-3}	λ /J·(m·s℃)$^{-1}$	C_p /J·(kg·℃)$^{-1}$	T_m	Q /J·mol^{-1}	n	K
400 MPa Grade	6900	25.1	702.0	1500℃	124500	0.4	$1.67×10^{-7}$
800 MPa Grade	6900	25.1	702.0	1500℃	249000	0.4	$2.9×10^{-3}$

The grain growth in HAZ of the above two steels was simulated under three welding heat input levels named as high level, medium level and low level as shown in Table 10.3.

The simulated final grain structures in the HAZ of 400 MPa fine-grained steel for various welding conditions are shown in Figure 10.1. It is noted that the region near the fusion line experiences significant grain growth during welding. The closer the location to the fusion line, the coarser the grain size. This is expected, since the grain-size change depends on the temperature. The higher the temperature at a site, the larger the final grain size.

Table 10.3　Welding conditions

Heat Input Levels	Current /A	Voltage /V	Speed v/mm · s^{-1}
Low	52	19.6	5.6
Medium	79	22.0	5.6
High	115	25.4	5.6

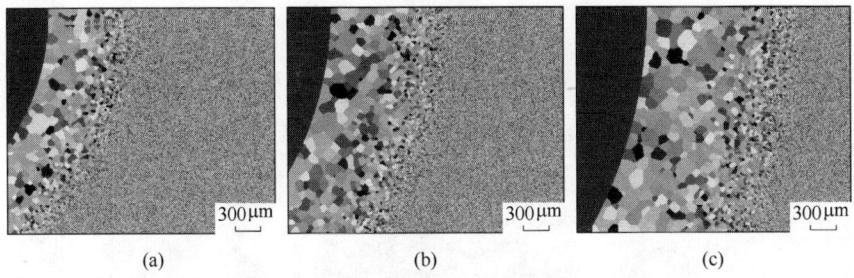

(a)   (b)   (c)

Figure 10.1 Comparison of the simulated grain structure under various
welding heat-input conditions:
(a) 182 J/mm; (b) 310.4 J/mm; (c) 521.6 J/mm

The grain size was estimated by using statistic method. It was found that the average grain size is around 70~80 μm under low heat input condition, the average grain size is around 100~110 μm under medium heat input condition and the average grain size is around 120~150 μm under high heat input condition, as shown in Figure 10.2.

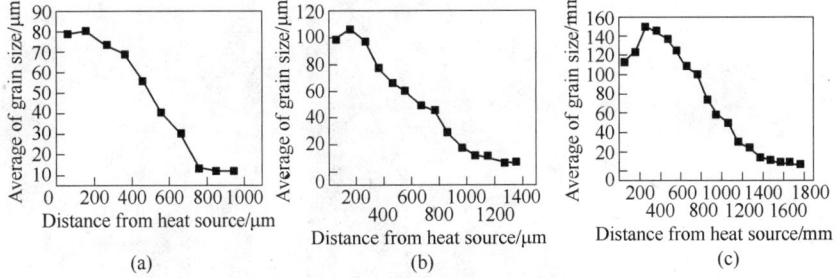

(a)   (b)   (c)

Figure 10.2 Comparison of the average grain sizes under various
welding heat-input conditions:
(a) 182 J/mm; (b) 310.4 J/mm; (c) 521.6 J/mm

10.2.1.4 Experimental identification

The actual grain morphological appears in HAZ of 400 MPa steel, under the above three heat input conditions, were shown in Figure 10.3. The grain size was measured in accordance with the procedure defined in YB7T5148—93. The measured results were summarized in Table 10.4. It is noted that the simulated results are of good accuracy.

Table 10.4 Comparison of the simulated grain size with that of measured values

Measured value and Simulated value	Low heat input	Medium heat input	High heat input
Measured value	69 μm	105 μm	127 μm
Simulated value	75 μm	105 μm	135 μm

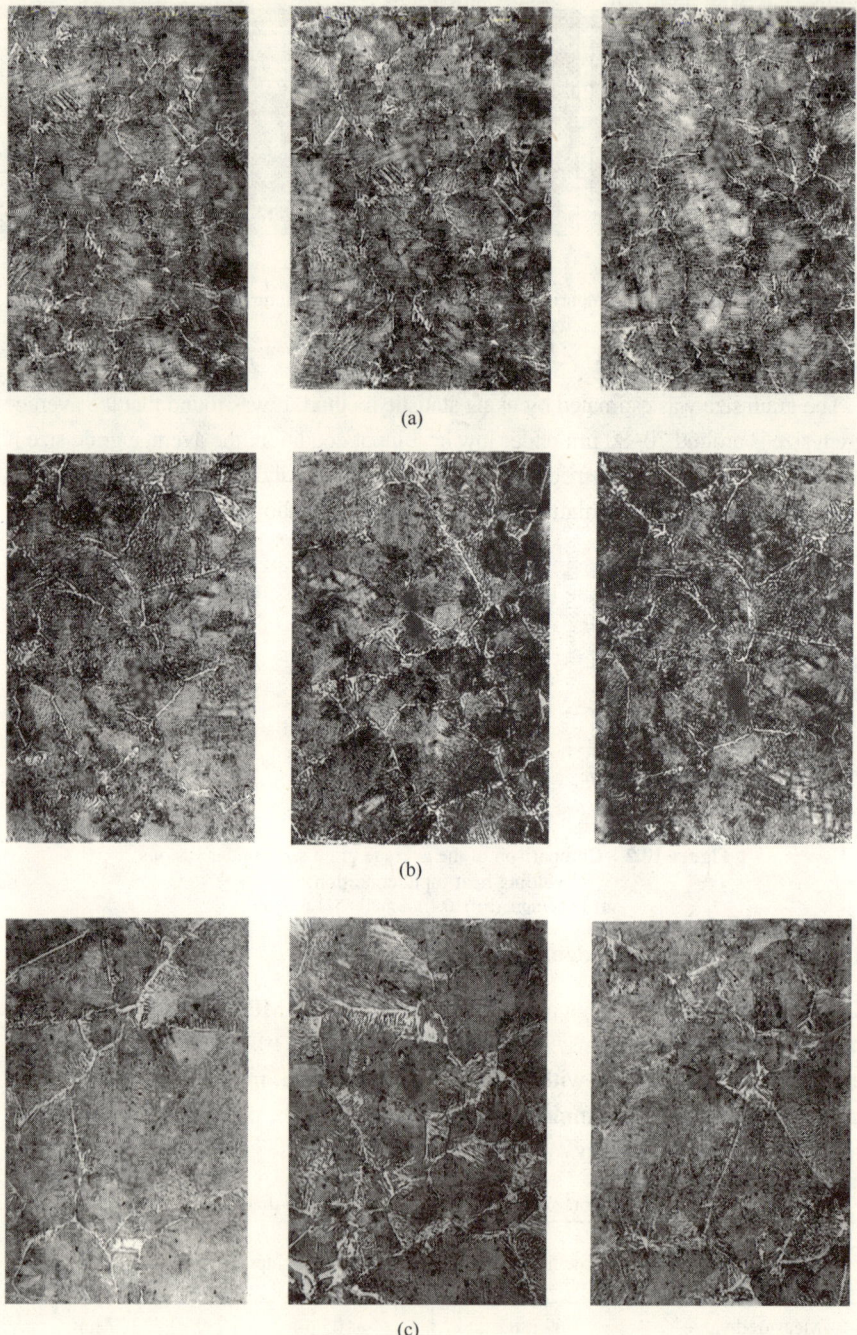

Figure 10.3　Coarse grained HAZ morphological appears under various
welding heat-input conditions:
(a) 182 J/mm; (b) 310.4 J/mm; (c) 521.6 J/mm (×100)

10.2.2 *Fluid flow in welding pool of ultra fine grain steel*

The heat flow and the fluid flow in the weld pool can significantly affect the temperature gradients, cooling rates and solidification structure. In addition, the fluid flow and the convective heat transfer in the weld control the penetration and shape of the weld pool. Often, the critical variable that controls variation in the pool geometry is the amount of surface-active minor elements that are present in commercially available material. In iron-base alloys, sulfur and oxygen are the surface-active trace elements most commonly present (Zhao Y Z, 2006; Lu S P, 2002; Hsieh R I, 1999).

The behavior of fluid flow and the influence of active elements addition, especially oxygen and sulfur, in the welding pool of a novel TIG process—active flux TIG(A-TIG) could be demonstrated as follows.

10.2.2.1 Mathematical model

(A) Governing Equations

In order to simplify the mathematical model, the following assumptions have been made: 1. the flow is Newtonian, incompressible and laminar; 2. all of the physical properties of the liquid and solid metals are constant; 3. the spatially-distributed heat and current fluxes falling on the free surface have Gaussian characteristics; 4. Boussinesq approximation can be employed.

Because that:

1. The heat flux of the workpiece surface is symmetrical due to Gaussian distribution;
2. The geometry of the workpiece is also symmetrical;
3. The heat losses and the mechanical boundary conditions of the workpiece is symmetrical.

The resulted temperatures and fluid patterns in the welding pool are symmetrical to the plane of $y=0$. For convenience, the symmetry plane ($y=0$) in the longitudinal direction is assumed, so that the computations need to be done in only half of the region of the workpiece.

In Figure 10.4, the arc moves in the positive x-direction at constant speed u_x. Let u, v, and w represent the x, y, z directional velocities in the coordinate system respectively, the governing equations, including the continuity, momentum and energy equations, may be written as follows:

$$\frac{\partial(\rho u)}{\partial x}+\frac{\partial(\rho v)}{\partial y}+\frac{\partial(\rho w)}{\partial z}=0 \tag{10.6}$$

$$-\frac{\partial(\rho u_x u)}{\partial x}+\frac{\partial(\rho uu)}{\partial x}+\frac{\partial(\rho vu)}{\partial y}+\frac{\partial(\rho wu)}{\partial z}=\frac{\partial}{\partial x}\left(\mu\frac{\partial u}{\partial x}\right)+\frac{\partial}{\partial y}\left(\mu\frac{\partial u}{\partial y}\right)+\frac{\partial}{\partial z}\left(\mu\frac{\partial u}{\partial z}\right)-\frac{\partial P}{\partial x}+S_x$$

$$\tag{10.7}$$

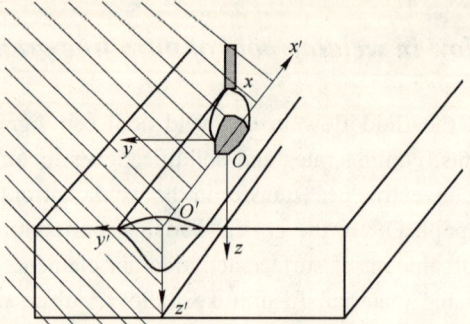

Figure 10.4   Schematic diagram of the weld and the coordinate systems

$$-\frac{\partial(\rho u_x v)}{\partial x}+\frac{\partial(\rho uv)}{\partial x}+\frac{\partial(\rho vv)}{\partial y}+\frac{\partial(\rho wv)}{\partial z}=\frac{\partial}{\partial x}\left(\mu\frac{\partial v}{\partial x}\right)+\frac{\partial}{\partial y}\left(\mu\frac{\partial v}{\partial y}\right)+\frac{\partial}{\partial z}\left(\mu\frac{\partial v}{\partial z}\right)-\frac{\partial P}{\partial y}+S_y \qquad (10.8)$$

$$-\frac{\partial(\rho u_x w)}{\partial x}+\frac{\partial(\rho uw)}{\partial x}+\frac{\partial(\rho vw)}{\partial y}+\frac{\partial(\rho ww)}{\partial z}=\frac{\partial}{\partial x}\left(\mu\frac{\partial w}{\partial x}\right)+\frac{\partial}{\partial y}\left(\mu\frac{\partial w}{\partial y}\right)+\frac{\partial}{\partial z}\left(\mu\frac{\partial w}{\partial z}\right)-\frac{\partial P}{\partial x}+S_z$$

$$(10.9)$$

$$-\frac{\partial}{\partial x}(\rho u_x h)+\frac{\partial}{\partial x}(\rho uh)+\frac{\partial}{\partial y}(\rho vh)+\frac{\partial}{\partial z}(\rho wh)=\frac{\partial}{\partial x}\left(k\frac{\partial T}{\partial x}\right)+\frac{\partial}{\partial y}\left(k\frac{\partial T}{\partial y}\right)+\frac{\partial}{\partial z}\left(k\frac{\partial T}{\partial Z}\right)+S_h \quad (10.10)$$

where ρ is density, k is thermal conductivity, μ is viscosity, P is pressure, h is enthalpy, S_x, S_y and S_z are the component of the body forces. The body force consists of the electromagnetic force and buoyancy force:

$$S_{x,y,z}=(J\times B)_{x,y,z}+\rho g_{x,y,z}\beta(T-T_f) \qquad (10.11)$$

where J is the current density convector; B is the magnetic induction vector; β is the coefficient of volume expansion; T_f is the reference temperature.

S_h is the source term that accounts for the latent heat of melting and convective transport of latent heat in the two-phase region:

$$S_h=-\left[\frac{\partial}{\partial x}(\rho u\Delta H)+\frac{\partial}{\partial y}(\rho v\Delta H)+\frac{\partial}{\partial z}(\rho w\Delta H)\right]+\frac{\partial}{\partial x}(\rho u_x\Delta H) \quad (10.12)$$

The latent heat (ΔH) is assumed to be proportional to the liquid mass fraction (f_l) in the weld pool. In the present study, the latent heat is absorbed or released according to the following relation:

$$f_l=\frac{T-T_l}{T_l-T_s} \text{ for } T_s\leqslant T\leqslant T_l \qquad (10.13)$$

where T_l is the liquidus temperature and T_s is the solidus temperature.

(B) Boundary conditions

(a) At the top surface

The model considers the heat flux from the arc at the top surface of workpiece as a specified symmetric Gaussian distribution described by:

$$q(r) = \frac{3UI\eta}{\pi r^2} \exp\left[\frac{-3(x+y)^2}{r^2}\right] \tag{10.14}$$

where U is the voltage, I is the current, η is the process efficiency, r is the effective radius of heat flux distribution.

(b)   At the other surfaces

Heat that losses from the metal to its surroundings due to convection and radiation can be written as:

$$q_{loss} = h_c(T - T_0) + \sigma\varepsilon\left(T^4 - T_0^4\right) \tag{10.15}$$

where T_0 is the atmospheric temperature; h_c is the heat transfer coefficient; σ is the Stefan-Boltzmann constant; ε is the radiation emissivity.

(c)   Along the symmetrical plane

Along the plane of the symmetry ($y=0$), the following boundary conditions are defined for the velocity components:

$$\frac{\partial u}{\partial y} = 0 \qquad \frac{\partial w}{\partial y} = 0 \qquad v = 0 \tag{10.16}$$

(d)   Surface tension

At the surface of the weld pool, the Marangoni effect was incorporated by equating the stress to the spatial gradient of surface tension:

$$-\mu\frac{\partial u}{\partial z} = \frac{\partial\gamma}{\partial T}\times\frac{\partial T}{\partial x} \qquad -\mu\frac{\partial v}{\partial z} = \frac{\partial\gamma}{\partial T}\times\frac{\partial T}{\partial y} \tag{10.17}$$

Experimental surface tension data are seldom available for any material throughout the temperature range of interest. Since it is difficult to experimentally obtain surface tension data at all temperatures and compositions of interest, in the calculations presented here a developed formula to calculate the surface tension was used. The relation between surface tension and the temperature is given by

$$\gamma(T) = \gamma_m - A(T - T_m) - RT\Gamma_s\ln(1 + K_{seg}a_i) \tag{10.18}$$

where

$$K_{seg} = k_1\exp\left(\frac{-\Delta H^\ominus}{RT}\right)$$

The value of the temperature coefficient of surface-tension $\partial\gamma/\partial T$ for containing surface active element can be obtained by differentiating Equation 9.18with respect to T:

$$\frac{\partial\gamma}{\partial T} = -A - R\Gamma_s\ln\left(1 + K_{seg}a_i\right) - \frac{K_{seg}a_i}{\left(1 + K_{seg}a_i\right)}\frac{\Gamma_s\left(\Delta H^\ominus\right)}{T} \tag{10.19}$$

where γ is the surface tension of the solution at the temperature T; γ_m is the surface tension of the pure metal at the melting point T_m; A is constant in surface tension coefficient, 4.3×10^{-4} N / m $\cdot$ K; R is gas constant, 8314.3 J/kg $\cdot$ Mole $\cdot$ K; Γ_s is surface excess at saturation, 2.03×10^{-8} kg Mole/m^2(O), 1.30×10^{-8} kg Mole/m^2(S);

K_{seg} is equilibrium constant for segregation; k_1 is constant related to entropy of segregation, 1.38×10^{-2}(O), 3.18×10^{-2}(S); $\Delta H^{\ominus}$ is standard heat of adsorption, 146.3×10^3 kJ/kg Mole(O), 166.2×10^3 kJ/kg Mole(S); a_i is activity of surface active element (mass% O or S).

It is seen that $\partial \gamma / \partial T$ is a function of both temperature and composition and is negative for pure metals. In alloys containing surface active solutes $\partial \gamma / \partial T$ depends on temperature, T, the equilibrium constant for segregation, K, and the activity of the surface species, a_i. Figure 10.5 (a) and (b) show $\partial \gamma / \partial T$ of Fe-O and Fe-S systems varying as a function of oxygen and sulfur content and temperature separately. Surface-active elements present in the base metal segregate preferentially to the weld pool surface, reducing the surface tension of the base metal. As shown in Figure 10.5(a) the heats containing oxygen initially exhibit a positive $\partial \gamma / \partial T$. As the temperature increases beyond a critical temperature, $\partial \gamma / \partial T$ becomes negative. For example, for oxygen content of 150

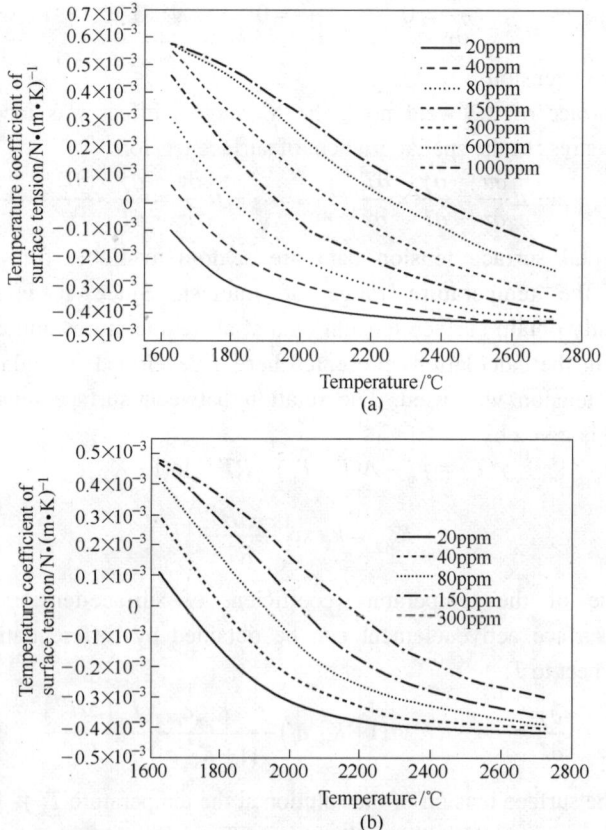

Figure 10.5　Temperature coefficients of surface tension ($\partial \gamma / \partial T$) of Fe-O system (a) and Fe-S system (b) vary with oxygen and sulfur content and temperature

ppm, $\partial\gamma/\partial T$ is positive until approximately 1950℃. As the melt surface temperature increases beyond this temperature, $\partial\gamma/\partial T$ becomes negative. From Figure 10.5 we can find the following characters: (1) the basic characteristics of the surface tension *vs.* temperature curves have been changed due to the addition of surface-active element in steels; (2) at the same temperature, the value of the surface tension decreases as the content of oxygen or sulfur increases; (3) the temperature at which the maximum surface tension occurs increases as the oxygen content increases. For different surface-active element content, $\partial\gamma/\partial T$ changes from a negative value to a positive value at different temperature.

10.2.2.2　Numerical method

A system of 250×30×20 (*i*×*j*×*k*) grid points was utilized for the welding domain of 100mm×25mm×10mm. Spatially nonuniform grids were used in the weld-pool region because of the higher temperature and velocity gradients. To solve the governing equations with the associated source terms numerically, a general thermo-fluid-mechanics computer program, PHOENICS code was used. The thermo-physical properties and welding conditions are listed in Table 10.5.

Table 10.5　Data used for heat transfer calculations

Nomenclature	Symbol	Value	Nomenclature	Symbol	Value
Solidus temperature/℃	T_S	1397	Latent heat of Melting/J • kg^{-1}	L	2.675×10^5
Liquidus temperature/℃	T_L	1450	Radiation emissivity	ε	0.4
Viscosity/kg • (m•s)$^{-1}$	Vs	0.006	Coefficient of thermal expansion /K^{-1}	β	10^{-4}
Thermal conductivity of solid/J • (m • s • K)$^{-1}$	Ks	25.1	Thermal conductivity of liquid /J • (m • s • K)$^{-1}$	K_l	83.6
Specific heat of liquid /J • (kg·K)$^{-1}$	C	702	Magnetic permeability /H • m^{-1}	μ_0	1.26×10^{-6}
Density/kg • m^{-3}	ρ	7200	Arc efficiency	η	0.75
Welding current /A	I	160	Welding voltage /V	u_w	14
Abient temperature /℃	T	25			

Generally, the heat transfer in the liquid pool occurs in the combination of convection and conduction modes. Peclet number, which is the measure of relative heat importance by heat convection and conduction, is defined as follows:

$$pe = \frac{L \cdot v_{max}}{2\alpha_l} \tag{10.20}$$

where v_{max} is the maximum surface velocity, α_l is the thermal diffusivity of liquid and L is the characteristic length of the weld pool, which can be taken as the weld pool without or with low active element content. In the deep and narrow weld pool containing certain active element, L can be taken as the depth of the weld pool.

Figure 10.6 to Figure 10.8 show the temperature fields and the flow patterns when free of active element and when oxygen and sulfur concentration are 200ppm respectively. With different surface-active element concentrations, the flow patterns

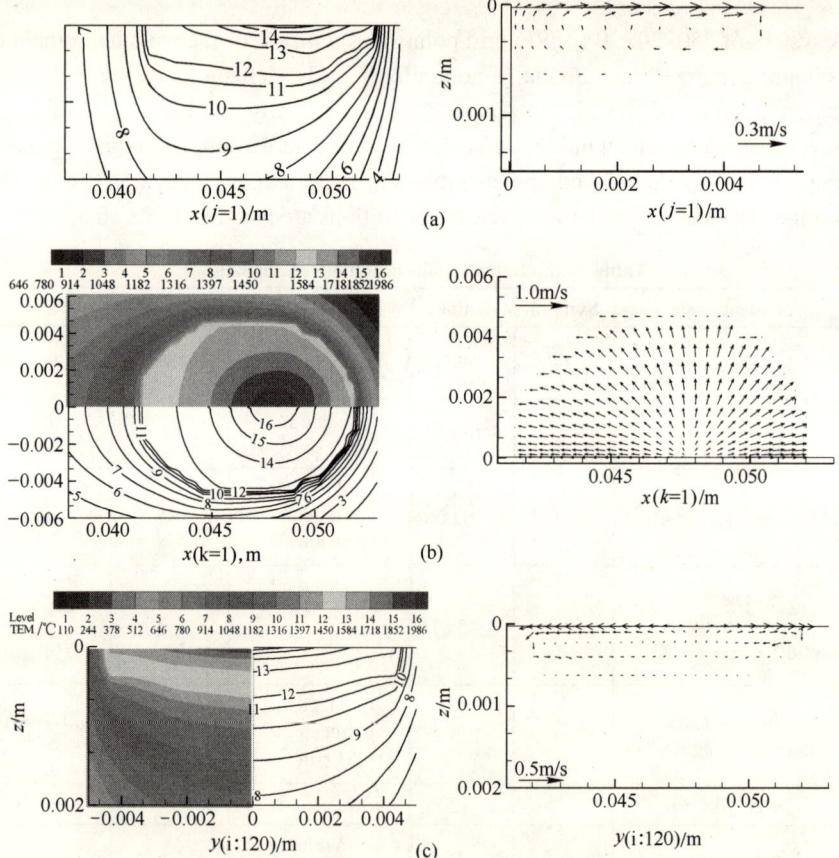

Figure 10.6　Temperature and velocity fields at [O, S] = 0 ppm

(a) Temperature and velocity fields in the *xz* face; (b) Temperature and velocity fields in the *xy* plane; (c) Temperature and velocity fields in the *yz* plane

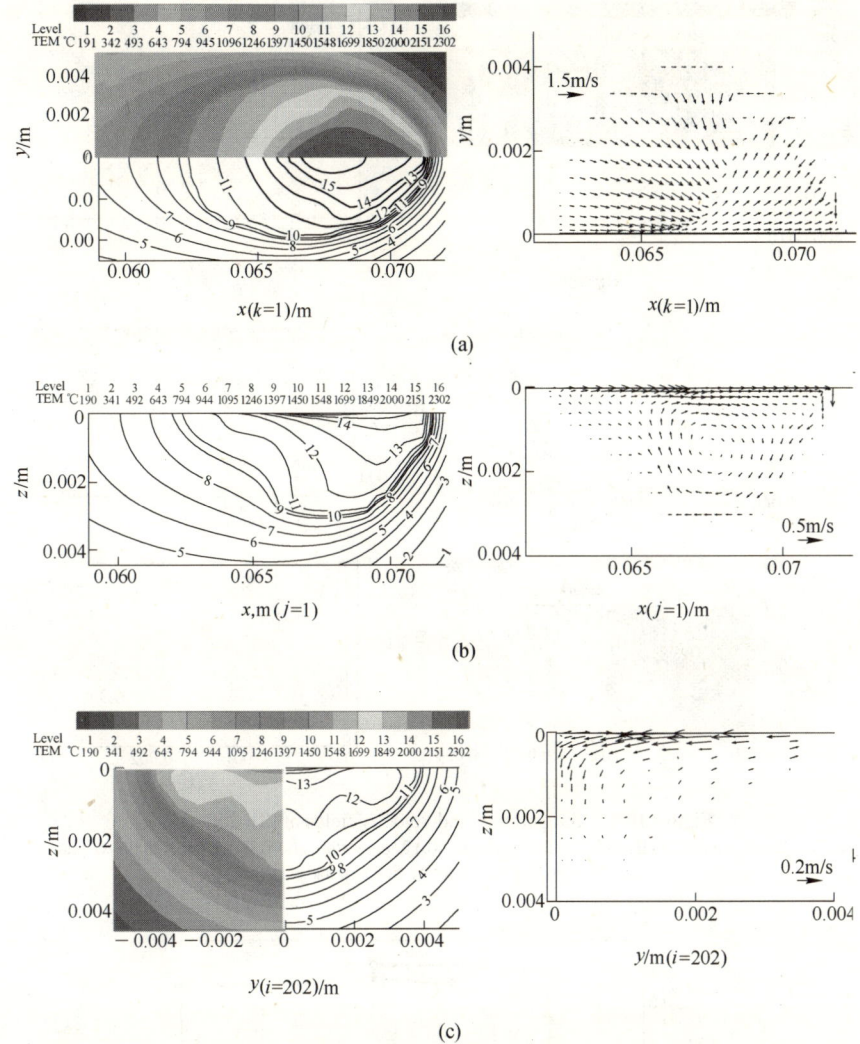

Figure 10.7 Temperature and velocity fields at [O]=200 ppm

(a) Temperature and velocity fields at xy face; (b) Temperature and velocity fields at xz face; (c) Temperature and velocity fields at yz face

and temperature distributions in the weld pool have an appreciable difference. The surface-active elements change the sign of $\partial\gamma/\partial T$, which dominates the fluid flow and controls the development of the weld pool. When $\partial\gamma/\partial T$ is positive, the surface tension increases inward from the edge as the temperature increases and the surface tension force pull the liquid metal flow toward the center and downward. This flow patterns transfer the arc energy from the surface to the weld bottom and the weld pool exhibits narrow and deep shape. When $\partial\gamma/\partial T$ is negative, the maximum

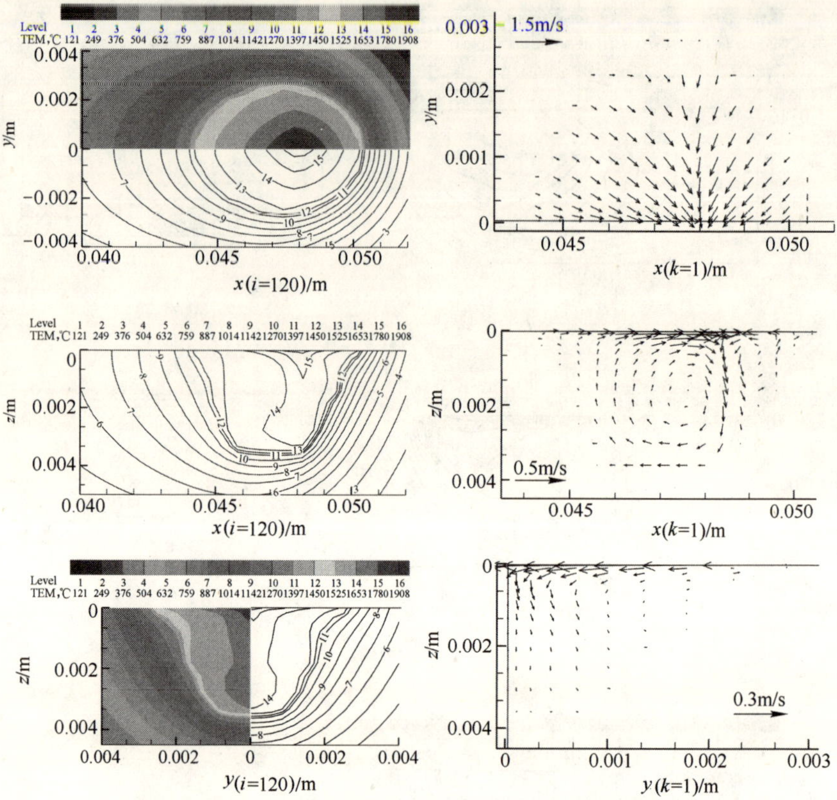

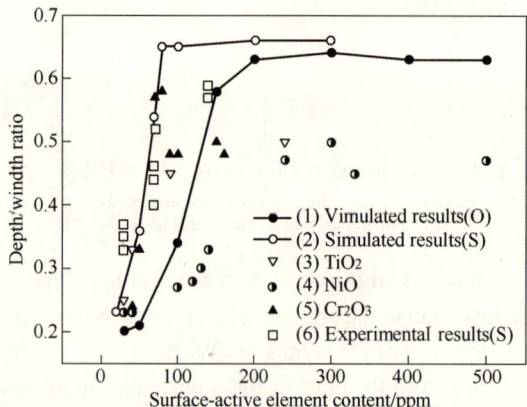

Figure 10.8 Temperature and velocity fields at [S]=200 ppm
(a) Temperature and velocity fields in the xy plane; (b) Temperature and velocity fields in the xz plane;
(c) Temperature and velocity fields in the yz plane

Figure 10.9 Weld depth/width ratio vs. surface active element content

surface tension occurs at the edge of the pool and the fluid flows from the center to the edge, causing the pool shallow and wide.

In Figure 10.9, line (1) and line (2) are the calculated results that the depth/width ratios vary with the oxygen and sulfur content respectively. The two curves increase sharply first and then remain constant with increasing surface-active elements content. The surface-active element doesn't have an appreciable influence on the depth/width ratio when oxygen content beyond 200 ppm and sulfur content beyond 80 ppm. Comparing the above two curves, the sulfur has stronger effect on the depth/width ratio than oxygen at the same content. Data (3), (4), (5) are the experimental results that give the changes of weld depth/width ratios with the oxygen content for the flux Cr_2O_3, NiO, TiO_2. Data (6) is the experimental results that give the changes of weld depth/width ratios with different sulfur content. Comparing the experimental and simulated results, the weld depth/width ratio has the same trend: increases sharply first and then remains a constant with increasing surface active element. The calculated results are agreed well with the experimental results.

10.3   Welding of Fine Grained Carbon Steel Plate

10.3.1   *Laser welding of low carbon steel*

Fine grained steels have ferrite grains in the grade of micrometer or sub-micrometer. The strength and toughness of the steels are greatly increased because of their fine grain size. Problems may occur when these steels are used in welding structures. After welding, the microstructure of heat-affected zone (HAZ) will be changed and the mechanical properties may deteriorate, including occurring of brittle zones and softened zones(Inoue T, 1990; Kanetsuki Y, 1998; Gianetto J A, 1997).

High temperature heat treatment used to change the microstructure and mechanical properties of welded joint shouldn't be used for fine grained steel because the process will change the microstructure and lower the mechanical properties of base metal (Hanus F E, 1995).So it is necessary to get qualified welded joint without post welding heat treatment. Laser is a high energy density power, which results in immediate melting of metal and the conduction of heat to base metal is reduced. The width of HAZ is reduced and the degree of the effects of thermal cycle on the mechanical properties of base metal is limited. In this part the effects of laser welding on microstructure and mechanical properties of fine grained steel are discussed.

10.3.1.1   Experiment material and equipment

3 mm thick plate of fine grained steel is used for experiment. The average

ferrite grain size of the steel is 6 μm. Its yielding strength is 360 MPa and tensile strength is 460 MPa. Chemical compositions of the steel are shown in Table 10.6.

Table 10.6　Chemical compositions of fine grained steel（mass%）

C	Si	Mn	P	S	Al	Cu	Cr	Mo	Ni
0.171	0.09	0.36	0.013	0.013	0.025	0.01	0.02	0.01	0.03

When the welding power is lower than 3 kW, a 3 kW CO_2 laser with $TEM_{00}+TEM_{01}$ beam mode is used and a ZnSe lens of 127 mm focal length is used to focus the laser beam. When the welding power is higher than 3 kW, a 6 kW CO_2 laser with TEM_{01}* beam mode is used and a paraboloid shaped copper mirror of 127 mm focal length is used to focus the laser beam. Ar is used to protect the melt pool. The welding power and welding speed are so matched that the plate can be completely penetrated.

Plasma arc welding and MAG welding are conducted to compare the results with those of laser welding. The parameters of the two arc welding methods are: current =115 A, voltage=28 V, and welding speed=0.25 m/min for plasma welding; current =200 A, voltage=26 V, and welding speed=0.4 m/min for MAG welding. These parameters are so chosen that the plate can be completely penetrated.

A Gleeble-1500 thermo-mechanical simulation machine is used to simulate the thermal cycles of coarse-grained HAZ (CGHAZ) and the specimens are used to test the impact toughness. Izod impact test specimens with cross section of 10 mm×2.5 mm and length of 75 mm are used for the test.

10.3.1.2　Weld shape and microstructure of welded joints

According to the energy density of laser welding, conduction welding or deep penetration welding may be realized, respectively. If the energy density of laser is high enough, the metal in the melt pool evaporates and a keyhole forms. Laser energy transfers to base metal through plasma in the hole and a deep and narrow weld is produced. Figure 10.10 shows the cross section shape of deep penetration laser welding, where parameters of power=2400 W and welding speed=1.0 m/min are used. Deep penetration laser welding enables us to reduce the number of layers needed to fully penetrate the plate. This is beneficial for the toughness of welded joint. If multi-layer welding is applied, the HAZ of former welding pass is heated to the temperature of Ac_1~Ac_3 by the thermal cycle of the next pass. The carbides in the coarse grain HAZ of the former welding pass decompose under the thermal cycle of next welding pass and the resulted diffusible carbon segregates in the austenite. The austenite islands of high-carbon content may transform to M-A constitutes which have low toughness(Lee S, 1992; Aihara S, 1992; Hrivnak I, 1995). The low heat input and narrow weld of laser welding produce welded joint of low transient stresses and low residual stresses and are beneficial for the prevention of solidification cracking and cold cracking(Dain Y, 1999; Tsai C L, 1998; Duhamel R F, 1997; Postacioglu N, 1997; Carmignani C, 1999).

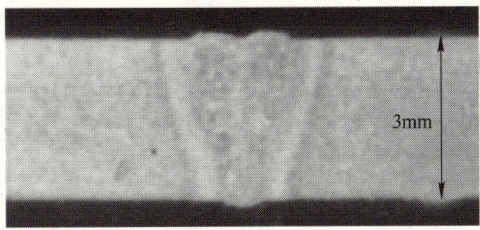

3mm

Figure 10.10 The cross section shape of deep penetration laser welding

Experiment steel acquires fine ferrite grains mainly by TMCP (thermomechanically controlled processing) and fast cooling. There is no micro-alloying element which can form particles of high temperature stability in the steel. After high temperature thermal cycle of arc welding, the microstructure transform into austenite and the austenite grains grow seriously at high temperature. Figure 10.11 (a) and (b) show the HAZ micrographs of MAG welding and plasma welding. The prior austenite grains grow to 200 μm. It indicates that it is necessary to add some micro-alloying elements to produce particles of high temperature stability, such as, adding Ti to produce TiN or Ti_2O_3 particles. These particles can pin the grain boundary at high temperature and inhibit the growth of austenite grains(Gianetto J A, 1997; Tian D W, 1996; Han J K, 1994; Iki H, 1998; Terada Y, 1998).

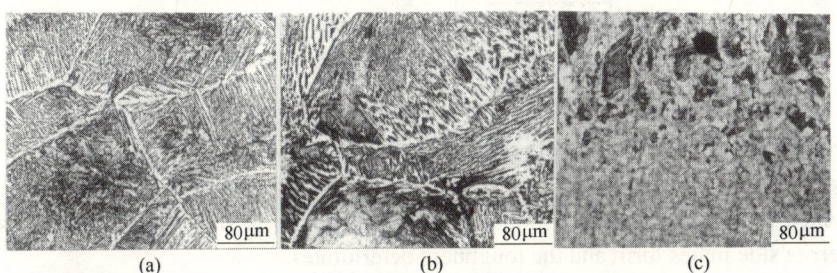

| (a) | (b) | (c) |

Figure 10.11 Coarse grain HAZ of MAG welding, plasma welding, and laser welding
(a) MAG welding(200 A, 26 V, 0.4m/min); (b) Plasma welding(115 V, 28 V, 0.25 m/min);
(c) Laser welding(3500 W, 1.6 m/min)

If laser power is used for welding, the temperature of thermal cycle rises and then drops rapidly. Experiment measurement shows that the rising rate of temperature is about 5000℃/s and cooling rate is about 800 ~1500℃/s at high temperature. The holding time above 800 ℃ is about 1 second. The short holding time of high temperature doesn't provide enough time for the growth of austenite grains, so small austenite grains are kept. Figure 10.11 (c) shows that the average prior austenite grain size is 20 μm, which is 1/10 of that of MAG welding and plasma welding. The width of HAZ of laser welded joint is 0.55 ~ 0.70 mm, much narrower than that of MAG welding, 3.8~6.8 mm, and that of plasma welding, 3.4~4.6 mm. Figure 10.12 and 10.13 show the comparisons of prior austenite grain sizes of coarse grained HAZ and the width of HAZ of laser welding, plasma arc welding, and MAG welding.

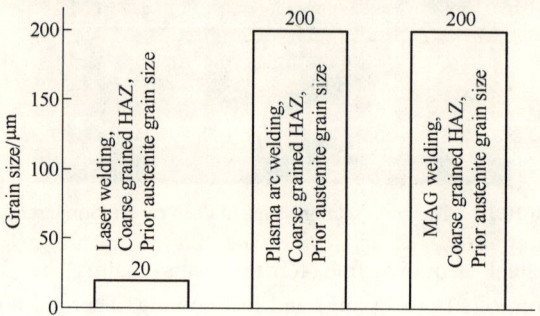

Figure 10.12　Prior austenite grain sizes of coarse grained HAZ

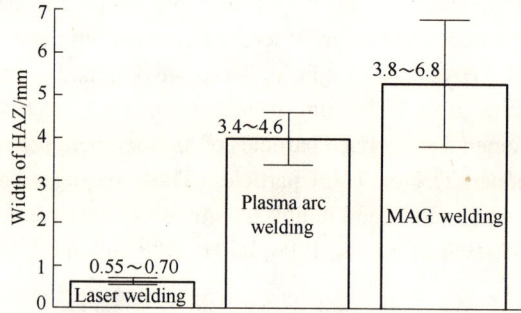

Figure 10.13　The width of HAZ of laser welding, plasma arc welding, and MAG welding

During welding of fine grained steel, HAZ metal transforms to austenite, which in turn transforms to different microstructure during cooling period according to cooling rate from 800 ℃ to 500 ℃. When cooling rate is fast, lower bainite which has good toughness forms. When cooling rate is slow, upper bainite and ferrite side plates form and the toughness deteriorates.

Figure 10.14 shows the microstructure of laser welded joint. The microstructure of weld metal are B_L + M + (P+F) (small amounts in grain boundary). The microstructure of coarse grain HAZ are B_L + M + (P+F) (small amounts). With the increase of input energy per unit distance, the amount of M decreases and the amount of P+F increases for both weld metal and coarse grain HAZ. The microstructure of the fine grain HAZ, the intercritical HAZ, and the base metal are F+P. The results show that if proper input energy per unit distance is adopted, the microstructure of weld metal and coarse grain HAZ mainly consist of lower bainite and low carbon martensite, which has good toughness, so the toughness of the welded joint will not deteriorate seriously. Figure 10.15 (a) and (b) are micrographs of coarse grain HAZ of MAG welding and plasma welding. The microstructure consists of upper bainite, proeutectoid ferrite, and ferrite side plates. For MAG welding there are large amount of ferrite side plates. For plasma welding there are large amount of upper bainite. These microstructure are detrimental to toughness. From this point of view, the shorter cooling time of laser welding from 800 ℃ to 500 ℃ is more beneficial for the produce of microstructure of higher toughness.

| Weld metal | Coarse grain HAZ | Fine grain HAZ | Intercritical HAZ | Base metal |

Figure 10.14   Microstructures of laser welded joint (P=4000 W, v=1.5 m/min)

(a)   (b)   (c)

Figure 10.15   Microstructure of HAZ metal at different welding speed (P=2400 W)
(a) v=0.6 mm/min; (b) v =0.8 mm/min; (c) v =1.0 mm/min

Figure 10.15 shows the microstructure of HAZ metal at different welding speed when laser power is 2400 W. The microstructure of HAZ metal is B_L + M (small amount) + P (small amount) at welding speed of 0.8 mm/min. At slower welding speed (v=0.6 mm/min), ferrite side plates occur. At faster welding speed (v=1.0 mm/min), the amount of martensite increases.

Figure 10.16 shows the transmission electro microscope (TEM) photos of the weld metal where the laser power is 2400 W and welding speed is 1.0 m/min. In Figure 10.16 (a), carbides precipitate from ferrite plates. This is the structure of lower bainite. The ferrite plates and carbides are fine. In Figure 10.16 (b), carbides precipitate from ferrite. The carbides are very small and they do not parallel with each other. In Figure 10.16 (c), small ferrite plate groups lie in different directions.

Between ferrite plates there are small carbides and inside ferrite plates there are fine carbide particles. Figure 10.16 (d) shows the martensite plates. Their size is small and the amount of the martensite is a small percentage in the whole microstructure. So the weld metal has good toughness (higher than that of base metal).

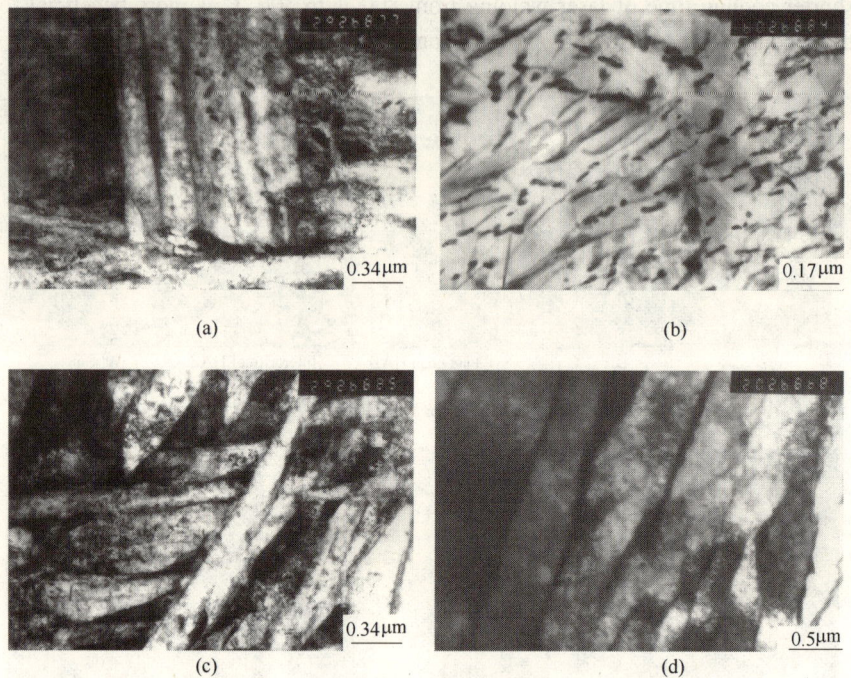

(a)

(b)

(c)

(d)

Figure 10.16   TEM Photographs of weld metal ((a)~(d))
(P=2400 W, v=1.0 m/min)

10.3.1.3   Mechanical properties of laser welded joint

Figure 10.17 shows the -40℃ impact energy values of the three zones of welded joint. The impact energy of weld metal is 25.3 J, which is higher than that of base

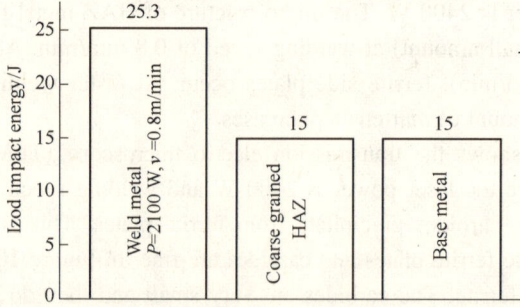

Figure 10.17   −40℃ Izod impact energy of the three zones of welded joint

metal, 15 J, if 2100 W laser power and 0.8 m/min welding speed were used. The thermal cycle of coarse grain HAZ of laser welding is simulated in thermo-mechanical simulation machine. The peak temperature is 1320℃ and cooling time from 800℃ to 500℃ is 1 second. Impact test shows that the impact energy of coarse grain HAZ is 15 J, the same as the value of base metal.

Figure 10.18 shows the micrographs of the fractured surfaces of Izod impact test by scanning electron microscope (SEM). The specimens are from the weld metal, coarse grain HAZ, and base metal, respectively. The parameters of laser welding are power=2100 W and welding speed=0.8 m/min. The fractured surface of weld metal (Figure 10.18 (a)) consists of small and deep dimples. It indicates that the metal is plastically deformed before fracture. So the metal has very good toughness. Figure 10.18 (b) and (c) show that the fractured surfaces of coarse grain HAZ metal and base metal consist of larger dimples. Their toughness is good but lower than that of weld metal.

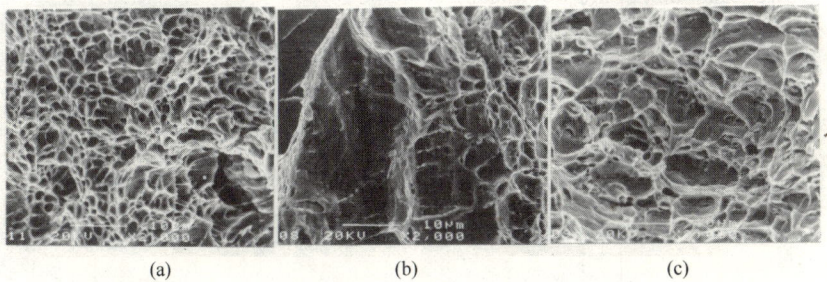

(a)　　　　　　　　(b)　　　　　　　　(c)

Figure 10.18　SEM micrographs of the fractured surfaces of Izod impact test
(a) Weld metal; (b) Coarse grain HAZ; (c) Base metal

There is no softened zone because the higher rolling temperature of the steel avoids the occurrence of recrystallization during thermal cycle. Figure 10.19 shows the hardness distributions of laser welded joints of the steel. When laser

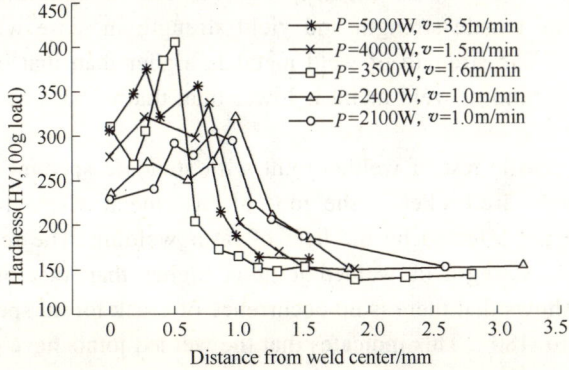

Figure 10.19　Hardness distribution of laser welded joint

powers are 2100 W or 2400 W and welding speed is 1 m/min, the highest hardness is lower than HV 325 and the weld metal and HAZ metal are not much hardened. When both laser power and welding speed are increased, the highest hardness of HAZ increases. So matching lower welding power with lower welding speed is beneficial for the prevention of cold cracking (Irving B, 1998). On the other hand, lower welding speed is also beneficial for the prevention of solidification cracking(Yurioka N, 1997) because solidification cracking occurs when the strain rate of weld metal in the brittle temperature zone is faster than the critical strain rate, and lower welding speed produces lower strain rate.

Figure 10.20 shows the hardness distribution of welded joints of laser welding, plasma welding, and MAG welding. Here the parameters of laser welding are power=2100 W and welding speed=1.0 m/min, and the parameters of plasma welding and MAG welding are the same as above. It is indicated that the hardness of laser welding is higher, but the width of hardened zone of laser welding is much narrower, than that of arc welding.

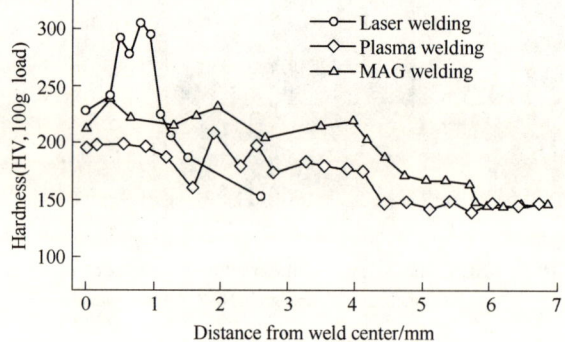

Figure 10.20　Hardness distribution of welded joints of laser welding,
plasma welding, and MAG welding

Figure 10.21 shows the relationship between the strength and the welding speed. Both the tensile strength and yield strength increase with increasing welding speed. The strength of weld metal is higher than that of base metal. The elongation ratio of weld metal is lower than that of base metal, as Figure 10.22 illustrates.

Transverse tensile test of welded joint with standard specimens shows that all the specimens are broken in the zone of base metal where the mechanical properties are not affected by the heat of laser welding. The results indicate that the tensile strength of welded joint is higher than that of base metal. Bending test shows that there is no occurrence of crack for all specimens when they are bent to 180° . This indicates that the welded joints have good bending ductility.

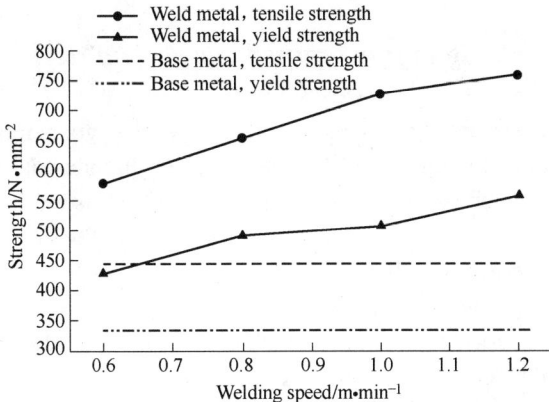

Figure 10.21   Relationship between strength and welding speed

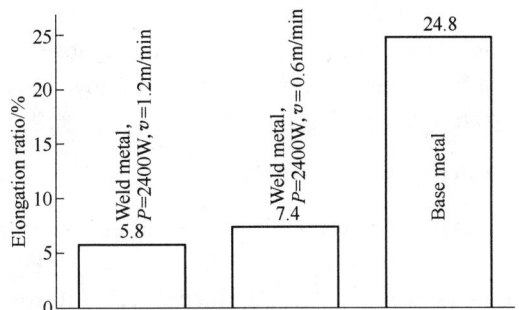

Figure 10.22   Elongation ratio of weld metal and base metal

10.3.1.4   Conclusions

Deep penetration laser welding produces weld of large depth and narrow width. The weld metal and HAZ is heated and then cools rapidly. The width of HAZ of laser welding is 0.55 ~ 0.70 mm, much narrower than that of arc welding, and the grain size of prior austenite is 1/10 of that of arc welding.

The weld metal and the coarse grain HAZ of laser welded joint mainly consist of lower bainite. The toughness of weld metal is higher than that of the base metal and the toughness of coarse grain HAZ is in the same level as that of the base metal.

Matching lower laser power with lower welding speed, the hardening tendency of coarse grain HAZ can be decreased. There is no softened zone. The tensile strength of the welded joint is higher than that of the base metal. The joint has good bending ductility as well.

10.3.2   *Arc welding of fine grained low carbon steel*

Theoretical analysis and experimental study show that grain refining increases both the strength and toughness of low carbon steel. In industrial production, the grain size of conventional low carbon steel, named Q235, is refined to 7 μm from 25 μm. Its yield strength is increased to 450 MPa from 200 MPa and its $-40\,^{\circ}\!C$ impact toughness reaches 94 J/cm^2.

During welding, the microstructure of heat-affected zone (HAZ) transforms from ferrite and pearlite to austenite, which transforms to different microstructure depending upon the cooling rate during cooling period (Kanetsuki, 1998; Gianetto J A, 1997; Lee S, 1992; Chen W, 2001). Weldability is crucial for engineering application of steel. It is shown that high energy density method welding, such as laser welding, can produce joint with limited width of HAZ and the grain growth tendency of HAZ is relatively small, which is beneficial for the mechanical properties of a welded joint (Peng Y, 2002). Because arc welding is the most widely used method in industry, it is meaningful to study the adaptability of the fine grained steel to arc welding.

10.3.2.1   Experiment material and method

A 6 mm thick fine grained low carbon steel plate is used for the experiment. Its microstructure is composed of ferrite and a little pearlite, as Figure 10.23 shows. The chemical compositions of the steel are listed in Table 10.7 and its mechanical properties are shown in Table 10.8. CO_2 gas metal arc welding (GMAW) and shielded metal arc welding (SMAW) are used for the experiment. Different heat input is used for experiment to test the adaptability of the steel to arc welding. A commercial welding wire and a welding rod are used as welding filler metals. The mechanical properties of deposited metal of the two welding material are shown in Table 10.9.

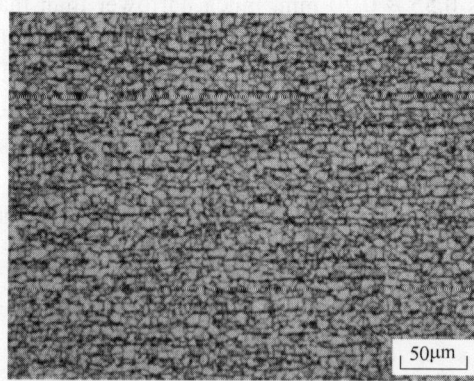

Figure 10.23   Microstructure of the steel

Table 10.7   Chemical compositions of the steel

w (C)	w (Si)	w (Mn)	w (P)	w (S)
0.09	0.18	1.14	0.020	0.006

Table 10.8   Mechanical properties of the steel

R_{eL} /MPa	R_m /MPa	Toughness/ J • cm^{-2}		
		0℃	−40℃	−60℃
450	525	95	94	93

Table 10.9   Mechanical properties of deposited metal

Mechanical properties	R_m/MPa	R_{eL}/MPa	A_5/%	A_{KV} (−30℃) / J
Welding wire	545	420	30	100
Welding rod	550	445	28	173

The test plates are machined into 60° groove for butt welding . No preheating is adopted before welding. For GMAW, when heat input of 4.99 kJ/cm is adopted three pass welding in one side is used. When heat input is between 8.64 to 20.23 kJ/cm one pass welding is adopted. For SMAW single pass welding in double side is adopted. The welding thermal cycles are recorded by thermocouples.

10.3.2.2   Experiment results and discussion

Welding heat input, cooling time from 800℃ to 500℃ ($t_{8/5}$)   and the cross sections of welded joints are shown in Table 10.10.

Figure 10.24 illustrates the hardness distribution of welded joints. The hardness of weld metal is higher than that of base metal. In HAZ, the hardness in the zone near to fusion line is the highest. The highest hardness is less than HV 215. Between HAZ and base metal there is a softened zone. The ratio of lowest hardness to the average hardness of base metal is between 0.93~0.97, which is not related to $t_{8/5}$. The width of softened zone increases with increasing $t_{8/5}$ and SMAW produces widest softened zone. Table 10.11 shows some characteristic data of HAZ.

Comparing the hardness data with the results of transversal tensile test of welded joint, it is found that when the width of softened zone is larger than 1.5mm, the broken zone is located in the softened zone. But the tensile strength is the same as that of base metal because of the less than 10% softening degree and the restraining strengthening effect.

Table 10.10   Welding heat input, $t_{8/5}$ and cross section of welded joint

Welding method	Heat input /kJ · cm^{-1}	$t_{8/5}$ /s	Cross section of welded joint
GMAW, (CHW-50C6, Φ1.2 mm)	4.99	4.4	
	8.64	7.5	
	11.78	9.6	
	14.92	11.8	
	20.23	16.1	
SMAW, (CHE 507, Φ3.2 mm)	18.5		
	13.3		

Table 10.11   Characteristic data of HAZ

$t_{8/5}$/s	Highest hardness in HAZ/HV	Lowest hardness in HAZ/HV	Ratio of lowest hardness of HAZ to the average hardness of base metal	HAZ Width /mm	Softened width in HAZ /mm
4.4	203	163	0.97	2.5	0.5
7.5	215	153	0.97	3.5	1.0
9.6	208	153	0.93	4.5	1.5
11.8	208	153	0.93	4.5	1.5
16.1	201	159	0.95	6.0	2.0
SMAW	180	145	0.94	5.5	3.0

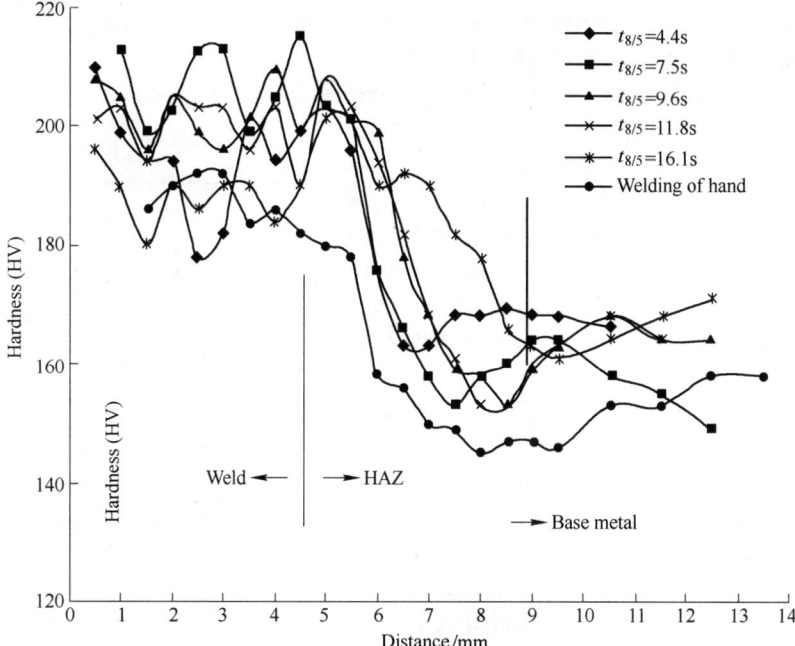

Figure 10.24 Hardness distribution of welded joints

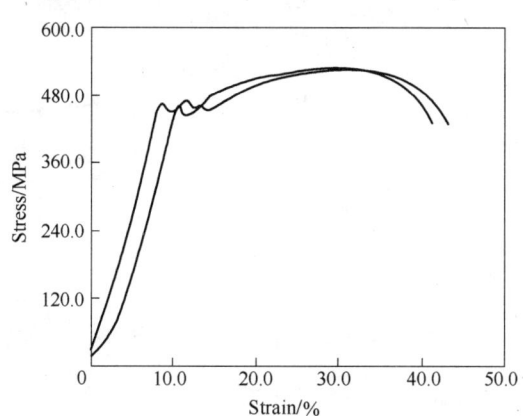

Figure 10.25 Stress-strain curve of welded joint

For GMAW, if the heat input is 14.92 kJ/cm or less than that, all the tensile specimens were broken in the base metal far from HAZ. If the heat input is 20.23 kJ/cm, some specimens were broken in the softened zone of HAZ. For SMAW all specimens were broken in the softened zone of HAZ because of its large softened zone width.

The transversal tensile strength of the welded joints is between 515~530 MPa. Because the material of welded joint is not homogeneous, only broken strength is significant data. But from the stress-strain curve (Figure 10.25) of tensile test it is shown that there are remarkable yield point and large elongation. The yield strength of welded joint is higher than 400 MPa.

Bending test was carried out on a pressure head of 15 mm diameter. No crack occurred when the specimens were bent to 180°. This indicates that the welded joints have good ductility. Sub-sized Charpy-V impact toughness test was conducted with the V-notch located on zones of weld metal (I), fusion line (II), HAZ (III) and base metal, as illustrated in Figure 10.26. The size of the specimens is 5 mm×10 mm×55 mm.

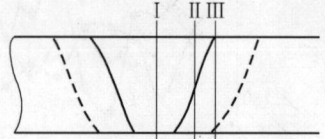

Figure 10.26   Diagrammatic sketch of notching position

Figure 10.27 presents the impact toughness of weld metal (a), fusion line (b) and HAZ (c). Because the welding wire is a commercial welding material, the low temperature toughness of weld metal is not high. For GMAW, the −40℃ impact toughness of the weld metal is between 28 and 50 J/cm². To get higher low temperature toughness, users are advised to choose high toughness welding wires (Weng Y, 2003). The −40℃ impact toughness of fusion line is between 37 and 49 J/cm², which is in a certain degree affected by the weld metal. The −40℃ impact toughness of HAZ is between 48 and 98 J/cm². This

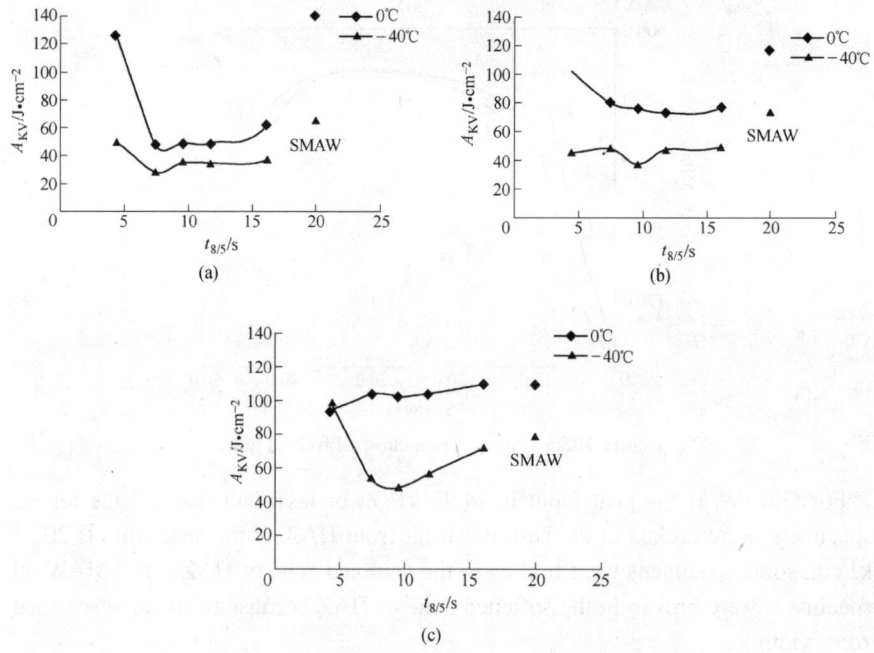

Figure 10.27   Toughness of welded joint
(a) Weld metal; (b) Fusion line; (c) HAZ

indicates that HAZ can reach acceptable good toughness when welding in wide heat input range. When low heat input (4.99 kJ/cm) is adopted the toughness of HAZ is the highest. For SMAW, the -40℃ impact toughness is 65 J/cm^2 for weld metal, 74 J/cm^2 for fusion line, and 76 J/cm^2 for HAZ, which are much higher than that of GMAW because the welding rod of higher toughness is adopted and the second side welding has the effect of heat treatment on the welding area of first side.

Figure 10.28 shows microstructure of HAZ of GMAW, where heat input is 8.64 kJ/cm. The zone near fusion line is coarse grained heat affected zone (CGHAZ), where the microstructure is Bainite and a little primary ferrite. Away from CGHAZ the microstructure is ferrite and a little pearlite. Farther from fusion line is the fine grain heat affected zone (FGHAZ), where the microstructure is fine ferrite and a little pearlite.

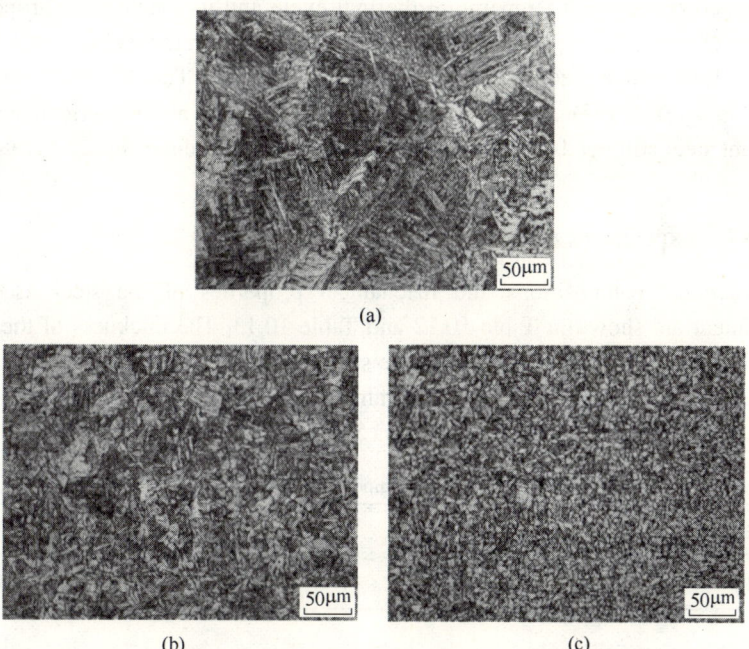

(a)

(b)   (c)

Figure 10.28   Microstructure of HAZ of GMAW, 8.64 kJ/cm
(a) CGHAZ; (b) Between CGHAZ and FGHAZ; (c) FGHAZ

10.3.2.3   Conclusions

1. The ultra-fine grained low carbon steel is suitable for arc welding in wide heat input range (5~20 kJ/cm).
2. There is a softened zone in the HAZ. However, the softened zone does not affect the tensile strength of the welded joint in the heat input range of 5~20 kJ/cm.

3. The welded joint has good ductility. The HAZ has acceptable good toughness when welding in a wide range of heat input.

10.3.3　Arc welding of fine grained atmospheric corrosion resistant steel

Atmospheric corrosion resistant steel is widely used as structural material because of its long service life and low cost. 09CuPTiNb is a kind of atmospheric corrosion resistant steel used in China. By refining the ferrite grain size from 25 μm to 7 μm, the tensile strength of the steel can be increased from 350 MPa to 560 MPa, and its Charpy V-notch impact toughness can reach as high as 135 J/cm^2 at -40℃. During welding the microstructure of heat-affected zone (HAZ) is changed by the high-temperature thermal cycle and its mechanical properties are also changed. Though some studies have been done on the weldability of fine grained low carbon steel (Peng Y, 2002; Peng Y, 2005; Tian Z, 2004; Peng Y, 2003; Peng Y, 1997), the weldability of fine grained atmospheric corrosion resistant steel still needs to be studied because its alloy elements may have much effect.

10.3.3.1　Experiment materials and procedure

The chemical compositions and mechanical properties of the steel used for experiment are shown in Table 10.12 and Table 10.13. The thickness of the steel plate is 6 mm. The microstructure of the steel, shown in Figure 10.29, consists of ferrite and a little pearlite. The ferrite grain size is 7μm . The yield strength of the steel is 485 MPa and its tensile strength is 560 MPa.

Table 10.12　Chemical compositions of experiment steel

C	Si	Mn	P	S	Cu	Ti	Nb
0.07	0.28	0.33	0.078	0.011	0.27	0.01	0.03

Table 10.13　Mechanical properties of experiment steel

R_m /MPa	R_{eL} /MPa	A_5 /%	CVE$_{-20℃}$/J · cm^{-2}	CVE$_{-40℃}$ /J · cm^{-2}
560	485	27	142	135

Gas metal arc welding (GMAW) was carried out and a flux cored wire with diameter of 1.2 mm was used as filler metal. Table 10.14 and Table 10.15 show the chemical compositions and mechanical properties of deposited metal, respectively. Butt welding of plate with V type 60° groove was adopted. CO_2

gas was used as shielding gas and no preheating was used. Different welding heat input, from 8.72 kJ/cm to 20.09 kJ/cm, was adopted. After welding, the welded joints were machined into specimens for tensile test, bending test, and 5mm×10 mm×55 mm Charpy V-notch impact test. The notch position for impact test is shown in Figure 10.30.

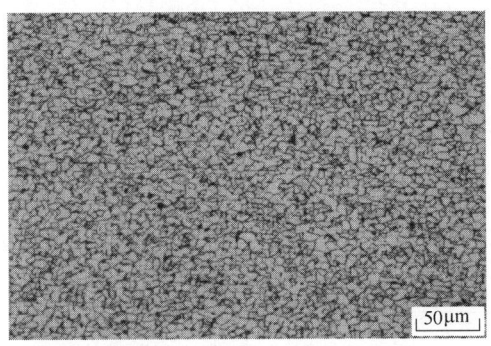

50μm

Figure 10.29 Microstructure of experiment steel

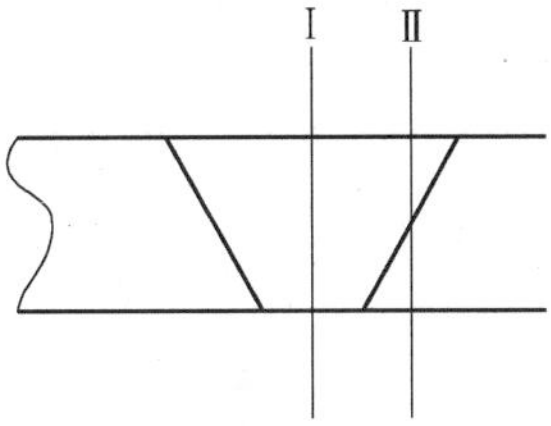

Figure 10.30 Notch position for impact test, I —in weld metal; II —cross fusion line

Table 10.14 Chemical compositions of deposited metal of flux cored wire

C	Si	Mn	P	S	Cu	Ni
0.039	0.17	0.87	0.017	0.010	0.34	0.73

Table 10.15 Mechanical properties of deposited metal of flux cored wire

R_m /MPa	R_{eL} /MPa	A_5 /%	CVE $_{-30℃}$ /J $\cdot$ cm^{-2}	CVE $_{-50℃}$ /J $\cdot$ cm^{-2}
490	430	30	168	53

10.3.3.2 Experiment results and discussion

Welded joints were machined into tensile and bending test specimens. The additional height of weld is smoothly removed for all specimens. Table 10.16 shows the results of tensile and bending test of welded joints. The broken position of tensile test is located in base metal zone away from weld and heat-affected zone (HAZ) for all specimens of joints produced by 8.72 kJ/cm, 11.85 kJ/cm, 15.91kJ/cm and 20.09 kJ/cm welding heat input. Bending test indicates that welded joints have good ductility.

Table 10.17 shows the results of $-40℃$ Charpy V-notch impact test of welded joints. When welding heat input is 8.72 kJ/cm, the impact energy of both weld metal and cross fusion line is high. With increasing heat input, the impact energy decreases rapidly. Combining the results of thermal simulation and welded joints, it is shown that welding with small heat input can produce welded joint with good toughness.

Table 10.16　Results of tensile and bending test of welded joints

Heat input /kJ $\cdot$ cm^{-1}	R_m /MPa	Broken position from fusion line /mm	R_{eL} /MPa	A /%	Cold bending ($d=3a$, 180°)	
8.72 (2 bead)	545	18	475	17.0	Obverse side	No crack
	540	22	465	23.5	Back side	No crack
11.85 (2 bead)	530	17	460	24.0	Obverse side	No crack
	530	26	455	24.5	Back side	No crack
15.91 (1 bead)	540	5	470	23.0	Obverse side	No crack
	535	9	475	24.5	Back side	No crack
20.09 (1 bead)	535	4	460	21.5	Obverse side	No crack
	535	3.5	465	21.5	Back side	No crack

Table 10.17　Results of −40℃ Charpy V-notch impact test of welded joints

Notch position		8.72 (2 bead) / kJ $\cdot$ cm^{-1}	11.85 (2 bead) /kJ $\cdot$ cm^{-1}	15.91 (1 bead) /kJ $\cdot$ cm^{-1}	20.09 (1 bead) /kJ $\cdot$ cm^{-1}
CVE$_{-40℃}$ /J $\cdot$ cm^{-2}	In weld metal	70，65，60	55，50，68	35，10，10	13，33，9
		65	58	18	18
	Cross fusion line	88，78，70	10，38，43	9，6，11	8，21，6
		79	30	9	12

　　The microstructure of coarse grain zone of HAZ is shown in Figure 10.31. For the joint of 8.72 kJ/cm heat input, almost all the microstructure is Bainite. For the joint of 11.85 kJ/cm heat input, the microstructure is Bainite and primary ferrite, and the grain size of prior austenite is large. For the joint of 15.91 kJ/cm heat input, more primary ferrite occurs along the austenite grain boundary. In the case of larger heat input, 20.09 kJ/cm, large amount of primary ferrite occurs and the ferrite grows to large size. It is indicated that with small heat input, such as 8.72 kJ/cm, better microstructure can be gotten. The microstructure coincides with the results of impact toughness test.

　　Figure 10.32 shows the hardness distribution of welded joints in the position of 1 mm under steel plate surface and the center of plate thickness. In HAZ the highest hardness is lower than 225 HV. It indicates that the steel has small hardening tendency. Between HAZ and base metal there is a softened zone. The softened width is narrow and the softening degree is small. During tensile the softened zone is strengthened by the restraining effect of harder zones. So the tensile strength of welded joint is not lowered.

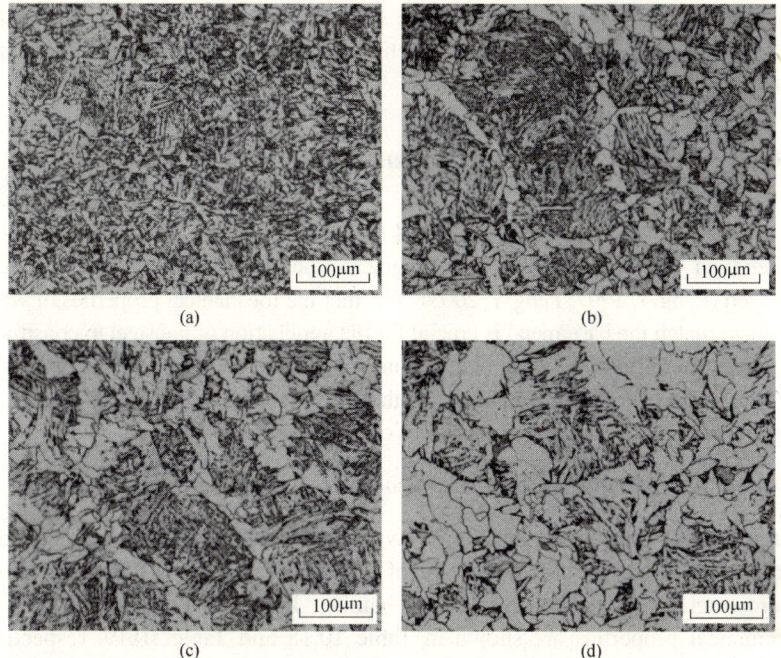

Figure 10.31 Microstructure of coarse grain HAZ of welded joint
(a)8.72kJ/cm; (b)11.85kJ/cm; (c)15.91kJ/cm; (d)20.09kJ/cm

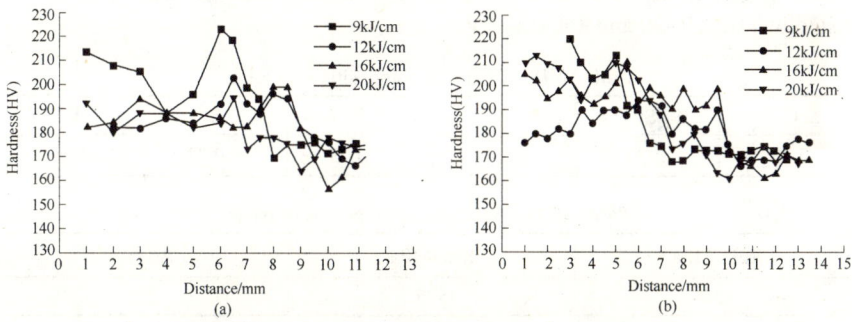

Figure 10.32 Hardness distribution of welded joints
(a) 1 mm under steel plate surface; (b) Center of plate thickness

10.3.3.3 Conclusions

1. The microstructure of coarse grain zone of HAZ consists of mainly Bainite when small heat input is used for welding. With larger heat input, more primary ferrite occurs.
2. The toughness of HAZ depends on welding heat input. With small heat input the toughness is good. The toughness decreases dramatically with increasing heat input.

3. The softening degree is small and the softened width is narrow in the softened zone of welded joint. The tensile strength of welded joint remains the same as that of base metal.

10.3.4   *Welding of 400 MPa grade fine grained rebar*

By refining the grain size of carbon steel rebar, its yield strength can be increased to higher than 400 MPa. After welding, the microstructure of fine grained carbon steel is changed (Peng Y, 1997; Peng Y, 2003). Whether the mechanical properties of welded joint can match the base metal is crucial for the application of the steel to construction structures. In this part the flash butt welding and electro-slag pressure welding, which are the most often used welding methods in construction, are discussed, and microstructure and mechanical properties of the welded joint were analyzed.

10.3.4.1   Experiment material and procedure

A rebar of 25 mm in diameter with average grain size of 7.8μm was used for experiment. It has the microstructure of ferrite and pearlite in the center and the microstructure in the outer part is bainite. Its chemical compositions and mechanical properties are shown in Table 10.18 and Table 10.19, respectively. Figure 10.33 shows the macro appearance and microstructure of longitudinal section of the rebar. Hardness distribution of the rebar is shown in Figure 10.34. Welding parameters of electro-slag pressure welding and flash butt welding are listed in Table 10.20 and Table 10.21.

Table 10.18   Chemical compositions of rebar

C	Si	Mn	P	S	V
0.20	0.30	0.55	<0.03	<0.03	0.02

Table 10.19   Mechanical properties of rebar

ReL /MPa	Rm /MPa	A5 /%
450	575	25

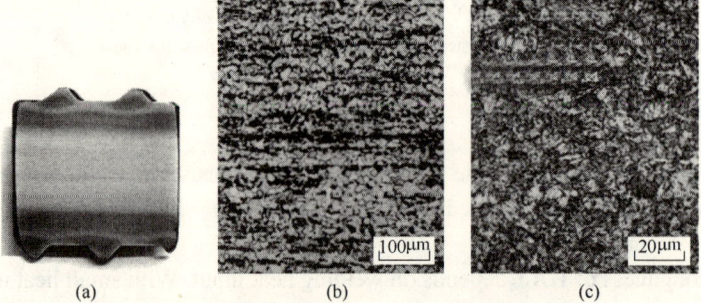

(a)   (b)   (c)

Figure 10.33   Macro appearance and microstructure of longitudinal section of rebar
(a) Macro appearance; (b)Inner part; (c) Outer part

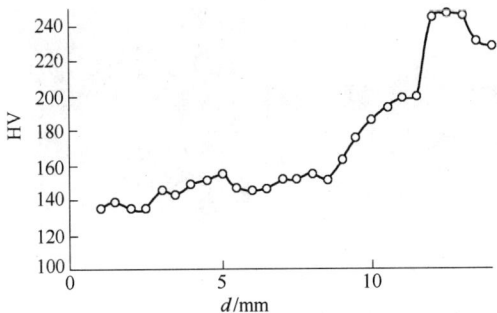

Figure 10.34 Hardness distribution of the rebar

Table 10.20 Parameters of the electro-slag pressure welding

Current /A	Welding voltage /V		Welding time /s	
	Arc period	Slag melting	Arc period	Slag melting
450	40~45	22~27	25	6

Table 10.21 Parameters of the flash butt welding

Electric voltage /V	Sticking out length /mm	Preheating length /mm	Flash length /mm	Forging length /mm	Flash time /s
7.17	40	6	12	7	8~12

10.3.4.2 Experiment results and discussion

Figure 10.35 shows the longitudinal section, microstructure of CGHAZ, and hardness distribution of electro-slag pressure welded joint. The width of weld in the axis position of rebar is very narrow and gradually becomes wider from the center to the outer part. The width of HAZ in the side that was put in the upper position during welding is 19 mm and the width of HAZ in the side that was put in the lower position during welding is 12 mm. The widths of HAZ of the two sides are very wide. The microstructure of CGHAZ is primary ferrite, acicular ferrite, and pearlite. In the inner part of rebar the hardness of CGHAZ is a little higher than that of base metal and the hardness of weld metal is much higher than that of HAZ. In the outer part the hardness of weld metal and HAZ is lower than that of base metal. Because the inner part occupies most of the cross section, the overall strength of the joint is not lowered.

Figure 10.36 shows the longitudinal section, microstructure of CGHAZ, and hardness distribution of flash butt welded joint. The weld is 0.5 mm wide and the HAZ width in each side is 17 mm. Its HAZ microstructure is similar to that of electro-slag pressure welding but contains more large plate ferrite and large acicular ferrite. Its hardness distribution is also similar to that of electro-slag pressure welded joint.

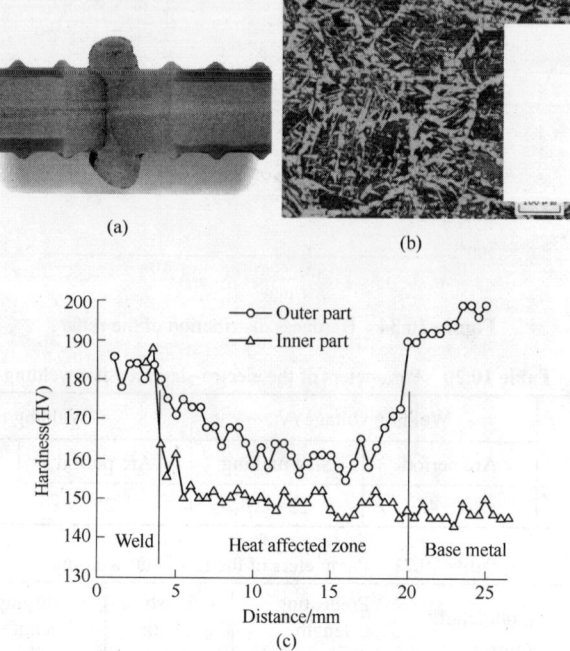

Figure 10.35   Longitudinal section, microstructure of CGHAZ, and hardness distribution of electro-slag pressure welded joint

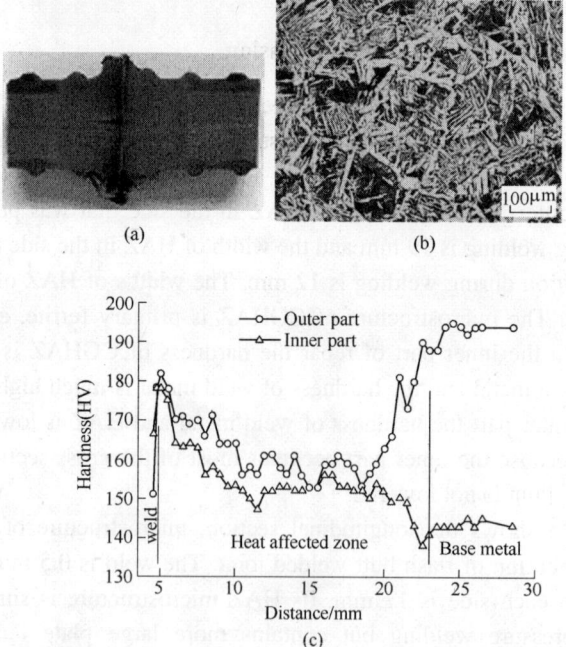

Figure 10.36   Longitudinal section, microstructure of CGHAZ, and hardness distribution of flash butt welded joint

Table 10.22 shows results of tensile test of welded joint. All the specimens of flash butt welded joint and electro-slag pressure welded joint were broken in the position of base metal. Cold bending tests indicate that when the specimens were bent to 90° no crack occurs. The experiment results indicate that the welded joints have qualified strength and ductility. Figure 10.37 shows specimens of tensile test and Figure 10.38 shows specimens of bending test.

Table 10.22 Results of tensile test of welded joint

Welding method	R_m /MPa	R_{eL} /MPa	Breaking position away from melting line /mm	Area contraction /%	Bending $d=4a$, 90°
Electro-slag pressure welding	570	415	135	60.4	No cracking
	580	450	120	63.5	No cracking
	580	435	29	55.2	No cracking
Flash butt welding	570	455	178	65.8	No cracking
	575	435	117	51.2	No cracking
	575	430	74	63.4	No cracking

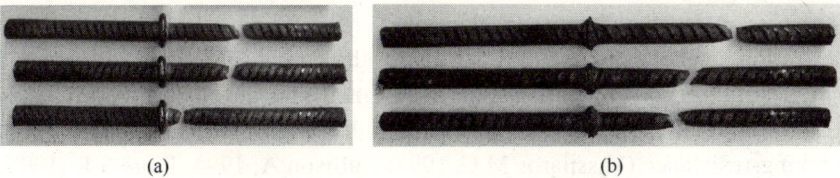

(a)　　　　　　　　　　　(b)

Figure 10.37 Specimens of tensile test
(a) Electro-slag pressure welding; (b) Flash butt welding

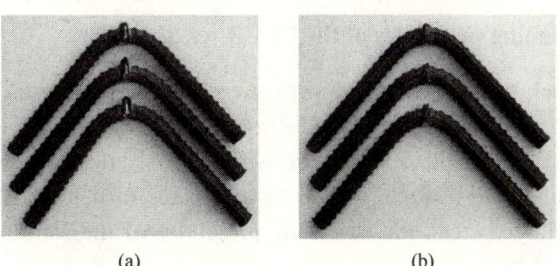

(a)　　　　　　　　　(b)

Figure 10.38 Specimens of bending test
(a) Electro-slag pressure welding; (b) Flash butt welding

10.3.4.3 Conclusions

Flash butt welding and electro-slag pressure welding of ultra-fine grained rebar can produce joints with qualified strength and cold bending ductility.

10.4   Welding of Ultra-Fine Structure Bainite Steel

10.4.1   *Development of ultra-low carbon bainitic high strength welding wire*[1]

The new generation high strength structural steels possess refined lath packages in its bainitic structure and thus not only high strength and toughness but also excellent weldabilty. After welding thermal cycle, the hardening of HAZ won't occur and the microstructure of HAZ are insusceptible to hydrogen induced cracking   (HIC). Therefore the requirements of preheat will be reduced as far as the base material is concerned. However, due to the lack of matching welding materials, conventional welding materials must be used. Consequently, the welding technology still needs strict controlling, especially, when thick plates and high restraint joints are adopted. The properties of the weld metal cannot satisfy the requirements and so do the properties of the welded joint. The weld metal becomes the "weak link" in the welded joint. Therefore, it is necessary to develop matching welding materials for the new generation steel. Thus a welding wire with the composition that will generate ULCB structure in the weld metal is designed and developed in this study. ULCB structure possessed high strength, high toughness and good cracking-resistance (Vassilaros M G, 1993; Cullison A, 1994; Fiore S R ,1995). In addition, its strength, ductility and low temperature toughness were insensitive to the heat input and cooling-rate.

10.4.1.1   Designing principles of the ULCB welding wires

Because the solid wire combined with the shielding gas with low oxidation potential has an advantage in producing high strength and toughness, the development of gas shielded solid wire is paid more attention to. According to the compositions, microstructure and characteristics of new 800 MPa ultra low carbon microalloyed steel, the designing principles of the welding wires are as follows:

1. The weld metal should have equivalent mechanical properties to the base metal. And neither preheating nor post welding heat treatment is required.
2. Ultra-low carbon is used.The carbon equivalent of the weld metal should becontrolled at low level to decrease the hardenability and the cracking susceptibility of the weld metal.

---

[1] The parts 10.4.1, 10.4.2 were written by Chengyong Ma.

3. The addition of alloying elements such as Mn, Ni, Mo etc. should be reasonable so that the transformation curves of ferrite and pearlite in the CCT diagram of the weld metal are retarded and the transformation curve of banite is spread. Consequently the weld metal insensitive to the cooling rate is guaranteed to obtain ULCB structure.
4. Micro-alloying elements will be added to refine the structure of the weld metal, and improve the properties of the weld metal.

10.4.1.2　Compositions and mechanical properties of ULCB wire deposited metals

Based on the above principles, 9 heats of welding wires of variant chemical compositions are produced and tested. Table 10.23 shows the chemical compositions of the deposited metal.

Table 10.23　Deposit analysis of the welding wires （mass%）

Welding wire	C	Mn	Si	P	S	Ni	Mo	Cr	Ti	B
W1	0.034	1.82	0.34	0.0037	0.0027	3.81	0.79	0.085	0.014	0.0042
W2	0.026	1.28	0.30	0.0044	0.0031	3.01	0.39	0.01	0.013	0.0031
W3	0.024	1.70	0.23	0.0038	0.0031	3.54	0.76	0.006	0.004	0.0007
W4	0.025	1.50	0.26	0.0044	0.0032	3.55	0.48	0.006	0.003	0.0018
W5	0.02	1.74	0.17	0.0058	0.0039	3.96	0.78	0.0648	0.01	0.0025
W6	0.02	1.80	0.25	0.0054	0.0047	3.88	0.97	0.0115	0.009	0.0024
W7	0.021	1.87	0.28	0.0068	0.0042	3.85	0.94	0.2677	0.015	0.0027
W8	0.046	1.81	0.20	0.0058	0.0045	3.84	0.78	0.0114	0.006	0.0023
W9	0.016	1.70	0.15	0.0057	0.0056	2.76	0.70	0.0207	0.007	0.0020

The mechanical properties of the as-deposited metals are summarized in Table 10.24. It can be seen that as the chemical compositions of the filler wire were varied, their mechanical properties also changed obviously. But it is evident that ULCB as-deposited metal possesses not only high strength, but also good ductility. What is more, excellent low temperature impact toughness was still obtained in the deposited metal as the strength was enhanced. W8 wire was taken for example. Although its tensile strength was as high as 840 MPa, the Charpy-V impact value of over 109 J at$-50℃$ was achieved.

Table 10.24　Mechanical property of deposited metal for 9 filler wires

Wire number	$R_{eL0.2}$/MPa	R_m/MPa	A_5/%	Z/%	$A_{KV}(-50°C)$/J
W1	760	830	20	70	39、37、37
W2	600	655	25	79	>147、>147、180
W3	660	760	22	74	>147、166、140
W4	630	690	25	74	>147、175、169
W5	720	775	22	76.5	>147、160、164
W6	710	795	21	73	69、140、124
W7	740	830	18.5	72	24、17、30
W8	790	840	18.5	66.5	109、117、119
W9	640	690	23.5	76	>147、140、135

The hardness is often used to evaluate the weldability, express the softening or hardening extent of materials. The compositions of the as-deposited metals may be scaled by the carbon equivalent (CEN). The calculating results of CEN are showed in Table 10.25and the formula of calculation is seen in equation (10.21) and (10.22) (Zou Z F, 1990).

$$CEN=C+A(C)\times[Si/24+Mn/6+Cu/15+Ni/20+(Cr+Mo+V+Nb)/5+5B] \tag{10.21}$$

where：
$$A(C)=0.75+0.25\tan[20\times(C-0.12)] \tag{10.22}$$

Table 10.25　CEN of deposited metal

No.	W1	W2	W3	W4	W5	W6	W7	W8	W9
CEN	0.3992	0.2684	0.3451	0.3045	0.3655	0.3835	0.4146	0.3993	0.3121

The correlation between the CEN and the microhardness of deposited metal can be established directly (see Figure 10.39). It can be found that with the increase of the CEN, the hardness of the as-deposited metal increases, the hardenability tendency of the ULCB as-deposited metal intensifies and the microstructure becomes hard.

Similarly the relation curve can be established between the CEN and the strength of various as-deposited metal (seen Figure 10.40). It can be seen that the yield strength and tensile strength of ULCB as-deposited metal are directly proportional to the CEN, and the changing trends of two curves are similar. Since the CEN directly depend on the content of the carbon and alloying elements in the as-deposited metal, the strength can be connected with the chemical compositions of the as-deposited metal. That is to say that the strength of the as-deposited metal can be estimated according to the CEN.

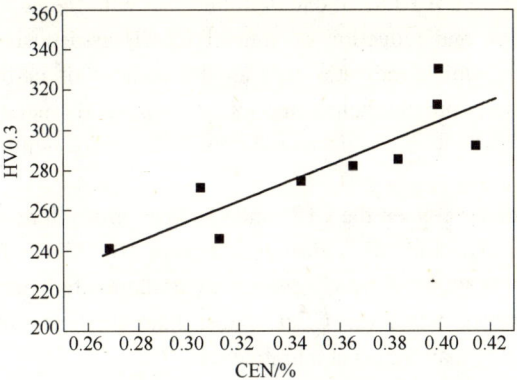

Figure 10.39 Relation curve between the hardness and the CEN of various as-deposited metal

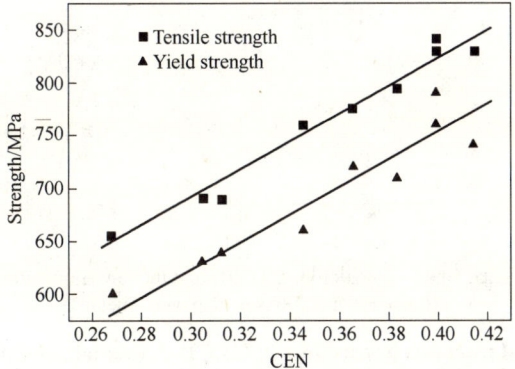

Figure 10.40 Relation curve between the CEN and the strength of various as-deposited metal

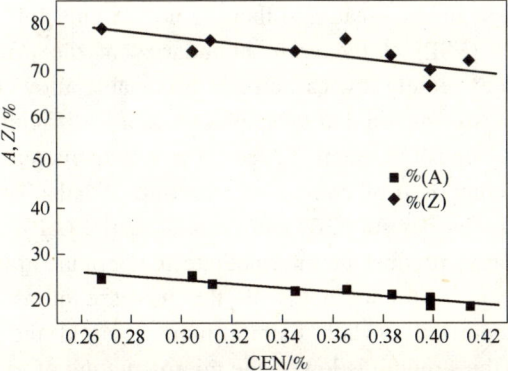

Figure 10.41 Relation curve between the CEN and the ductility of various as-deposited metal

The relation curve between the CEN and the ductility of various as-deposited metal is plotted in Figure 10.41. It can be found that with the increase of the CEN, both the elongation and reduction of area of ULCB as-deposited metal show a trend of decrease, which indicates that as the content of carbon and alloying elements increases, the hardenability of as-deposited metal enhances and meanwhile the ductility of as-deposited metal decreases with the increase of strength.

The relation curve between the CEN and the low temperature impact toughness of various as-deposited metal is shown in Figure 10.42. It is found that when the CEN is over 0.39, the impact energy of as-deposited metal is decreased remarkably. However, when the CEN is less than 0.39, the impact energy of as-deposited metal is maintained at a high level.

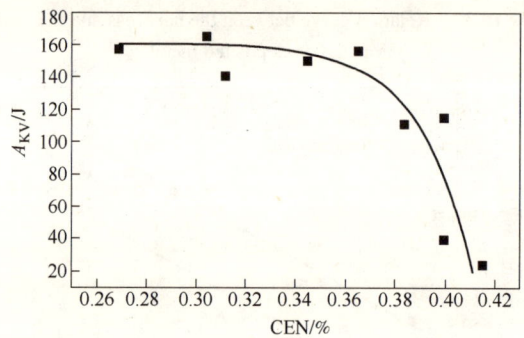

Figure 10.42   Relation of the CEN and the low temperature toughness in various as-deposited metal

10.4.1.3   Optical microstructure of the ULCB deposited metals

Figure 10.43 shows the optical micrographs of the as-deposited metal from the 9 different welding wires. It can be seen that the grain boundary of the primary austenite is very clean and clear, and there is no pro-eutectoid ferrite (PF) and ferrite side-plates (FSP) at the grain boundaries of the primary austenites. Moreover, due to extremely low carbon and reasonable alloy elements, there is no martensitic transformation that takes place and it is difficult that the carbide appears in the as-deposited metal. Instead, the microstructure of as-deposited metal is mainly composed of composite structure of lath-like bainite without carbide (LB), granular bainite (GB) and acicular ferrite (AF), which are all the phase transformation product of intermediate temperature transformation. By comparison, it can be found that with the increase of as-deposited metal strength, the proportion of lath bainite increases and the amount of AF decreases. When the strength is lower, the microstructure of as-deposited metal mainly consists of AF, and the amount of LB is less. Here, AF is coarser and the aspect ratio of AF piece is about four to one (see Figure 10.43 (c)). As the strength is upgraded to 700 MPa or so, the microstructure of as-deposited metal becomes fine obviously, and AF is very fine, but the amount of LB doesn't change significantly. When the strength is further increased up to 800 MPa, LB becomes the main microstructure of as-deposited metal gradually, the amount of AF is reduced greatly, and the appearance of AF is also changed obviously. The aspect ratio of AF increases up to eight to one, or even higher (see Figure 10.43（a）,（h）). But it is notable that when the amount of LB is increased to obtain higher strength, if good impact toughness is needed, the alloying elements must be added properly, so that fine and compact lath of bainite can be gained. As to W7 welding wire, because the content of alloy elements such as Cr, Mo is more, its carbon equivalent is higher, and a large amount of coarsened lath of bainite is formed in the as-deposited metal, its low temperature impact toughness is very low (see Figure 10.43（h）). From this, it can be concluded that in order to gain high strength and toughness in the as-deposited metal, the traditional design idea of AF couldn't meet the challenge and the new design idea of ULCB must be adopted. Thus the microstructure of as-welded metal is mainly composed of fine LB without carbides and different proportion of GB and AF, therefore, good combination of strength and toughness is achieved.

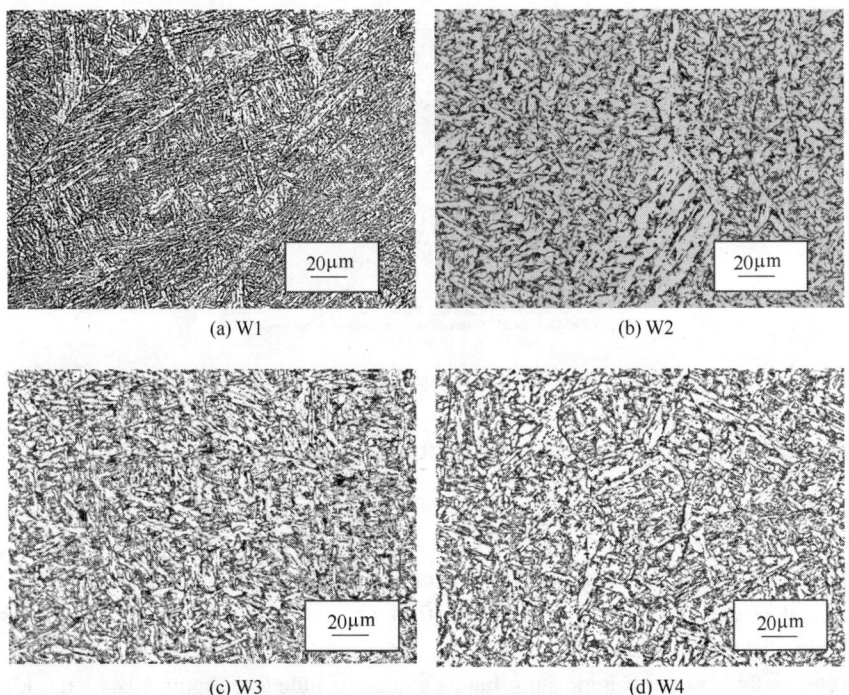

(a) W1

(b) W2

(c) W3

(d) W4

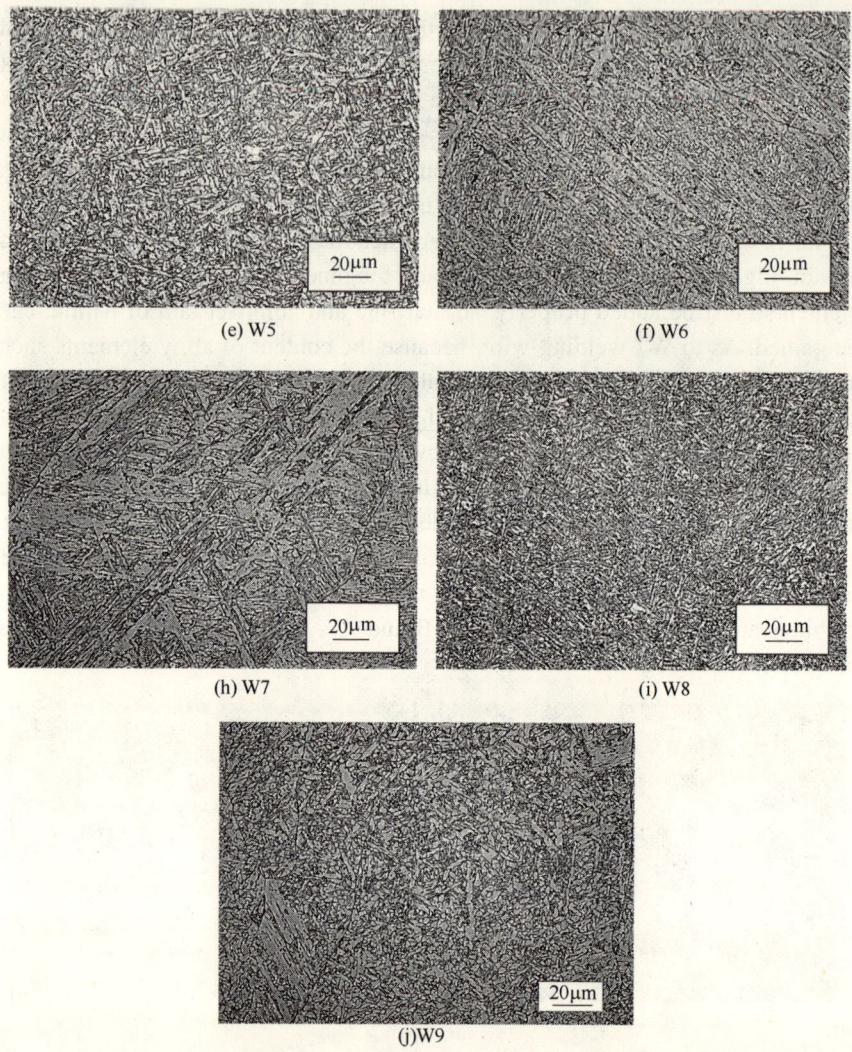

Figure 10.43   Optical microstructure of ULCB wire deposited metals

10.4.1.4   Fine microstructure of ULCB wire deposited metals

TEM photographs of ULCB wire as-deposited metal are shown in Figure 10.44. It can be found the fine structure in the ULCB as-deposited metal mainly consists of the lath-like bainitic ferrite with high dislocation density. In addition to bainite lath, some GB and AF can also be found (see Figure 10.44（b）,（c）), and there also exists high density dislocation in the GB and AF. The thin film of residual austenite may be seen occasionally between bainitic laths, but its amount is little (see Figure 10.44（d）). A small quantity of insular spherical inclusions are located in the as-deposited metal, and

AF can nucleate at this nucleus (see Figure 10.44（c）). Besides, the TEM photographs show that there is no second phase precipitation in the lath bainites.

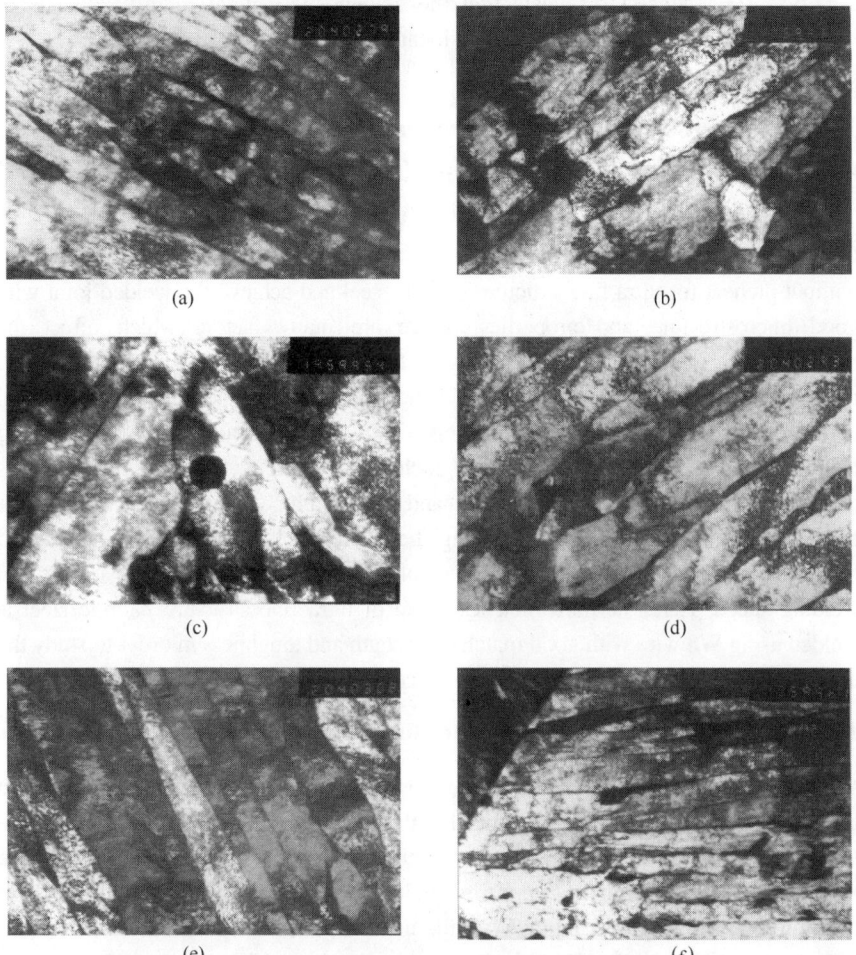

(a)

(b)

(c)

(d)

(e)

(f)

Figure 10.44 TEM photographs of ULCB wire as-deposited metal
(a)Bainite lath; (b)Bainite lath and granular bainite; (c)AF with the nucleus of inclusion;
(d)Residual austenite; (e)Bainite lath; (f)Bainite lath

10.4.1.5 Conclusions

1. The design idea of compositions for ULCB gas metal arc welding wire is put forward, and from this, ULCB welding wire with high strength and toughness, especial good low-temperature toughness has been developed successfully.
2. With the increase of carbon equivalent, the strength and hardness of ULCB as-deposited metal increase, but the toughness and ductility fall.
3. The microstructure of the ULCB as-deposited metal is mainly composed of

carbide-free lath bainite, granular bainite and acicular ferrite (AF), which are the transformation products of super-cooling austenite in the middle temperature region. TEM analysis reveals that the as-deposited metal mainly consists of lath-like bainitic ferrite with high dislocation density.

10.4.2   *Microstructures and properties of the GMAW welded joint of the ultra fine structure bainitic steel*

One of the purposes of developing ULCB welding wire is to realize the welding without preheat for ultra fine structure bainitic steel and achieve the welded joint with good microstructure and properties. There are many factors which affect the microstructure and properties, including welding materials, weldability of the base metal, and practical welding technology. When the welding material and parent metal is determined, the microstructure and properties of welded joint are up to the welding technology. The welding parameters include preheating temperature, interpass temperature, heat input, geometry of joint and welding procedure, etc. Heat input is one of the most important factor influencing the microstructure and properties of weld metal and it reflects the collective effect of welding current, welding voltage and welding speed. Here, 12 mm thick test plate of ultra fine structure bainitic steel is welded using W8 wire with good match of strength and toughness in order to study the effect of different heat input on the microstructure and properties.

10.4.2.1   Weld microstructure of ultra fine grained bainitic steel

Weld microstructure not only includes crystallized structure directly generated from liquid metal solidification, but also the microstructure from the solid phase transformation in the subsequent continuous cooling process. The structure morphology of columnar grains in weld has great relations with welding technology, primarily heat input. With the increase of heat input from 10 kJ/cm, 20 kJ/cm to 30 kJ/cm, the width of columnar grains in weld increases. The average widths at three heat inputs are respectively about 25 μm, 38 μm and 70 μm. It is considered that different heat input will result in different cooling rate of weld. Generally, large heat input corresponds with low cooling rate and vice versa. As the cooling rate is lower, the overheating degree in the vicinity of fusion line is large, which will inevitably make the columnar grains of weld coarsen. In addition, the increase of heat input results in the reduce of temperature gradient in the front edge of pool solidification. Since the growth direction of the columnar grain is in accord with the direction of the largest temperature gradient, the growth rate of columnar crystal along the length direction reduces. And in the width direction with little temperature gradient, owing to the low cooling rate, the columnar crystal grows up easily. In a word, with the increase of heat input, the width of primary columnar grains in weld increases gradually.

As the continuous cooling process goes along, the primary columnar grains will undergo solid phase transformation, which can be observed at room temperature. Figure 10.45 shows the typical micrography of the surface bead under different heat input. It can be found that the primary ferrite and side-plate ferrite are almost removed completely in the weld metal, and the lath bainite, acicular ferrite (AF) and granular bainite are the main microstructure components under different heat inputs. By further comparison, it can be seen that the morphology and amount of various microstructure in the weld are different evidently under different heat inputs. As the heat input is 10 kJ/cm, the fine and compact lath-like bainite is the main as-welded microstructure, AF also has a certain proportion and its size is larger, and GB has a small proportion (see Figure 10.45（a）). As the heat input is 20 kJ/cm, the fine AF becomes the main as-welded microstructure and· the amount of lath-like bainite reduces greatly. As the heat input is 30 kJ/cm, AF is still the main weld microstructure. However, it is notable that at the same time, AF start coarsening , the microstructure begins equiaxed, the amount of GB increases, and the lath-like bainite becomes coarse (see Figure 10.45（c）).

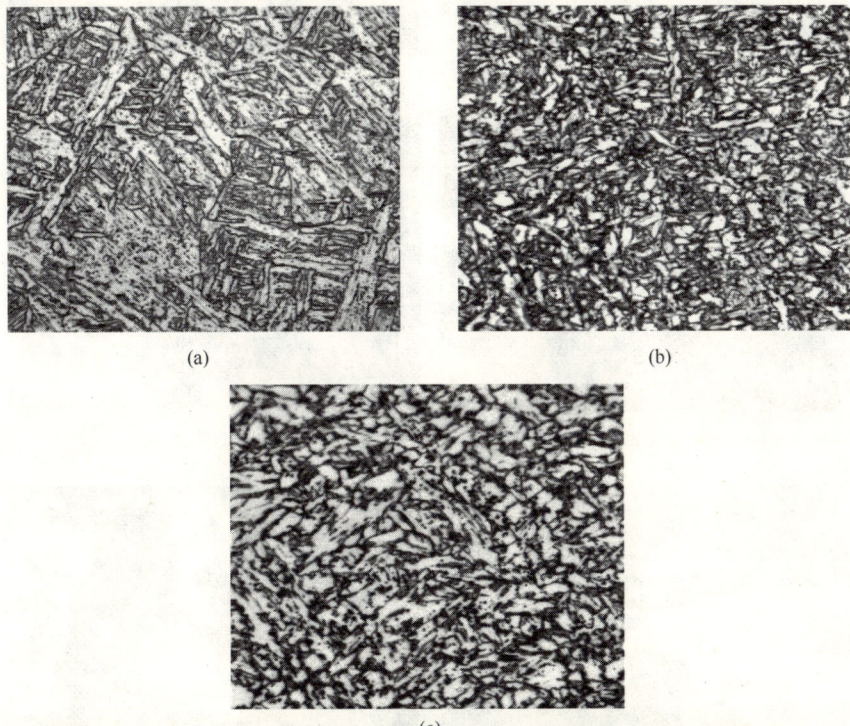

(a) (b)

(c)

Figure 10.45　Typical micrography of the surface bead under different heat inputs
(a)10 kJ/cm; (b)20 kJ/cm; (c)30 kJ/cm

Figure 10.46 shows the TEM photography of as-welded microstructure under different heat input. From Figure 10.46（a）,（b）,（c）,（d）, the fine microstructure of the bainite ferrite lath and AF in weld at the heat input of 10 kJ/cm can be seen. Figure 10.46（e）;（f）,（g）,（h）shows the fine microstructure of the bainite lath and AF in weld at the heat input of 20 kJ/cm. Figure 10.46（i）,（j）,（k）,（l）shows the fine microstructure of the bainite ferrite lath, equiaxed GB and AF with the inclusion nucleus in weld at the heat input of 30 kJ/cm. Apparently, the bainite ferrite lath, GB and AF all have high dislocation density. In addition, it is still found that with the increase of heat input, the average width of bainite ferrite lath increases to some extent, which will influence the mechanical properties of the weld metal.

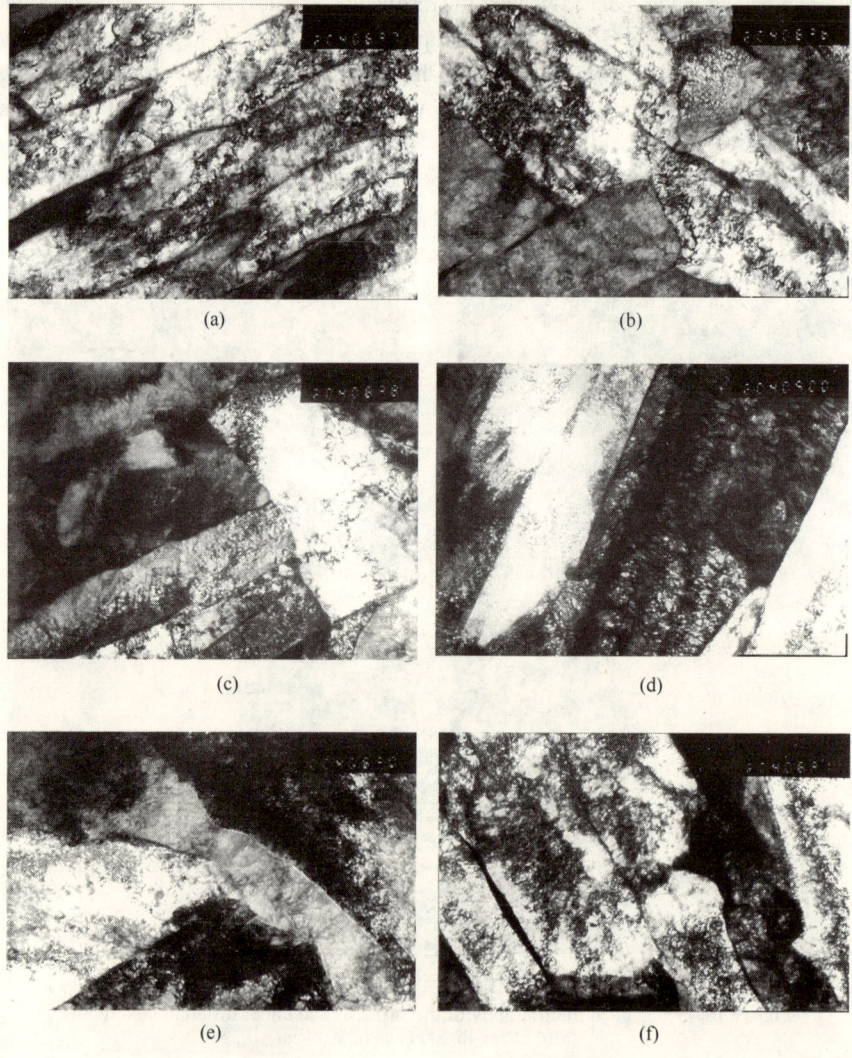

(a)

(b)

(c)

(d)

(e)

(f)

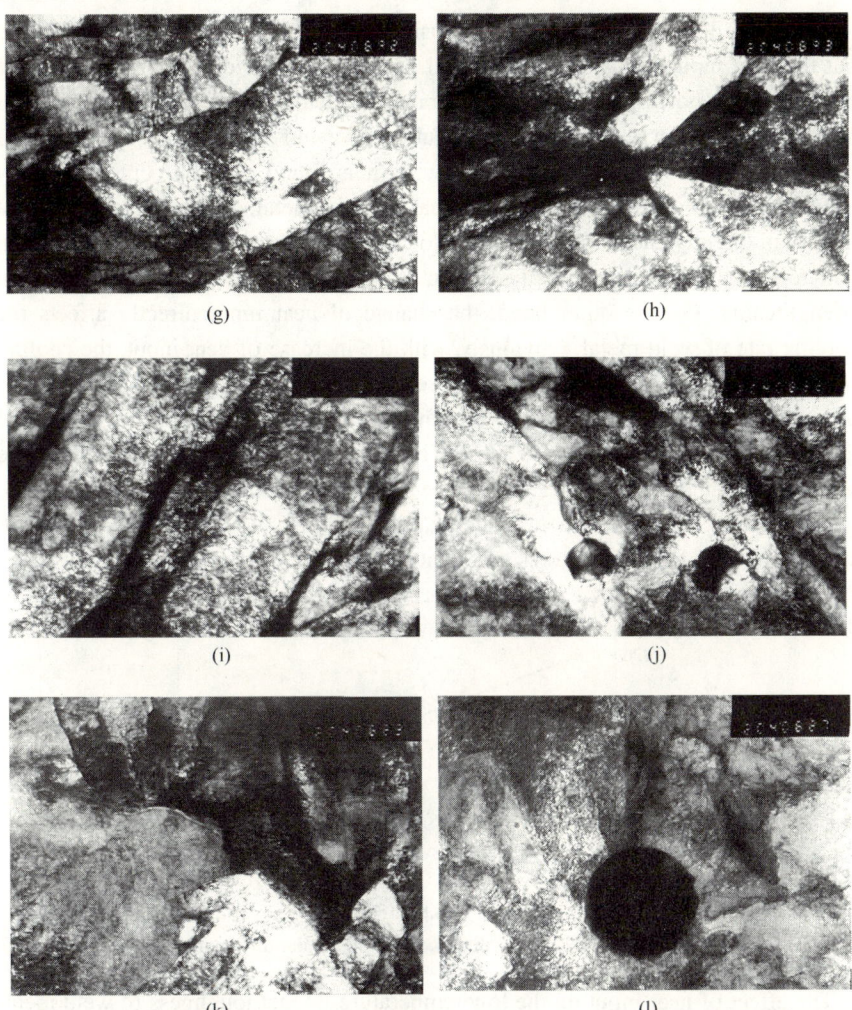

Figure 10.46   TEM photography of as-welded microstructure under different heat inputs
(a)10 kJ/cm; (b)10 kJ/cm; (c)10kJ/cm; (d)10 kJ/cm; (e)20kJ/cm; (f)20kJ/cm; (g)20kJ/cm;
(h)20 kJ/cm; (i)30 kJ/cm;(j)30 kJ/cm;(k)30 kJ/cm;(l)30 kJ/cm

10.4.2.2   Mechanical properties of weld metal in ultra-fine grained bainitic steel

The effect of heat input on the tensile strength is shown in Figure 10.47. Firstly, it
is seen that high strength of welded joint is obtained under different heat inputs.
The tensile strengths under three heat inputs all exceed 90% of the base metal
tensile strength. In particular, the tensile strength reaches 820 MPa at the heat input
of 10 kJ/cm, which is equivalent to that of the ultra-fine structure bainitic steel. In
addition, it can be obviously seen that with the increase of heat input, the strength
of the welded joint decreases gradually. Theoretically, the mechanical properties of

joint mainly depend on the alloy compositions and its cooling rate after welding, but the heat input influences mechanical properties of welding joint by changing both alloy compositions and its cooling rate. On the one hand, the increase of heat input can result in the increase of dilution of weld metal. By comparison of compositions between base metal and wire, it is found that the content of alloy elements in parent metal is far below that in weld metal. So the increase of heat input will directly cause the reduce of alloy concentration in the weld metal, which will result in the declination of solution strengthening and phase transformation strengthening. On the other hand, the change of heat input directly affects the cooling rate of weld metal. Obviously, with the increase of heat input, the cooling rate of weld metal decreases. The increase of cooling rate promotes the generation of quench-hardening structure and the reverse is true. To sum up, the strength of joint shows a trend of decrease with the increase of heat input. However, because of the design idea of ULCB, in the range of cooling rate adopted, the microstructure of all weld metal is the bainite structure. As a result, the change of strength in weld metal is not so significant as that of traditional high strength weld.

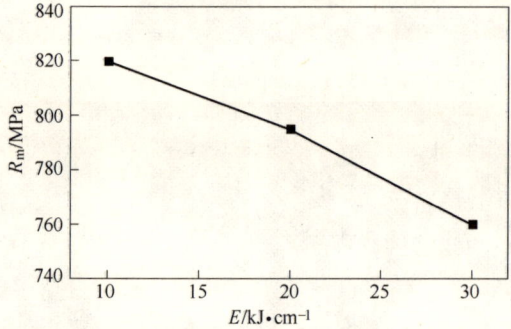

Figure 10.47 Tensile strength of welded joint under different heat input

The effect of heat input on the low temperature impact toughness of weld metal is shown in Figure 10.48. Firstly, it can be seen that good low temperature impact toughness of weld metal is obtained under different heat inputs using ULCB wire. On the one hand, due to adopting ULCB structure, the reduction of carbon content benefits the depress of weld brittleness. On the other hand, as a compensation of lowering carbon, a given amount of Ni and Mn is added, which are beneficial to the increase of strength for weld metal and don't affect much the toughness of the weld metal. Especially, Ni not only decreases the friction resistance of weld metal, σ_i and pinning constant, k_y, but also increases the fault energy, promotes the cross slipping of screw dislocation and enhances the work consumed for the crack propagation. Consequently, high strength and good toughness are obtained simultaneously.

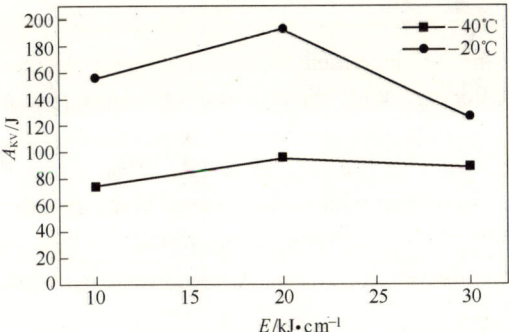

Figure 10.48 Low temperature toughness of welded joint under different heat input

The effect of heat input on the hardness of welded joint is shown in Figure 10.49. It can be found that the influence of heat input on the hardness in the welded joint are notable. With the increase of heat input, the softening tendency of welded joint becomes obvious. When the heat input is 30 kJ/cm, the whole welded joint softens and the width of the soften zone is the largest. This will definitely result in a drop of strength of the welded joint. When lower heat input is used, the width of the softened zone decreases greatly.

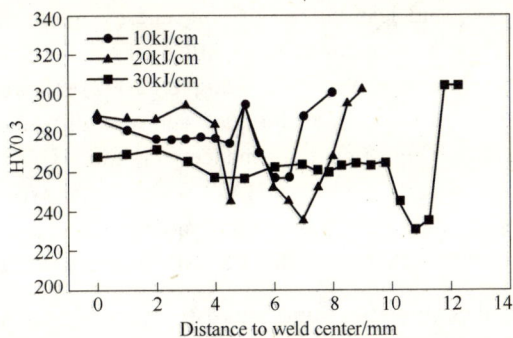

Figure 10.49 Effect of heat input on the microhardness of weld metal

10.4.2.3 Conclusions

1. Using ULCB wire, a joint with good combination of strength and toughness can be obtained in new 800 MPa grade ultra fine structure bainitic steel. The tensile strengths under three heat inputs all exceed 90% of base metal tensile strength. In particular, the weld metal achieves good low temperature toughness in such high strength.
2. The width of primary columnar crystal increases with the increase of heat input. The pre-eutectoid ferrite and side-plate ferrite are almost removed completely in the structure of the weld metal, and the lath bainite, acicular ferrite (AF) and granular bainite are the main microstructure components under different heat

inputs.

3. When the heat input is increased, the tensile strength decreases gradually. The HAZ shows softening. With the increase of heat input, the softened zone increases.

4. Under TEM, the bainite ferrite lath, GB and AF all have high dislocation density. In addition, it is found that with the increase of heat input, the average width of bainite ferrite lath increases to some extent, which will influence the mechanical properties of weld metal.

10.4.3❶   *Laser welding of ultra-fine microstructural bainitic steel*

Welding is one of the key techniques in the research of 800MPa ultra-fine microstructural bainitic steel (UFMBS) and it is very important to study the weldability of the steel, because it is mostly used in the structural fabrications need to be welded. As an advanced method, laser welding (Chen W Z, 2001; Zhang X D, 2004; Zhang X D, 1999), a high power density welding process with the characteristic of high heating and cooling rate, has many advantages compared to conventional arc welding process, such as much narrower heat affected zone (HAZ) and less kinetic driving energy for grain growth. Laser welding is one of the best methods of welding UFMBS (Zhang X D, 2004a; 2004b; Zhao L, 2004; Peng Y, 2002; Wang C, 2002). However, UFMBS is obtained by special processing technique, and the different laser welding conditions have also significant influence on the HAZ, especially the coarse-grained heat-affected zone (CGHAZ) which is the worst section of the weld joint. Therefore, the microstructure and mechanical properties of the HAZ in laser welding of 800 MPa grade UFMBS will be discussed in this section.

10.4.3.1   Chemical compositions and microstructure of base metal

The chemical compositions (mass fraction in %) of UFMBS is shown in Table 10.26. The microstructure of UFMBS is the lath bainite and granular bainite, as Figure 10.50 shows. The size of its prior austenite grain is about 12 μm, and that of the bainitic ferrite (BF) lath package is about 8 μm.

Table 10.26   Chemical compositions (mass fraction in %) of UFMBS

C	Si	Mn	P	S	Cu	Ni	Mo	Nb	Ti	Al	B
0.035	0.251	1.502	0.012	0.003	0.538	0.304	0.156	0.043	0.021	0.029	0.0012

---

❶ The part 10.4.3 was written by Wuzhu Chen and Lin Zhao.

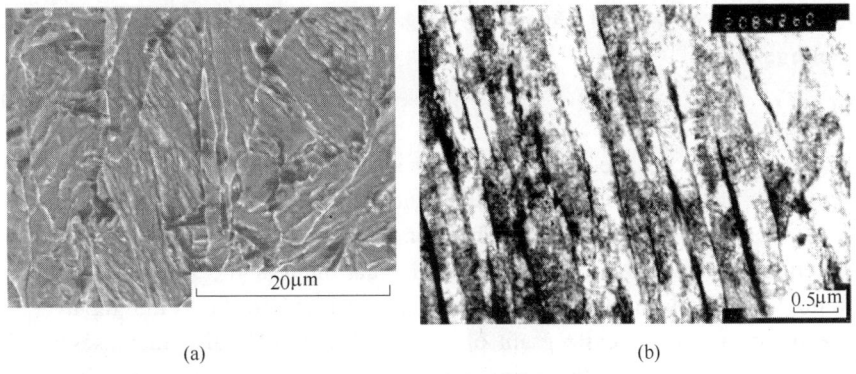

(a)   (b)

Figure 10.50 Microstructure of UFMBS
(a) OM photo; (b) TEM photo

10.4.3.2 Experimental procedure

A 4kW laser was used to perform welding experiments. Argon was used to protect the melt pool. Full-penetration welding of 6 mm thick UFMBS plate was carried out without feeding of filler wire under four kinds of welding conditions, as shown in Table 10.27.

Table 10.27 Laser welding conditions

Weld No.	Laser power /kW	Welding speed /m • min^{-1}	Heat input /J • mm^{-1}	CGHAZ corresponding $t_{8/5}$ /s
1	4	0.60	400	4
2	4	0.45	533	5.5
3	4	0.36	667	7.5
4	4	0.30	800	10

Because the CGHAZ of laser welding of UFMBS is very narrow, a thermal simulation test experiment was carried out to investigate the fine microstructure and the mechanical properties of CGHAZ, and a Gleeble-1500 thermal simulator was used in the experiment. Considering the fast heating characteristic of laser welding and the ability of the thermal simulator, the specimens were heated to 1350℃ in one second. In the light of the laser welding conditions (shown in Table 10.27) and the related database (Wang C, 2002; Wang C, 2001), the cooling time from 800℃ to 500℃ ($t_{8/5}$) of laser welding is usually less than 10 s. In order to investigate the influence of the welding conditions on the microstructure in the larger range of laser welding heat input, the chosen range of $t_{8/5}$ was 0.3~30 s which is a quite wide heat input range for laser welding. In the experiment, the size of specimens used for thermal simulation is 10.5 mm ×6mm ×55mm and $t_{8/5}$ was 0.3 s, 3 s, 6 s, 8 s,

15s and 30 s. Argon and water were used to control the cooling rate during the cooling period.

10.4.3.3   Grain size

Figure 10.51 shows the size of the prior austenite grain of the CGHAZ. From Figure 10.51(a), it could be clearly found that the size of the prior austenite grain increases with increasing heat input. The average size of the prior austenite grain is about 32.5 μm when the heat input is 400 J/mm, and is about 50 μm when the heat input is 800 J/mm. Figure 10.51(b) shows that the average size of the prior austenite grain of the simulated HAZ also increases as $t_{8/5}$ increases. The size of the prior austenite grains of the CGHAZ increases slightly comparatively. The change of grain size of the CGHAZ can be also found from optics micrograph shown in Figure 10.52. According to the data above, the size of the prior austenite grain has largely grown up compared with the base metal.

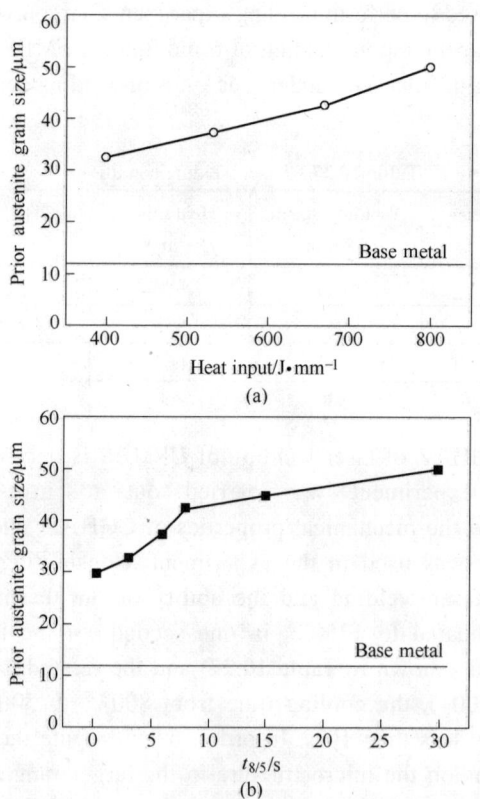

Figure 10.51   Influence of $t_{8/5}$ on grain size of CGHAZ

(a) laser welding; (b) thermal simulation

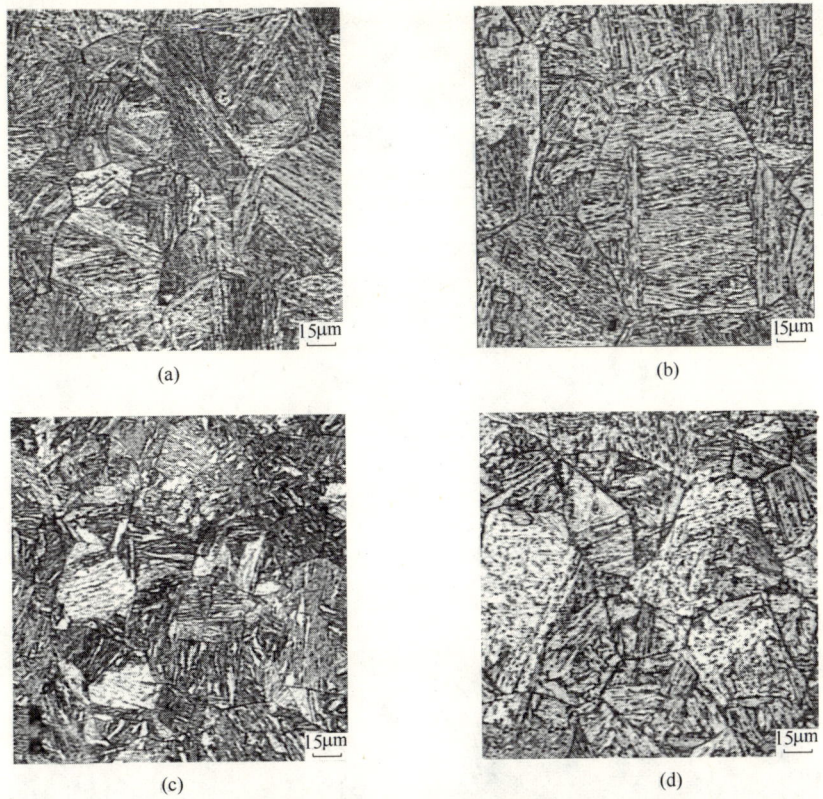

(a)

(b)

(c)

(d)

Figure 10.52 OM photos of CGHAZ
(a) CGHAZ of laser welding (400 J/mm); (b) CGHAZ of laser welding (800 J/mm);
(c) thermal simulation ($t_{8/5}$=0.3 s); (d) thermal simulation ($t_{8/5}$=30 s)

10.4.3.4 Microstructure of CGHAZ

(A) Effect of $t_{8/5}$ on microstructure of CGHAZ

Figures 10.53 and 10.54 show the microstructures of the CGHAZ at different $t_{8/5}$. The microstructure in the CGHAZ of UFMBS under laser welding conditions is predominately composed of granular bainite while $t_{8/5}$ is 0.3~30 s. The granular bainite consists of bainitic ferrite (BF) lath (black field in Figure 10.54) and martensite-austenite (M-A) constituent (white islands in Figure 10.54). M-A constituent exists between BF laths, and there is high dislocation density in BF lath. From Figure 10.54, it could also be clearly found that the change of $t_{8/5}$ can obviously affect the morphology of M-A constituent.

(B) Effect of $t_{8/5}$ on fine structure of M-A constituent

Figure 10.55 shows the fine structure of the M-A constituent (TEM). Figure 10.55(d) shows that there are two phases in the M-A constituent shown as Figure 10.55(a). Figure 10.55(b) shows the dark field image of γ phase, and it is residual

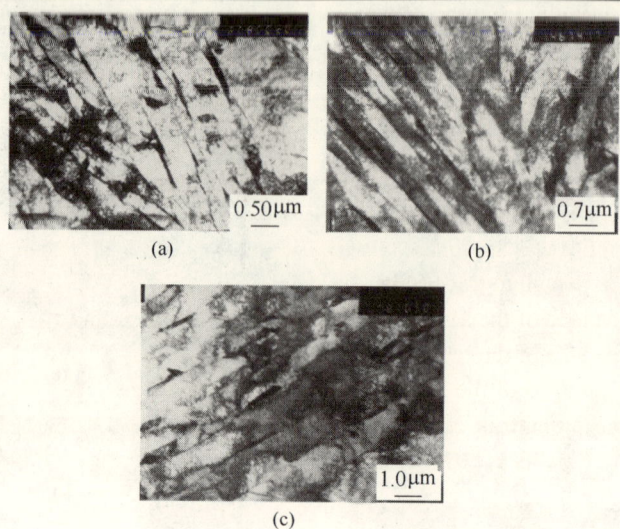

(a)   (b)

(c)

Figure 10.53 TEM microstructures of CGHAZ, granular bainite consisting of BF lath and island-like M-A constituent, high dislocation density in BF lath

(a) $t_{8/5}$=0.3 s; (b) $t_{8/5}$=6 s; (c) $t_{8/5}$=30 s

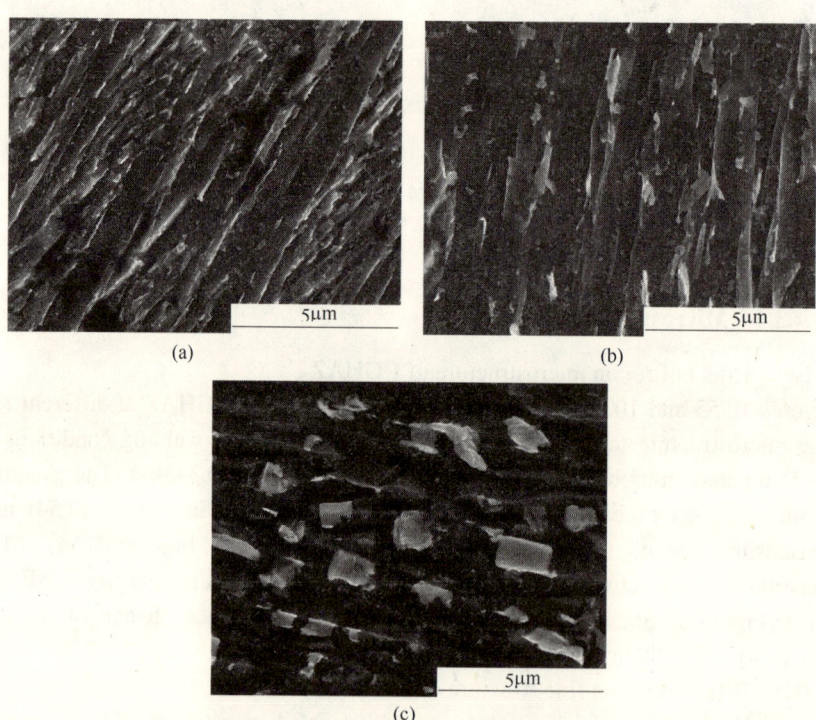

(a)   (b)

(c)

Figure 10.54 SEM morphologies of CGHAZ, morphology of M-A constituent obviously changing

(a) $t_{8/5}$=0.3 s; (b) $t_{8/5}$=6 s; (c) $t_{8/5}$=30 s

austenite. Figure 10.55(c) shows the dark field image of α phase, which is twinned martensite, and the twinned substructure of martensite can be clearly observed. With TEM observation time after time, the result indicates that all M-A constituent consists of the twinned martensite and the residual austenite while $t_{8/5}$ is 0.3~30 s.

On the other hand, the volume fraction of the residual austenite in the M-A constituent is also one of the key factors that reflect the fine structure of the M-A constituent, and it was approximately measured by using TEM image method. The method was divided into three steps:

1. Measure the area of the M-A constituent (S_{M-A}) in TEM image;
2. Measure the area of the residual austenite in the M-A constituent (S_{RA});
3. Calculate the ratio of the residual austenite (SRA/SM-A). The volume fraction of residual austenite in M-A constituent changes from 42% to 36% when $t_{8/5}$ increases from 0.3 s to 30 s and the change of that is negligible.

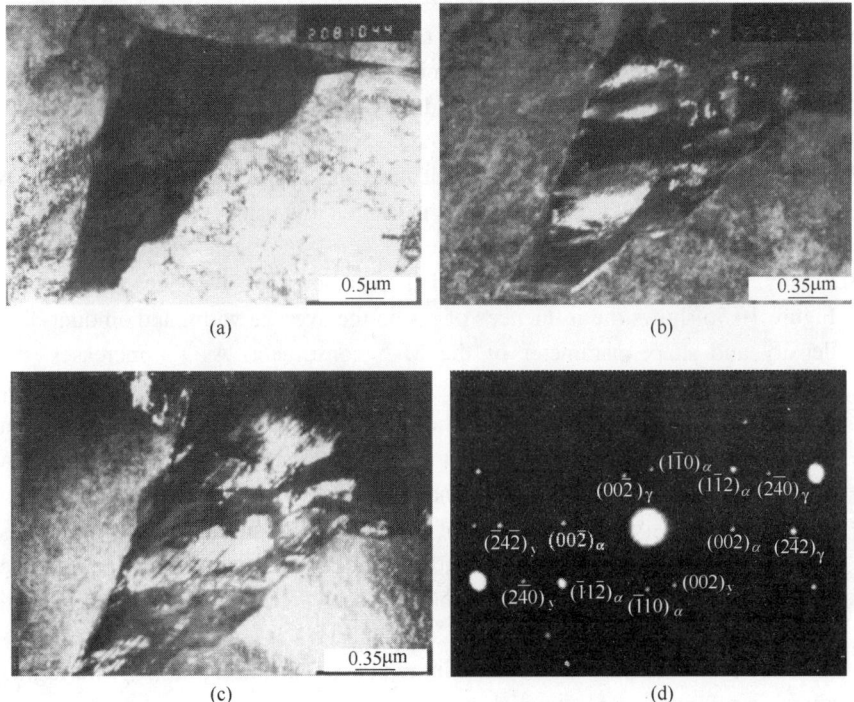

Figure 10.55 Fine structure of M-A constituent (TEM)
(a) M-A constituent; (b) residual austenite in M-A (dark field image);
(c) martensite in M-A (dark field image); (d) electron diffraction pattern of M-A

(C) Effect of $t_{8/5}$ on morphology of M-A constituent

The morphology of the M-A constituent can obviously change as $t_{8/5}$ increases. In order to quantitatively describe the morphology of the M-A constituent, four characteristic parameters that describe the morphology of M-A is proposed and defined, and only the integration of all the four parameters can entirely describe the morphology characteristic of the M-A constituent (Zhao L, 2006a; 2006b; 2006c). The four characteristic parameters are the average width, amount, line density and shape parameter of the M-A constituent. In statistics, the average width a (μm) can represent the size of the M-A constituent, the area fraction of the M-A constituent S (%) in planar coordinate can represent the amount of the M-A constituent, the number per mm N (mm^{-1}) can describe the line density of the M-A constituent. As to the shape of the M-A constituent, there are the elongated M-A constituent and the massive M-A constituent. Because the shape difference of the M-A constituent can greatly affect the toughness, the shape must be quantitatively divided. The M-A constituent which aspect ratio is less than 3 is defined as the massive M-A constituent, and that which aspect ratio is not less than 3 is defined as the elongated M-A constituent. The shape parameter of the M-A constituent R (%) is the number ratio of the massive M-A constituent that can describe the shape of the M-A constituent. The method for measurement of the four characteristic parameters under each welding condition is illustrated as following:

1. Not less than 60 SEM images are randomly chosen, and there are not less than 50 M-A islands in each SEM image;
2. The average width, amount, linear density and shape parameter of the M-A constituent in each SEM image are measured by using the Image-Pro Plus software package;
3. Finally, the mean of the four characteristic parameters of all images is calculated. Figure 10.56 shows the influences of $t_{8/5}$ on the average width and amount, line density and shape parameter of the M-A constituent. As $t_{8/5}$ increases, the average width and amount of the M-A constituent in the CGHAZ under laser welding conditions increase and the line density of the M-A constituent decreases. When $t_{8/5}$ is from 0.3 s to 30 s, the shape parameter of the M-A constituent increases and the main shape of the M-A constituent changes from elongated to massive. The variation of the morphology of the M-A constituent is determined by the phase transformation process of the granular bainite. The cooling rate is very fast and the cooling process is extremely nonequilibrium under the laser welding conditions. Commonly, faster cooling rate corresponds to lower initial temperature of the bainite phase transformation (B_s) and higher phase transformation rate, which reduces the activity of the carbon atom and increases the difficulty of diffusion process in austenite. It causes the average width, amount and shape parameter of the M-A constituent to be smaller and the linear density of the M-A constituent to be higher. Thus, as $t_{8/5}$ increases, the average width, amount and shape parameter of the M-A constituent increase, while the linear density of the M-A constituent decreases.

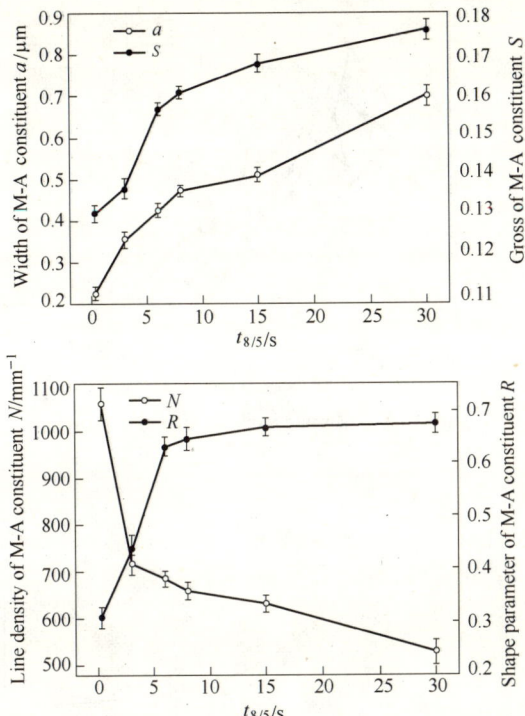

Figure 10.56 Influences of $t_{8/5}$ on average width and amount
(a) line density and shape parameter (b) of M-A constituent

10.4.3.5 Hardness and strength of CGHAZ

(A) Hardness distribution of welded joint

Figure 10.57 shows the hardness distribution of the welded joint. The average hardness of the weld metal is between 300 and 340 HV, and the maximal hardness of the HAZ is about 350 HV. The maximal hardness of the HAZ decreases when the heat input decreases. From Figure 10.57 it can be concluded that the hardness of laser welding HAZ of UFMBS is higher than that of the base metal (273 HV). It also indicates that the softening of HAZ is not a problem in laser welding of UFMBS.

(B) Tendency of hardness and strength of CGHAZ

Figure 10.58 shows the hardness of the CGHAZ at different $t_{8/5}$. The hardness of the CGHAZ decreases from 368 to 294 HV as $t_{8/5}$ increases. Figure 10.59 shows the tensile strength of the CGHAZ at different $t_{8/5}$. The strength of the CGHAZ decreases from 1136 to 847 MPa as $t_{8/5}$ increases. From Figures 10.58 and 10.59, it can be concluded that the CGHAZ of laser welding of UFMBS has higher hardness and strength than those of the base metal (273 HV and 814 MPa).

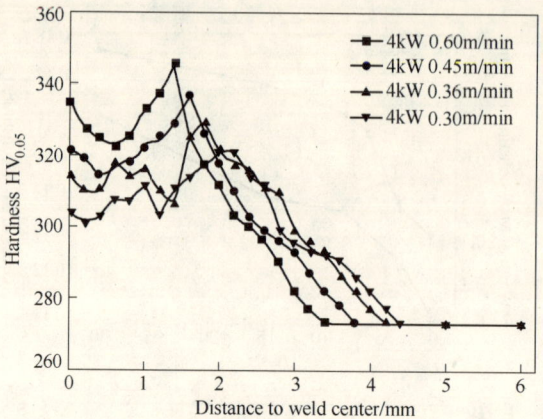

Figure 10.57 Hardness distribution of welded joint

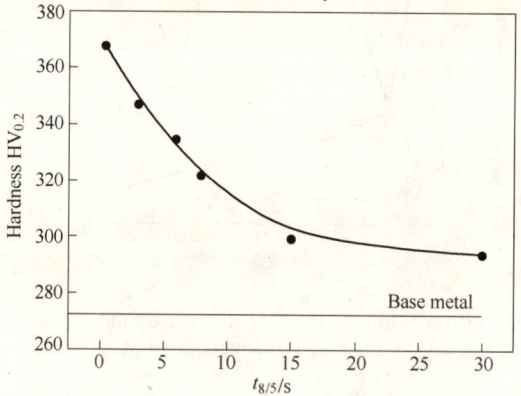

Figure 10.58 Hardness of CGHAZ at different $t_{8/5}$

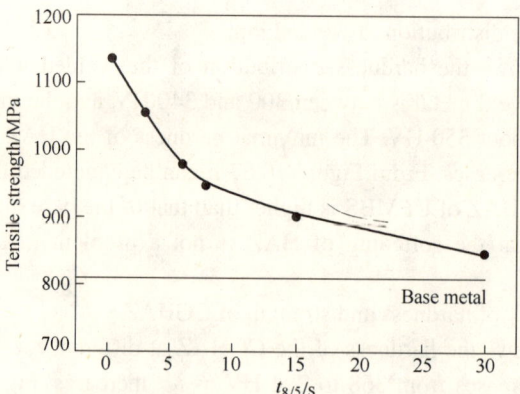

Figure 10.59 Tensile strength of CGHAZ at different $t_{8/5}$

(C) Analysis of hardness and strength

The hardness and strength of the CGHAZ are primarily determined by BF laths.

BF laths at different $t_{8/5}$ were carefully observed by using TEM, and the observation result indicates that the cooling rate ($t_{8/5}$) can obviously affect the dislocation density in BF laths of the CGHAZ, as shown in Figure 10.60. It can be found that the dislocation density of phase transformation in BF laths of the CGHAZ induced by fast cooling of welding is higher than that of deformation and phase transformation in BF laths of the base metal. With shorter $t_{8/5}$, the cooling rate of welding HAZ is faster, and the dislocation density in BF laths is increased. Thus, the hardness and strength of the CGHAZ are higher than those of the base metal because of the high dislocation density induced by phase transformation, and the hardness and strength increase with the decrease of $t_{8/5}$.

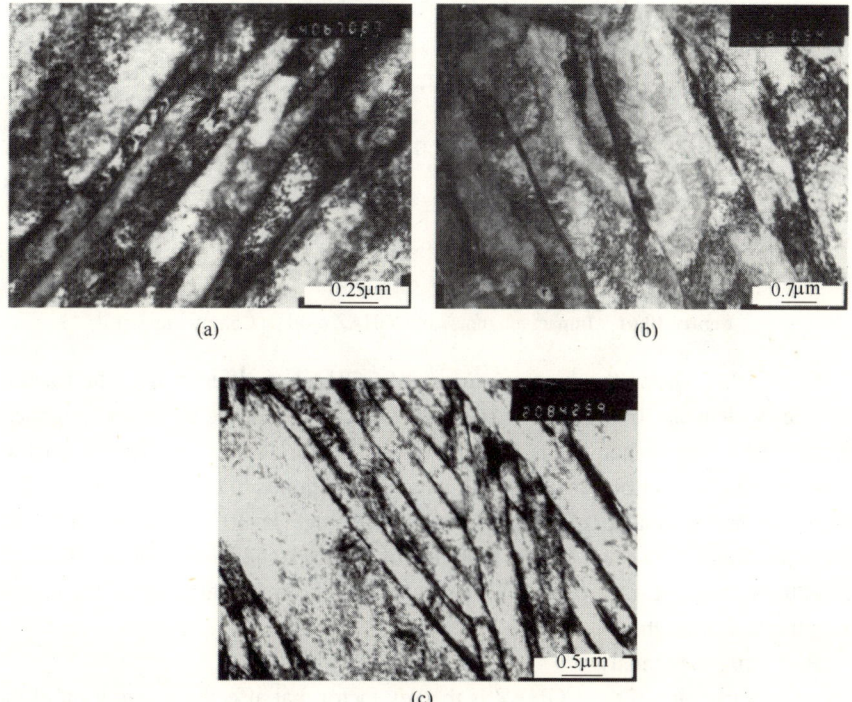

(a)   (b)

(c)

Figure 10.60   Dislocation density in BF laths of base metal and CGHAZ
(a) $t_{8/5}$=0.3 s; (b) $t_{8/5}$=30 s; (c) Base metal

10.4.3.6   Toughness of CGHAZ

(A)   Impact toughness of CGHAZ

Figure 10.61 shows the change of $-40\,^{\circ}\text{C}$ impact toughness of the CGHAZ with cooling rate. The varied trend of the impact toughness of the CGHAZ with $t_{8/5}$ appears a curve which top value is at the $t_{8/5}$ of 6 s. As $t_{8/5}$ increases, the impact toughness of the CGHAZ increases at first and then decreases. The impact energy of the CGHAZ is much higher than that of the base metal (63 J) when $t_{8/5}$ is between 3 s and 15 s. The impact energy reaches the top (98 J) when $t_{8/5}$ is 6 s. Furthermore, higher or lower $t_{8/5}$ will lead to lower impact energy than that of base metal. It indicates that the excellent low temperature toughness can be achieved in CGHAZ under appropriate laser welding conditions, although grains grow in this region. According to the curve of the toughness with $t_{8/5}$, better impact toughness can also be obtained if $t_{8/5}$ is controlled in appropriate range for other welding methods.

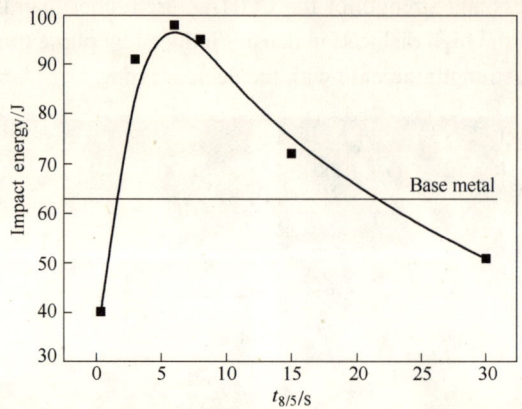

Figure 10.61   Impact toughness of CGHAZ (–40℃ Charpy impact)

Figure 10.62 shows the fracture surface of CGHAZ at different $t_{8/5}$. The fracture surface is cleavage fracture when $t_{8/5}$ is 0.3 s, corresponding to lower toughness (Figure 10.62(a)). When $t_{8/5}$ is 6 s or 8 s, the fracture surface is ductile fracture (Figure 10.62(b) and Figure 10.62(c)), which corresponds to higher toughness. The fracture surface is also cleavage fracture when $t_{8/5}$ is 30 s (Figure 10.62(d)), corresponding to lower toughness than that of Figure 10.62(b) and Figure 10.62(c). Thus the fracture surface of the CGHAZ can also show the variation of the impact toughness at different $t_{8/5}$.

(B)   Toughness analysis

The microstructure of the CGHAZ is the key factor that affects the variation of the impact toughness at different $t_{8/5}$. The granular bainite is the dominant microstructure of the CGHAZ during the laser welding of UFMBS. For the granular bainite, BF lath is toughness phase, and M-A constituent is brittle phase. So M-A constituent determines the toughness of the granular bainite. As the fine structure and the formation of the M-A constituent are similar, the toughness of the granular bainite is determined by the average width, amount, line density, and the shape parameter of the M-A constituent (Matusda F, 1996; Yin G G, 2001; Qian B W, 1995; Tian D W, 1997; Lam K Y, 1993; Fang H S, 2001; Chen J H, 1984; Matusda F, 1994; Matusda F, 1993; Zhao L, 2007; Zhao L, 2005). When $t_{8/5}$ is about 0.3 s, the line density of the M-A constituent is larger and the major shape

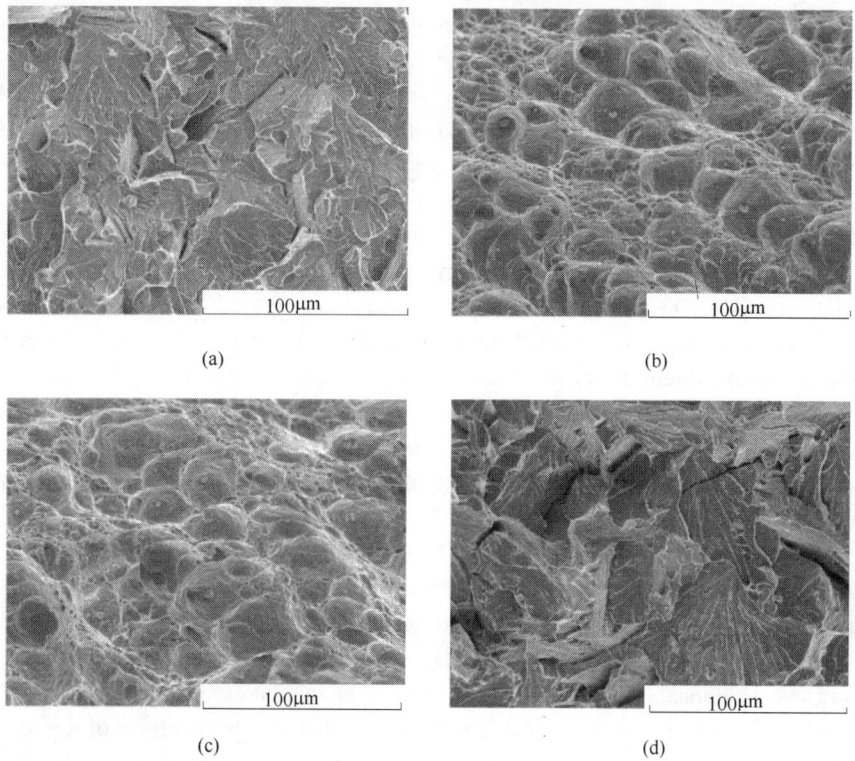

(a)   (b)

(c)   (d)

Figure 10.62   Fracture surface of CGHAZ
(a) $t_{8/5}$=0.3 s; (b) $t_{8/5}$=6 s; (c) $t_{8/5}$=8 s; (d) $t_{8/5}$=30 s

of the M-A constituent is elongated, though the average width and amount of the M-A constituent are smaller. Some researchers suggested that the decrease in the shape parameter of the M-A constituent tends to have an adverse effect on the fracture toughness (Matusda F, 1996; Yin G G, 2001). The microcrack or microhole can be easily induced at the interface between the bainitic ferrite matrix and the elongated M-A constituent when the bainitic ferrite is heavily deformed, and the elongated M-A constituent do not have a significant plastic deformation ability. Qian et al. (1995) proposed that the M-A constituent does not cause much harm on the toughness when the aspect ratio of the M-A constituent is close to 1. So the toughness of the granular bainite decreases as the shape parameter of the M-A constituent decreases. The line density can describe the interval of the M-A constituent. The smaller the interval of the M-A constituent, the lower the toughness (Tian D W, 1997; Lam K Y, 1993). Therefore, the impact energy of the CGHAZ is lower because of the large reduction of the shape parameter of the M-A constituent and the increase of the line density of the M-A constituent when $t_{8/5}$ is 0.3 s. When $t_{8/5}$ is close to 30 s, the average width and the amount of the M-A constituent are remarkably increased though the main shape of the M-A constituent is massive. The increase in the average width of the M-A constituent can promote the spread of fracture or the spread of fracture requires less energy (Fang H S, 2001). Furthermore, the larger the average width of the M-A constituent, the smaller the load to initiate the formation of the new crack nucleus, and the smaller the impact value (Chen J H, 1984). Moreover, the increase in the amount of the M-A constituent can block the slip of the bainitic ferrite matrix. The reduction of the slip distance for the deformation of the bainitic ferrite matrix can reduce the impact toughness (Matusda F, 1994; Matusda F, 1993). Therefore, the toughness of the CGHAZ dramatically decreases because of the remarkable increase of the average width and amount of the M-A constituent as $t_{8/5}$ is 30 s. When $t_{8/5}$ is between 3 and 15 s, the average width, amount, line density, and the shape parameter of the M-A constituent are proper. Consequently, the excellent low temperature toughness can be obtained, and the impact energy of the CGHAZ is much higher than that of the base metal when $t_{8/5}$ is between 3 and 15 s.

(C)   Toughness model

According to toughness analysis of the CGHAZ above, the influence of the morphology of M-A constituent on the toughness attributes to the combined effect of its four characteristic parameters, namely the average width, amount, line density and shape parameter of the M-A constituent on the toughness. The integration of all the four parameters can entirely describe the morphology characteristic of the M-A constituent. Similar results have been observed in HSLA and pipeline steels. Four rules regarding the M-A constituent influence on toughness can be summarized as follows (Zhao L, 2005; Zhao L, 2004a; 2004b; 2004c):

1. The toughness increases as the average width of the M-A constituent decreases;
2. The toughness increases as the amount of the M-A constituent decreases;
3. The toughness increases as the line density of the M-A constituent decreases;
4. The toughness increases as the shape parameter of the M-A constituent increases.

According to the above analysis, the toughness of the CGHAZ is determined by the integration of the four characteristic parameters. Hence the impact energy can be expressed with Equation (10.23) as the function of the characteristic parameters:

$$CVN = f(a,S,N,R) \qquad (10.23)$$

where CVN is impact energy at $-40°C$, a is the average size of M-A constituent, S is the amount (area fraction) of M-A constituent, N is the line density of M-A constituent, R is the shape parameter of M-A constituent.

Based on the facture mechanics analysis and experimental results, the influence of each of the four characteristic parameters on the toughness is correlative, so the relation between them is multiplied. Thus CVN can be also expressed as:

$$CVN = g(a^{\eta} \cdot S^{\gamma} \cdot N^{\varphi} \cdot R^{\theta}) \qquad (10.24)$$

where η, γ, φ, θ represent the influence grade of the four characteristic parameters on the toughness, respectively.

Hence the quantitative relation between the four characteristic parameters and the toughness that is defined as UFMBS toughness model can be written as:

$$CVN = \alpha + \beta \cdot a^{\eta} \cdot S^{\gamma} \cdot N^{\varphi} \cdot R^{\theta} \tag{10.25}$$

According to the experimental results above and correlated references, the following can be obtained:

$$-\theta \approx \eta \approx \gamma \approx \varphi \approx 1 \tag{10.26}$$

So UFMBS toughness model can be rewritten as:

$$CVN = \alpha + \beta \cdot a \cdot S \cdot N \cdot R^{-1} \tag{10.27}$$

The coefficients α, β can be obtained using simple linear regression method. So under this experimental condition, UFMBS toughness model is expressed as:

$$CVN = 254 - 2.13 \times \left(a \cdot S \cdot N \cdot R^{-1} \right) \tag{10.28}$$

Based on expression (10.27), a characteristic factor of the M-A constituent is defined as F:

$$F = a \cdot S \cdot N \cdot R^{-1} \tag{10.29}$$

So UFMBS toughness model can be rewritten as a function that include F:

$$CVN = \alpha + \beta \cdot F \tag{10.30}$$

From expression (10.29, 10.30), it can be concluded that the characteristic factor of the M-A constituent F is the multiplied result based on the effect of the four characteristic parameters on the toughness. F is linear with the toughness, and the toughness increases as F decreases.

The relationship between the characteristic factor of the M-A constituent and $t_{8/5}$ is shown in Figure 10.63. It indicates that the characteristic factor of the M-A constituent F decreases at first and then increases as $t_{8/5}$ increases, and F reaches foot value at which the toughness reaches top value when $t_{8/5}$ is 6 s.

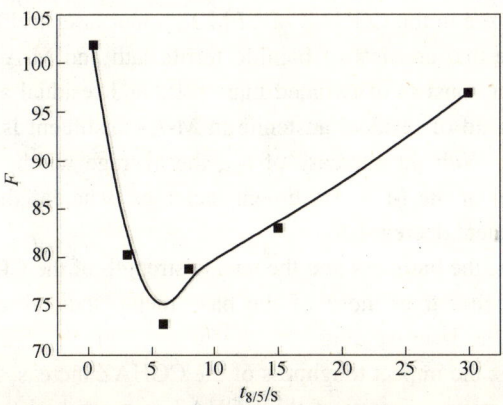

Figure 10.63   Relationship between characteristic factor of M-A constituent and $t_{8/5}$

The UFMBS toughness model is not only applicable to the simulated CGHAZ of UFMBS, but also applied to the toughness analysis and evaluation of the base metal and the laser welded joint of UFMBS steel. Table 10.28 shows the calculated and measured values of *CVN* of the base metal and the CGHAZ of laser welded joint of 6 mm UFMBS plate. It can be deduced that the characteristic factor of the M-A constituent *F* of the base metal is 90. In the light of UFMBS toughness model, the calculated value of *CVN* of the base metal is 62 J, and the measured value of that is 63 J. Under actual laser welding conditions, *F* of the CGHAZ is lower than that of the base metal, and it can be forecasted that the toughness of the CGHAZ is higher than that of the base metal. The calculated values coincide with the measured value.

Table 10.28   Calculated and measured values of *CVN* of the base metal
and CGHAZ of laser welded joint

No.	Welding condition		$t_{8/5}$	F	CVN ($-40°C$)	
					Calculated value[①]	Measured value
1	Base metal			90	62 J	63 J
2	Laser welding CGHAZ	4 kW 0.36 m/min	7.5 s	81	81 J	84 J
3	Laser welding CGHAZ	4 kW 0.30 m/min	10 s	86	71 J	74 J

① The values of CVN are calculated by using expression (10.28).

10.4.3.7   Conclusions

1. The size of the prior austenite grains of the CGHAZ increases with increasing heat input, and it grows up a great deal compared with the base metal.
2. The microstructure in the CGHAZ of UFMBS under laser welding conditions is granular bainite that consists of bainitic ferrite lath and M-A constituent. The M-A constituent consists of twinned martensite and residual austenite, and the change of the ratio of residual austenite in M-A constituent is negligible when $t_{8/5}$ is 0.3~30 s. With the increase of $t_{8/5}$, the average width, amount, and the shape parameter of the M-A constituent increases, whereas the line density of the M-A constituent decreases.
3. As $t_{8/5}$ increases, the hardness and the tensile strength of the CGHAZ decreases, but they are higher than those of the base metal, indicating the absence of softened zone after laser welding.
4. As $t_{8/5}$ increases, the impact toughness of the CGHAZ increases at first and then decreases. The impact energy of the CGHAZ is much higher than that of the base metal when $t_{8/5}$ is between 3 and 15 s. It indicates that the excellent low

temperature toughness can be obtained under appropriate laser welding conditions. The variation in the impact toughness of the CGHAZ at different $t_{8/5}$ is mainly determined by the average width, amount, line density, and the shape parameter of the M-A constituent.

5. The UFMBS toughness model relates the four morphology characteristic parameters of M-A to the low temperature toughness of granular bainite. With the model, the toughness of the granular bainite can be predicted and quantitatively evaluated. The calculated toughness values of the base metal and real laser welded CGHAZ are close to the measured value.

References

Aihara S, Okamoto K (1992) Influence of Local Brittle Zone on HAZ Toughness of TMCP Steels. Welding Research Council Bulletin,No.373:33-44

Anderson M P, Srolovttz D J, Grest G S and Sahni P S (1984) Computer Simulation of Grain Growth – I .Kinetics, Acta Metall.,32(5) : 783-791

Carmignani C, Mares R, Toselli G (1999) Transient Finite Element Analysis of Deep Penetration Laser Welding Process in a Singlepass Butt-welded Thick Steel Plate. Computer Methods in Applied Mechanics and Engineering, Vol.179, No, 3:197-214

Chen J H, Kikuta Y, Araki T, Yoneda M, Matsuda Y (1984) Micro-Fracture Behavior Induced By M-A Constituent (Island Martensite)In Simulated Welding Heat Affected Zone of HT80 High Strength Low Alloyed Steel.Acta Metall,32(10):1779-1788

Chen W Z, Peng Y, Wang C, Bao G, Tian Z L(2001) Welding Thin Plate of 400 MPa Grade Ultra-fine Grained Steel Using CO_2 Laser. International Symposium on Ultrafine Grained Steels(ISUGS 2001), Fukuoka,Japan: 252-255

Chen W, Peng Y, Wang C , Bao G, Tian Z (2001) Welding Thin Plate of 400MPa Grade Ultra-fine Grained Steel Using CO_2 Laser. Proceedings of the International Symposium on Ultrafine Grained Steels (ISUGS 2001), September 20-22, Fukuoka,Japan, the Iron and Steel Institute of Japan, pp 252-255

Cullison A (1994) Two Paths, One Goal:A Consumable to Weld HSLA 100. Welding Journal. (8), pp 51-53

Dain Y, Kapadia P D, Dowden J M (1999) Distortion Gap Width and Stresses in Laser Welding of Thin Elastic Plates.Journal of Physics D:Applied Physics, Vol.32, No.2:168-175

Duhamel R F (1997) Laser Beam Welding of a Restrained Joint. Welding Journal, Vol.76, No.4:65-71

Fang H S, Liu D Y, Xu P G, et al (2001)The ways to improve strength and toughness of bainitic steel.Mater.Mech.Eng,25(6):1-5 (in Chinese)

Fiore S R (1995) The Development of Welding Electrodes For Producing Low Carbon Bainitic Ferrite Weld Deposits. Welding and Weld Automation in Shipbuilding.

Proceedings of the TMS Materials Week'95 Symposium in Cleveland, Ohio. Oct.29-Nov.2, pp 135-150

Gianetto J A, Braid J E M, Bowker J T, Tyson W R (1997) Heat-affected Zone Toughness of a TMCP Steel Designed for Low-temperature Applications. Journal of Offshore Mechanics and Arctic Engineering, Transactions of the ASME,Vol.119, No.2:134-144

Hamatani H, Miyazaki Y, Otani T, Ohkita S (2007) Minimization of heat-affected zone size in welded ultra-fine grained steel under cooling by liquid nitrogen during laser welding.Materials Science Forum Vols.539-543,4063-4068

Han J K, Lee J B, Chang R W (1994) Recent Developments in TMCP Steels. International Journal for the Joining of Materials,Vol.6,No.3:121-125

Hanus F E (1995) Flame Straightening Shape Control of TMCP Steels. OMAE Proceedings of the 1995 14th International Conference on Offshore Mechanics and Arctic Engineering, Vol.3, Jun.18-22, Copenhagen, Den:371-376

Hrivnak I (1995) Weldability of Modern Steel Materials. ISIJ International, Vol.35, No.10:1148-1156

Hsieh R I, Pan Y T and Liou H Y (1999) The Study of Minor Elements and Shielding Gas on Penetration in TIG Welding of Type 304 Stainless Steel, Journal of Materials Engineering and Performance. 8(1): 68-73

Iki H, Nagayoshi A, Sueda K, Ohnishi K, Arimochi K(1998)Development of High-strength Steel Plate for Offshore Structures Produced by TMCP.OMAE Proceedings of the 1998 17th International Conference on Offshore Mechanics and Arctic Engineering, Jul.5-9, Lisbon, Portugal, 6pp Paper: OMAE98-2181 PIOSEB

Inoue T, Hagiwara Y (1990) Fracture Behavior of Welded Joints with HAZ Undermatching. Proceedings of the Ninth International Conference on Offshore Mechanics and Arctic Engineering, Volume III:Materials Engineering-Part A, Feb.: 253-260

Irving B (1998)Weld Cracking Takes on Some New Twists.Welding Journal,Vol.77,No. 8:37-40

Kanetsuki Y, Katsumata M (1998) Effects of Heating and Cooling Rate on Transformation Behaviors in Weld Heat Affected Zone of Low Carbon Steel. Journal of the Iron and Steel Institute of Japan, Vol.84, No.2, Feb.: 109-114

Kang J H, Torizuka S (2007) Dynamic recrystallization by large strain deformation with a high strain rate in an ultralow carbon steel. Scripta Materialia, Volume 57, Issue 11,1048-1051

Kawaguchi Y (2002) Mechanical properties of welded joints of ultra-fine grained steels, ICASS, May 22-24,Tsukuba,Japan

Lam K Y, Wen C, Tao Z (1993) Interaction between microcracks and a main crack in a semi-infinite medium. Engineering Fracture Mechanics,44(5): 753-761

Lancaster J F (1980) Metallurgy of Welding, third edition, ISBN 0 04 669008 5

Lee S, Kim B C, Kwon D (1992) Correlation of Microstructure and Fracture Properties in Weld Heat-affected Zones of Thermomechanically Controlled Processed Steels. Metallurgical Transactions A,Vol.23 A: 2803-2816

Lu S P, Tanaka M and Nogi K (2002) Weld Penetration and Marangoni Convection with

Oxide Fluxes in GTA Welding, Materials Transactions, 43(11):2926-2931

Majta J, Muszka K (2007) Mechanical properties of ultra fine-grained HSLA and Ti-IF steels. Materials Science and Engineering: A, Volume 464,Issues 1-2,186-191

Matsuda F, Fukada Y, Okada H et al (1996) Review of mechanical and metallurgical investigations of marten-site-austenite constituent in welded joints in Japan. Welding in the World, 37(3):134-154

Matsuda F, Ikeuchi K, Liao J (1993)Weld HAZ toughness and its improvement of low alloy steel SQV-2A for pressure vessels(Report 1).Trans. JWRI,22(2):215-221

Matusda F, Ikeuchi K, Okada H, et al (1994)Effect of M-A Constituent of Fracture Behavior of 780 and 980 MPa Class HSLA Steels Subject to Weld HAZ Thermal Cycle. Trans. JWRI, 23(2): 231-238

Máthis K, Rauch E F (2007) Microstructural characterization of a fine-grained ultra low carbon steel.Materials Science and Engineering:A, Volume 462,Issues 1-2,248-252

Murty S V S N, Torizuka S, Nagai K (2005) Ferrite grain size formed by large strain-high Z deformation in a 0.15C steel,Materials Transactions,46,11,2454-2460

Murty S V S N, Torizuka S, Nagai K, Kitai and Kogo Y (2005) Dynamic recrystallization of ferrite during warm deformation of ultrafine grained ultra-low carbon steel, Scripta Materialia,53,6,763-768

Peng Y, He C, Tian Z, Zhang X, Ma C, Xiao H, Chen Y (2005)Study of Arc Welding of Fine Grained Low Carbon Steel, ISUGS Part of Proceedings of the Joint International Conference of HSLA Steels and ISUGS 2005, November 8-10, Sanya, Hainan, China, 295-299

Peng Y, Tian Z, Chen W, Wang C, Bao G (2003) Laser Welding of Ultra-fine Grained steel SS400, Journal of Iron and Steel Research International, Vol.10, No.3, 32-36

Peng Y, Xu Z (1997) Effect of welding thermal cycle on the microstructures and toughness of Nb-V-Ti microalloyed Steel.Iron and Steel, 32(2):53-56

Peng Y, Tian Z, He C, Ma C (2003) Microstructures and mechanical properties of welding HAZ of 400 MPa ultra-fine grained steel. Transactions of the China Welding Institute, 24(5),21-24

Peng Y, Tian Z, He C, Zhang X, Xiao H (2003) Effect of Welding Thermal Cycle on the Microstructure and Mechanical Properties of Ultra-fine Grained Carbon Steel, Materials Science Forum ,Vol.426-432,No.2,1457-1462

Peng Y, Tian Z, Wang C, Chen W, Bao G, Zhao L (2002) Study of Welding Ultra-fine Grained Ferrite Steel by CO_2 Laser. Steel Research, Vol.73,No.11, pp 508-512

Peng Y, Wang C, Chen W Z, Zhao L, Tian Z L (2002) The parameter-related microstructural characteristics of laser autogenously produced weld metal of ultra fine grained steel. Proceding of the 4th Workshop on High Performance Structural Steels for 21st.Century,Pohang,Korea: 299-302

Postacioglu N, Kapadia P, Dowden J M (1997) Thermal Stress Generated by a Moving Elliptical Weldpool in the Welding of Thin Metal Sheets. Journal of Physics D:Applied Physics,Vol.30,No.16:2304-2312

Qian B N, Li J L, Si C Y ,Yi Y Y (1995)Effect of C, Al and Ti on the toughness of HAZ of HSLA steel., Chin.J. Mater.Res.,9(2):119-124 (in Chinese)

Shi Y W, Chen D,Lei Y P and Li X Y (2004) HAZ Microstructure Simulation in Welding of a Ultra Fine Grain Steel, Computational Materials Science,31:379-388

Srolovttz D J,Anderson M P,Sahni P S and Grest G S (1984) Computer Simulation of Grain Growth – II .Grain Size Distribution, Topology and Local Dynamics, Acta Metall., 32(5):793-802

Terada Y, Ishikawa H, Chijiiwa R, Tomioka K, Takamoto T, Itsubo G, Tamehiro H (1998) High-strength Titanium-oxide Bearing Tether Pipe for Tension Leg Platform. Proceedings of the 1998 8th International Offshore and Polar Engineering Conference ,Part 4 (of 4),May 24-29, 1998,Vol.4,Montreal, Can:131-137

Tian D W, Karjalainen L P, Qian B N, Chen X F (1997)Cleavage Fracture Model for Granular Bainite in Simulated Coarse-Grained Heat-Affected Zones of High-Strength Low-Alloyed Steels. JSME International Journal Series A,40(2):179-188

Tian Z, et al. (2002) Welding of ultra-fine grained carbon steels, Workshop on New Generation Steel,13-16 Beijing,China,pp 108-112

Tian Z, Peng Y, He C, Zhang X, Shi Y, Xiao H, Ma C (2004) Weldability of 400 MPa Grade Ultra-fine Grained Carbon Steel, Proceedings of Second International Conference on Advanced Structural Steels, ICASS 2004, April 14-16, Shanghai, China, 898-906

Tian D W, Karjalainen L P, Qian B, Chen X(1996)Nonuniform Distribution of Carbonitride Particles and Its Effect on Prior Austenite Grain Size in the Simulated Coarse-grained Heat-affected Zone of Thermomechanical Control-processed Steels. Metallurgical and Materials Tansactions A,Vol. 27A:4031-4038

Tsai C L, Liaw M L, Teng J I (1998) Effect of Residual Stresses on Design Assessment of Partial Penetration Laser Welds in a Pressure Valve Component. Welding Journal,Vol.77,No.10: 403-410

Vassilaros M G, Czyryca E J (1993) The Development of High-Strength, Cooling-Rate Insensitive Ultra-Low-Carbon Steel Weld Metals. Key Engineering Materials Vol.84-85, pp 587-601

Wang C (2002) Study of Laser Welding of 400 MPa Super Steel and Its Weldability [Dissertation], Tsinghua University, Beijing (in Chinese)

Wang C, Peng Y, Bao G, Zhang Y Q, Chen W Z, Tian Z L (2001) Calculation and detection of thermal cycle of laser deep penetration welding. Electric Welding Machine, 31(4):14-15,21.(in Chinese)

Wang C, Zhang X D, Chen W Z, Zhao L, Tian Z L (2002) Modeling and experimental study on HAZ grain growth in laser welding of ultra-fine grained steel. Applied Laser, 22(2):181-184 (in Chinese)

Weng Y (2003) Ultra-fine Grain Steel, Metallurgical Industry Press, China, pp 616-712

Yin G G,Gao J S, Hong Y C, et al (2001) The microstructure and toughness of HAZ in low carbon Ti-Nb series steel after welding. Transaction of the China Welding Institute, 22(2):71-74 (in Chinese)

Youn J G, Park T D (2002) Effect of heat input on properties of the ultra-fine grained steel weldments,ICASS 2002,May 22-24,Tsukuba,Japan

Yurioka N(1997) TMCP Steels and Their Welding. Welding in the World, Vol.43, No.2:2-17

Zhang X D , Wang C, Chen W Z, Bao G, Tian Z L (1999) Thermal Cycle of CO_2 Laser Beam Welding and Effect on Mechanical Property of Joint. Applied Laser, 19(5):272-275 (in Chinese)

Zhang X D, Chen W Z, Wang C, Zhao L, Peng Y, Tian Z L (2004) Factors affecting mechanical properties of laser welded joint of 400 MPa grade ultra-fine grained ferrite steel. Proceeding of ICASS : 998-1002

Zhang X D, Chen W Z, Wang C, Zhao L, Peng Y, Tian Z L (2004) Microstructures and Toughness of Weld Metal of Ultra-Fine Grained Ferritic Steel by Laser Welding. Journal of Materials Science & Technology, 20(6):755-759

Zhang X D, Chen W Z, Bao G, Zhao L (2004) Improvement of Weld Quality Using a Weaving Beam in Laser Welding. Journal of Materials Science & Technology, 20(5):633-636

Zhao L, Chen W Z, Zhang X D (2006)Microstructure and mechanical properties of laser welded heat-affected zone in new ultra-low carbon bainitic steel.Chinese Journal of Lasers, 33(3):408-412 (in Chinese)

Zhao L, Chen W Z, Zhang X D (2006)Microstructure and Mechanical Properties of Laser Welded Joint of NULCB Steel. Laser Technology, 30(4):344-346 (in Chinese)

Zhao L, Chen W Z, Zhang X D, Shan J G (2007) Study on Laser Welded Heat-Affected Zone in New Ultra-Low Carbon Bainitic Steel. Journal of University of Science and Technology Beijing (English edition), 14(2):136-140

Zhao L, Chen W Z, Zhang X D, Shan J G(2006) Structure character of M-A constituent in CGHAZ of new ultra-low carbon bainitic steel under laser welding conditions. Journal of materials science and technology,22(3):382-386

Zhao L(2004) Study on Laser Weldability of New Ultra-Low Carbon Bainitic Steel [Dissertation], Tsinghua University, Beijing, p.54 (in Chinese)

Zhao L, Zhang X D, Chen W Z (2004) Microstructure character in laser welding of 800MPa grade RPC steel.Applied Laser.24(6):371-374 (in Chinese)

Zhao L, Zhang X D, Chen W Z, Peng Y, Tian Z L (2005) Microstructure and mechanical properties of laser welded CGHAZ of RPC steel. Transactions of the China Welding Institution, 26(6): 5-8(in Chinese)

Zhao L, Zhang X D, Chen W Z, Peng Y, Tian Z L (2004) Microstructure and toughness of HAZ of 800MPa grade RPC steel by laser welding. Proceedings of SPIE, Vol.5629:209-216

Zhao L, Zhang X D, Chen W Z, Peng Y, Tian Z L (2004) Microstructure and mechanical properties of laser welded HAZ of 800 MPa grade RPC ultra-fine microstructure low-alloy steel. Proceeding of ICASS :974-978

Zhao L, Zhang X D, Chen W Z (2005)Toughness of heat-affected zone of 800MPa Grade low alloy steel. Acta Metallurgica Sinica,41(4):392-396 (in Chinese)

Zhao Y Z, Zhou H P and Shi Y W (2006) The Study of Surface Active Element on Weld Pool Development in A-TIG Welding, Modelling Simul.Mater.Sci.Eng.14:331-349

Zou Z F, Zhang W Y (1990) Welding Metallurgy and Metal Weldability. Beijing: Mechanical Industry Publishing House. p.227

Subject Index